THE ORIGIN
OF
SPECIES REVISITED

*The Theories of Evolution and
of Abrupt Appearance*

The marker for Darwin's grave in Westminster Abbey

Originally Published by

Philosophical Library
New York

THE ORIGIN
OF
SPECIES REVISITED

The Theories of Evolution and of Abrupt Appearance

VOLUME I: SCIENCE

by
W. R. Bird

Regency

Nashville, Tennessee

Published in Nashville, Tennessee, by Thomas Nelson, Inc., and distributed in Canada by Lawson Falle, Ltd., Cambridge, Ontario.

Library of Congress Cataloging-in-Publication Data

Bird, W. R., 1954–
    The Origin of Species Revisited: The Theories of
    Evolution and of Abrupt Appearance

    Includes index (name and subject).
    1. Science—Biological Evolution—Biochemical
    Evolution—Cosmic Evolution.
    2. Philosophy of Science—Philosophy of Religion—History of
        Science—Educational Theory—Constitutional Law.
I. Title.
QH371.B58   1987, 1988, 1989
ISBN Vol. I 0-8407-6845-1

Printed in the United States of America

1 2 3 4 — 95 94 93 92

TABLE OF CONTENTS

VOLUME I

133641

ACKNOWLEDGMENTS

Sincere thanks are expressed to many evolutionist, nonevolutionist, discontinuitist, and creationist scientists, philosophers, and others including the following. No agreement is implied on the part of these individuals with the content of this book, and all responsibility for error rests with the author.

For the biology, biochemistry, and physics issues, appreciation is expressed to Russell G. Akridge, Ph.D., physics; Walter L. Bradley, Ph.D., professor of materials science at Texas Tech U.; Harold Coffin, Ph.D., geology; Carl B. Fliermans, Ph.D., microbiology; Wayne Frair, Ph.D., professor of biology at King's C.; Robert V. Gentry, professor of physics at Columbia Union C.; Duane T. Gish, Ph.D., biochemistry; Ronald Good, Ph.D., emeritus professor of botany at U. Hull; Hilton Hinderliter, Ph.D., professor of physics at Pennsylvania State U.; James W. Hugg, Ph.D., physics; D. Russell Humphreys, Ph.D., physicist at Sandia National Laboratories; Dean H. Kenyon, Ph.D., professor of biology at San Francisco State U.; Soren Løvtrup, Ph.D., professor of biology at U. Umea; Frank L. Lyon, Ph.D., former assistant professor of microbiology at Tulane Medical School; Norman Macbeth, J.D.; W. Scot Morrow, Ph.D., assistant professor of biochemistry at Wofford C.; Wilbert H. Rusch, Sr., biology; Giuseppe Sermonti, Ph.D., professor of genetics at U. of Perugia; Charles B. Thaxton, Ph.D., chemistry; Emmett L. Williams, Ph.D., physics; Kurt Wise, Ph.D. candidate in paleontology at Harvard U.; Hubert P. Yockey, Ph.D., micro-biology; and others unnamed.

For the philosophy, theology, history, education, and constitutional issues, appreciation is expressed to Larry Azar, Ph.D., professor of philosophy at Iona C.; Ronald H. Brady, Ph.D., professor of philosophy at Ramapo C.; James Carper, Ed.D., professor of education at U. of Mississippi; David Caudill, J.D.; Robert J. Clinkert, Ph.D., education; Peter D. Fehlner, Ph.D., editor of *Miles Immaculatae*; Russell French, Ed.D., professor of education at U. of Tennessee; Norman L. Geisler, Ph.D., theology; Rabbi Jonah Gewirtz, D.T.L., theology; Edward J. Larson, Ph.D., professor of history of science at U. of Georgia; John N. Moore, Ed.D., former professor of science education at Michigan State U.; William G. Most, Ph.D., professor of classics at Loras C.; Paul A. Nelson, philosophy of science graduate student at U. of Chicago; Huston Smith, Ph.D., emeritus professor of philosophy at Syracuse U.; Robert C. Walton, Ph.D., chairman and professor of church history at U. of Munster; William Young, Ph.D., professor of philosophy at U. of Rhode Island; and others unnamed.

For other assistance, appreciation is expressed to Kevin Wirth, Cathy Edwards, Cynthia Turner, George Turner, Beth Reach, Thomas T. Anderson and A. Morgan Brian, Jr.

Preface
by Dr. Gareth J. Nelson

All facts fit all theories. That is a fact of life. Facts fit some
theories better than other theories, and that is another fact of life,
one which enables science to progress, when a better theory is
created by the human spirit. In this book the lawyer W.R. Bird
compares two theories, evolution and abrupt appearance. He argues
that the facts of life and of the universe fit them both, but fit the
theory of abrupt appearance as well as or better than the theory of
evolution.

Mr. Bird's is not the first attempt to argue this case, nor will it be
the last, but it is perhaps the most scholarly effort among many of
this kind to appear in recent years. In this respect it contrasts
starkly with most, and perhaps all, of the "creation science" literature that has so far been published.

I do not know for whom Mr. Bird has written this book. Its argument will not convince my evolutionist colleagues that they are
wrong in their judgment that evolution is the better theory. Creationists might rejoice to have this book, as comprehensive and well
written as it is, to champion their cause, but it is a book rather
different from their usual fare, and I suspect that they will find it
very difficult to understand in any depth. So it probably will not
convince them that they are wrong in their judgment, either. Some
of my more cynical colleagues will see the book as a political document, and I probably will be chastised by them for writing this
preface, as if in doing so I give aid and comfort to an enemy of true
science. So why do I write a preface to a book that might merely
confirm everyone in his point of view?

I do so because the book has virtue as criticism of evolutionary theory. It has virtue even though its criticism is loaded like the proverbial pair of dice. Indeed, when Mr. Bird rolls for evolutionary theory, who would expect anything but snake eyes to come up? Still, he rolls the dice with style. He rolls them over and over again with the same result.

I may be too optimistic to expect my colleagues to learn much if anything from Mr. Bird's effort. But there is something in his book for all of them, and they need no prompting from me to explore its pages. Many will look into it if only to see how their own words are treated therein. Citing and quoting so widely in the recent literature, Mr. Bird creates a captive audience. Indeed, in one way or another we have all—all the way to the Supreme Court of the United States—been captured by the evolution/creation controversy, in which Mr. Bird has played a prominent role.

Mr. Bird is concerned with origins and the evidence relevant thereto. He is basically correct that evidence, or proof, of origins—of the universe, of life, of all of the major groups of life, of all of the minor groups of life, indeed of all of the species—is weak or nonexistent when measured on an absolute scale, as it always was and will always be. He is correct also that what evidence there is, is sometimes, even often, exaggerated by evolutionists. Yes, they load their own dice, for they, too, are human. They, too, play to the gallery, to the jury, and to the judges. Were they entirely wise rather than adversarial they would never claim to have done the impossible: to have proved the correctness of their views by offering evidence of origins of things. One might just as well attempt to prove stability by offering as evidence a pyramid balanced on its apex. A point—an origin—is where the evidence, like stability, disappears.

I would have found interesting an attempt by Mr. Bird to deal with the geographic distribution of life—with biogeography, a topic inexplicably missing from his argument. The facts of geographic distribution are not in short supply. They have been considered the most convincing evidence of evolution. Not since the 1830's, when the lawyer Charles Lyell published his *Principles of Geology*, have they been adequately reviewed in the context of abrupt appearance. This omission is not a fatal flaw of Mr. Bird's argument, for doubtless he could roll snake eyes for biogeography, too. Yet who knows?—I may as well be wildly optimistic—maybe the facts of distribution would tip the balance of his judgment in favor of evolution. After all, lawyers, too, are only human. Charles Lyell eventually became convinced that he was wrong. Why not W.R. Bird?

Gareth J. Nelson*
Chairman and Curator
Department of Herpetology and Ichthyology
The American Museum of Natural History
New York, New York 10024

[Dr. Nelson*, an evolutionist, is the coauthor of *Systematics and Biogeography*, "is chiefly responsible for the transformation" in cladistics, according to Colin Patterson*, and is a nationally respected zoologist and a department chairman at one of the world's leading museums. He also teaches biology at City University of New York, and earned his Ph.D. degree in zoology at University of Hawaii.]

Preface
by Dr. Dean H. Kenyon

Thanks to W.R. Bird we now have a first-rate, comprehensive summary of all the major facets of the current controversy on the subject of origins. Those who have felt the need for a clearly organized, richly documented scholarly compendium treating not only the major criticisms of evolutionary theory (as applied to biochemical, biological, and cosmic origins), but also containing the principal positive arguments supporting the alternative theory of abrupt appearance, will not be disappointed by Mr. Bird's impressive new work, *The Origin of Species Revisited*. In addition to the scientific discussion the book also presents detailed, documented analyses of philosophic, historical, educational, and constitutional dimensions of the subject or origins. Both the scientifically literate layman and the professional scientist will find this two-volume set uniquely valuable both as a reference manual and as a work to be read and savored from cover to cover.

In the short space of a preface it is difficult to do justice to all the reasons why I am enthusiastic about this book. I will mention only a few additional points. First, a caveat to my fellow scientists: This work is not a technical treatise written at the level of papers in professional journals. While it clearly identifies and documents, for example, the positive arguments supporting abrupt appearance (of the universe, the first life, and the various sorts of living organisms) as a creditable and substantial scientific alternative to the macro-evolutionary doctrine, these arguments are not complete as stated, in that this work follows in general the approach of Darwin's *The Origin of Species*. The discussion is meant to be suggestive of the main points of each argument, and these points are thoroughly documented. (The book has more than 5,000 references.) But the reader will have to do the required homework to fill in the gaps and answer the questions raised. I would not have separated the arguments in quite the same way as Mr. Bird has done. For example, in Chapter 4, I would have combined the Information Content argument with the Thermodynamics argument. But this relatively minor point along with an occasional quibble about terminology do not significantly detract from the overall great merit of the book.

Why do I say *great* merit? The reason is that this book, better than any other of which I am aware, presents an intellectually balanced discussion of competing substantial claims in the scientific study of origins and its related issues. The structure of claim-counterclaim-critique, perhaps more familiar now to lawyers than to scientists (Charles Darwin was adept at this form of argument), is repeated in all sections of *The Origin of Species Revisited*. The aim is not to refute or establish one particular view, but in the author's words, to defend "the viability of alternate positions," and to support "the fair and uncensored teaching in educational institutions of all scientific theories of origins." As a scientist and educator I have immense respect for this approach. Students of the subject of origins, and indeed of any important subject, need to see that there are solid competing positions deserving of careful study. W.R. Bird's book provides the reader with a splendid means of gaining that perspective. I am sure that many of my colleagues will join me in saluting him with a hearty "well done!"

Dean H. Kenyon
Professor of Biology
San Francisco State University
San Francisco, California 94132

[Dr. Kenyon is one of America's leading nonevolutionist scientists, and teaches biology and evolution at San Francisco State University. He performed original research for years on the origin of life, published many technical articles on that topic, and co-authored the book *Biochemical Predestination* during his evolutionist days. He earned his Ph.D degree in biophysics at Stanford University.]

INTRODUCTION

For I am well aware that scarcely a single point is discussed in this volume on which facts cannot be adduced, often apparently leading to conclusions directly opposite to those at which I have arrived. A fair result can be obtained only by fully stating and balancing the facts and arguments on both sides of each question . . ..
—Charles Darwin*,
in *Introduction* to
The Origin of Species[1]

Charles Darwin* published in 1859 his epochal "The Origin of Species by Means of Natural Selection or the Preservation of Favoured Races in the Struggle for Life." That single volume has had a massive influence not only on the sciences, which increasingly are built on evolutionary assumptions, but on the humanities, theology, and government.

Darwin's* revolution in science grew from the concept that one or a few original single-celled organisms evolved into invertebrates, then into fish, then into amphibians, then into reptiles, then into lower mammals, then into primates, then into man.[2] Darwin* speculated,[3] and others proposed, that the original single-celled organ-

---

*Scientists cited in this book, unless otherwise indicated, are not proponents of, and their quoted statements are not intended as endorsements of, either the theory of abrupt appearance or the theory of creation. However, their quoted statements are acknowledging data that some nonevolutionist scientists interpret as supporting the theory of abrupt appearance better than the theory of evolution or as undermining the theory of evolution or significant aspects.

1

isms themselves evolved from nonlife.[4] That evolutionary view soon combined with concepts that the physical universe has evolved from primordial chaos to its present order,[5] that concepts of the deity and inspired writings evolved in changing cultures, that human knowledge and values evolved in a universe without absolute truth, and that governmental institutions and their foundational documents do and in fact should evolve in form and meaning.[6]

On the centennial of Darwin's* book, the scientific community was still divided over a viable mechanism to explain the assumed evolution from nonlife to life and from single-celled life to all plants and animals in their vast complexity.[7] In the following quarter century, a growing scientific challenge arose to critical elements of Darwinian evolution,[8] and an even faster growing scientific challenge emerged about the truth of Darwinian evolution itself.[9] The dissent seems to be so widespread as to indicate a Kuhnian revolution in science and a paradigm shift.[10]

The challenge to critical elements of Darwinism came from many directions: initially anti-selectionists and evolutionary saltationists who found natural selection inadequate to propel microevolution into macroevolution or to explain a fossil record of systematic gaps;[11] recently punctuated equilibria advocates who replace the mechanism of biological evolution and its misreading of microevolution and of the fossil record,[12] transformed cladists and some pheneticists who question the truth of evolution or its relevance to classification,[13] and neutral selectionists, nonequilibrium thermodynamics proponents, and structuralists;[14] and generally specialists in every field who find no persuasive evidence of Darwinian evolution in their own field but assume that the evidence is present in another field.

Many paleontologists, while supposing that the evidence for Darwinian macroevolution is in another field, concede that "no real evolutionist, whether gradualist or punctuationist, uses the fossil record as evidence in favour of the theory of evolution . . ." (Ridley* [15]). Although reliance is often placed on evolutionary trees, "phylogenies grew up like weeds" for "even organisms with no fossils available" (Boyden* [16]), and are "meaningless waffle" (Charig* [17]). Many evolutionists look to the field of classification or systematics for the key evidence, but "much modern taxonomy has abandoned its Darwinian, historicist or genealogical approach" (Oldroyd* [18]), such as the transformed cladists who "have taken more or less extreme measures to sever their ties" from evolutionary biology and are "at odds with evolutionary thinking" (Beatty*[19]). Comparative anatomists often look to another discipline, because so widespread are convergences and parallelisms that "[m]ore often than not functional comparisons turned up phylogenetic paradoxes instead of parallels" (Ross* [20]). Comparative embryologists frequently despair that "[a]natomically homologous parts in different related organisms appear to have quite different embryonic origins," which "is almost impossible to reconcile with . . . neo-Darwinian theory . . ." (Oldroyd*[21]). Many comparative biochemists also look to other disciplines for proof of Darwinism and macroevolution, because "[t]here is no avoiding the serious nature of the challenge to the whole evolutionary framework implicit in these findings" of regular evolutionary anomalies (Denton* [22]). Population geneticists often conclude that population genetics is "like a complex and exquisite machine" that "from the other end has issued—nothing" and "explains nothing" (Lewontin* [23]). And that completes the circle around the various major arguments for Darwinism and macroevolution. Some evolutionists write that to "a minority, neo-Darwinism is coming apart at the seams," while others are equally critical of punctuated equilibria and other alternatives.[24] The effect is that "Darwinism is under attack" (Leith*):

> It is therefore of immediate concern to both biologist and layman that *Darwinism is under attack*. The theory of life that undermined nineteenth-century religion has *virtually become a religion itself* and in its turn is being threatened by fresh ideas. The attacks are certainly not limited to those of the creationists and religious fundamentalists who deny Darwinism for political and moral reasons. The main thrust of the *criticism comes from within science itself*. The doubts about Darwinism represent a political revolt from within rather than a siege from without.
>
> What is even more surprising is that these doubts are arising *simultaneously from several independent branches of science*. With a growth in the appreciation of the philosophy of science . . . has come a *doubt about whether Darwinism is, strictly speaking, scientific*. Is the theory actually testable—as good theories must be? Is the idea of natural selection based on a tautology, a simple restatement of some initial assumptions? From within biology the doubts have come from *scientists in half a dozen separate fields*. Many palaeontologists are unconvinced by the supposed gradualness of Darwinian evolution; they feel that the evidence points to abrupt change—or else to no change at all. Some geneticists question Darwin's explanation for the 'origin of species', feeling that natural selection may have virtually nothing to do with the events that lead to the appearance of new species. Among other scientists, for example, among immunologists, embryologists, and taxonomists, the

same feeling seems to be growing: there is a lot more to evolution than Charles Darwin envisaged, and even the modern synthesis of evolutionary ideas—called neo-Darwinism . . . —seems inadequate in many respects.

. . . In the past ten years has emerged a *new breed of biologists* who are considered scientifically respectable, but who have their *doubts about Darwinism.*[25]

The even more serious challenge to Darwinian evolution itself developed from an eminent group of leading non-Darwinian evolutionists who embrace evolution but deny Darwinian mechanisms, a surprising number of nonevolutionist scientists who cannot accept the theory of creation but are at best agnostic toward evolution, and a remarkable number of nonevolutionary discontinuitist and creationist scientists. Among the noncreationists, Løvtrup* recently published *Darwinism: The Refutation of a Myth* (1987); Holbrook* attacked the influence of Darwinism in *Evolution and the Humanities* (1986); Denton* wrote *Evolution: A Theory in Crisis* (1985) and concluded that "[n]either of the two fundamental axioms of Darwin's macroevolutionary theory . . . has . . . been validated by one single empirical discovery or scientific advance since 1859";[26] Midgley* identified nonscientific aspects in *Evolution as a Religion* (1985); Ho* and Saunders* edited *Beyond Neo-Darwinism* (1984) and concluded that "evolution theory is in crisis";[27] Ambrose* summarized his research in *The Nature and Origin of the Biological World* (1982); Leith* catalogued the dissent in *The Descent of Darwin: A Handbook of Doubts about Darwinism* (1982); Sermonti* and Fondi* published *Dopo Darwin: Critica all' Evoluzionismo* (1980), which "opposes the evolutionary view" and concludes "that a stationary view accounts better for the observed facts than an evolutionary view";[28] and Grassé wrote *The Evolution of Living Organisms* (trans. 1977) to "launch a frontal assault on all forms of Darwinism."[29] "In fact, throughout the past century there has always existed a significant minority of first-rate biologists who have never been able to bring themselves to accept the validity of Darwinian claims."[30] These technical books and numerous scholarly articles generally converge on anti-Darwinian and often anti-macroevolutionist views:

The overriding supremacy of the *myth* has created a widespread *illusion* that the theory of evolution was all but proved one hundred years ago and that all subsequent biological research—paleontological, zoological and in the newer branches of genetics and molecular biology—has provided *ever-increasing evidence for Darwinian ideas. Nothing could be further from the truth.* The fact is that the evidence was so patchy one hundred years ago that even Darwin himself had increasing doubts as to the validity of his views, and the only aspect of his theory which has received any support over the past century is where it applies to microevolutionary phenomena. His general theory, that all life on earth had originated and evolved by a gradual successive accumulation of fortuitous mutations, is still, as it was in Darwin's time, a *highly speculative hypothesis entirely without direct factual support* and very far from that self-evident axiom some of its more aggressive advocates would have us believe.[31]

Darwinians have always realized that, "given a number of basic facts, one can spin any number of explanatory hypotheses to account for them" (Ruse*[32]). More and more of the anti-Darwinian evolutionists and anti-macroevolutionists are applying that principle to call for "the consideration of some other explanation of the facts" (Good*[33]):

> The fundamental inherent difficulty in the study of evolution is that this great natural process involves time dimensions of a magnitude quite out of proportion to the duration of human life or even to the sum of human experience, and the observer has therefore to *rely on indirect, or circumstantial evidence.* Hence beliefs that are often referred to as *theories of evolution* are, *more accurately, only working hypotheses.* This is a very important matter because the essence of a *hypothesis* is that it is an opinion suggested by the available evidence, but *not one which precludes the possibility of some alternative.* A hypothesis may well be substantiated when more corroborative details are forthcoming, but until then *there is no logical reason for excluding the consideration of some other explanation of the facts.* So, while it may be justifiable to believe that evolution affords a reasonable explanation of the facts of nature, *it is not justifiable to maintain that no other explanation is possible or permissible.*[34]

Some scientists even argue that, because "it is the duty of a scientist to tell the truth as he sees it when this truth is relevant to important public issues," "the political position taken by many opponents of the creationists offends my liberal instincts" as an "ethical" matter (Tipler*[35]).

Another challenge to Darwinism and macroevolution came from the theory of creation. As a *New Republic* article said, the "leading participants on the creationist side—who are often portrayed as Bible-thumpers, but have science Ph.D.s—are in fact scientists" (Bethell*[36]). Their unifying bond is less and less consensus in biblical interpretation (because much diversity exists),[37] or even consensus in biblical allegiance (because many reject the inerrancy if not the inspiration of religious texts).[38] Instead, that bond is an agreement that the existing scientific evidence renders Darwinian evolution questionable, and in fact better supports the theory of creation as an alternate scientific explanation. Seven of the fifteen judges of the U.S. Court of Appeals for the Fifth Circuit agreed that the theory of creation is "scientific evidence" that "has no direct religious reference whatever,"[39] and two of the nine justices of the U.S. Supreme Court agreed.[40] They correctly point out that concepts of creation always have been a basic part of science,[41] and are still a vital part of cosmology: "we may defend the concepts of age, First Event, and creation as they are encountered in all current cosmological contexts" (North* [42]). However, the creationist position has more often than not been based on negative evidence (weaknesses of evolution) rather than on affirmative evidence (scientific data and scientific interpretation supporting a theory of creation).[43] It has received extensive criticism.[44]

A century and a quarter after Darwin's *The Origin of Species*, the growing dissent and doubt is collected in this book, *The Origin of Species Revisited: The Theories of Evolution and of Abrupt Appearance*. By the "theory of abrupt appearance" is meant the scientific theory that the universe, the first life, and plants and animals appear abruptly in complex form and in a discontinuous manner, in contrast with the progressive and ultimately continuous nature of the theory of evolution. That theory of abrupt appearance is a broad category that includes many nonevolutionist approaches such as nineteenth century typological views, theories of discontinuity and natural group systematics, and of panspermia and directed panspermia, and scientific theories of creation to the extent they rely solely on empirical evidence, just as the theory of evolution is a broad category that includes neo-Darwinian and punctuated equilibria approaches, non-Darwinian evolutionary approaches, scientific theories of mechanism and reductionism, and views of theistic evolution. This book defends the viability of alternate positions to Darwinian evolution, and supports the fair and uncensored teaching in educational institutions of all scientific theories of origins.

In doing so, this book is unique in several ways. First, this volume outlines affirmative lines of scientific evidence supporting the theory of abrupt appearance that are parallel to the affirmative lines of evidence or arguments supporting evolution, and assesses whether evolution is so firmly proved that alternative explanations cannot exist. Second, Volume II addresses the definition of science in the context of the evolution controversy, and assesses whether the features of natural law, testability, and falsifiability are necessary demarcation lines between science and nonscience, as well as whether they exclude abrupt appearance theories or evolutionary theories from the scientific domain. Third, the book analyzes what characteristics render a concept religious, and assesses whether the theory of abrupt appearance is or can be as nonreligious as the theory of evolution. That includes scrutiny of the role of religion and science in the history of the evolution controversy, and the feasibility and utility of presenting alternate explanations under educational theory. Fourth, this book describes the constitutional concepts of academic freedom and separation of church and state in relation to public school instruction in all scientific theories of origins, including nonevolutionary theories, and thereby provides a defense of uncensored instruction.

In summary, this book compares the scientific, nonreligious, and constitutional natures of the theory of abrupt appearance and the theory of evolution. Its thesis follows Darwin's* point that was quoted above: "A fair result can be obtained only by fully stating and balancing the facts and arguments on both sides of each question . . . ." The author does not endorse any particular view of abrupt appearance or evolution—only the "fair result" of "fully stating and balancing" all the evidence. In each discipline, virtually all citations are to evolutionist and other noncreationist sources, except for the few that are clearly defined as creationist for definitional or historical purposes. In quoting those specialists, the point emphatically is not that they support either discontinuous abrupt appearance or creation in any sense, but simply that they acknowledge the existence of empirical data that others find to support the theory of abrupt appearance more than the theory of evolution, or that they concede the existence of serious difficulties with the theory of evolution. This qualification is indicated by an asterisk after an evolutionist's and noncreationist's name, in order to avert the criticism that any researcher's views or words are misrepresented. The criticism is inevitable, but unwarranted, that the book redefines the nonevolutionist side of the conflict. It does not in that the nonevolutionist (or discontinuitist) position has always been much broader than the theory of creation, and there is no reason why this book need discuss one subcategory (a scientific theory of creation) rather than the broad category (the scientific theory of abrupt appearance). Similarly, discussion of evolution need not focus solely on the subcategory of biological macroevolution without cosmic evolution and biochemical evolution, or on the subcategory of neo-Darwinism without the punctuated equilibria, non-Darwinian, and other subcategories. Moreover, Darwinism has been drastically redefined from classical to neo-Darwinian views and now to punctuated equilibria views,[45] and many components such as species selection similarly have had "repeated redefinition."[46]

A Kuhnian revolution[47] may be occurring in the widespread acceptance of the theory of abrupt appearance (the revolutionary enterprise), coupled with the widespread criticism of the theory of evolution (the possible failure of the governing science paradigm), both as growing trends. The unprecedented antagonism shown by many evolutionists[48] may simply reflect the principle that "[n]ormal science, for example, often suppresses fundamental novelties because they are necessarily subversive of its basic commitments" (Kuhn* [49]). The general public certainly supports the trend: a massive majority (86% to 8%) of the national public supports teaching the theory of creation in public schools rather than just evolution (AP-NBC News poll[50]), including nearly equal supermajorities of Protestants and Catholics (Stacey* and Shupe* [51]); more than two-thirds of lawyers nationally agree (56% to 26%) and find dual instruction constitutional (63% to 26%) (American Bar Association-commissioned poll[52]); majorities (80% at Ohio State, 56% at Oberlin) of university students at secular institutions agree (Fuerst* [53], Zimmerman* [54]); two-thirds (67% to 25%) of public school board members concur (American School Board Journal poll[55]); and a substantial minority (42.3% to 53.7%) of even public school biology teachers favors the theory of creation over the theory of evolution (Austin Analytical Consulting poll[56]).

Many evolutionists agree that all scientific theories of origins— even the theory of creation—should be taught. Provine* of Cornell writes that "creationism should be taught along with evolutionism in grade schools and high schools . . . in the science classroom," because "creationism is a viable, understandable and plausible theory for the creation point" although it is his "opinion that it is a wrong theory."[57] Stonehouse* of Cambridge says that a recent creationist book "may convince you . . . that there is more in the Creationist argument than scientists are generally willing to concede," and "that uncritical acceptance of Darwinism may be counterproductive."[58] Morrow* writes that balanced treatment is good because "[s]tudents would have available a realistic set of options to explore."[59] Thompson notes that "[s]tudents should be exposed to both sides of the coin regarding biological change—the doctrine of creation and that of evolution," and that "[c]reationists are now espousing one of the arguments of Clarence Darrow's ardent defense of Scopes: that the theory of the beginning should not be taught to the exclusion of another."[60] Solomon* agrees that both explanations should be taught because "[n]othing is so unscientific as . . . seeking to suppress or conceal dissent rather than grappling with it."[61] Alexander* concurs that "a comparison of the two alternatives can be an excellent exercise in logic and reason."[62] Anderson* and Kilbourn* agree that at least "an argument for teaching special-creation can be made."[63]

The U. S. Supreme Court recently has ruled for the first time on the constitutional issue of "balanced teaching of creation-science and evolution" in public schools. The Court overturned a Louisiana law that required balanced treatment, on the ground that the particular legislature's purpose was to advance religion, although the opinion did not say that teaching the theory of creation would necessarily advance religion.[64] The majority opinion expressly reaffirmed that teachers "already possess" a "flexibility . . . to supplant the present science curriculum with the presentation of theories, besides evolution, about the origin of life," and that teachers are "free to teach any and all facets of this subject" of "all scientific theories about the origins of humankind."[65] Justice Scalia, joined by Chief Justice Rehnquist, went further and argued as follows: "Infinitely less can we say (or should we say) that the scientific evidence for evolution is so conclusive that no one could be gullible enough to believe that there is any real scientific evidence to the contrary," while on the other hand that they "have no basis on the record to conclude that creation-science need be anything other than a collection of scientific data supporting the theory that life abruptly appeared on earth."[66] In fact, the U.S. Court of Appeals split narrowly on those issues (eight to seven), with the seven dissenting judges concluding firmly that balanced treatment "does not infringe the constitution," that "evolution is not established fact and that there is strong evidence that life and the universe came about in a different manner" in the view of many scientists, and that the theory of creation is "scientific evidence . . . for the sudden appearance of highly developed forms of life."[67]

Even John Scopes*, who fought for the right to teach evolution in an age of opposite bigotry to today's evolutionary orthodoxy, said that "[e]ducation, you know, means broadening, advancing, and if you limit a teacher to only one side of anything the whole country will eventually have only one thought. . . . I believe in teaching every aspect of every problem or theory."[68]

W. R. Bird
Atlanta, Georgia
October 1987

Notes

A note about footnote style that follows *A Uniform System of Citation*: Articles in periodicals are cited by author, title italicized, volume number, journal, first page, relevant page, and date; *e.g.*, footnote 15 (unless the journal does not use sequential pagination for each volume). Essays collected in books are cited by author, title italicized, book title, first page, relevant page, editor, and date; *e.g.*, footnote 27. Books are cited by author, title italicized, relevant page, and date; *e.g.*, footnote 1 (unless unpublished; *e.g.*, footnote 50). Legal cases and statutes are cited in legal style; *e.g.*, footnote 39.

[1] C. Darwin*, *The Origin of Species* 2 (1st ed. 1859, repr. 1964).

[2] *E.g.*, Thompson*, *Biology, Zoology, and Genetics* 1 (1983); Ch. 3 introduction.

[3] 2 *The Life and Letters of Charles Darwin* 202 (F. Darwin*ed. 1887).

[4] *E.g.*, T. Dobzhansky*, F. Ayala*, G. Stebbins* & J.Valentine*, *Evolution* 351-64 (1977); Ch. 5 introduction.

[5] *E.g.*, *id.* at 349-50; C. Sagan*, *Cosmos* 246-47 (1980); Section 7.1.

[6] Sections 13.5, 14.1.

[7] Section 3.3.

[8] Sections 3.2(d)-(e), 3.3.

[9] Section 3.2(d) & (f).

[10] Section 9.1(d).

[11] Section 15.2(a).

[12] Section 3.2(c).

[13] Section 3.2(e).

[14] Section 3.2(d).

[15] Ridley*, *Who Doubts Evolution?*, 90 New Scientist 830, 831 (1981); Section 3.4(a).

[16] A. Boyden*, *Perspectives in Zoology* 117 (1973); Section 3.4(b).

[17] Charig*, *Systematics in Biology: A Fundamental Comparison of Some Major Schools of Thought*, in Problems of Phylogenetic Reconstruction 411-12 (K. Joysey* & A. Friday* eds. 1982).

[18] Oldroyd*, *Charles Darwin's Theory of Evolution: A Review of Our Present Understanding*, 1 Biology & Philosophy 133, 154 (1986); Section 3.4(c).

[19] Beatty*, *Classes and Cladists*, 31 Systematic Zoology 25, 29, 31 (1982).

[20] Ross*, *Illusion and reality in comparative physiology*, 59 Canadian J. Zoology 2151, 2153 (1981); Section 3.4(d).

[21] Oldroyd*, *Charles Darwin's Theory of Evolution: A Review of Our Present Understanding*, 1 Biology & Philosophy 133, 154 (1986); Section 3.4(e).

[22] M. Denton*, *Evolution: A Theory in Crisis* 291 (1985); Section 3.4(f).

[23] R. Lewontin*, *The Genetic Basis of Evolutionary Change* 11-12, 189 (1974) (italics deleted); Section 3.4(g).

[24] Cracraft*, *Book Review of Beyond Neo-Darwinism*, 1 Cladistics 300, 300 (1985) (not necessarily Cracraft's* own view of neo-Darwinism); Section 3.2(b) and 3.3(f).

[25] B. Leith*, *The Descent of Darwin: A Handbook of Doubts about Darwinism* 10-11 (1982) (italics added).

[26] M. Denton*, *Evolution: A Theory in Crisis* 345 (1985).

[27] Ho* & Saunders*, *Preface*, to Beyond Neo-Darwinism ix, ix (M. Ho* & P. Saunders* eds. 1984).

[28] Sermonti*, *Life as a non-historical reality*, 73 Rivista di Biologia 551, 564-66 (1980).

[29] Dobzhansky*, *Book Review of The Origin of Living Organisms*, 29 Evolution 376, 376 (1975).

[30] M. Denton*, *Evolution: A Theory in Crisis* 327 (1985).

[31] *Id.* at 77 (italics added).

[32] Ruse*, *The Ideology of Darwinism*, in Darwin Today 233 (E. Geissler* & W. Scheler* eds. 1983).

[33] R. Good*, *Features of Evolution in the Flowering Plants* 2 (1974).

[34] *Id.* (italics added).

[35] Tipler*, *How to Construct a Falsifiable Theory in Which the Universe Came Into Being Several Thousand Years Ago*, 2 Philosophy of Science Association 873, 874, 893 (1984).

[36] Bethell*, *A Challenge to Materialism*, New Republic, Aug. 1, 1983, at 34, 36.

[37] Section 15.3(c).

[38] Sections 15.2(a) & 13.2.

[39] Aguillard v. Edwards, 778 F.2d 225, 226, 227 (5th Cir. 1985) (en banc) (Gee, J., dissenting with Clark, C.J., and Reavley, Garwood, Higginbotham, Hill, and Jones, JJ.).

[40] Edwards v. Aguillard, 482 U.S. (June 19, 1987) (Scalia, J., dissenting with Rehnquist, C.J.).

[41] Section 13.4.

[42] J. North*, *The Measure of the Universe* 405 (1965).

[43] R. Shapiro*, *Origins: A Skeptic's Guide to the Creation of Life on Earth* 257 (1986); Ruse*, *Creation-Science Is Not Science*, in Creationism and the Law 150, 156 (M. La Follette* ed. 1983).

[44] The following are only the books, without adding the many articles. *Creationism, Science, and the Law: The Arkansas Case* (M. La Follette* ed. 1983); N. Eldredge*, *The Monkey Business* (1982); P. Kitcher*, *Abusing Science: The Case Against Creationism* (1982); M. Ruse*, *Darwinism Defended* 283-329 (1982); R. Shapiro*, *Origins: A Skeptic's Guide to the Creation of Life on Earth* 248-65 (1986); D. Futuyma*, *Science on Trial: The Case for Evolution* (1983); N. Newell*, *Creation and Evolution: Myth or*

Reality? (1982); J. Zetterberg*, *Evolution Versus Creation: The Public Education Controversy* (1983); D. Nelkin*, *The Creation Controversy: Science or Scripture in the Schools* (1982); *Science and Creationism* (A. Montagu* ed. 1983).

[45] Sections 3.2(a)-(c).

[46] Hoffman* & Hecht*, *Species Selection As a Causal Process: A Reply*, 19 Evolutionary Biology 275, 275 (1985).

[47] T. Kuhn*, *The Structure of Scientific Revolutions* (2d ed. 1970).

[48] Sections 9.7 & 10.5.

[49] T. Kuhn*, *The Structure of Scientific Revolutions* 5 (2d ed. 1970).

[50] NBC News & Associated Press, November National Poll 15 (Nov. 24, 1981).

[51] Stacey* & Shupe*, *Religious Values and Religiosity in the Textbook Adoption Controversy in Texas*, 25 Rev. Religious Research 321, 326 (1984).

[52] *Lawpoll*, Am. Bar Ass'n J., Jan. 1987, at 35.

[53] Fuerst*, *University student understanding of evolutionary biology's place in the creation/evolution controversy*, 84 Ohio J. Science 218 (1984).

[54] Zimmerman*, *The Evolution-Creation Controversy: Opinions from Students at a "Liberal" Liberal Arts College*, 86 Ohio J. Science 134, 134 (1986).

[55] *Finding: Let kids decide how we got here*, Am. School Bd. J., Mar. 1980, at 52, 52.

[56] Austin Analytical Consulting, Opinion Poll for Biology Teachers question 8 (1986).

[57] *Scientists Abandon Evolution*, Contrast, Mar.-Apr. 1982, at 1, 3.

[58] Stonehouse*, *Introduction*, to M. Pitman, Adam and Evolution 9, 12 (1984).

[59] Letter from Dr. W. Scot Morrow* to Dr. Major Rhodes* (Jan. 1, 1981).

[60] A. Thompson*, *Biology, Zoology, and Genetics: Evolution Model vs. Creation Model* 2, 271 (1983) (although he does not view the theory of creation as scientific).

[61] P. Davis & E. Solomon*, *The World of Biology* 414 (1974).

[62] Alexander*, *Evolution, Creation, and Biology Teaching*, in Evolution versus Creationism 90, 91 (J. Zetterberg* ed. 1983) (although he does not support legislation of curriculum or regard the theory of creation as scientific).

[63] Anderson* & Kilbourn*, *Creation, Evolution, and Curriculum*, 67 Science Education 45, 53-54 (1983) (although they do not regard the theory of creation as scientific).

[64] Edwards v. Aguillard, 482 U.S. (June 19, 1987).

[65] *Id.* at 8, 9.

[66] *Id.* at 25, 20 (Scalia, J., dissenting, with Rehnquist, C.J.).

[67] Aguillard v. Edwards, 778 F.2d 225, 226 (5th Cir. 1985) (en banc) (dissenting opinion).

[68] P. Davis & E. Solomon*, *The World of Biology* 414 (1974).

PART I

What Are the Theories of Evolution and Abrupt Appearance?

The theory of abrupt appearance involves the scientific evidence that natural groups of plants and animals appeared abruptly but discontinuously in complex form, and also that the first life and the universe appeared abruptly but discontinuously in complex form. It is different from theories of creation, although they share some historical roots in the great scientists of the nineteenth century, differing particularly in its totally empirical basis.

The empirical evidence of discontinuity is widely acknowledged in science. Many evolutionists write that biological "observed discontinuities" result from the "sudden emergence of major adaptive types, as seen in the abrupt appearance in the fossil record of families and orders" (Davis*),[1] that " 'discontinuities are almost always and systematically present at the origin of really high categories' " (Kitts*),[2] and that further "discontinuities" arise from the "regular absence of transitional forms [that] is an almost universal phenomenon" for "almost all orders of all classes" (Simpson*).[3] Others see a "discontinuity between the two forms" of prokaryotes and eukaryotes (Margulis*),[4] and between apes and man (Dobzhansky* et al.).[5] Evolutionists also write of the cosmic "beginnings, the First Event," which "involve a discontinuity which has often been said to constitute a limit to that which may be known" (North*),[6] and which are often called "singularities" because of that discontinuity (Tipler*).[7]

13

The theory of evolution, by contrast, centers around the "common ancestry" of all organisms[8]—or macroevolution—which involves evolution "from primordial life, through unicellular and multicellular organisms, invertebrate and vertebrate animals, to man...."[9] It also includes the evolution of life from nonlife, and the evolution of the universe by the big bang.[10]

There are no religions that embrace a theological belief in abrupt appearance, but there are religions that hold evolutionist beliefs. Nevertheless, the scientific theories are independent of any religions, which have merely consistent beliefs.

Notes

[1]   Davis*, *Comparative Anatomy and the Evolution of Vertebrates*, in Genetics, Paleontology, and Evolution at 64, 74 (G. Jepsen*, E. Mayr* & G. Simpson* eds. 2d ed. 1963) (affirming evolution).

[2]   Kitts*, *Paleontology and Evolutionary Theory*, 28 Evolution 458, 467 (1974) (affirming evolution).

[3]   G. Simpson*, *The Major Features of Evolution* 360-61 (1953) (affirming evolution).

[4]   L. Margulis*, *The Origin of Eukaryotic Cells* 27 (1970) (affirming evolution).

[5]   T. Dobzhansky*, F. Ayala*, G. Stebbins* & J. Valentine*, *Evolution* 453 (1977) (affirming evolution).

[6]   J. North*, *The Measure of the Universe* 400-01 (1965) (affirming cosmic evolution).

[7]   Tipler*, *How to Construct a Falsifiable Theory in Which the Universe Came into Being Several Thousand Years Ago*, 2 Philosophy of Science Association 873, 874-75 (1984) (affirming cosmic evolution).

[8]   F. Ayala* & J. Valentine*, *Evolving: The Theory and Processes of Organic Evolution* 1 (1979).

[9]   Dobzhansky*, *Evolution*, in 10 Encyclopedia Americana 734, 748 (1982).

[10]   T. Dobzhansky*, F. Ayala*, G. Stebbins* & J. Valentine*, *Evolution* 9 (1977).

CHAPTER 1

Definitions of the Theory of Evolution and the Theory of Abrupt Appearance

> *Education, you know, means broadening,*
> *advancing, and if you limit a teacher to*
> *only one side of anything the whole coun-*
> *try will eventually have only one thought,*
> *be one individual. I believe in teaching*
> *every aspect of every problem or theory.*
> —John T. Scopes*,
> at the *Scopes* trial[1]

Proponents sometimes define evolution merely as change. The press often ignores the theory of abrupt appearance, and uses the theory of creation synonymously with Genesis. This chapter assesses the accuracy of those definitions (Section 1.1), and compares evolution and abrupt appearance with religion (Section 1.2).

---

*Scientists cited in this book, unless otherwise indicated, are not proponents of, and their quoted statements are not intended as endorsements of, either the theory of abrupt appearance or the theory of creation. However, their quoted statements are acknowledging data that some nonevolutionist scientists interpret as supporting the theory of abrupt appearance better than the theory of evolution or as undermining the theory of evolution or significant aspects.

Figure 1.1
Charles Darwin*, author
of The Origin of Species

1.1 The Definitions of Evolution and Abrupt Appearance

a. The Scientific Meanings of Evolution

(1) Aspects of Evolution. "Evolution" has three major scientific aspects, which are described by leading evolutionists Dobzhansky*, Ayala*, Stebbins*, and Valentine*:

> During the century and more since Darwinism came into being, the concept of evolution has been applied not only to the *living world* but to the nonbiological as well. Thus, we speak of the evolution of the entire *universe*, the *solar system* and the *physical earth*, apart from the organisms that inhabit it. As we shall show in Chapter 11 ("Cosmic Evolution and the Origin of Life"), the origin of life is best explained as the outcome of precellular *chemical evolution*, which took place over millions of years.[2]

Their book is one of the "[t]wo textbooks of evolution [that] now dominate the field," according to another leading evolutionist, Stephen Jay Gould* of Harvard.[3]

The same phases of evolution are mentioned by Mayr* of Harvard, "our greatest living evolutionary biologist" according to Gould*.[4]

Man's world view today is dominated by the knowledge that the universe, the stars, the earth and all living things have evolved through a long history that was not foreordained or programmed, a history of continual, gradual change shaped by more or less directional natural processes consistent with the laws of physics. *Cosmic evolution* and *biological evolution* have that much in common.
. . ..
. . . [See "*Chemical Evolution and the Origin of Life*" by Richard E. Dickerson, p. 70].[5]

Thus, evolution includes biological evolution, biochemical evolution, and cosmic evolution:

a. Biological evolution (or organic evolution):	Evolution of *organisms* all from one or more common ancestors, so that single celled organisms evolved into invertebrate animals and plants, then vertebrate fish, then amphibians, then reptiles, then birds and lower mammals, then primates, then man ("macroevolution")[6]
b. Biochemical evolution (or chemical evolution):	Evolution of the *first life* from nonlife[7]
c. Cosmic evolution (or stellar evolution):	Evolution of the *universe*, including galactic clusters, galaxies, stars, and solar systems.[8]

Similar terms and definitions are given in a multitude of other standard works on evolution, written by Blum*,[9] Huxley*,[10] Fox* and Dose*,[11] Ponnamperuma*,[12] Olson*,[13] and a number of others.[14]

Thus, evolution is not restricted to biological evolution. Dobzhansky*, a geneticist at Rockefeller University, instead stated "that the concept of evolution is much broader":

Although this article is concerned with *biological evolution*, it should be recognized that the concept of evolution is much broader. . . . There is also *cosmic*, or inorganic, *evolution*, and evolution of human culture. One of the theories advanced by cosmologists sets the beginning of cosmic evolution between 5 and 10 billion years ago. The *origin of life*, which started biological evolution, took place 3 or 4 billion years ago.[15]

Darwin* himself did not limit evolution to the biological arena, but wrote of the possibility "that all the conditions for the first production of a living organism" were present "in some warm little pond."[16]

(2) Difference from Mere Change. The basic meaning of "evolution" is not merely change. Instead,

> Clearly, a definition of organic evolution is needed that includes all of its aspects and at the same time *distinguishes between evolution and mere change....Transformation* is a better concept than "change"....[17]

In fact, discontinuitist scientists agree that change (microevolution) occurs in organisms and the universe and limit their objections to large scale transmutation (macroevolution).[18]

Biological evolution, in contrast to mere change, according to Ayala* and Gould*, is the view that all plants and animals descended from a common ancestor:

> The millions of diverse living species we find around us in the modern world are all descended from a *common ancestor* that lived in the remote past (Fig. 1.1). The processes that have brought this diversity about are collectively called evolution.[19]

> evolution[.] The process by which all organisms have arisen by descent from a *common ancestor.*[20]

Biological evolution is similarly defined to include common ancestry by Maynard Smith*,[21] Patterson*,[22] and others.[23] That descent from common ancestors involves change "from primordial life, through unicellular and multicellular organisms, invertebrate and vertebrate animals, to man. . .," in the words of the late Dobzhansky* and others.[24] That is the view of biological evolution taught in most science textbooks in public schools.[25]

The scientific basis of evolution is discussed in detail in Chapters 3, 5, and 7.

b. The Scientific Meaning of the Theory of Abrupt Appearance

The theory of abrupt appearance is defined as scientific interpretations of scientific data postulating origin through discontinuous abrupt appearance in complex form. That "theory that life abruptly appeared on Earth" is the general "competitive theory of origins" to the "theory of evolution," according to Klein*.[25A] That theory of abrupt appearance points to the scientific evidence for sudden emergence that punctuated equilibria advocates and other scientists stress, but it is important to note that the theory of abrupt appearance interprets that evidence in terms of discontinuity and relies on other lines of evidence, whereas punctuationists interpret that evidence in terms of continuity and evolution. Thus, many structuralists such as Webster* write of "apparent, empirical discontinuity," while others such as Denton* propose "that life might be fundamentally a discontinuous phenomenon."[26] The theory of abrupt appearance also relies on the scientific evidence that many big bang theorists find to support a sudden emergence of the universe, but it is also important to state that the theory of abrupt appearance interprets that evidence to show the discontinuity not only of the origin of matter and energy but of the origin of galaxies and stars. In this book, proponents of the theory of abrupt appearance, thus, are called discontinuitists. The empirical data and scientific interpretations that some discontinuitist scientists offer are summarized in Chapters 2, 4, and 6.

(1) Scientific Meaning of Abrupt Appearance. The term "abrupt appearance" is widely used in the biological and astrophysical literature about origins. In biology, for example, advocates of evolutionary punctuated equilibria describe the fossil record of sudden or abrupt appearances, and Raup* and Stanley* are typical:

> Unfortunately, the origins of most higher categories are shrouded in mystery; commonly new higher categories *appear abruptly* in the fossil record without evidence of transitional ancestral forms.[27]

Many neo-Darwinians also recognize the abrupt appearances in the fossil record, such as Ayala* and Valentine*:

> Most taxa at these high levels *appear abruptly* in the fossil record. . . .
> . . ..
> . . .Most orders, classes, and phyla *appear abruptly* and commonly have already acquired all the characters that distinguish them.[28]

(As noted above, those evolutionists believe in evolutionary or continuous, rather than discontinuous, abrupt appearance.[29]) Many information scientists discuss the sudden appearance of vast information content in living forms.[30] Large numbers of similar citations appear in Sections 2.1 and 2.4.

In cosmology, advocates of the evolutionary big bang theory often speak of the sudden or abrupt appearance of the universe, while proponents of the evolutionist inflationary universe theory refer to the sudden or abrupt appearance of matter and energy. Their views are discussed in Sections 7.1 and 7.2. (Their interpretation involves singularities but not necessarily nonnaturalistic causes and events.[31])

The term "discontinuity" is also widely used in biological and cosmic evolutionary literature, as discussed on page 13.

(2) Aspects of Abrupt Appearance. The "theory of abrupt appearance" has three aspects parallel to evolution:

> *a. Biological*   Abrupt appearance in complex form of genera
> *abrupt*   or families of *organisms*, while acknowledg-
> *appearance:*   ing both genetic variation ("microevolution")
>   in all natural groups within genetic limits and
>   extinction of some natural groups
> *b. Biochemical* Abrupt appearance in complex form of the
> *abrupt*   *first life*
> *appearance:*
> *c. Cosmic*   Abrupt appearance in complex form of the *uni-*
> *abrupt*   *verse*, including galactic clusters, galaxies,
> *appearance:*   stars, and the solar system.

The following sections discuss affirmative lines of scientific evidence that constitute the theory of abrupt appearance, giving seven affirmative scientific arguments for biological abrupt appearance, five for biochemical abrupt appearance, and six for cosmic abrupt appearance. Examples of this scientific evidence are the abrupt appearance of complex organisms in the fossil record, the systematic gaps between natural groups of organisms in that fossil record up to the present, and the widespread anomalies in anatomy and biochemistry between presumably close relatives.

These affirmative lines of scientific evidence are not entirely new concepts. In fact, the underlying empirical data for biological abrupt appearance were essentially stated 125 years ago by Professor Louis Agassiz of Harvard, and some of the evidence for cosmic abrupt appearance was presented 300 years ago by Sir Isaac Newton, as described later.[32] Much of the evidence has been outlined recently by Professor Dean H. Kenyon of San Francisco State University.[33]

This theory of abrupt appearance is different from the theories of creation, vitalism, panspermia, and similar concepts. Discontinuous abrupt appearance is a more general theory and a more scientific approach than scientific views of creation, vitalism, or panspermia, although they can be formulated as submodels of abrupt appearance. The various theories can be outlined as follows:

The Theory of Evolution	*The Theory of Abrupt Appearance*
Theory of continuity (macroevolution, biochemical evolution, cosmic evolution)	Theory of discontinuity (steady state, natural group systematics,[34] nineteenth century systematics or typology,[35] etc.)
Theories of Darwinian evolution (either neo-Darwinism/natural selection or punctuated equilibria)	Theory of abrupt appearance (biological abrupt appearance, biochemical abrupt appearance, cosmic abrupt appearance)
Theories of non-Darwinian evolution (saltations, macromutations, neutral mutations, structuralism, some transformed cladistics, neo-Lamarckism, etc.)	Theories of panspermia and directed panspermia[36]
Theories of theistic evolution	Theories of nontheistic forces (creative intelligence,[37] great origins thesis,[38] vitalism,[39] etc.)
	Theories of creation (nomothetic[40] or miraculous)

A theory of discontinuity is described in steady state terms by Sermonti* (a noted professor of genetics at University of Perugia and vice president of the 14th International Congress of Genetics) and Fondi* (professor of paleontology at University of Siena):

> If we wish to keep to the substance of the matter, the new scientific *Weltanschauung* not only brings to mind the ideas of many distinguished men such as Goethe, Cuvier, Linnaeus, Vico, Leibniz, Paracelsus, Cusano and Aristotle, but . . . the traditional view of a *cosmos* or *systema naturae* perceived as a *static whole*. . .

> The result we believe must be striven for can therefore only be the following: biology will receive *no advantage* from following the teachings of Lamarck, *Darwin* and the modern hyper-Darwinists; indeed, it must as quickly as possible leave the narrow straits and *blind alleys* of the evolutionistic myth and resume its certain journey along the open and illuminated paths of tradition.[41]

The theory of discontinuity was integral to nineteenth-century systematics:

> [T]he doctrine of continuity has always necessitated a *retreat from pure empiricism*, and contrary to what is widely assumed by evolutionary biologists today, *it has always been the anti-evolutionists, not the evolutionists, in the scientific community who have stuck rigidly to the facts and adhered to a more strictly empirical approach.*

Even in classical times Aristotle's opposition to the evolutionism of the pre-Socratics was based on his acute observation of nature and his appreciation of the facts of biology. It was, again, the actual facts that led *Linnaeus, Cuvier* and *most of the professional biologists* of the seventeenth, eighteenth and early nineteenth centuries to favour a *discontinuous* view of nature. . . .

. . . When, half a century later, *Agassiz* referred to the notion of continuity in its new Darwinian guise as "a phantom" *he was speaking as a true empiricist. It was Darwin the evolutionist who was retreating* from the facts.[42]

Some variants of the theory of discontinuity involve nontheistic forces such as the "great origins thesis" of Huston Smith* (a philosopher of science until recently at Syracuse University and before that at Massachusetts Institute of Technology):

All that the thesis requires is that *we derive from Something that is superior to ourselves* by every measure of worth we know. These transcendent objects include the ultimates of the great religious traditions— Allah, God, Brahman, Śūnyatā, the Tao, the Great Spirit—as well as philosophical ultimates, provided that they exceed human beings in intrinsic worth. Clearly included, for example, is the Neoplatonic One from which beings proceed by emanation rather than creation, and the Whiteheadian God whose primordial and consequent natures conspire to work upon the world their everlasting lure. I hope this latitude in the Great Origins thesis will keep it from being dismissed as Creationism.[43]

(3) Historical Basis for the Definition. The term "creation" has been defined in a similar way by many scientists over the last century and a quarter, as origin through discontinuous "causes unknown," "endowed from the beginnings of their existence with all their characteristics." That sort of use at the time of Darwin*—a use that did "not imply God"—is summarized by Cannon*, a history professor at University of California at Berkeley:

The reason is simple. The theory of separate *creation* explains nothing because there was no theory of separate *creation*. There was only a theory of *separate* creation. The word "creation" in English scientific writings of the mid-nineteenth century merely means, "They got there somehow." It does not imply God, and is used quite casually by Charles Lyell himself. The term "the creation of species" is equivalent to the phrase "the origination of species by cause or causes unknown." Darwin's famous use of ridicule about creation is in his "Historical Sketch" attached to the third and later editions of the Origin in which he attacked Richard Owen for saying that "creation" means, to the zoologist, "a process he knows not what." Owen was, however, quite correct, and the passage actually makes Darwin, not Owen, look ridiculous. Even for

Louis Agassiz, creation only meant that organized beings are "endowed from the beginning of their existence with all their characteristics," just as an embryo is endowed with the characteristics of the youth and the man.

On the other hand, *separate* creation is a phrase which applies to at least three distinct scientific controversies. . . .[44]

Leakey*, the paleoanthropologist, recognizes the same historical relation of creation to abrupt appearance:

Geologists of the 1830s were convinced that they had discovered the dawn of life in this strata, called the Cambrian, and no hypothesis save special *creation* was deemed adequate to account for the *sudden appearance* of Cambrian fossils. Rocks older than the Cambrian were, so it seemed, completely devoid of fossils. In the second place, the various strata each generally had its own characteristic fossil flora and fauna and the transitions between strata were *abrupt*. This suggested to geologists the probability of successive wholesale *creations* and extinctions. . . .[45]

Charles Darwin* himself used the "term of creation, by which I really meant 'appeared' by some wholly unknown process."[46] Another anti-creationist, Draper*, in his widely read book in 1896, acknowledged that the primary component of creation is "abrupt appearance":

They incline us to view favorably the idea of transmutations of one form into another, rather than of sudden creation.

Creation implies an abrupt appearance, transformation a gradual change.

In this manner is presented to our contemplation the great theory of Evolution. . . .[47]

Agassiz of Harvard, "America's leading biologist"[48] and the leading creationist scientist of his time, further defined the theory of creation as follows:

All attempts to explain the origin of species may be brought under two categories: viz. 1st, some naturalists admitting that all organized beings are *created*, that is to say, *endowed from the beginning of their existence with all their characteristics*, while 2d, others assume that they arise spontaneously.[49]

Others over a century ago, such as Hooker*, used the term creation in the sense of "appearing or originating."[50]

Creation was similarly defined over a quarter century ago by Dr. Evan Shute, also a creationist:

The lower four-fifths of the rock of the earth's crust is lifeless. Then life *suddenly appears*, is at once general across the earth, and promptly demonstrates most of the types we now know. This is not the evidence the evolutionist wants, and is quite fatal to his claims. *This is Creation*.[51]

The term was so used three decades ago by Gold*, Bondi*, and Hoyle* in the continuous creation (or steady state) hypothesis to describe the abrupt appearance from nothing of hydrogen atoms.[52]

(4) Scientific Uses of Creation. The term "creation" is widely used in this decade by Guth*, Steinhart*, Tryon*, and others in science literature describing the inflationary universe theory to refer to the abrupt appearance "from nothing" of all matter and energy in the universe.[53] Typical examples are as follows:

> The idea that the universe has been *created from "nothing"* by a process of quantum mechanical tunnelling was first suggested by Tryon [1] and by Fomin [2]. It has received renewed attention, both as a way of circumventing the problem of the initial singularity [3], and because the universe may then start out as a (quasi-) de Sitter space-time, allowing inflation and solving a number of outstanding cosmological problems [4-10]. . . .[54]

> Abstract. A non zero probability amplitude for the *appearance* of a multidimensional universe of $(1 + d)$ dimensions is found. . . .
> Some recent computations [3] have indeed shown that there exists a finite amplitude for the *creation* of an universe in an inflationary phase from the vacuum. The idea is to reinterpret the usual compact de Sitter instanton as giving this amplitude by the well known W.K.B. semiclassical formula.[55]

The term is currently used by many evolutionist advocates of the big bang theory to describe the abrupt appearance of the universe.[56] One of its primary proponents, Gamow*, described the big bang as "The Creation of the Universe,"[57] and Silk*, similarly describes that theory as "The Left Hand of Creation."[58] Creation is used in biological theories as well, such as by Hoyle and other advocates of the panspermia theory to describe the abrupt appearance in complex form of microbes in space.[59] These and many other scientific uses of the term creation are treated in Section 13.1.

The theory of creation has been defined differently by various people and groups, but the above definition is the one most generally accepted by its supporters. Because it seems fair to let each camp define its own name, this definition of the theory of creation will be used in this book. However, the camps cannot conclusively determine the scientific and non-religious nature of their views, so those issues will be scrutinized respectively in this volume and in the second volume.

The linkage occasionally of "creation" with "science" is not necessarily an unusual name for a scientific area. Many writers refer to "evolutionary science," such as the scientist who named the neo-Darwinian synthesis,[60] Gould*,[61] and others.[62] Textbooks and authors refer to "biological science,"[63] as well as to "life science," "physical science," "environmental science," and similar areas.[64] Other examples are the natural sciences, nuclear science, information science, and computer science. The congruity or incongruity of pairing "creation" with "science" will be discussed further.[65]

(5) Misconceptions about Abrupt Appearance. There are several misconceptions about the theory of abrupt appearance. It does *not* necessitate reference to a creator or ad hoc explanation based on acts of a creator, for several reasons. First, "abrupt appearance" is properly defined as scientific data and scientific interpretations that indicate discontinuous abrupt appearances but not supernatural causes (Chapters 2, 4, and 6). Second, "abrupt appearance" is a term widely used in science without any reference to or explanation by a creator (Section 13.1). Third, abrupt appearance is a viewpoint held by some scientists who do not believe in a creator and offer a creator-less explanation (Sections 13.1(f) and 13.2). Fourth, however, many evolutionist writings refer to a creator without being religious, and modern science historically arose in a context of belief in a creator (Sections 13.3-13.4). Discussion of the scientific evidence that discontinuitist scientists offer (fossils, morphology, information content, probability, genetics, comparative biochemistry, etc.) simply does not require discussion of a creator.

The theory of abrupt appearance does *not* essentially involve appearance "from nothing," because that concept is not necessary to discontinuous abrupt appearance in complex form. However, the concept of origin "from nothing" or "ex nihilo" is not necessarily religious.[66] Some evolutionist physicists and astronomers, such as Guth* of MIT, Tryon* of Hunter, and Vilenkin* of Tufts, currently advocate the inflationary universe theory with its premise that the universe appeared "ex nihilo":

> Recently there has been some serious speculation that the actual creation of the universe is describable by physical laws. In this view the universe would originate as a quantum fluctuation, starting *from absolutely nothing.* . . . From a historical point of view probably the most revolutionary aspect of the inflationary model is the notion that all the matter and energy in the observable universe may have emerged from almost nothing.[67]

Others who advocated the steady state (or continuous creation) theory, such as Bondi* of University of London and Hoyle* (then of

Cambridge), argued on the basis of mathematical calculations that hydrogen atoms appear abruptly "out of nothing."[68] Many proponents of the big bang theory, such as Margenau* of Yale (past president of the American Association of the Philosophy of Science and a collaborator with Einstein*, Heisenberg*, and Schrödinger*), suggest that "science has definitely shown the non-contradiction of creation out of nothing."[69]

The theory of abrupt appearance does *not* involve "kinds" of plants or animals, because that concept is generally outside the realm of empirical data and scientific interpretations. It instead involves "natural groups."[70] However, even the term "kinds" is widely used by evolutionists in a nontechnical and nonreligious sense.[71]

The theory of abrupt appearance also does *not* essentially involve "catastrophism" or a "worldwide flood", because those concepts are not part of the origin of the universe, the first life, and the various organisms. Many catastrophists are not discontinuitists,[72] and many discontinuitists are not catastrophists.[73] In fact, Morris made that distinction between the theories of abrupt appearance or creation and the theory of catastrophism, although he is a leading exponent of both creation and castastrophism:

> As with the evidence for a young earth, there is a great amount of sound scientific evidence for catastrophism, rather than uniformitarianism, in earth history including good geologic and ethnologic evidence for a worldwide flood. There is no good reason why all these scientific data should not be incorporated in public instruction. However, this question is quite distinct from the basic creation-evolution question, and should be kept separate in public school classrooms and textbooks. In other words, there are three basic questions at issue here:
> (1) Special creation versus naturalistic evolution as the ultimate explanation of the universe, life and man.
> (2) Age of the earth; ancient earth versus young earth.
> (3) Uniformitarianism versus catastrophism (including not only intermittent local catastrophism, but also a global cataclysm) as the basic framework of interpretation in earth history.
> Each of these issues can and should be treated as a separate issue in public education. They are related issues of course, but each is important in its own right and is capable of discussion and evaluation quite independently of the others. . . .[74]

Finally, the theory of abrupt appearance does *not* essentially involve a "relatively recent inception" or "young age" of the universe and life, because the scientific evidence for biological abrupt appearance, biochemical abrupt appearance, and cosmic abrupt appearance does not depend at all on any particular time frame. Many who recognize a possibility of a young age are not discontinuitists,[75] and many or most discontinuitists reject a young age.[76] Again, Morris stresses the distinction in connection with the theory of creation:

> The scientific creation model is *not* tied to the young earth concept at all, despite its very wide misunderstanding on this point. The basic evidences for creation and against evolution (e.g., the gaps in the fossil record, the laws of thermodynamics, the complexity of living systems) are completely independent of the age of the earth or the date of creation. Creationists therefore do not propose that creationism be tied in public schools to a recent creation. On the other hand, there are many sound scientific evidences that the earth is young—far more numerous and based on data at least as good as the few evidences for an old earth—and apparently the only reason for not including these in public education is the fact that the evolution model requires an old earth before it can be considered feasible at all. The creation model does not depend on a young earth, but evolution does imply an old earth. . . .[77]

Because the theory of abrupt appearance does not require any particular time frame for the universe or life, it does not require any particular time frame for the abruptness of "abrupt appearance." It can adopt for biological abrupt appearance the geological "abruptness" of biological macroevolutionists.

The theory of abrupt appearance involves a concept of discontinuity that the theory of evolution excludes, and citations of evolutionist acknowledgments of abrupt appearances are not meant to imply evolutionist agreement with total discontinuity. However, discontinuitist scientists conclude that the abrupt appearances cited are explained more plausibly by discontinuity than by continuity.

Summary. As defined in one of the "[t]wo textbooks of evolution [that] now dominate the field" (Gould*[78]), "the concept of evolution has been applied not only to the living world" (biological evolution), but to "the origin of life . . . as the outcome of precellular chemical evolution" and to "the evolution of the entire universe, the solar system and the physical earth" ("cosmic evolution") (Dobzhansky*, Ayala*, Stebbins*, and Valentine*[79]). Thus, a proper definition "distinguishes between evolution and mere change," and recognizes that "[t]ransformation is a better concept than 'change' "(*id.*[80]).

The theory of abrupt appearance involves the same aspects: the discontinuous abrupt appearance in complex form of the universe (cosmic abrupt appearance), of the first life (biochemical abrupt appearance), and of plants and animals (biological abrupt appearance). That theory builds on the empirical evidence of abrupt appearance that many evolutionists recognize, but adds that the more logical scientific interpretation of that evidence involves discontinuity rather than continuity. The theory of abrupt appearance differs from the historical theory of creation, particularly in the totally empirical basis of the theory of abrupt appearance and its categorization into affirmative lines of scientific evidence. However, the theories share some historical roots in the great scientists such as Agassiz of Harvard, who held to a scientific theory of creation based on data that organisms appear "endowed from the beginning of their existence with all their characteristics" (Agassiz[81]). Darwin* himself referred to the "theory of creation" and to the "term of creation, by which I really meant 'appeared' by some wholly unknown process" (Darwin*[82]), and the next generation understood too that "[c]reation implies an abrupt appearance" (Draper*[83]). In its context at the time of Darwin*, the "word 'creation' in English scientific writings of the mid-nineteenth century ... does not imply God" (Cannon*[84]). This book is about the theory of abrupt appearance, as contrasted with the theory of creation, and specifically about the scientific evidence of which the theory of abrupt appearance consists. *Abusus non tollit usum.*

1.2 The Religious Meanings of Evolution and Creation

a. A Comparison of Evolutionist Religions and the Scientific Theory of Evolution

In contrast to evolutionary science, there are numerous evolutionist religions (religions holding to theological beliefs in evolution). Although most people are aware of some creationist religions, they are often not aware that parallel evolutionist religions (whether explicit or implicit) exist and even fall in every theological category. The following are evolutionist religions of Protestant, Catholic, Jewish, and non-Judeo-Christian faiths:

Figure 1.2
Evolutionist religions,
such as Buddhism

Theological Category	*Evolutionist Religions*
a. *Protestant*:	Theological Liberalism and Neo-Orthodoxy, Religious Humanism and Unitarianism
b. *Catholic*:	Neo-Modernist Roman Catholicism
c. *Jewish*:	Reform Judaism and Humanistic Judaism
d. *Non-Judeo-Christian*:	Buddhism and most Hinduism, Secular Humanism and other Humanist faiths, Nontheistic religions and Atheism.

These evolutionist religions are discussed with extensive documentation in a later section.[85]

b. A Comparison of Creationist Religions and the Theory of Abrupt Appearance

In contrast to the theory of abrupt appearance, there are creationist religions just as there are evolutionist religions. Although most people are aware of the existence of creationist religions, they are often not aware that those religions span the theological spectrum just as evolutionist religions do. The following are creationist faiths that are not just Protestant but Catholic, Jewish, and non-Judeo-Christian:

Theological Category	Creationist Religions	Evolutionist Religions
a. Protestant:	Conservative Evangelicalism and Fundamentalism; Church of Christ and Seventh-day Adventism	Theological Liberalism and Neo-Orthodoxy Religious Humanism and Unitarianism
b. Catholic:	Orthodox Roman Catholicism and Eastern Orthodoxy	Neo-Modernist Roman Catholicism
c. Jewish:	Orthodox Judaism	Reform Judaism and Humanistic Judaism
d. Non-Judeo-Christian:	Islam (Muslims) and some Hinduism.	Buddhism and most Hinduism, Secular Humanism and other Humanist faiths, Nontheistic religions and Atheism.

These creationist religions and their evolutionist religion counterparts are discussed in a later section.[86] The point made here is that the scientific theory of abrupt appearance is as different from creationist religions as the scientific theory of evolution is from evolutionist religions.

Summary. There are no religious bodies that hold to a belief in the theory of abrupt appearance, but there are many religious groups that have a doctrinal belief in evolution, such as Theological Liberalism, Neo-Orthodoxy, Religious Humanism, Neo-Modernist Catholicism, Reform Judaism, and Buddhism. The religious denominations that have theological beliefs in creation are equally diverse, and hold a view very different in content from the theory of abrupt appearance, in that the former but not the latter includes God, days of creation, created kinds, Adam and Eve, a fall into sin, Noah's flood, and other biblical concepts. *Non semper ea sunt quae videntur.*

Notes

[1]   P. Davis & E. Solomon*, *The World of Biology* 414 (1974).

[2]   T. Dobzhansky*, F. Ayala*, G. Stebbins* & J. Valentine*, *Evolution* 9 (1977).

[3]   Gould*, *Darwinism Defined: The Difference between Fact and Theory*, Discover, Jan. 1987, at 65.

[4]   Gould*, *Balzan Prize To Ernst Mayr*, 223 Science 255, 255 (1984).

[5]   Mayr*, *Evolution*, Scientific Am., Sept. 1978, at 47, 47, 51 (italics added).

[6]   The general scientific use of the term "biological evolution" is shown at the beginning of Chapter 3.

[7]   The general scientific use of the term "biochemical evolution" is documented at the beginning of Chapter 5.

[8]   The general scientific use of the term "cosmic evolution" is shown at the beginning of Chapter 7.

[9]   The following definition is given by Blum*:

Most works dealing with organic evolution focus attention on its strictly *biological aspects*, disregarding to a great extent those physical factors that have determined the basic pattern along which living systems could subsequently develop. To understand these factors and restrictions, one needs to go back to the *origin of life*, and beyond into the domains of terrestrial and *cosmic evolution*.

H. Blum*, *Time's Arrow and Evolution* 4 (3d ed. 1968) (italics added).

[10]   Huxley*, *At Random*, in 3 Evolution after Darwin 41, 42 (S. Tax* ed. 1960) ("[I]t is evolution, in the broad sense, that links *inorganic* nature with life, and the *stars* with earth, and matter with mind, and animals with man.") (italics added).

[11]   S. Fox* & K. Dose*, Molecular Evolution and the Origin of Life 67 (1972) ("The ideal concept of the several evolutionary sequences on the atomic and molecular level as treated in Chapters 2-5 is summarized by the following flowsheet: Origin of the Universe [;] Evolution of stars and elements[;] ... Production of micromolecules in huge amounts ... [;] Formation

of macromolecules by condensation of micromolecules.") (italics deleted).

   12   He defines "Darwinian evolution" as follows: "We think of the process as having taken place in stages, from *inorganic evolution* to *organic evolution* and then to *biological evolution*." C. Ponnamperuma*, *The Origins of Life* 39 (1972) (italics added).

   13   E. Olson* & J. Robinson*, *Concepts of Evolution* 10 (1975) (*"Evolution-ism* is the doctrine that the *universe*, including *inorganic* and organic matter in all its manifestations, is the product of gradual and progressive development.") (italics added).

   14   *E.g.*, Wilson*, *The Origin of Life*, in Did the Devil Make Darwin Do It? 85, 86 (D. Wilson* ed. 1983) (*"Evolution*, which is the strongest natural explanation, holds that the gross features of the *universe*—including galaxies, solar systems and planets; the transition from *non-living matter to living organisms*; and the *diversity of life forms*, including human beings— all arose as a consequence of the innate proclivities of matter and energy, as expressed by the laws of nature.") (italics added); Price*, *Some Social and Philosophical Implications of the Origin and Synthesis of Life*, in Molecular Evolution at 461, 461-62 (D. Rohlfing* & A. Oparin* eds. 1972) ("One facet of this is the role of order in evolution. From the *big bang* onward, the major steps leading to human society here on Earth have had some common features . . .. This has unquestionably been a factor throughout *chemical and biological evolution*.") (italics added); J. Jarrett*, *Philosophy for the Study of Education* 346 (1969) (on evolutionary view of Herbert Spencer*); Abbagnano*, *Positivism*, 6 Encyclopedia of Philosophy 414, 416 (P. Edwards* ed. 1967) ("Darwin's doctrines made possible the formulation of the idea of a natural and necessary progress of the whole universe, beginning with a *cosmic* nebula and, through the uninterrupted development of the *inorganic* and *organic* world, continuing into the 'superorganic' development of the human and historical world.") (italics added).

   15   Dobzhansky*, *Evolution*, in 10 Encyclopedia Americana 734, 734 (1982) (italics added). Sir Julian Huxley* wrote similarly:

> I am quite aware that many people object to the use of the term evolution for anything but the transformations of living substance. But I think this is undesirably narrow. Some term is undoubtedly needed for the comprehensive process in all its aspects, and no other convenient designation exists at present save that of evolution. The over-all process of evolution in this comprehensive sense comprises *three main phases*. . . . We may call these three phases the inorganic or, if you like, *cosmological*; the organic or *biological*; and the human or psycho-social.

J. Huxley*, *Evolution in Action* 10 (1964) (italics added).

   16   Letter from Charles Darwin* to Sir Joseph Hooker* (1871), in 2 *The Life and Letters of Charles Darwin* 202 (F. Darwin* ed. 1887).

   17   T. Dobzhansky*, F. Ayala*, G. Stebbins* & J. Valentine*, *Evolution* 8 (1977) (italics added). *See also* Gruner*, *On Evolution and Its Relation to Natural Selection*, 16 Dialogue 708, 709 (1977) ("This becomes clear when we

reflect on what is meant by 'evolution'. When applied to organic nature the term does not refer merely to change or even gradual change.").

[18] *E.g.*, W. Stansfield*, *The Science of Evolution* 9 (1977) ("For example, the assertation that populations of organisms can change in their genetic composition from one generation to another (i.e., evolve) is undisputed, even by the creationists.").

[19] F. Ayala* & J. Valentine*, *Evolving: The Theory and Processes of Organic Evolution* 1 (1979) (college textbook).

[20] S. Luria*, S. Gould* & S. Singer*, *A View of Life* 767 (1981) (college textbook).

[21] J. Maynard Smith*, *The Theory of Evolution* 152 (1958) ("The theory of evolution holds that existing plants and animals have originated by descent with modification from one or a few simple ancestral forms.").

[22] C. Patterson*, *Evolution* 145 (1978) ("The first is the general thesis that evolution has occurred—all animal and plant species are related by common ancestry . . ..").

[23] Thomson*, *Marginalia: The Meanings of Evolution*, 70 Am. Scientist 529, 529 (1982); W. Stansfield*, *The Science of Evolution* 3 (1977) ("Evolution is a scientific theory proposing that higher forms of life have descended from lower forms").

[24] T. Dobzhansky*, *Evolution*, 10 Encyclopedia Americana 734, 748 (1982); A. Thompson*, *Biology, Zoology, and Genetics* 1 (1983); *see* Chapter 3.

[25] *E.g.*, R. Oram*, *Biology: Living Systems* 118, 248-67, 277-94, 602-23, 73T-80T, 142T-45T (3d ed. Teacher's Ed. 1979) (high school text) ("evolved from a single, original, common ancestor").

[25A] Klein*, *Preface*, to L. Sunderland, Darwin's Enigma 5, 5 (1985).

[26] Webster*, *The nature and scope of structuralist analysis in biology*, 80 Rivista di Biologia (Biology Forum) 173, 175 (1987); M. Denton*, *Evolution: A Theory in Crisis* 353 (1985).

[27] D. Raup* & S. Stanley*, *Principles of Paleontology* 372 (2d ed. 1978) (italics added).

[28] F. Ayala* & J. Valentine*, *Evolving: The Theory and Processes of Organic Evolution* 258, 266 (1979) (italics added).

[29] Section 2.1(b).

[30] Sections 2.4 & 4.1.

[31] Section 10.2(a) (2).

[32] Chapters 2 & 4.

[33] Sections 2.1, 2.2 & 2.7. For example, Dr. Dean H. Kenyon, a creationist scientist with a Ph.D. degree from Stanford and a professorship at San Francisco State University, concludes that the theory of creation is scientific and credible:

It is my conviction that if any professional biologist will take adequate time to examine carefully the assumptions upon which the *macroevolutionary* doctrine rests, and the observational and laboratory evidence that bears on the problem of origins, he/she will conclude that there are *substantial reasons for doubting* the truth of this doctrine. Moreover, I believe that a *scientifically sound creationist view* of origins is not only *possible*, but is to be *preferred* over the evolutionary view.

. . ..

We have seen that evidence often taken to support a naturalistic chemical *origin of life*, actually, upon close analysis, points in another direction, namely, toward the conclusion that the first life was *created*. The data of *molecular biology*, especially the details of the genetic-coding and protein-synthesizing systems, lend further powerful support to this view. *Probability* arguments applied to the problem of the origin of genetic information also confirm the creationist view of origins.

Laboratory data and theoretic arguments concerning the origin of the first life lead one to doubt the evolution of subsequent forms of life. The *fossil record* and other lines of evidence confirm this suspicion. In short, when all the available evidence is carefully assessed in toto, the *evolutionary story of origins appears significantly less probable than the creationist view.*

Kenyon, *The Creationist View of Biological Origins*, NEXA Journal, Spring 1984, at 28, 28, 33 (italics added).

[34]   *E.g.*, Charig*, *Cladistics: A Different Point of View*, in Evolution Now 121, 121 (J. Maynard Smith* ed. 1982) (" 'Transformed Cladistics' is— 'natural order systematics'.").

[35]   *E.g.*, Simpson*, *Editorial Essay*, 7 Precambrian Research 101, 102 (1978) ("In pre-Darwinian days the abrupt appearances of new taxa, then already known and even more impressive than now, was commonly interpreted as indicating that each taxon had been divinely created at about the time of its appearance in the sequence. . . ."); note 42.

[36]   F. Hoyle & N. Wickramasinghe, *Evolution from Space: A Theory of Cosmic Creationism* (1984); F. Crick*, *Life Itself: Its Origin and Nature* (1981).

[37]   E. Ambrose*, *The Nature and Origin of the Biological World* 143 (1982).

[38]   Note 43.

[39]   H. Bergson*, *L'Evolution Créatrice* (1907).

[40]   N. Gillespie*, *Charles Darwin and the Problem of Creation* 26-27 (1979); Sections 15.2(a) (1) & 10.2(b).

[41]   G. Sermonti* & R. Fondi*, *Dopo Darwin: Critica all' Evoluzionismo* (1980), translated in Montalenti*, *Darwinism today*, 77 Scientia 21, 29 (1983).

[42]   M. Denton*, *Evolution: A Theory in Crisis* 353-54 (1985).

[43]   Smith*, *Two Evolutions*, in On Nature 42, 47 (L. Rouner* ed. 1984).

[44]   Cannon*, *The Bases of Darwin's Achievement: A Revaluation*, 5 Victorian Studies 109, 131 (1961) (italics in original, footnotes omitted).

[45]   Leakey*, *Introduction*, to The Origin of Species 14-15 (R. Leakey* ed. 1979) (italics added).

[46] 2 *The Life and Letters of Charles Darwin* 202-03 (F. Darwin* ed. 1903).

[47] J. Draper*, *History of the Conflict Between Religion and Science* 246-47 (1896) (italics added).

[48] Gould*, *Catastrophes and Steady State Earth*, Natural History, Feb. 1975, at 15, 15-16.

[49] *Prof. Agassiz on the Origin of Species*, 30 Am. J. Science 142, 149 (1860), excerpted from 3 L. Agassiz, *Contributions to the Natural History of the United States* (1860).

[50] N. Gillespie*, *Charles Darwin and the Problem of Creation* 29 (1979); Elders*, *The Philosophical and Religious Background of Charles Darwin's Theory of Evolution*, 37 Doctor Communis 32, 38 (1984) (address to Royal Spanish Academy of Science).

[51] E. Shute, *Flaws in the Theory of Evolution* 5 (1961) (first italics added). Shute wrote at a time when the evidence for Precambrian microfossils was not compelling.

[52] Section 13.1(e).

[53] Section 13.1(c).

[54] Pollock*, *On the Creation of an Inflationary Universe from "Nothing"* . . ., 167B Physics Letters 301, 301 (1986) (italics added).

[55] Alvarez*, *Quantum Creation of Multidimensional Universes*, 30 Zeitschrift für Physik (Particles & Fields) 157, 157 (1987) (italics added).

[56] Section 13.1 (b).

[57] G. Gamow*, *The Creation of the Universe* (1955).

[58] J. Silk*, *The Big Bang: The Creation and Evolution of the Universe* (1980).

[59] F. Hoyle & N. Wickramasinghe, *Evolution from Space: A Theory of Cosmic Creationism* (1984). *See also* 2 *Oxford English Dictionary* 1152 (1971); Sections 13.1-13.2.

[60] J. Huxley*, *Evolution in Action* 9 (1964).

[61] Gould*, *The promise of paleobiology as a nomothetic, evolutionary discipline*, 6 Paleobiology 96, 108 (1980).

[62] W. Stansfield*, *The Science of Evolution* (1977).

[63] *E.g.*, Biological Sciences Curriculum Study*, *Biological Science: Molecules to Man* (3d ed. 1973 & 1976); Biological Sciences Curriculum Study*, *Biological Science: An Interaction of Experiments and Ideas* (3d ed. 1977).

[64] *E.g.*, *Physical Science Investigations* (1976); *Physical Science Investigations* (rev. ed. 1979); *Introductory Physical Science* (4th ed. 1982); *Physical Science Text-Workbook* (1982); *Challenges: Physical Science* (1973); *Introduction to Environmental Science* (1980); *Environmental Science: The Way the World Works* (1981); *Physical Science* (4th ed. 1982); *Earth Science* (1973).

[65] Chapters 9-10 (definitions of science and the theory of creation), and Chapters 12-14 (religion and the theory of creation).

[66] Section 13.1(c)-(d).

[67] Guth* & Steinhardt*, *The Inflationary Universe*, Scientific Am., May

1984, at 116, 128. *See also* Tryon*, *What Made the World?*, New Scientist, Mar. 8, 1984, at 14, 16 ("In 1973, I proposed that our Universe had been created spontaneously from nothing (*ex nihilo*), as a result of established principles of physics.").

[68]   H. Bondi*, *Cosmology* 144 (1968) ("It should be clearly understood that the creation here discussed is the formation of matter not out of radiation but *out of nothing*."); F. Hoyle, *The Nature of the Universe* 125 (1950).

[69]   Margenau*, *Modern Physics and the Turn to Belief in God*, in The Intellectuals Speak Out About God 39, 42 (R. Varghese* ed. 1984). *See also* H. Pagels*, *Perfect Symmetry: The Search for the Beginning of Time* (1985) (appearance by big bang "out of absolutely nothing").

[70]   The concepts of genus and family are standard terms of biological classification, as discussed at the beginning of Chapter 2. The word "types" has been used by many nonevolutionist and creationist scientists since before 1860 (by Agassiz), and is a scientific term different in meaning from "kinds," as also summarized at the beginning of Chapter 2.

[71]   *E.g.*, W. Stansfield*, *The Science of Evolution* 98, 511 (1977); A. Boyden*, *Perspectives in Zoology* 117 (1973); S. Stanley*, *Macroevolution* 193 (1979); N. Eldredge* & I. Tattersall*, *The Myths of Human Evolution* 8 (1982) ("another kind of early man"); E. Mayr*, *The Growth of Biological Thought* 251 (1982) ("Actually the term ['species'] is often applied to all sorts of objects, in the sense of 'kinds of' "); A. Kluge*, *Chordate Structure and Function* 10 (2d ed. 1977) ("Classification is the formal arrangement of similar kinds of organisms into groups . . . ."); R. Good*, *Features of Evolution in the Flowering Plants* 1 (1974); Ayala*, *Biological Evolution: Natural Selection or Random Walk?*, 62 Am. Scientist 692, 692 (1974) ("The origin and kinds of organism. . ."); Hull*, *Karl Popper and Plato's Metaphor*, in 2 Advances in Cladistics 177, 177, 188 (N. Platnick* & V. Funk* eds. 1980); Eldredge*, *An Extravagance of Species*, Natural History, June 1980, at 47, 50; Valentine*, *The Evolution of Multicellular Plants and Animals*, Scientific Am., Sept. 1978, at 141, 158; Manser*, *The Concept of Evolution*, 40 Philosophy 18, 27 (1965); S. Luria*, S. Gould*, & S. Singer*, *A View of Life* 636 (1981); D. Raup* & S. Stanley*, *Principles of Paleontology* 104 (2d ed. 1978); A. Wallace*, *The World of Life* 12-13 (1911) ("The reader may therefore rest assured that there is no mystery in the word *species*, but that he may take it as meaning the *same as kind* in regard to animals and plants in a state of nature.") (italics added).

[72]   *E.g.*, Heylmun*, *Should We Teach Uniformitarianism?*, 19 J. Geological Educ. 35, 36-37 (1971); I. Velikovsky*, *Worlds in Collision* (1950).

[73]   Those scientists who describe themselves as discontinuitists or creationists split about evenly on acceptance or rejection of catastrophism and a worldwide flood. Those rejecting catastrophism and a worldwide flood include the discontinuitists and creationists in Section 15.3(c)(2), such as Edward Hitchcock, Adam Sedgwick, and James Dana. Historically, great scientists advocating a worldwide flood include Sir Isaac Newton, Nicholas

Steno, William Whiston, John Woodward, Georges Cuvier, Timothy Dwight (president of Yale), and William Buckland (professor of geology at Oxford). This is further discussed in Section 15.3(c)(2).

[74] H. Morris, *Creation and Its Critics* 27 (1982).

[75] *E.g.*, Tipler*, *How to Construct a Falsifiable Theory in Which the Universe Came Into Being Several Thousand Years Ago*, 2 Philosophy of Science Association 873 (1984) (rejecting short age view but finding it theoretically possible); Kazmann*, *It's About Time*, Geotimes, Sept. 1978, at 18, 19 (describing but not endorsing evidence for a young age).

[76] Those scientists who describe themselves as discontinuitists or creationists similarly split about evenly on a young age or multibillion-year age of the universe, earth, and life. Those in the twentieth century advocating a multibillion year age include the discontinuitists and creationists listed in Section 15.3(c)(1). Those creationist or discontinuitist scientists in the nineteenth century advocating an old age include Agassiz, Philip H. Gosse, John William Dawson, and James Dana. *E.g.*, 1 L. Agassiz, *Contributions to the Natural History of the United States* 53, 56 (1857). Historically, great scientists advocating a young age include Sir Isaac Newton, Johannes Kepler, and Lord Kelvin. This is further discussed in Section 15.3(c)(1).

[77] H. Morris, *Creation and Its Critics* 25-26 (1982) (italics in original).

[78] Gould*, *Darwinism Defined: The Difference between Fact and Theory*, Discover, Jan. 1987, at 65.

[79] Note 2.

[80] Note 17.

[81] Note 49.

[82] Note 46.

[83] Note 47.

[84] Note 44.

[85] Section 14.1.

[86] Section 14.2.

PART II

Whether the Theories of Abrupt Appearance and Evolution Are Scientific?

The Origin of the Various Living Organisms

The biological theory of abrupt appearance consists of at least seven lines of affirmative scientific evidence, involving fossils, information content, probability, genetics, and comparative biology. Although some evolutionists discount and even discredit a discontinuity-oriented interpretation of the patterns of nature, many openminded scientists would agree with an Agnostic evolutionist physicist:

> I think, however, that we must go further than this and admit that the only acceptable explanation is creation. I know that this is anathema to physicists, as indeed it is to me, but we must not reject a theory that we do not like if *the experimental evidence supports it.*[1]

Biological abrupt appearance indeed has scientific difficulties and needs further research, but those conditions are shared by biological evolution.

The biological theory of evolution, on the other hand, is not compellingly established, and indeed "evolutionary theory is in crisis," in the words of evolutionist scientists Saunders* and Ho*.[2] In fact, "scientists who utterly reject evolution may be one of our fastest-growing controversial minorities," according to Hatfield*.[3] There

39

are "some among the biologists who feel that much of the fabric of [evolutionary] theory accepted by the majority today is actually false," and "a generally silent group of students engaged in biological pursuits who tend to disagree with much of the current thought," Olson* notes.[4] Darwinism is even more in crisis than macroevolution, as a new evolutionist book shows under the title *Darwinism: The Refutation of a Myth:*

> Micromutations do occur, but the theory that these alone can account for evolutionary change is either falsified, or else it is an unfalsifiable, hence metaphysical theory.
>
> I suppose that nobody will deny that it is a great misfortune if an entire branch of science becomes addicted to a false theory. But this is what has happened in biology: for a long time now people discuss evolutionary problems in a peculiar 'Darwinian' vocabulary—'adaptation,' 'selection pressure,' 'natural selection,' etc.—thereby believing that they contribute to the *explanation* of natural events. They do not, and the sooner this is discovered, the sooner we shall be able to make real progress in our understanding of evolution.
>
> I believe that one day the Darwinian myth will be ranked the greatest deceit in the history of science. When this happens many people will pose the question: How did this ever happen? . . .[5]

Notes

[1]   Lipson*, *A Physicist Looks at Evolution*, 31 Physics Bulletin 138, 138 (1980).

[2]   Ho* & Saunders*, *Preface*, to Beyond Neo-Darwinism ix, ix (M. Ho* & P. Saunders* eds. 1984).

[3]   Hatfield*, *Educators Against Darwin*, Science Digest Special, Winter 1979, at 94, 94.

[4]   Olson*, *Morphology, Paleontology, and Evolution*, 1 Evolution after Darwin 523, 523 (S. Tax* ed. 1960).

[5]   S. Lóvtrup*, *Darwinism: The Refutation of a Myth* 422 (1987) (italics in original).

CHAPTER 2

Theories of Abrupt Appearance and Empirical Evidence: Biological Abrupt Appearance of Living Organisms

> *I look with confidence to the future—to young and rising naturalists, who will be able to view both sides of the question with impartiality....*
> —Charles Darwin*,
> in *The Origin of Species*[1]

Definitions. "Biological abrupt appearance" describes the origin of plants, animals, and microorganisms as through "discontinuous abrupt appearance in complex form," as a scientific interpretation of empirical evidence.[2] The abrupt appearance is of "natural groups" of organisms in complex form, and discontinuity appears to exist between those groups, in the view of discontinuitist scientists.

"Natural groups" were the unit of classification used by most pre-Darwinian biologists such as Linnaeus,[3] and are still used by

---

*Scientists cited in this chapter, unless otherwise indicated, are not proponents of, and their quoted statements are not intended as endorsements of, either the theory of abrupt appearance or the theory of creation. However, their quoted statements are acknowledging data that some nonevolutionist scientists interpret as supporting the theory of abrupt appearance better than the theory of evolution.

41

many systematists such as transformed cladists.[4] In fact, classification is "based on a study of 'natural groups' found in nature," in the view of most systematists such as Mayr*.[5] A natural group of a particular organism might be a genus, a family, or sometimes a species,[6] because generally accepted classification is rather subjective at and above the species level,[7] and because "[t]here is probably no other concept in biology that has remained so consistently controversial as the species concept," Mayr* states.[8] The natural group as the unit of discontinuous abrupt appearance in complex form has a long history in nonevolutionist thought.[9]

The term "type" historically was often used to refer to a natural group, by Linnaeus, Agassiz,[10] Sedgwick,[11] and others.[12] The term type presently occurs frequently in scientific literature relating to classification[13] and is used in generally accepted terminology of classification, although the modern meaning differs from natural groupings.[14]

"Biological evolution," in contrast to biological abrupt appearance, is the view held by the majority of scientists. It proposes that "the first living cell 'evolved' into complex multicellular forms of life; these 'evolved' into animals without backbones. Fish evolved into amphibia, amphibia into reptiles, reptiles into birds and mammals, early mammals into primates, and primates into man."[15] Part of biological evolution is that all fish, amphibians, reptiles, birds, lower mammals, apes, human beings, and other organisms evolved from a "common ancestor," as Ayala* of University of California at Davis and Gould* of Harvard stress:

> The millions of diverse living species we find around us in the modern world are all descended from a *common ancestor* that lived in the remote past (Fig. 1.1). The processes that have brought this diversity about are collectively called evolution.[16]
>
> Evolution[.] The process by which all organisms have arisen by descent from a *common ancestor*.[17]

There is much disagreement among evolutionists over the gradual or punctuated nature and the mechanism (Darwinism) of this common ancestry and descent (macroevolution),[18] and even much questioning about whether macroevolution occurred,[19] but macroevolution is a key element of biological evolution.[20]

Affirmative Evidence. The biological theory of abrupt appearance consists of empirical evidence and scientific interpretations, and those follow at least seven affirmative lines, in the view of many discontinuitist scientists:

2.1 Paleontology argument:
Empirical evidence of systematic abrupt appearances
2.2 Paleontology argument:
Empirical evidence of systematic gaps
2.3 Comparative morphology argument:
Empirical evidence of systematic similarity and stasis
2.4 Information content argument:
Natural laws of information science
2.5 Probability argument:
Natural laws of statistics
2.6 Genetics argument:
Natural law of limited change
2.7 Comparative discontinuity argument:
Empirical evidence from classification, comparative anatomy, and comparative biochemistry.

The purpose of this chapter is to outline, rather than to present comprehensively, this scientific evidence, and to do so in the words of evolutionists with the data that they recognize, rather than by reliance on any creationist scientists.

In summary, the paleontology arguments are based on the abrupt appearance of complex organisms in the fossil record, and the systematic gaps between fossil organisms (Sections 2.1-2.2). The comparative morphology argument is founded on the similar structure of even the oldest fossil organisms and their modern-day counterparts, and the general nonchange (stasis) of organisms from their first fossil appearance to the present or to their extinction (Section 2.3). The information content argument concerns the vast information content of the least complex as well as the most complex living organisms and their complex parts, and the abrupt appearance in incredible complexity of that information content (Section 2.4). The probability argument is based on the greater mathematical probability of abrupt appearance, and the infinitely small probability of evolution, of complex features, of complex molecules, and of organisms with symbiotic relationships (Section 2.5). The genetics argument is founded on the genetic limits on viable change or transformation of natural groups of organisms (Section 2.6). Finally, the comparative discontinuity argument involves the evidence for discontinuous ancestry rather than common ancestry of natural groups of organisms, in the form of widespread anomalies in the comparative fields of systematics, anatomy, and biochemistry (Section 2.7).

These lines of evidence are affirmative in the sense that, if true, they support the theory of abrupt appearance. They are not negative in the sense of merely identifying weaknesses of evolution. Nor do they depend on any assumption that the theories of abrupt appearance and evolution are the only scientific alternatives, except for the probability argument in part.

Historical Foundation. These affirmative lines of evidence for abrupt appearance are not newly proposed data, although their specific formulation may be different from past discussions. In fact, the underlying concepts were advocated more than 125 years ago by Professor Louis Agassiz of Harvard, "America's leading biologist" of the time according to Gould*,[21] who made "reputable claims" according to Eldredge*.[22] Agassiz wrote as follows of the scientific evidence underlying the (1) paleontology argument of abrupt appearance, (2) paleontology argument of systematic gaps, (3) comparative morphology argument, (4) information content argument, (5) probability argument, and (6) genetics argument:

[1] Species *appear suddenly* and disappear suddenly in progressive strata. That is the fact proclaimed by Palaeontology . . ..

. . .

[2] The geological record, even with all its imperfections, exaggerated to distortion, tells now what it has told from the beginning, that the *supposed intermediate forms* between the species of different geological periods are *imaginary* beings, called up merely in support of a fanciful theory.

. . ..

[3] But it stands recorded now as before, that the animals known to the ancients are *still in existence*, exhibiting to this day the characters they exhibited of old.

. . .

[4] [Mr. Darwin] has lost sight of the most striking of the features, and the one which pervades the whole, namely, that there runs throughout Nature unmistakable *evidence of thought*, corresponding to the mental operations of our own mind, and therefore intelligible to us as thinking beings, and unaccountable on any other basis than that they owe their existence to the working of intelligence; and no theory that overlooks this element can be true to nature.

. . ..

[5] [Mr. Darwin] would also have us believe that the most *perfect organs* of the body of animals are the product of gradual improvement, when eyes as perfect as those of the Trilobites are preserved with the remains of these oldest animals.

. . .

[6] What ought to be shown, if the transmutation theory is to stand, is that these favored individuals diverge from their specific type, and *neither* Darwin nor anybody else has furnished a single fact to show that they *go on diverging.*

. . ..

The fact is that throughout all geological times each period is character-ized by definite specific types, belonging to definite genera, and these to definite families, referable to definite orders, constituting definite classes and definite branches, built upon definite plans.

. . ..

The origin of all the diversity among living beings remains a mystery as totally unexplained as if the book of Mr. Darwin had never been written, for *no theory unsupported by fact, however plausible it may appear, can be admitted in science.*[23]

Scientific Nature. The theory of abrupt appearance is scientific. It consists of the empirical evidence and scientific interpretation that is the content of this chapter. The theory of abrupt appearance also satisfies the various definitions of science in a manner comperable to evolution, as discussed in Chapters 9-10. Its many testable and falsifiable claims are summarized in Sections 10.3(a) and 10.4(a).

The theory of creation similarly can be scientific, a number of its opponents concede. An Agnostic physicist and Fellow of the Royal Society, to whom the theory of creation is "anathema," recently concluded that the scientific evidence better supports that theory than evolution:

I think, however, that we must go further than this and admit that *the only acceptable explanation is creation.* I know that this is anathema to physicists, as indeed it is to me, but we must not reject a theory that we do not like if *the experimental evidence supports it.*[24]

A recent commentator who strongly opposes the theory of creation has conceded that it can be scientific:

Although, in the final analysis, creationism may prove to be ill founded, *it could, nevertheless, be put forward in a scientific spirit* if it were presented merely as a model that accommodated the fossil data.[25]

A noted philosopher of science has similarly acknowledged that the theory of creation makes scientific, testable, falsifiable, "empirical claims," although he violently rejects it, in his criticism of a court decision:

By arguing that the tenets of Creationism are neither testable nor falsifi-able, Judge Overton (like those scientists who similarly charge Creation-ism with being untestable) deprives science of its strongest argument against Creationism. Indeed, if any doctrine in the history of science has ever been *falsified*, it is the set of claims associated with "creation-science." Asserting that Creationism makes no *empirical claims* plays directly, if inadvertently, into the hands of the creationists by immunizing their ideology from empirical confrontation.   The correct way to combat Creationism is to confute the *empirical claims* it does make, not to pretend that it makes no such claims at all.[26]

Other leading evolutionists, such as Gould* and Raup*, have similarly conceded that the theory of creation involves "some testable statements."[27]

One evolutionist author even observes that "today it is the conventional neo-Darwinians who appear as the conservative bigots and the unorthodox neo-Sedgwickians [discontinuitist scientists] who rate as enlightened rationalists prepared to contemplate the evidence."[28]

The following sections discuss the affirmative evidence or empirical claims offered by the theory of abrupt appearance.

Figure 2.1
The "sudden appearance
of whole groups": section
in The Origin of Species
(original first edition)

On the sudden appearance of whole groups of Allied Species.—The abrupt manner in which whole groups of species suddenly appear in certain formations, has been urged by several palæontologists, for instance, by Agassiz, Pictet, and by none more forcibly than by Professor Sedgwick, as a fatal objection to the belief in the transmutation of species.   If numerous species, belonging to the same genera or families, have really started into life all at once, the fact would be fatal to the theory of descent with slow modification through natural selection.

2.1 The Paleontology Argument: Empirical Evidence of Systematic Abrupt Appearances

Paleontology, or scientific study of the fossil record,[29] generally reflects two things: (1) the systematic abrupt appearances of natural groups of fossilized complex organisms and (2) the systematic gaps between different natural groups of fossil organisms. These two factors, discontinuitist scientists suggest, support biological abrupt appearance and render biological evolution less plausible. The point is that the abrupt appearances are systematic, but not that there are no ambiguous cases for the emergence of higher categories (there are) or that there are no examples of gradual change at the subspecies or species level (there are). Those ambiguous cases and microevolutionary changes are discussed in the next chapter. The systematic rule remains significant.

The systematic abrupt appearances of complex life and the systematic gaps between living forms have been acknowledged by such leading evolutionist scientists as Gould*, a brilliant paleontologist at Harvard, Raup*, a noted geologist and dean of the Field Museum of Natural History, and Stanley*, a prominent paleontologist at Johns Hopkins, as well as by many others quoted in following paragraphs:

> Increasing diversity and multiple transitions seem to reflect a determined and inexorable progression toward higher things. But the *paleontological record supports no such interpretation.* There has been *no steady progress* in the higher development of organic design. We have had, instead, vast stretches of *little or no change* and one evolutionary *burst* that created the entire system.[30]

> Unfortunately, the *origins of most higher categories are shrouded in mystery*; commonly new higher categories *appear abruptly* in the fossil record *without* evidence of *transitional ancestral forms.*[31]

Those systematic abrupt appearances and systematic gaps are "almost always" the case at the species level, and are characteristic of "nearly all" the higher categories, as Gould* and Simpson* note:

> *New species* almost always *appeared suddenly* in the fossil record with *no intermediate links* to ancestors in older rocks of the same region.[32]

> In spite of these examples, it remains true, as every paleontologist knows, that *most new species, genera, and families* and that *nearly all new categories above the level of families appear in the record suddenly* and are *not* led up to by known, gradual, completely continuous *transitional sequences.*[33]

Together these form "the classic dilemma of paleontology since Cuvier's time—the absence of transitional forms between major alterations of *Bauplan* (the apparently sudden origin of new morphologies . . .)."[34]

In summary, these abrupt appearances (a) are not fully explainable by conventional rationalizations, but have fundamental implications for theories of origins, and (b) are systematic, involving every phylum in the "Cambrian explosion," and encompassing every major stage of Darwinian evolution. The systematic gaps, or lack of intermediate forms, are discussed in the next section.

a. Implications of Abrupt Appearances

(1) Rationalizations for Abrupt Appearances. The reason for abrupt appearances and gaps can no longer be attributed to the "imperfection of the fossil record," as it was by Darwin* when paleontology was a young science. With over 200,000,000 catalogued specimens of about 250,000 fossil species,[35] many evolutionist paleontologists such as Stanley* argue that the fossil record is sufficient:

> In part, the role of paleontology in evolutionary research has been defined narrowly because of a *false belief*, tracing back to Darwin and his early followers, *that the fossil record is woefully incomplete.* Actually, the record is of *sufficiently high quality* to allow us to undertake certain kinds of analysis meaningfully at the level of the species.[36]

Gould*,[37] Eldredge* and Tattersall*,[38] Kitts*,[39] and Raup* agree. [40] For example, Raup*, whose Field Museum of Natural History has one of the largest fossil collections in the world, writes:

> Well, we are now about 120 years after Darwin and the *knowledge of the fossil records has been greatly expanded.* We now have a quarter of a million fossil species but the situation hasn't changed much. The record of evolution is still surprisingly jerky and, ironically, *we have even fewer examples of evolutionary transition that we had in Darwin's time. . . .*[41]

The general adequacy of the fossil record can be seen in two direct ways. First, the great majority of living orders and living families have been found in the fossil record, as is evident in the following data derived from Romer's* classic treatise:

Number of living orders of terrestrial vertebrates found as fossils		42
Number of living orders of terrestrial vertebrates		43
	Percentage fossilised	97.7%
Number of living families of terrestrial vertebrates found as fossils		261
Number of living families of terrestrial vertebrates		329
	Percentage fossilised	79.1%
Number of living families of terrestrial vertebrates found as fossils excluding birds		156
Number of living families of terrestrial vertebrates excluding birds		178
	Percentage fossilised	87.8%[42]

Thus, according to Denton*, a molecular biologist,

[W]hen estimates are made of the percentage of living forms found as fossils, the percentage turns out to be surprisingly high, suggesting that the fossil record may not be as bad as it is often maintained. Of the 329 living families of terrestrial vertebrates 261 or 79.1% have been found as fossils and, when birds (which are poorly fossilised) are excluded, the percentage rises to 87.8% . . ..[43]

The same is true of species and genera in the fossil record, as Simpson* of Harvard is quoted as observing:

G. G. Simpson recently estimated the percentage of *living species* recovered as fossils in one region of North America and concluded that, *at least for larger terrestrial forms, the record may be almost complete!* In another approach he compared the number of *living genera* of various categories such as insectivores, carnivores, etc. in a particular region with the numbers of fossil genera of the same categories in a region of similar ecological make-up in the past. . . .

These comparisons and some other considerations suggest that surely half and probably two-thirds or more of the Middle Oligocene genera are known and that those not yet known are mainly carnivores (individually much less abundant than herbivores) and very small mammals (with less recoverability than large mammals by previous collecting methods).[44]

Even from the earliest periods of life, "about one in 10 durably skeletonized phanerozic marine invertebrate species is known" in fossils, Valentine* and Erwin* add.[45]

Second, there are some instances where the fossil record is perfectly continuous for periods dated at ten million years, and in which organisms still "appear suddenly with no intermediate forms," as Ambrose* recognizes.[46]

The reason for abrupt appearances and gaps is similarly not the smallness of populations where evolution presumably occurs, because such populations would not remain small for thousands of years, as noted by Ayala*.[47] The punctuated equilibria viewpoint, which proposes that evolutionary events occur primarily in small populations, is further discussed in the next chapter.[48]

(2) Affirmative Evidence for a Theory of Abrupt Appearance. Systematic abrupt appearances and systematic gaps in the fossil record are an affirmative evidence in support of the theory of abrupt appearance. They are also an affirmative evidence for the theory of creation, as Thompson* and Clark* both recognize:

Rather than supporting evolution, the *breaks* in the known fossil record *support the creation* of major groups with the possibility of some limited variation within each group.[49]

Thus so far as concerns the major groups of animals, the creationists seem to have the better of the argument.[50]

Draper* recognized that "[c]reation implies an abrupt appearance," in contrast to transformation.[51]

Historically, abrupt appearances and gaps were interpreted by most geologists immediately before Darwin* (and most prominent scientists upon hearing his theory[52]) as evidence for abrupt or "sudden appearance," as Leakey* recognizes:

> Geologists of the 1830s were convinced that they had discovered the dawn of life in this strata, called the Cambrian, and no hypothesis save *special creation* was deemed adequate to account for the *sudden appearance* of Cambrian fossils. Rocks older than the Cambrian were, so it seemed, completely devoid of fossils. In the second place, the various strata each generally had its own characteristic fossil flora and fauna and the *transitions between strata were abrupt*. . . .[53]

Darwin* himself recognized the critical problem for evolution vis-à-vis alternative theories posed by "The sudden appearance of whole groups of Allied Species" (one section in his *Origin of Species*) and by the systematic absence of "innumerable transitional links":[54]

> At one point [Darwin] observed, "innumerable transitional forms must have existed but why do we not find them embedded in countless numbers in the crust of the earth?"; in another place he said, "why is not every geological formation and every stratum full of such intermediate links? Geology assuredly does not reveal any such finely graduated organic chain, and this perhaps is the *greatest objection which can be urged against my theory*."[55]

Yet some diehard Darwinians, well described by Leach* as among "the conventional neo-Darwinians who appear as the conservative bigots" by refusing "to contemplate the evidence,"[56] insist that ". . . every fossil is consistent with the idea of evolution"![57] The fossil evidence is very different from facile statements and shows their "bigotry" against the actual data.

The explanation of abrupt appearances and systematic gaps, it is important to stress, differs totally between evolutionist and discontinuitist scientists. Discontinuitist scientists suggest that abrupt appearances and systematic gaps are explained most naturally and logically by discontinuity or unrelatedness of the natural groups of plants and of animals. Darwinian evolutionists attempt to reconcile abrupt appearances and systematic gaps with common ancestry (macroevolution) in a number of different ways, such as punctuated equilibria, an imperfect fossil record, or small population change, that are assessed in Chapter 3. Thus, the following quotations from all evolutionist researchers acknowledge the empirical evidence of systematic abrupt appearances or systematic gaps, but do not and should not be read to concede discontinuous ancestry rather than common ancestry or to abandon Darwinian macroevolution.

Interpretation of fossils is unavoidable, because "fossils, by themselves, tell us nothing," and their meaning "must be reached within inferences that invoke biological theories," according to Kitts*.[58] The same fossils give rise to different inferences by various evolutionists as well as by discontinuitist scientists.

b. The Fossil Record of Abrupt Appearances

(1) Systematic Nature of Abrupt Appearances. The systematic abrupt appearances of complex organisms in the fossil record have been noted by many evolutionist scientists. Species typically appear abruptly, as summarized by Gould*:

> The history of most fossil species includes two features particularly inconsistent with gradualism:
>
> 1. *Stasis.* . . .
>
> 2. *Sudden appearance.* In any local area, a species does not arise gradually by the steady transformation of its ancestors; it appears all at once and "fully formed."[59]

"Most" fossil species appear abruptly, in the concurring view of Kemp*, curator of the University Museum at Oxford:

> [P]aleontology is now looking at what it actually finds, not what it is told that it is supposed to find. As is now well known, *most fossil species appear instantaneously* in the record, persist for some millions of years *virtually unchanged*, only to disappear abruptly—the "punctuated equilibrium" pattern of Eldredge and Gould. . . .[60]

A similar point is made by Raup*:

> Instead of finding the gradual unfolding of life, what geologists of Darwin's time, and geologists of the present day, actually find is a highly uneven or jerky record; that is, *species* appear in the sequence *very suddenly*, show little or no change during their existence in the record, then abruptly go out of the record. And it is not always clear, in fact it's rarely clear, that the descendants were actually better adapted than their predecessors. In other words, biological improvement is hard to find. . . .[61]

Ager* writes that, "whether at the level of orders or species, we find—over and over again—not gradual evolution, but the sudden explosion of one group at the expense of another."[62]

Higher categories also typically appear abruptly, as conceded by Ayala* and Valentine*:

> The tree of life consists of numerous major branches—there are about

25 major living subdivisions (*phyla*) of the animal kingdom alone, *all with gaps* between them that are not bridged by known intermediates. ...
Most taxa at these high levels *appear abruptly* in the fossil record. ...[63]

. . ..

Most orders, classes, and phyla *appear abruptly* and commonly have already acquired all the characters that distinguish them.

. . ..

We are forced to the conclusion that most of the really novel taxa that appear suddenly in the fossil record did in fact *originate suddenly*.[64]

"Most new higher taxonomic groups and, therefore, most novel morphologies appear suddenly in the fossil record," Erwin* and Valentine* add.[65] That systematic abrupt appearance is "real" and will not be solved by "further collecting" of fossils, as Davis* observes:

The sudden emergence of major adaptive types, as seen in the *abrupt appearance* in the fossil record of *families and orders*, continued to give trouble. The phenomenon lay in the genetical no man's land beyond the limits of experimentation. A few paleontologists even today cling to the idea that these gaps will be closed by further collecting, i.e., that they are accidents of sampling; but most regard the observed discontinuities as real and have sought an explanation for them.

The origin of new adaptive types, as opposed to their subsequent evolution, is the crux of the whole adaptive question, whether from the standpoint of paleontology or of neobiology.[66]

Many other evolutionist scientists have published similar acknowledgments of the systematic abrupt appearance of species[67] and higher categories.[68]

The meaning of "abrupt" is not necessarily instantaneous. A single fossil or group may have been deposited rapidly, but a widely occurring category may be described by geologists as appearing "abruptly" in a geological sense, by which they mean tens of thousands of years. Use of the term "abrupt" by discontinuitist scientists as well as evolutionist scientists may mean instantaneous appearance or geologically abrupt appearance, depending on the context. This book, in quoting evolutionist references to abruptness, does not mean to imply that the quotations involved instantaneousness unless their context so indicated. Systematic abrupt appearance, whether instantaneous or geologically abrupt, simply supports the abrupt appearance explanation and weakens the macroevolutionary explanation, in the view of discontinuitist scientists.

(2)The Abrupt Appearances of All Major Phyla in the Cambrian Explosion. The major period of abrupt appearance is often called the "Cambrian explosion":

When confronted with the *abrupt appearance* of many new families of a higher taxon, some workers have sought an explanation in the imperfection of the fossil record. The most general problem to which this approach has been taken is the apparently *sudden appearance* in the fossil record of the diverse classes of *invertebrates* that characterize the Cambrian system. In fact, it was Darwin, the first worker seriously faced with the "Cambrian problem," who . . . wrote in *On the Origin of Species* (1859, p. 308) "The case at present must remain inexplicable; and may be truly urged as a valid argument against the views [evolution by natural selection] here entertained."[69]

That Cambrian explosion of invertebrates is generally acknowledged,[70] as exemplified in Schopf*:

> The beginning of the Phanerozoic Aeon of earth history, about 600 million years ago, is marked in the fossil record by the *sudden, widespread appearance* of numerous types of invertebrate animals and macroscopic algae. This *"explosion" of advanced life forms*, an event that apparently occurred within a period of only ten or twenty million years, has *puzzled paleontologists* for more than a century. In Charles Darwin's day, for example, when the Precambrian was thought to be entirely devoid of fossils, this abrupt beginning of the fossil record presented a major dilemma, a problem that Darwin thought would require convincing explanation if his theory of evolution were to be ultimately accepted. . . .[71]

Few evolutionists feel that the Cambrian explosion has been adequately and fully explained.

Vertebrate fish also probably appeared in the Cambrian explosion, according to Repetski* and Cygan* and Koucky*,[72] so that the explosion would include every major animal phylum.[73] Looking from paleontology to paleobotany, many land plants as well appeared in that explosion.[74]

The most simple forms of life, it is true, do not first appear in the Cambrian explosion. However, the fossil "evidence is as yet equivocal" on their appearance, as Schopf* further notes:

> First, it is now known that *microfossils*—or at least microscopic objects that closely resemble microfossils—occur in several Archean deposits. The oldest of these occur in carbonaceous sediments of the Swaziland Sequence of the eastern Transvaal, South Africa, sediments ranging in age from about 3100 to 3400 million years. These microscopic bodies, however, are of very simple morphology (figure 3). Although they apparently occur in considerable abundance, *they do not have the structural complexity* (such as being demonstrably multicelled or having well defined, regular surface ornamentation) *that would make their biological interpretation wholly convincing.* Moreover, and perhaps most perplexing, they bear at least superficial *resemblance to organic spheroids*

that are known to be entirely of non-biological origin, such as the spheroidal bodies produced abiotically in laboratory experiments designed to
simulate events that may have occurred on the primitive earth and the
spheroidal "organized elements" known to occur in some carbonaceous
meteorites. Thus, while it is possible, and perhaps likely, that at least
some of these fossil-like objects are actually microfossils (and while it is
true that they are so regarded by many workers), *the evidence is as yet
equivocal.* Further studies are needed to define their true nature.[75]

*(3) The Abrupt Appearance of Every Major Stage of Darwinian
Evolution.* That abrupt appearance of complex life characterizes
nearly every major category of organisms and every alleged stage in
the evolutionary process. For invertebrates (animals without backbones), "all major invertebrate phyla appear suddenly"[76] and trilobites appear in an "explosion."[77]

Fish appear abruptly in complex form in the fossil record, as noted
by Ommanney*, an evolutionist authority on fish:

> How this *earliest chordate stock* evolved, what stages of development
> it went through to eventually give rise to truly fishlike creatures, we *do
> not know.* Between the Cambrian when it probably originated, and the
> Ordovician when the first fossils of animals with really fishlike charac-
> teristics appeared, there is a *gap of perhaps 100 million years* which we
> will probably never be able to fill. But in the 45 million years which
> followed, up to the Devonian when fishes experienced a *veritable explo-
> sion in population and species*, some very significant events took place
> which shaped their future for all time.[78]

An example is the way that osteostracan fish "burst upon the
scene," according to Stahl*:

> The origin of Osteostraci is much more *mysterious* than their disappear-
> ance. An investigator who seeks to know the steps by which these forms
> came into existence finds himself confronting one of the most perplexing
> problems in the study of vertebrate evolution. The earliest known osteo-
> stracans, those found in Silurian deposits, show all the typical character-
> istics of the group. No one has found any older fossils whose structure is
> *clearly antecedent* to the osteostracan pattern. When a vertebrate group
> seems to *burst upon the scene* in this fashion, paleontologists can say
> only that they may possess fossils of the ancestral forms which they
> have not properly identified or that the progenitors of the group were too few
> in number or too fragile to leave remains that were likely to be found....[79]

Other examples are the appearance of antiarch fish with "fully
formed" peculiar appendages, and of gnathostome fish with "fully
functional" hinged lower jaws.[80]

Reptiles similarly appear abruptly in complex form.[81] For example, turtles appear as turtles with unclear ancestry, as Carroll*
points out:

The earliest and most primitive turtles, placed in the suborder Progano-chelydia, are known from the Upper Triassic of Germany. Descriptions of these forms, by Jaekel (1916) and others, indicate that they are already unquestionably turtles in most features of their anatomy and show little, if any, affinity with other groups of reptiles. . . . At present the ancestry of turtles is subject to considerable speculation (p. 9).[82]

Birds also appear abruptly in complex form in the fossil record.[83]

Mammals appear suddenly in complex form, arising in an "explosion" summarized by Ager*:

> Other explosions, such as *Cambrian trilobites* or *Tertiary mammals*, are much more obvious. The latter are particularly interesting because they lay doggo for well over 100 million years before putting in their successful takeover bid. . . .
>
> The point emerges that, if we examine the fossil record in detail *whether at the level of orders or of species*, we find—over and over again—not gradual evolution, but the *sudden explosion* of one group at the expense of another.[84]

Primates appear abruptly in complex form in the fossil record, as acknowledged by Johansen*, an evolutionist authority:

> *Modern gorillas, orangutans, and chimpanzees spring out of nowhere*, as it were. They are here today; they have no yesterday.[85]

Man, finally, also appears abruptly in complex form.[86]

For plants, the same thing is true: "vascular plants . . . arose almost simultaneously."[87] Flowering plants made an "explosive" appearance, in the view of Gray* and Boucot*,[88] and in fact leave the troubling possibility of appearing "de novo," in the estimation of Good*, professor emeritus of botany at University of Hull:

> For one paramount reason, namely the *absence of any effective palaeontological history* of these plants, the answer can only be that their direct influence on this problem is comparatively small, but more indirectly many of their features, and especially their huge numbers, give them considerable significance. If a new biological type is not the result of transformism it must, as far as we are capable of judging, arise *in some way within the meaning of the words de novo*, and that is something quite beyond our experience. That we have no such experience, however, is not in itself a reason for excluding the possibility of an origin of this sort in all cases, through it does afford reasonable grounds for doubting whether this has ever been a general and wide-spread phenomenon, because if this had been the case the less likely that we should continue to be without any evidence of it. On this argument then the very numbers of the Flowering Plants tend to support the opinion that they are, at least in all essentials, the result of biological transformism. At the same time we cannot totally ignore the possibility that occasionally in time and space, if no more frequently, there may have been involved an event of a different kind.[89]

Summary. Many evolutionists acknowledge that "[n]ew species almost always appeared suddenly in the fossil record with no intermediate links to ancestors in older rocks of the same period" (Gould*[90]), and that "[u]nfortunately, the origins of most higher categories are shrouded in mystery; commonly new higher categories appear abruptly in the fossil record without evidence of transitional ancestral forms" (Raup* and Stanley*[91]). Those and other evolutionist spokesmen do not mean to endorse the theory of abrupt appearance and particularly its element of discontinuity; they instead embrace the theory of macroevolution with continuity from single-celled life to fish, to amphibians, to reptiles, to mammals. However, the scientific evidence that they observe is more logically explained by the theory of abrupt appearance, according to its advocates. The problem is not "that the fossil record is woefully incomplete," because "the record is of sufficiently high quality to allow us to undertake certain kinds of analysis" (Stanley*[92]). The abrupt appearances are not just the exceptional cases: of the "25 major living subdivisions (phyla) of the animal kingdom alone," "[m]ost taxa at these high levels appear abruptly in the fossil record" (Ayala* and Valentine*[93]), and "whether at the level of orders or species, we find—over and over again—not gradual evolution, but the sudden explosion of one group at the expense of another" (Ager*[94]). Darwin* conceded that "The sudden appearance of whole groups of Allied Species" posed a serious difficulty for his theory (Darwin*[95]), while Thompson* admits that, "[r]ather than supporting evolution, the breaks in the known fossil record support the creation of major groups with the possibility of some limited variation within each group" (Thompson*[96]). *Natura facit saltum*.

2.2 The Paleontology Argument: Empirical Evidence of Systematic Gaps

Systematic gaps between the higher categories of fossil organisms, and between the various natural groups of organisms, also characterize the fossil record at every major step in the postulated process of biological evolution, according to many evolutionists as well as nonevolutionist scientists. The gaps persist (a) in general, (b) with profound implications for origins, and (c) at every step: (1) between microorganisms and invertebrate animals, (2) between invertebrates and vertebrate fish, (3) between fish and amphibians

Figure 2.2
The systematic gaps between categories: "true of all the thirty-two orders of mammals" (Simpson*); "the 'missing links' have for the most part remained missing" (Russell*)

and between amphibians and reptiles, (4) between reptiles and birds and lower mammals, and (5) between lower mammals, primates, and man. Further evidence comes from the systematic stasis between groups, which is separately discussed in the following section.

a. Gaps in General

"Gaps among known orders, classes, and phyla are systematic and almost always large," as Simpson*, the noted Harvard paleontologist, acknowledges:[97]

> This *regular absence of transitional forms* is an *almost universal* phenomenon, as had long been noted by paleontologists. It is true of *almost all orders of all classes of animals*, both vertebrate and invertebrate. *A fortiori*, it is true also of the *classes, themselves*, and of the *major animal phyla*, and it is apparently also true of *analogous categories of plants*.
>
> . . ..
>
> . . .Even apart from that, the recognition and interpretation of such discontinuities is interesting and is a necessary, frequently also a practical and useful, part of the paleontological profession. Moreover, it is a *fact* that *discontinuities are almost always and systematically present* at the origin of really *high categories*, and, like any other systematic feature of the record, this requires explanation.
>
> . . ..

... There remains, however, the point that for still higher categories discontinuity of appearance in the record is not only frequent but also *systematic*. Some break in continuity *always occurs in categories from orders upwards*, at least, although the break may not be large or appear significant to most students.[98]

Kitts* concurs with Simpson* about the "systematic" discontinuities for higher categories of classification:

The "fact that discontinuities are *almost always and systematically present* at the origin of really *high categories*" is an item of genuinely historical knowledge because it rests necessarily upon historical inferences.[99]

Gaps are not just systematic, but unexceptional, for the twenty-five phyla (highest divisions) of the animal kingdom, and no common ancestor groups are known, according to Ayala* and Valentine*:

[T]here are about 25 major living subdivisions (phyla) of the animal kingdom alone, *all with gaps* between them that are not bridged by known intermediates. ... Furthermore, it is unusual to find fossils that are the immediate common ancestors of major branches. In fact, there are *no* extinct fossil groups known that are the *common ancestors* of two or more living phyla, and the common ancestral stocks of *only a few classes* (out of many score) have been found.[100]

Even where Valentine* sees common ancestor groups (which are discussed in Section 3.4(a)), he does not see transitional forms "for any of the phyla or classes appearing" in the Precambrian to Ordovician:

THE QUESTION OF THE MISSING ANCESTORS (INTERMEDIATES)

If ever we were to expect to find ancestors to or intermediates between higher taxa, *it would be in the rocks of late Precambrian to Ordovician times*, when the bulk of the world's higher animal taxa evolved. Yet *transitional alliances are unknown or unconfirmed for any of the phyla or classes* appearing then [see Olson, 1981]. The question, then, is what factors have conspired to prevent the appearance of ancestral lineages.[101]

Others concur such as Patterson*[102] and Russell* on the systematic nature of gaps.[103]

Yet, the absence of transitional forms to bridge these gaps is the "trade secret of paleontology," as Gould* states:

The *extreme rarity of transitional forms* in the fossil record persists as the trade secret of paleontology. The evolutionary trees that adorn our textbooks have *data only at the tips* and nodes of their branches; the rest is inference, however reasonable, not the evidence of fossils.[104]

In fact, "the [fossil] record fails to contain a single example of a significant transition," Woodruff* observes,[105] particularly at higher categories, Russell*[106] and Simpson*[107] state. Many evolutionist scientists, such as Gould* and Eldredge*,[108] Raup*,[109] and Olson*[110] note this. For example, Patterson* says:

> I fully agree with your comments on the *lack of direct illustration of evolutionary transitions* in my book. If I knew of any, fossil or living, I would certainly have included them. . . . I will lay it on the line—*there is not one such fossil for which one could make a watertight argument.* The reason is that statements about ancestry and descent are not applicable in the fossil record. Is Archaeopteryx the ancestor of all birds? Perhaps yes, perhaps no: there is no way of answering the question. It is *easy enough to make up stories* of how one form gave rise to another, and to find reasons why the stages should be favoured by natural selection. But such stories are not part of science, for there is no way of putting them to the test.[111]

Thus, Raup* concedes that "[t]he evidence we find in the geologic record is not nearly as compatible with [D]arwinian natural selection as we would like it to be. . . . In other words, there are not enough intermediates."[112] (The small handful of alleged transitional forms are discussed in Section 3.4.) The statistical significance of these gaps is evident in comparing the quarter billion catalogued fossils with the 3-5 kingdoms, 35-50 phyla, 100-130 classes, 600-2,000 orders of animals, 50,000 vertebrate species, and 600,000 insect species.[113]

b. Gaps and Theories of Origins

These systematic gaps, if not adequately explained, are very damaging if not fatal to macroevolution and Darwinism, as Kitts* concedes:

> Despite the bright promise that *paleontology* provides a means of "see-ing" evolution, it has presented some *nasty difficulties* for evolutionists the most notorious of which is the presence of *"gaps"* in the fossil record. *Evolution requires intermediate forms* between species and *paleontology does not provide them.*[114]

In fact, T. H. Huxley*, who was "Darwin's bulldog" and chief exponent, wrote that "if it could be shown that this fact [gaps between widely distinct groups] had always existed, the fact would be *fatal* to the doctrine of evolution."[115] Moore* acknowledges that, "[i]f the hypothesis of evolution, which assumes that all of today's species are the descendants of a few original forms, is true, there should have been connecting forms between the major groups (phyla, classes, orders)."[116] The explanations are further discussed elsewhere of an imperfect fossil record (Section 2.1(a)), of speciation only in small populations (Section 3.3(f)), and of common ancestor groups rather than common ancestor fossils (Section 3.3(f)).

The existence of systematic gaps between fossil natural groups, moreover, is affirmative and not just negative evidence, supporting the theory of abrupt appearance and not just undermining the theory of evolution, in the view of both evolutionist and discontinuitist scientists cited in the preceding section. In parallel, Gillespie* observes that "creationism predicted . . . that no transitional fossils would be discovered,"[117] and such historical creationist scientists as Wollaston claimed the absence of transitional links as part of the "great body of facts" in support of "the law of creation."[118] Johnson* concurs that "[t]he almost universal absence of fully documented transitions between species (*a key creationist argument*) has recently been underlined by scientists like Eldredge and Gould."[119]

Good*, an evolutionary botanist, notes that the "gaps in many places" leave open the "distasteful" possibility of "some other explanation" such as appearance "de novo" of some categories:

> It is true that some phases of the record show, especially along certain lines, successions of forms so closely knit as to make it hard to resist the conclusion that they do indeed represent direct series of transformations in which each has given rise to its immediate successor in time, but it is also true, and in a much more real way, that the *record not only has gaps in many places*, but that these are *often just where the absences of reliable positive information is most frustrating* and disturbing.
>
> Recapitulating, although there may be many germane, as well as more collateral, reasons for believing that the biological past has been a gradual transformism of the kind depicted in current theories of evolution, there is no decisive evidence that this has been the case and thus there are *no proper grounds for excluding* from free consideration the possibility that the facts may be, at least in part, susceptible to *some other explanation*. That there has been progressive change with time seems to admit of no argument, but what kind of change may have been most largely involved and how far that change has been consistent in rate and sort are questions that still remain unanswered.
>
> However distasteful this conclusion may be it is a fair and correct assessment of the situation regarding evolutionary theories today . . . .[120]

Gould* and Eldredge* acknowledge that "morphological gaps" and "stasis" (lack of change) are affirmative "classes of information," although they often have been "ignored by evolutionists as 'no data.' "[121] They add the following:

> We wanted to expand the scope of relevant data by arguing that morphological breaks in the stratigraphic record may be real, and that *stasis is data*—that each case of stasis has as much meaning for evolutionary theory as each example of change.[122]

By the same reasoning, gaps constitute affirmative classes of information and data; they record the relative stasis of the organisms separated by the gaps.

c. Gaps at Each Evolutionary Step

(1) Gap between Microorganisms and Invertebrate Animals. The gap between microorganisms and the complex Cambrian invertebrate animals is the "major mystery of the history of life," according to Simpson*.[123] Part of that gap is the jump, in both living and fossil organisms, from one-celled organisms to more than twenty-celled organisms, with nothing in between. Dobzhansky*, Ayala*, Stebbins*, and Valentine* similarly state that

> the *gap between Protista and the animal kingdom*, which according to the present treatment is synonymous with the Metazoa, is so great that the *origin of Metazoa is still obscure* . . ..
>
> . . ..
>
> . . .Although there is a good fossil record of the major groups that have well-mineralized skeletons, the origins and earliest evolution of the metazoan phyla *cannot be documented* from fossil evidence. . . .[124]

That "good fossil record" removes a potential excuse for the systematic gaps among insects.[125] The same is true for the systematic gaps among brachiopods, according to Ager* of Imperial College, a paleontologist:

> It must be significant that nearly all the evolutionary stories I learned as a student . . . have now been '*debunked*'. Similarly, my own experience of more than twenty years *looking for evolutionary lineages* among the Mesozoic Brachiopoda has proved them equally elusive.[126]

In general, invertebrates are "largely immune to the 'poor fossil record' argument," because "these creatures, unlike the vertebrates, have records that for major segments of geologic time are widely distributed in space and are also well studied."[127]

(2) Gap between Invertebrates and Vertebrate Fish. A similar gap exists between invertebrates and the earliest chordate fish, and that is a "gap of perhaps 100 million years" in the view of Ommanney*.[128] Romer*, a Harvard paleontologist, adds:

> In sediments of late Silurian and early Devonian age, numerous fishlike vertebrates of varied types are present, and it is obvious that a long evolutionary history had taken place before that time. But of that history we are mainly ignorant.[129]

White*, former president of the Linnean Society, reaches a similar conclusion about fish generally and lungfishes particularly (about which he is an authority):

> Whatever ideas authorities may have on the subject, the *lungfishes, like
> every other major group of fishes* that I know, have their *origins firmly
> based in nothing.*[130]

Similar gaps exist for a large number of forms of fish, such as the
antiarchs with their unusual appendages and gnathostomes with
hinged lower jaws:

> The evolution of the armored, spine-like pectoral fins of the antiarchs
> constitutes a special problem and one that is far from being resolved.
> *When the antiarchs appear* in the Lower Devonian, they possess, fully
> formed, the peculiar appendages that W. Gross has dubbed "arthropte-
> rygia" because of their superficial resemblance to arthropod limbs. *No
> fossil* has been found bearing appendages *recognizably transitional*
> between those of antiarchs and any other group of placoderms. . . .
> Paleontologists agree that the antiarchs must have diverged from
> arthrodiran stock very early in the history of the jawed fishes. Little
> progress has been made in understanding how the fins might have
> developed from the arthrodiran pattern. . . .
> While the evolution of paired appendages among the placoderms and
> acanthodians was foreshadowed by a number of structures at the ostra-
> coderm level, the appearance of jaws in these fishes was not. The mouth
> in ostracoderms was edged by dermal bone in such a way that its aper-
> ture could be changed very little; *in the first gnathostomes* the hinged
> lower jaw existed in a fully functional condition, making possible the
> enlarged gape and forceful closure that provided at once a new mecha-
> nism for food getting, defense, and offense. There is *no* evidence in the
> fossil record of *stages transitional* to the jaw apparatus that proved
> indispensable then and thereafter to the success of the vertebrates.[131]

(3) Gap between Fish and Amphibians. A "broad evolutionary
gap not bridged by fossil materials" appears between fossil fish and
amphibians, as noted by Romer*.[132] Moreover, the "transition
between the Paleozoic amphibians and the 'modernized' forms is
almost completely a blank . . .."[133] This gap, along with the gap
between amphibians and reptiles and other stages, is further discussed in Section 3.4.

(4) Gaps between Reptiles and Birds and Lower Mammals. Systematic gaps also exist between fossil reptiles and birds, so that
"there is no fossil evidence of the stages through which the remarkable change from reptile to bird was achieved."[134] *Archaeopteryx*
fossils "do not count,"[135] rather than being an intermediate form,
and appear at the same point in the fossil record as the earliest
modern birds,[136] as discussed later.[137]

Systematic gaps persist between fossil reptiles and lower mammals, as noted by Russell*, a morphologist and a former president of
the Linnean Society:

"Missing links" have for the most part remained *missing*. Even in the *Mammals*, whose geological history is *comparatively well documented, serious gaps* in the record occur just at the time when the primary *differentiation of the Orders* is taking place. . . . A specially striking example is provided by the *Bats*. They appeared in the Middle Eocene with their wings fully differentiated, and since that time, some 50-55 million years ago, the Bat's wings have not essentially progressed, though they have become more diversified (Simpson, p. 119). The Bats, *we must assume*, have evolved, like the other mammalian Orders, from the *primitive insectivores* of Upper Cretaceous and Paleocene times, but of this great transformation, involving an entirely new mode of life, and a high degree of structural specialisation, we have so far *no record*. So also with the Whales, as we have already seen. Though in this case primitive forms are known, these are not ancestral to the modern whales, which are *not* linked to the primitive mammalian stock by any *known intermediate forms*.[138]

The synapsids are not intermediates, in the view of many biologists, as discussed in the next chapter.[139]

(5) Gaps between Lower Mammals, Primates, and Man. There are gaps between all thirty-two mammal orders, which Simpson* describes:

> The earliest and most primitive members of every order already have the basic ordinal characters, and in no case is an approximately continuous series from one order to another known. In most cases the break is so sharp and the gap so large that the origin of the order is speculative and much disputed.[140]

Similar systematic gaps characterize the alleged transformation from lower mammals to primates: "In spite of recent findings, the time and place of origin of order Primates remains shrouded in mystery," Simons* notes.[141] Kelso* concurs that "the transition from insectivore to primate is not documented by fossils."[142]

Finally, systematic gaps prevail between fossil apes and man, as recognized by Zuckerman*:

> For example, no scientist could logically dispute the proposition that man, without having been involved in any act of divine creation, evolved from some ape-like creature in a very short space of time—speaking in geological terms—*without leaving any fossil traces* of the steps of the transformation.[143]

There is a massive gap that scientists can fill with "belief, preconception, and personal opinion," according to Zihlman* and Lowenstein*:

> Unfortunately, the fossil record for hominids (the human family) and pongids (the ape family) is *almost totally blank* between four and eight million years ago—an irresistible *tabula rasa* on which to inscribe belief, preconception, and personal opinion.[144]

Others have noted that gap.[145]

Summary. "The extreme rarity of transitional forms in the fossil record persists as the trade secret of paleontology" (Gould*[146]). In fact, "the record fails to contain a single example of a significant transition" (Woodruff*[147]). Those gaps are systematic: "The regular absence of transitional forms is an almost universal phenomenon," "is true of almost all orders of all classes of animals, both vertebrate and invertebrate," "is true also of the classes . . . and of the major animal phyla, and . . . is apparently also true of analogous categories of plants" (Simpson*[148]). Such "discontinuities are almost always and systematically present at the origin of really high categories" (Kitts*[149]). Huxley* had conceded that, "if it could be shown that this fact [gaps between widely distinct groups] had always existed, the fact would be fatal to the doctrine of evolution" (Huxley*[150]), and Good* admits that the "gaps in many places" leave open the "distasteful" possibility of "some other explanation" such as "de novo" appearance (Good*[151]). Such "morphological breaks in the stratigraphic record" are affirmative data, just as "stasis is data" (Gould* and Eldredge*[152]).

The evolutionary tree begins with "the gap between Protista and the animal kingdom, . . . Metazoa, [which] is so great that the origin of Metazoa is still obscure" (Dobzhansky*, Ayala*, Stebbins*, and Valentine*[153]). The next branch in the tree is "fishes that . . . have their origins firmly based in nothing" (White*[154]), and then between fish and amphibians is a "broad evolutionary gap not bridged by fossil materials" (Romer*[155]). For the next branch "there is no fossil evidence of the stages through which the remarkable change from reptile to bird was achieved" (Swinton*[156]); *Archeopteryx* fossils "do not count" (Gould* and Eldredge*[157]). In the limb to mammals, " [m]issing links' have for the most part remained missing" (Russell*[158]), and for all thirty-two mammal orders "[i]n most cases the break is so sharp and the gap so large that the origin of the order is speculative and much disputed" (Simpson*[159]). Moving to the top of the tree, "[i]n spite of recent findings, the time and place of origin of order Primates remains shrouded in mystery" (Simons*[160]), and "man . . . evolved from some ape-like creature . . . without leaving any fossil traces of the steps of the transition" (Zuckerman*[161]). *Dum tacent clamant.* Thus, "we cannot totally ignore the possibility that occasionally . . . there may have been an event of a different kind" involving "de novo" appearance (Good*[162]).

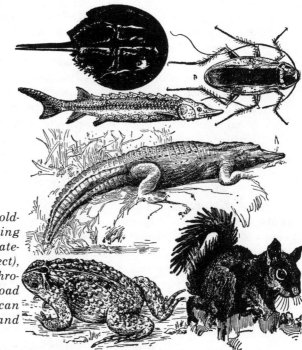

Figure 2.3
The similarity of the oldest fossils and living organisms in every category: cockroach (insect), horseshoe crab (arthropod), sturgeon (fish), toad (amphibian), American alligator (reptile), and squirrel (mammal)

2.3 The Comparative Morphology Argument: Empirical Evidence of Systematic Similarity and Stasis

Morphology refers to outward features or structure. A comparative morphology argument has long been used to support evolution.

The comparative morphology argument for biological abrupt appearance is based on (a) the systematically similar structure of fossilized organisms and their modern day counterparts, and (b) the general nonchange (stasis) of organisms from their first fossil appearance to the present or to their extinction. The related considerations of comparative anatomy are discussed in Section 2.7(b).

a. Systematic Similarity of Fossils and Modern Day Counterparts

The systematically similar structures of fossilized organisms and their modern day counterparts (if not extinct) are described by Grassé*:

Biologists find it hard to admit that, in their basic structure, *present living beings differ* [*hardly*] *at all from those of the past.* To begin with, such a supposition seems contrary to the scientific spirit. But facts are facts; *no new broad organizational plan has appeared for several hundred million years*, and for an equally long time numerous species, animal as well as plant, have *ceased evolving.*[163]

The point is not that they are identical, because present organisms of a genus or family differ widely among themselves, but that they are systematically similar. Nevertheless, many are so virtually identical that they are referred to as "living fossils."[164] Many examples can be given for every level of the evolutionary sequence.

"Among single-celled organisms, the discovery, during the past decade, of survivors from a very remote past has been equally remarkable, though here it is a matter of finding essentially modern forms as Precambrian fossils," including some dated at "1.9 billion years old."[167] The same is true of some bacteria.[166]

Among invertebrates, fossil insect wings are often "essentially identical" to modern wings,[167] and fossil cockroaches are also virtually identical to modern forms.[168] The modern horseshoe crab, also an arthropod, is "nearly identical" to its fossil forms.[169] Some modern squid "have not changed much" from their ancestors dated at 400 million years old:

> This specimen of E. elfriedae shows that alloteuthis-like animals *have not changed much* over 400 Myr [million years], and means that previous concepts of such forms must be revised.
>
> . . ..
>
> ...If we consider the timetable and the fact that the fossil record shows few closely related forms [of cephalopods], then more questions arise, especially as to the origin of these animals. How long did it take to evolve from a primitive nautiloid to Eoteuthis, and where might one hope to find connecting forms?[170]

Many other mollusks are living fossils such as Cephalocarida,[171] *Neopilinia, Neomphalus, Neritopsis,*[172] certain snails such as *Campanile symbolicum,*[173] *Distoma melanioides,*[174] and Nautilus.[175] The same is true of the bryozoan *Nellia tenella,*[176] the coelenterate coral *Heliopora,*[177] the brachiopod *Lingula,* as well as many ants.[178]

Among fish, bowfin fishes have changed "next to nothing" in a history dated at 100 million years, according to Stanley*:

> As a first example, we can consider the bowfin fishes. ... No more than two bowfin species are known to have existed at any one time .... What has happened to the bowfin fishes during their long history of more than one hundred million years? *Next to nothing!* ... The bowfins of seventy or eighty million years ago must have lived very much as their lake dwelling descendants do today. ... .[179]

Gars also have "hardly chang[ed]" in morphology:

> If hardly changing in morphology and low taxonomic diversity count, gars are prime living fossils. However, no one species has an impressive longevity, at least as measured by known specimens. . . .[180]

Other living fossils include lungfishes,[181] the teleostean fish *Chanidae*,[182] *Denticeps clupeoides*,[183] the osteichthyans *Polypterus* and *Erpetoichthys*,[184] sturgeons,[185] the neopterygian *Amia*,[186] and the coelacanths that were thought to be long extinct until caught by fishers.[187]

Among amphibians, many modern frogs and toads are quite similar to ancient fossil forms, as Stahl* describes:

> The living forms have been set apart in the order Apoda (Gymnophiona) but are often thought of as having at least a connection with the salamanders and newts of the order Urodela (Caudata). Those animals and the frogs and toads which are members of the order Anura (Salientia) have been found as fossils, but *known extinct forms are essentially modern* in structure and give no hint of the older amphibians from which they have descended. Most of the urodelan and anuran fossils come from rocks of the Cenozoic era, which began only 65 million years ago. *The specimens can usually be assigned to families that have living representatives* or even to extant genera. Remains from the Mesozoic era are much more sparse: less than a dozen frogs and about the same number of urodeles have been described. . . . The others are of Jurassic and Cretaceous age and already exhibit the skeletal modifications that distinguish the members of the modern orders from the labyrinthodonts and lepospondyls.[188]

For reptiles, many crocodiles and alligators are "living fossils," in Meyer's* words:

> Nile crocodiles and American alligators belong to a group of reptiles called broad-nosed crocodilians. In the warmer parts of the world, broad-nosed crocodilians are the largest predators to walk on land. They are *living fossils in the sense that they resemble ancient forms* in the shapes and the ruggedness of their heads and bodies.[189]

The lizard-like *Sphenodon* and soft-shelled turtles have a close similarity between fossil and modern forms.[190]

Among mammals, living fossils are also numerous. "An Eocene bat looks just like a modern bat," Mayr* concedes,[191] and "the Bat's wings have not essentially progressed" in a period dated at 50 million years, Russell* points out.[192] Ancient squirrels "differ in no important ways" from modern ones, according to Emry*:

> In the sense that they represent the least derived family of a very diverse order, squirrels in general might be called *living fossils*. The recently discovered skeleton of Protosciurus (perhaps the oldest squirrel fossil) shows that *the earliest recognized sciurid is strikingly similar* in its

osteology to living Sciurus. In the sense that it has evolved very little from what is apparently the primitive squirrel morphotype, Sciurus is a living fossil.

. . ..

By about 35 million years ago, squirrels had evolved that seem to *differ in no important ways* from their living relative Sciurus. Since Sciurus is so similar to what is apparently the primitive squirrel morphotype, it seems to fit the concept of "living fossil." . . .[193]

Tragulids also have "frozen" in form:

I have chosen the families Tapiridae and Tragulidae as examples of *living fossils* . . .. Apparently, these groups have remained in essentially the same habitat since these times and so have become *"frozen" in their evolution.* The evidence for this viewpoint comes from four different areas:

. . ..

3. Studies of the morphology of both living and fossil forms show that *little post-Eocene change has occurred.*[194]

Other mammal living fossils include elephant shrews,[195] tree shrews,[196] tarsiers,[197] bovids,[198] and tapirs,[199] as well as opossums, pangolins, new world porcupines, and aardvarks.

This systematic similarity and stasis each affirmatively supports biological abrupt appearance, and renders biological evolution less plausible, discontinuitists suggest. That point was made about data underlying the theory of creation by the renowned scientists whom Darwin* mentioned and disputed:

All these men [Cuvier, Owen, Agassiz, Barrande, Falconer, Forbes, Lyell, Murchison, and Sedgwick] were paleontologists or geologists, and special *creation* . . . was commonly recognized by them to have *strong empirical evidence in the fossil series* which seemed to support the idea that species appeared full-blown suddenly, endured unchanged, and became extinct without leaving descendants.[200]

For example, Sedgwick, professor of geology at Cambridge, found affirmative support for the theory of creation in the empirical fact that "a few of the types have endured, with specific modifications, through all succeeding ages of the earth."[201] As one noted evolutionist scientist stated recently, "if the hypothesis of evolution is true, the species that lived in the remote past must be different from the species alive today."[202]

b. Systematic Stasis from First Appearance to Present

The widespread stasis (general non-change[203]) of organisms from their first fossil appearance to the present (or to their extinction) is the other side of the coin of systematically similar structure. Stasis is described by Gould* as the general rule:

> The history of most fossil species includes two features particularly inconsistent with gradualism:
> 1. *Stasis*. Most species exhibit no directional change during their tenure on earth. They appear in the fossil record looking much the same as when they disappear; morphological change is usually limited and directionless.
> 2. *Sudden appearance*. . . .[204]

It is characterized by Eldredge* and Tattersall* as "the most obvious single fact about biological evolution—nonchange":

> Expectation colored perception to such an extent that the *most obvious single fact about biological evolution—nonchange*—has seldom, if ever, been incorporated into anyone's scientific notions of how life actually evolves. If ever there was a myth, it is that evolution is a process of constant change.
>
> The data, or basic observations, of evolutionary biology are *full of the message of stability*. Change is difficult and rare, rather than inevitable and continual. Once evolved, species with their own peculiar adaptations, behaviors, and genetic systems are remarkably conservative, *often remaining unchanged for several millions of years.*[205]

No new phyla, classes, and orders of organisms have appeared for a period dated at tens of millions of years or more, as Grassé* stated at the beginning of this section. In the "vast stretches of little or no change" between evolutionary bursts, "there has been no addition of basic designs since the Cambrian explosion," Gould* notes.[206] Taylor* elaborates:

> The fact[is] that subsequently *no new phyla have appeared, and no new classes and orders*. This fact, which has been much ignored, is perhaps the most powerful of all arguments against Darwin's generalisation.[207]

That aspect of stasis is not explained, but is only repeated in other words, by calling this the age of stabilization.[208]

Summary. Grassé* notes that, "in their basic structure, present living beings differ [hardly] at all from those of the past" (Grassé*[209]), and in all features, many organisms of all higher categories are so nearly identical to their oldest traces that they are called "living fossils" (Eldredge* and Stanley*[210]). Yet "the most obvious single fact about biological evolution—nonchange—has seldom, if ever, been incorporated into anyone's scientific notions of how life actually evolves" (Eldredge* and Tattersall*[211]). That stasis is not just the exception, but the rule: "Most species exhibit no directional change during their tenure on earth. They appear in the fossil record looking much the same as when they disappear" (Gould*[212]). Darwin* lamented that Cuvier, Owen, Agassiz, Barrande, Falconer, Forbes, Lyell, Murchison, and Sedgwick were noted "paleontologists or geologists, and special creation . . . was commonly recognized by them to have strong empirical evidence in the fossil series which seemed to support the idea that species appeared full-blown suddenly, endured unchanged, and became extinct" (Gillespie*[213])—affirmative evidence for the theory of abrupt appearance. *Semper idem.*

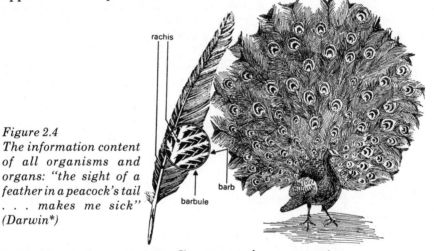

Figure 2.4
The information content
of all organisms and
organs: "the sight of a
feather in a peacock's tail
. . . makes me sick"
(Darwin)*

2.4 The Information Content Argument: Natural Laws of Information Science

The information content argument for the theory of abrupt appearance is based on the vast information content of all organisms from the least complex to the most complex, and the corresponding necessity for a plausible source for that information. "Information content" is a scientific measure of the information, as contrasted with random arrangement, of any nonrandom sequence.[214] The only plausible source of the vast information content in all organisms is biological abrupt appearance, according to discontinuitist scientists, and its origin through biological evolution is virtually impossible.

Information content analysis is applicable to biology, as the scientists cited in this section maintain implicitly by applying it. Brooks* and Wiley* make the point explicitly:

Two concepts figure prominently in our formulation of the core hypothesis: *entropy and information.* These concepts are important for three reasons: (1) they provide a connection between biological processes and natural physical laws showing that biological systems are not governed by special laws of biology, (2) they provide a means for demonstrating the plausibility of nonrandom internally driven evolutionary change, and (3) they provide the conceptual link for the auxiliary hypotheses. . . .[215]

This information content can be considered (a) at the level of complex essential molecules and (b) at the level of complex organs or other features.

a. Information Content of Complex Molecules

Complex molecules that are essential to particular organisms often have such a vast information content as to make the theory of abrupt appearance more probable and to make the theory of evolution effectively impossible.

One example is the information content of essential enzymes, which is unimaginably vast according to famous astronomer Hoyle, formerly a professor at Cambridge and director of its Institute of Theoretical Astronomy, and mathematician-astronomer Wickramasinghe:

The essence of his argument last week was that the *information content* of the higher forms of life is represented by the number $10^{40,000}$— representing the specificity with which some 2,000 genes, each of which might be chosen from 10^{20} nucleotide sequences of the appropriate length, might be defined. Evolutionary processes would, Hoyle said, require several Hubble times [each Hubble time is the time since the postulated big bang] to yield such a result. The chance that higher life forms might have emerged in this way is *comparable* with the chance that "*a tornado sweeping through a junk-yard might assemble a Boeing 747 from the materials therein.*"[216]

Even if all 2,000 enzymes, which the 2,000 genes produce, were not essential to life, or if enzymes of differing composition would suffice, the information content of those genes remains incredible. Criticism of Hoyle's calculation is discussed in Section 4.2.

Another example is the information content of the DNA and RNA of which genes consist, which is vast for all organisms, as Dawkins* describes:

As I mentioned at the end of Chapter 1, *there is enough information capacity in a single human cell to store the Encyclopaedia Britannica,* all 30 volumes of it, *three or four times over.* I don't know the comparable figure for a willow seed or an ant, but it will be of the same order of staggeringness. There is enough storage capacity in the DNA of a *single lily seed or a single salamander sperm* to store the *Encyclopaedia Britannica 60 times over.* Some species of the unjustly called 'primitive' *amoebas* have as much information in their DNA as *1,000 Encyclopaedia Britannicas.* [217]

The information content of the DNA-RNA coding system of higher organisms is even more vast, Denton* states:

> To the sceptic, the proposition that the *genetic programmes of higher organisms,* consisting of something *close to a thousand million bits of information,* equivalent to the sequence of letters in a small library of *one thousand volumes,* containing in encoded form countless thousands of intricate algorithms controlling, specifying and ordering the growth and development of billions and billions of cells into the form of a complex organism, were composed by a purely random process is simply an affront to reason. But to the Darwinist, the idea is accepted without a ripple of doubt—the paradigm takes precedence! [218]

The problem is exponentially increased by the need for simultaneous development of information content and molecular functions, as Eigen* (a Nobel Prize recipient) notes:

> The primitive *RNA strands* that happened to have the right *backbone* and the right *nucleotides* had a second and crucial advantage. They alone were capable of stable self-replication. They were simultaneously both the source of instruction (through the base-pairing rules) and the target molecules to be synthesized according to that instruction. Here at the molecular level are the roots of the old puzzle about the chicken or the egg. Which came first, *function or information*? As we shall show, neither one could precede the other; *they had to evolve together.* [219]

The precise sequence of nucleotides in DNA and RNA, and of amino acids in proteins, has a vast information content for all the various organisms.

b. Information Content of Complex Features

Complex organs and other features also have an incredibly large information content that renders biological abrupt appearance more plausible, in the estimation of many discontinuitist scientists, and that effectively precludes biological evolution, in the analysis of many evolutionist scientists as well. That is particularly true in light of the harmfulness or uselessness of nearly all imaginable intermediate stages in the evolution of complex organs and features.

One example is the human brain, which has an information content equivalent to 20,000,000 books, as astronomer Sagan* notes:

> The information content of the human brain expressed in bits is probably comparable to the total number of connections among the

neurons—about a hundred trillion, 10^{14} bits. If written out in English, say, that information would fill some twenty million volumes, as many as in the world's largest libraries.[220]

It is important to note that Sagan* is not speaking of acquired knowledge, but of the brain's "circuitry." The human brain was so troubling to the co-founder of biological evolution, Alfred Russel Wallace*, that he saw its complexity as precluding human evolution and requiring "creation" of man:

> A brain one-half larger than that of the gorilla would . . . fully have sufficed for the limited mental development of the savage; and we must therefore admit that the large brain he actually possesses could never have been solely developed by any of those laws of evolution, whose essence is, that they lead to a degree of organization exactly proportionate to the wants of each species, never beyond those wants. . . . *Natural selection* could only have endowed *savage man* with a *brain a few degrees superior to that of an ape*, whereas he *actually possesses one very little inferior to that of a philosopher.*[221]

A further example is the eye with its complex lens, retina, optical nerves, and other parts. Darwin* wrote in 1860 that "the eye to this day gives me a cold shudder,"[222] and explained his reasons as follows:

> To suppose that the eye, with all of its inimitable contrivances for adjusting the focus to different distances, for admitting different amounts of light, and for the correction of spherical and chromatic aberration, could have been *formed by natural selection*, seems, I freely confess, *absurd* in the highest possible degree. Yet reason tells me, that if numerous gradations from a perfect and complex eye to one very imperfect and simple, each grade being useful to its possessor, can be shown to exist; if further, the eye does vary ever so slightly, and the variations be inherited, which is certainly the case; and if any variation or modification in the organ be ever useful to an animal under changing conditions of life, then the difficulty of believing that a perfect and complex eye could be formed by natural selection, though insuperable by our imagination, can hardly be considered real.[223]

Although Darwin's* conjecture was that the absurdity of forming a complex eye by natural selection would be overcome, the "numerous gradations from a perfect and complex eye to one very imperfect and simple" do not exist in nature and remain highly improbable, and his wish that "each grade [is] useful to its possessor" multiplies the improbability. Any imaginable intermediate grade in the biological evolution of the eye would be useless if not harmful, as Hardin* notes:

> *How then are we to account* for the evolution of such a *complicated organ*

as the eye? . . . *If even the slightest thing is wrong*—if the retina is missing, or the lens opaque, or the dimensions in error—the eye *fails* to form a recognizable image and is consequently useless. Since *it must be either perfect, or perfectly useless*, how could it have evolved by small, successive, Darwinian steps?[224]

Further complicating the problem, the eyes of many different organisms seem to be totally unrelated and thus must have evolved separately, as Duke-Elder* points out in his classic fifteen-volume work on ophthalmology:

> The curious thing, however, is that in their distribution the eyes of the invertebrates form no series of contiguity and succession. Without obvious phylogenic sequence, their occurrence seems haphazard; analogous photoreceptors appear in unrelated species, an elaborate organ in a primitive species, or an elementary structure high in the evolutionary scale, and the same animal may be provided with two different mechanisms with different spectral sensitivities subserving different types of behaviour.[225]

The eye of the trilobite, as of all invertebrates, had incredible information content:

> [T]he lens systems were very different from what we now have. Riccardo Levi-Setti (a Field Museum research associate in geology and professor of physics at the University of Chicago) has recently done some spectacular work on the optics of these lens systems. Figure 7 shows sketches of a common type of trilobite lens. Each lens is a doublet (that is, made up of two lenses). . . . The shape of the boundary between the two lenses is unlike any now in use—either by humans or animals. But the shape is nearly identical to designs published independently by Descartes and Huygens in the seventeenth century.
>
> The Descartes and Huygens designs had the purpose of avoiding spherical aberration and were what is known as aplanatic lenses. The only significant difference between them and the trilobite lens is that the Descartes and Huygens lenses were not doublets—that is, they did not have the lower lens. But, as Levi-Setti has shown, for these designs to work underwater where the trilobites lived, the lower lens was necessary. Thus, the trilobites 450 million years ago *used an optimal design* which would require a well trained and imaginative optical engineer to develop today—or one who was familiar with the seventeenth century optical literature.[226]

The vertebrates similarly have highly complex eyes—which apparently could not have evolved from the invertebrate eyes, according to Prince*:

> One of the essential and most important differences between vertebrate and invertebrate eyes is that in the former the receptors (light sensitive cells) point outward toward the choroid (inverted), whereas in the inver-

tebrates they mostly point inward toward the lens (verted). But for that obstacle we should have been deluged with theories on the original evolution of the vertebrate eye from the invertebrates.[227]

Of course, every separate evolution of the eye exponentially increases the information content problem.

Another example is the feather with its vane, which is fringed with barbs, which in turn are fringed with barbules, which contain tiny hooks. Darwin* recovered from his cold shudder over the eye but suffered recurrent sickness over the feather:

> I remember well the time when the thought of the eye made me cold all over, but I have got over this stage of the complaint, and now small trifling particulars of structure often make me very uncomfortable. The sight of a *feather* in a peacock's tail, whenever I gaze at it, *makes me sick.*[228]

Seventeen such inexplicable problems are listed by Goldschmidt*, a late professor at Berkeley:

> hair in mammals; feathers in birds; segmentation of arthropods and vertebrates; the transformation of the gill arches in phylogeny; teeth; shells of mollusks; ectoskeletons; compound eyes; blood circulation; alternation of generations; statocysts; ambulacral system of echinoderms; pedicellaria of the same; cnidocysts; poison apparatus of snakes; whalebone; and primary chemical differences like hemoglobin versus hemocyanin.[229]

Five similar marvels are listed by Russell*,[230] and eight others by Hardy*.[231] Other complex features with vast information content are the python's hinged jaws, insect warning colors, bee food dances, and spider webs.[232]

Those complex organs or features until fully formed are generally of no evolutionary value and in fact are harmful, as recognized by Gould*:

> Even though we have no direct evidence for smooth transitions, can we invent a reasonable sequence of intermediate forms, that is, viable functioning organisms, between ancestors and descendants? Of *what possible use are the imperfect incipient stages* of useful structures? What good is half a jaw or half a wing? The concept of *"preadaptation"* provides the conventional answer by permitting us to argue that incipient stages performed different functions. But a *plausible story is not necessarily a true one,* and, in any case, the issue is not, can *preadaptation* save gradualism in some cases, but rather, does it *permit us to invent a tale of continuity* in most or all cases? I submit, although it may only reflect my lack of imagination, that the answer is no, and I invoke two recently supported cases of discontinuous change in my defense.[233]

The counterattack that Gould* launches against discontinuitist use of a design argument is related to Gould's* forthright cynicism of the incipient stage "tales." His counterattack is that apparent imperfections in nature show the absence of design.[234] Although Gould's* counterattack only involves a design argument, which this book does not defend, rather than an information content argument, it is relevant to the amount of information (rather than randomness) in biological systems. Denton* gives a powerful reply, although he does not accept any creationist view or a design argument:

> It is, of course, possible to allude to certain sorts of apparent "imperfections" in life, where an adaptation conveys the impression that nature often makes do in an opportunistic sort of way, moulding the odd lucky accident into something resembling an "imperfect" adaptation. This is the thrust of Gould's argument in his discussion of the curiously elongated bone in the hand of a panda which it uses as a kind of thumb. Yet, just as a few missing links are not sufficient to close the gaps of nature, *a few imperfect adaptations which give every impression of having been achieved by chance are certainly, amid the general perfection of design in nature, an insufficient basis on which to argue for the all-sufficiency of chance.* Such imperfections only serve to highlight the fact that, in general, biological adaptations exhibit, as Darwin confessed: "a perfection of structure and coadaptation which justly excites our admiration."[235]

Darwin* recognized that the biological theory of evolution would be disproved, and the biological theory of creation would be supported, if such complex organs could not be explained by numerous small steps:

> If it could be demonstrated that any *complex organ* existed, which could not possibly have been formed by numerous, successive, slight modifications, my theory would absolutely *break down.* But I can find no such case.[236]

Even if Darwin* were wrong about the need for gradual changes, punctuationists as well as neo-Darwinians must concede the need for numerous relatively slight modifications to produce any complex trait—and for the addition of a ponderous amount of information.

The vast information content of complex molecules and of complex organs is affirmative evidence for biological abrupt appearance and strong contrary evidence against biological evolution, as Hoyle and Wickramasinghe point out:

> From the beginning of this book we have emphasized the enormous *information content* of even the simplest living systems. The information *cannot in our view be generated by what are often called 'natural' processes,* as for instance through meteorological and chemical processes occurring at the surface of a lifeless planet. As well as a suitable

physical and chemical environment, a large initial store of information was also needed.[237]

Summary. The "genetic programmes of higher organisms [consist] of something close to a thousand million bits of information, equivalent to the sequence of letters in a small library of one thousand volumes, . . . specifying and ordering the growth and development of billions and billions of cells" (Denton*[238]). Similarly, the "information content of the human brain expressed in bits is . . . 10^{14} bits," which "would fill some twenty million volumes" (Sagan*[239]). And for human enzymes "the information content . . . is represented by the number $10^{40,000}$," so that the "chance that higher life forms might have emerged in this way is comparable with the chance that 'a tornado sweeping through a junkyard might assemble a Boeing 747 from the materials therein' " (Hoyle and Wickramasinghe[240]).

Darwin* conceded that, "[i]f it could be demonstrated that any complex organ existed, which could not possibly have been formed by numerous, successive, slight modifications, my theory would absolutely break down," although he assumed that none would be found (Darwin*[241]). Goldschmidt* listed seventeen of the almost innumerable complex features with vast information content: "hair in mammals; feathers in birds; segmentation of arthropods and vertebrates; the transformation of the gill arches in phylogeny; teeth; shells of mollusks; ectoskeletons; compound eyes; blood circulation; alternation of generations; statocysts; ambulacral system of echinoderms; pedicellaria of the same; cnidocysts; poison apparatus of snakes; whalebone; and primary chemical differences like hemoglobin versus hemocyanin" (Goldschmidt*[242]). Those examples are probably only a small part "of further as yet undreamt of depths of ingenuity and complexity" (Denton*[243]). Proponents of the theory of abrupt appearance suggest that "the enormous information content of even the simplest living system . . . cannot in our view be generated by what are often called 'natural' processes" (Hoyle and Wickramasinghe[244]). *Vel caeco appareat.*

Figure 2.5
The improbable inter-
dependency of the yucca
moth and yucca plant
(from the text used by
Scopes): "perfection of*
the mutual adaptation"
(Mayr)*

2.5 The Probability Argument: Natural Laws Reflected in Statistics

The probability argument is based on the higher mathematical probability of abrupt appearance, and the infinitesimally small probability of evolution, (a) of complex organisms, (b) of complex features, and (c) of symbiosis between various organisms.

Two clarifications must be made about statistical laws. First, statistical observations are not themselves natural laws, but measure the normal distribution of consequences of natural laws. Analogously, genetic statistics measure the normal distributions of outcomes of genetic laws. Second, the fact that something occurs does not mean that its occurrence by a particular process is probable, unless that process is the only possible process for its occurrence. For example, the existence of plants and animals does not necessarily mean that their occurrence by macroevolution is probable, except under the circular assumption that complex life can only arise through macroevolution. It is surprising that many of the very scientists who fault some discontinuitist scientists for assuming that the improbability of evolution shows the probability of abrupt appearance (on the assumption that there are only two possible alternatives), then themselves assume that the existence of life shows the probability of macroevolution (i.e., assume that there is only one possible alternative).

This probability argument is the only argument for the theory of biological abrupt appearance that is most applicable if abrupt appearance and evolution are the only possible alternatives, and that issue is discussed in Chapter 11. Even if they are not the only general scientific alternatives, many discontinuitist scientists suggest that the theory of abrupt appearance is the most probable of the possible explanations of biological order.

a. Probability of Complex Organisms

The mathematical probability of occurrence of complex organisms is terribly low for biological evolution and higher for biological abrupt appearance. Schutzenberger* of the University of Paris, at a conference on "Mathematical Challenges to the Neo-Darwinian Interpretation of Evolution," concluded that the probability of evolution by mutation and natural selection is "not conceivable":

> We believe that it is *not conceivable*. In fact if we try to simulate such a situation by making changes randomly at the typographic level . . . on computer programs we find that we have no chance (i.e., less than $1/10^{1000}$) even to see what the modified program would compute; it just jams.
>
> . . ..
> . . .Thus to conclude, we believe that there is a *considerable gap in the neo-Darwinian theory of evolution*, and we believe this gap to be of such a nature that it *cannot be bridged within the current conception of biology*.[245]

Noda* also finds serious probability problems.[246]

Eden* of Massachusetts Institute of Technology reaches a similar conclusion of "high implausibility,"[247] and finds the probability of evolution to be unimaginably small:

> If randomness is taken to mean that a uniform probability is assigned to each possible independent substitution or addition, the chance of emergence of man is *like the probability of typing at random a meaningful library of one thousand volumes* using the following procedure: Begin with a meaningful phrase, retype it with a few mistakes, make it longer by adding letters, and rearrange subsequences in the string of letters; *then examine the result to see if the new phrase is meaningful.* Repeat this process until the library is complete.[248]

Note that Eden's* calculations do allow for a positive effect of natural selection. Ambrose* of University of London also finds that for the emergence of new species "the probability is so small in terms of the known age of the universe that it is effectively zero."[249]

These calculations have been criticized for not factoring in natural selection to modify randomness. The questionable effectiveness of natural selection in surmounting improbability through generating macroevolutionary change is treated later (Section 3.3(a)). Even if natural selection could yield some macroevolutionary change, a great degree of improbability would remain for several reasons. First, the necessary mutations must be random and that would be improbable.[250] Second, each significant change would require "additional harmonious adjustments ... in other parts of the body," as Steele* observes:

> Thus, a crucial problem of the hereditary adaptation process is that one "important" change can be expressed usefully in the organism (i.e., possesses Darwinian survival value) *only if additional harmonious adjustments are also made in other parts of the body.* A concept of "simultaneity" appears to be required in any better understanding of phylogenetic adaptation. . . .[251]

Third, the original change and harmonious adjustments would have to occur with near "simultaneity," because it is implausible that intermediate stages really would be useful:

> In the most part, however, conventional Darwinian theory rationalizes most adaptations by assuming that sufficient time has transpired during evolution for natural selection to provide us with all the biological adaptations we see on earth today. That the earth is very old cannot be debated, but *in reality the adaptive process must by necessity occur rather quickly (in one or at the most two breeding generations).*[252]

Other criticisms of probability calculations are discussed later.[253]

There is, of course, a difference between improbability and impossibility. However, such small probabilities are treated as impossibility under statistical rules, in the context of the possible number of events in the entire universe during its entire age.[254]

b. Probability of Complex Features

The probability of complex molecules is similar. For human proteins, the probabilities of biological evolution of each one (of over 200,000 proteins) are "the same as those against a random solution of the Rubik cube" (less than 1 chance in 1 billion):

> These odds are roughly the same as you could give to the idea of just one of our body's proteins having evolved randomly, by chance. However, we use about 200,000 types of protein in our cells. If the odds against the random creation of one protein are the same as those against a random solution of the Rubik cube, then the odds against the random creation of all 200,000 are almost unimaginably vast.[255]

For human blood types, the same improbability of biological evo-

lution is acknowledged by some evolutionists, and the same probability of biological abrupt appearance exists in the estimation of
many discontinuitist scientists. Hemoglobin in blood contains two
chains (alpha and beta), and evolutionists generally assume that
one evolved from the other.[256] Yet that transformation would require
at least 120 point mutations, with a very low probability under
evolutionary processes, according to Eden*.[257] Thus, Lipson* does
"not see how the haemoglobin molecule could have evolved,"
because it is so complex.[258]

For complex features, numerous examples of improbabilities can
be given. The behavior patterns of many insects "are of a high
degree of improbability," in the words of Russell*:

> The life-histories of insects, especially those that are parasitic in various
> ways on other animals, provide many examples of complexity, ingenuity
> and specialisation, both in their structural and in their behavioural
> aspect. Many are of a high degree of *improbability*, so much so that if the
> facts were not firmly established by competent observers the story would
> be dismissed as incredible. Take for instance the life-history of *Sitaris*,
> worked out with such skill and patience by Fabre (1918).[259]

"Whole books have been devoted to the discussion of such perfect
adaptations" as "the division of labour and the harmonious collab-
oration of individuals of various castes in colonies of social insects"
or "the orientation of nocturnally migrating birds."[260]

c. Probability of Symbiosis

The probability of symbiosis of organisms (interdependent relationships) also is higher for biological abrupt appearance and low
for biological evolution. One example is symbiosis of the yucca moth
and yucca plant, which Mayr* outlines:

> The Yucca moth is specifically adapted to the Yucca plant and depends
> on it throughout its life cycle (Rau, 1945). The Yucca plant in turn is
> adapted to be *fertilized by this insect and by no other*. The female moth
> collects a ball of pollen from several flowers, then finds a flower suitable
> for ovipositing. After depositing her egg in the soft tissue of the ovary, by
> means of a lance-like ovipositor, she pollinates the flower by pushing the
> pollen to the bottom of the funnel-shaped opening of the pistil. This
> permits the larva to feed on some of the developing seeds in the non-
> parasitized sectors of the fruit to permit the Yucca plant abundant repro-
> duction. This *perfection of the mutual adaptation* of flower and moth is
> indeed admirable. Yet, in addition to this pollination and egg-laying
> relationship, there are numerous other adaptations, such as the *emer-
> gence of the moths in early summer* some ten months after pupation,

precisely at the time when the Yucca plants are in flower. "Could blind chance have achieved such perfection?", ask the skeptics.[261]
This well-known example is widely cited.[262]

Other examples are the intra-cellular symbiotic relationships that Mayr* describes:

> Or, let us take the field of intra-cellular symbionts studied by Buchner and his students. Here we have *innumerable structures* which permit insects and other metazoans to *house* the bacteria, yeasts or other micro-organisms, which *supply enzymes* for the better utilization of the food of the host. Most of the host organisms have developed various *mechanisms in order to supply their offspring with the right kind of symbiotic micro-organisms.* The number of the sometimes almost incredible adaptations is legion (Buchner, 1953).[263]

Then there are "the obligatory association between termites and the wood-digesting protists that inhabit the termite gut," which is "essential for the survival of the partners";[264] the effect of the parasitic flatworm on ants; and the activities of the parasite-cleaning fish.[265]

These probability considerations constitute affirmative evidence for biological abrupt appearance, as well as serious weaknesses of biological evolution, in the view of many discontinuitist scientists and even of some evolutionists. John Stuart Mill, one of the greatest philosophers of the nineteenth century, found that "the adaptations in Nature afford a large balance of probability in favour of creation by intelligence" in assessing the existing evidence.[266] Salisbury* concurs that the statistical improbability of evolution leaves "creation" as at least a logical possibility.[267] Hoyle and Wickramasinghe similarly recognize the support of probability considerations for abrupt appearance:

> Any theory with a probability of being correct that is larger than one part in $10^{40,000}$ must be judged superior to random shuffling. The theory that *life was assembled by an intelligence* has, we believe, a *probability vastly higher* than one part in $10^{40,000}$ of being the correct explanation of the many curious facts discussed in preceding chapters. Indeed, such a theory is so obvious that one wonders *why it is not widely accepted* as being self-evident. The reasons are *psychological rather than scientific.*[268]

One aspect of the psychological reason for rejection of a theory of abrupt appearance, which Hoyle and Wickramasinghe mention, is that most biological evolutionists, after excluding biological abrupt appearance from consideration by definition, then fall prey to a "best-in-field fallacy" that ignores the improbability of biological evolution and selects it as the best contestant in an artificially limited field.[269]

Summary. At an international conference on "mathematical challenges to the neo-Darwinian interpretation of evolution," one participant (who reflected a widespread view in Europe) said, "to conclude, . . . there is a considerable gap in the neo-Darwinian theory of evolution . . . of such a nature that it cannot be bridged within the current conception of biology" (Schutzenberger*[270]). Another participant determined, "from a probabilistic point of view, the randomness postulate is highly implausible and . . . an adequate scientific theory of evolution must await the discovery and elucidation of new natural laws" (Eden*[271]). Other scientists have calculated that for the emergence of new species "the probability is so small in terms of the known age of the universe that it is effectively zero" (Ambrose*[272]). These improbabilities are multiplied in the numerous cases of symbiosis, such as between the yucca plant and yucca moth and the "innumerable structures which permit insects and other metazoans to house the bacteria, yeasts or other micro-organisms, which supply enzymes for the better utilization of the food of the host," by "sometimes almost incredible adaptations" (Mayr*[273]). Even noncreationists such as John Stuart Mill have found that "the adaptations in Nature afford a large balance of probability in favour of creation by intelligence" (Mill*[274]), while discontinuitists suggest that "[a]ny theory with a probability of being correct that is larger that one part in $10^{40,000}$ must be judged superior to evolution," so that the "theory that life was assembled by an intelligence . . . has a probability vastly higher" (Hoyle and Wickramasinghe[275]). While it is true that the force of this probability argument is greatest if the theories of abrupt appearance and evolution are the only alternatives, some persuasive force remains otherwise in the estimation of many discontinuitists. *Supremo optat collocare sisyphus in monte saxum.*

Figure 2.6
The genetic limits on viable change: mutations are "merely hereditary fluctuations around a medium position; . . . no final evolutionary effect. . . they modify what pre-exists" (Grassé*)

2.6 The Genetics Argument: Natural Law of Limited Change

The genetics argument for the theory of abrupt appearance is founded on the genetic limits on viable change or transformation of natural groups of organisms.[276] Genes, which govern the structure of an organism and limit variation in that structure, do change by mutation.[277] However, (a) the restricted *scope* of viable mutations and (b) the restricted *frequency* of viable mutations reflect genetic limits on viable change by macroevolution, and instead produce the systematic gaps between natural groups of organisms and between higher categories of organisms, according to some nonevolutionists as well as to discontinuitist scientists.

This argument for the theory of abrupt appearance is related to a scientific argument made over a century ago by "the most eminent paleontologists" of Darwin's* day, as he lamented in *The Origin of Species*:

> . . . the most eminent paleontologists, namely Cuvier, Agassiz, . . . etc. and all our greatest geologists, as Lyell, Murchison, Sedgwick, etc. have unanimously, often vehemently, maintained the immutability of species.[278]

In fact, a discontinuitist zoologist in the 1830s coined the term natural selection (which Eiseley* suggests was plagiarized by Darwin*[274]), and recognized that its conservative function imposed limits on change:

> Blyth (1810-73), a creationist, first published essays on *natural selection* in 1835, 1836 and 1837, over twenty years before Darwin published *The Origin of Species*. Loren Eiseley found evidence in Darwin's essays that, between 1842 and 1844, he had studied Blyth's work. Later, after Blyth went to Calcutta, Darwin corresponded with him, showing particular interest in his studies of animal variation. Blyth made no more of his notion of natural selection than the facts warranted. He drew attention to its *conservative function*, using it not to explain how species arose from preexisting species but rather why they remain constant. To him a type's pedigree was a distinct creation, kept fit and 'in form' against the hone of natural selection. Only the fittest would survive to reproduce. Inbuilt adaptive potential could be exploited . . ..[280]

Like modern discontinuitist scientists, Blyth saw no evidence for an innovative function for natural selection. Other early creationists such as Agassiz*, in the period before genetic laws were discovered, found the empirical evidence to support innate limits on viable change,[281] although modern discontinuitist scientists would not agree that those limits apply generally at the species level.

a. Genetic Limits from the Scope of Viable Mutations

The restricted scope of viable mutations is noted by Boyden*, a zoologist at Rutgers:

> To focus attention on the known genetic units themselves, we see in multiple allelic series, that when genes mutate they generally continue to affect the same characters in similar ways, in other words, even *genes are limited in their capacity for viable change.* It is understandable, then, that since the beginnings of our fossil records, there appear to have been no major types evolved from other major types, such evolution, if it did occur, having taken place before the *fixation of the original major phyletic types.*
>
> . . ..
>
> The last 600,000,000 years show no revolutionary changes in the apparent mechanisms of evolution or in their products. All the major types of animals likely to leave fossils are represented in the early Paleozoic rocks. This period of evolution is therefore characterized as much by the conservation of change as by the changes themselves. It is evident that in the processes of establishing the major animal types, *limits have been built into protoplasmic systems beyond which living patents cannot be extended.* Of evolution by gradual variation leading to

adaptive radiation there has been a great deal and in the Insecta for example almost infinite variability on a basic patent has taken place.... The evidences relating to the Age of Stabilization do lend themselves to interpretation on the Neo-Darwinian basis, *all this evolution being subspeciational* and completely graded in origin, and the gaps between species having been secondarily acquired.[282]

Such "subspeciational" change (below species-level change), and even some species-level change, is of course generally accepted by discontinuitist scientists as microevolution, but is very different from macroevolution.[283]

Grassé* similarly concludes that mutations have "no final evolutionary effect" because of genetic limits on the scope of viable ones. Mutations instead are

merely hereditary fluctuations around a medium position; a swing to the right, a swing to the left, but *no final evolutionary effect* ... they modify what pre-exists.

. . ..

...No matter how numerous they may be, mutations do *not produce any kind of evolution*.[284]

Thus, Grassé* applies to lower levels of classification the genetic limits that Boyden* sees at higher levels. Russell* concurs:

It would seem on the face of it that *gene mutations* provide a very unpromising raw material for large scale evolution. *Viable mutations* are of the same order as the *trivial differences* between intra-specific races, and as such seem quite *incapable of giving rise to the major divergences* of structuro-functional organisation which characterise large scale habit and habitat specialisation and typal diversification. Such, however, is the *faith* which the Neo-Darwinians place in the efficacy of natural selection that they have no difficulty in believing that macro-evolution can be accounted for in principle by the same factors that bring about micro-evolution.[285]

Further, many genes together govern most traits of an organism, so multiple beneficial mutations are required to bring a change of significant scope. Ambrose*, a cellular biologist at University of London, develops the point:

The difficulties in explaining the *origin of increased complexity* as a result of bringing *a 'cluster' of genes* together within the nuclei of a single organism in terms of probabilities, fade into insignificance when we recognise that there *must be a close integration of functions between the individual genes of the cluster*, which must also be integrated into the development of the entire organism. The improbability increases at an enormous rate as the number of genes increases from one to five. . . . The problem of bringing together the five mutated genes we are considering, within a single nucleus, and for them to 'fit' immediately into this vast complex of interacting units, is indeed difficult. When it is remembered that *they must give some selective advantage, or else become scattered once more within the population at large, due to interbreeding,* it seems impossible to explain these events in terms of random mutation alone.[286]

The genetic limits on the scope of viable microevolution are dramatically shown by breeding experiments (artificial selection) and the sterility or reversion of breeds beyond a point. That was the conclusion of Luther Burbank*, the greatest breeder of this century:

> I know from my experience that I can develop a plum half an inch long or one two and a half inches long, with every possible length in between, but I am willing to admit that it is hopeless to try to get a plum the size of a small pea, or one as big as a grape-fruit. . . . In short, there are *limits* to the developments possible, and these limits follow a law. . . .
>
> It is the law [of the reversion to the average]. Experiments carried on extensively have given us scientific proof of what we already guessed by observation: namely, that plants and animals all tend to *revert*, in successive generations, toward a given mean or average. . . . In short, there is undoubtedly a pull toward the mean which keeps all living things within more or less *fixed limitations.* . . .[287]

The limits on change through breeding similarly are recognized by Deevey*,[288] Eiseley*,[289] and Falcone*.[290]

b. Genetic Limits from the Frequency of Viable Mutations

Genetic limits involve an interplay of the scope and the frequency of viable mutations. The frequency of viable mutations is extremely low, both for point mutations and for other mutations.

The extreme infrequency of point mutations in DNA copying is summarized by Erwin* and Valentine* of the University of California at Santa Barbara:

> *Viable mutations* with major morphological or physiological effects are *exceedingly rare and usually infertile*; the chance of two identical rare mutant individuals arising in sufficient propinquity to produce offspring seems too small to consider as a significant evolutionary event. . . .[291]

Hoyle concurs:

> However, in actual cells the mistakes made when DNA is copied are far fewer than this, and mistakes like *point mutations* occur on average *only once in each complete copying of the whole 200,000 chains.* So *instead of throwing up large numbers of natural mutations for natural selection to act upon,* the copying of DNA seems to be remarkably accurate—not very helpful to the modern form of the Darwinian theory.[292]

Most of those mutations are harmful; the frequency of "non-harmful" mutations has been estimated at 1 in 1,000 by Ambrose*,[293]

Huxley*,[294] and Kendrew*.[295] That figure is much higher than the frequency of favorable mutations.

The more extreme infrequency of multiple mutations that are necessary to improve a structure or feature is described by Ambrose*:

> The frequency with which a single *non-harmful mutation* is known to occur is *about 1 in 1000*. The *probability that two* favourable mutations would occur is 1 in $10^3 \times 10^3$, *1 in a million*. Studies of *Drosophila* have revealed that large numbers of genes are involved in the formation of the separate structural elements. There may be 30-40 involved in a single wing structure. It is most *unlikely* that *fewer than five genes could ever be involved* in the formation of even the simplest new structure, previously unknown in the organism. The probability now becomes *one in one thousand million million*. We already know that *mutations in living cells appear once in ten million to once in one hundred thousand million*. It is evident that the probability of five favourable mutations occurring within a single life cycle of an organism is *effectively zero*.[296]

He then discusses the alternative to simultaneous multiple mutations in a single organism:

> Let us consider the alternative possibility that the five mutations occur spontaneously within a large population of interbreeding organisms. They will have to be brought together eventually in a single organism, if they are to generate the structure at a new level of complexity, favourable for natural selection.
>
> According to our definition, each of the genes we are considering is due to a mutation which will give rise to a hitherto unknown structure of additional complexity once it meets the other four genes in a single fertilised egg cell. It would indeed be *surprising* if any [one alone] of these mutations could, at the same time, modulate an existing structure in a manner which would be *selected favourably by natural selection. It is only when the five genes find themselves together that a selective advantage will emerge.* They are more likely to be present independently, within the population, as so-called *neutral genes*. . . . In the absence of a selective advantage, the probability of the five genes coming together simultaneously within a single organism, will be extremely small.[297]

Thus, the probability is about 1 in 1,000,000,000,000,000 that even five non-harmful mutations will occur in a single organism, or will occur in several organisms and then be recombined in a single organism, in the ordinary case when the mutations separately are neutral and thus not subject to natural selection. Even if that happens, those are only "non-harmful" mutations, and not necessarily favorable ones.

Even then, a non-harmful mutation must become established in the population of the organism, which takes on the average "10 million years" according to Wald*:

If you make a rough estimate . . ., it looks as if something of the order of 10 million years is needed to establish a mutation. That is, each of these single amino acid changes appears relatively frequently in individuals as pathology; but to establish one such change as a regular characteristic in a species seems to take something of the order of 10 million years.[298] It takes 321,444 generations for a slightly beneficial recessive gene to increase in its frequency from 1 in 1,000,000 to a mere 2 in 1,000,000 in a population, as analyzed by Dodson*.[299]

Summary. Although no one questions whether genes sometimes change by mutation, there is much dispute whether the scope and frequency of those changes can produce macroevolution rather than just microevolution. In connection with the scope of mutations, "genes are limited in their capacity for viable change" at the level of the "major types" (Boyden*[300]), and "mutations do not produce any kind of evolution" at the species level either because of genetic limits (Grassé*[301]). "Viable mutations are of the same order as the trivial differences between intra-speci[es] . . . and as such seem quite incapable of giving rise to the major divergences of structuro-functional organisation," contrary to "the faith which the Neo-Darwinians place" in mutation and natural selection (Russell*[302]). Most significant traits are governed by more than one gene, and the "improbability increases at an enormous rate as the number of genes increases" (Ambrose*[303]). In connection with the frequency of mutations, it "is most unlikely that fewer than five genes could ever be involved in the formation of even the simplest new structure," and the "probability now becomes one in one thousand million million," because the probability of each favorable gene mutation is at best one in a thousand (Ambrose*[304]). Then "to establish one such change as a regular characteristic in a species seems to take something of the order of 10 million years" (Wald*[305]). Thus, Alfred Russel Wallace*, the co-theorist with Darwin* of the evolutionary mechanism of natural selection, noted the antagonism of Mendel's genetic laws as limits: "But on the general relation of Mendelism to Evolution I have come to a very definite conclusion. This is, that it has no relation whatever to the evolution of species or higher groups, but is really antagonistic to such evolution!" (Wallace*[306]). Instead, discontinuitists such as Blyth note that natural selection fulfills a "conservative function" (Blyth[307]), explaining the stasis within and the gaps between natural groups, by the mechanism that is now known to be the genetic laws. *Naturam expelles furca tamen usque recurret.*

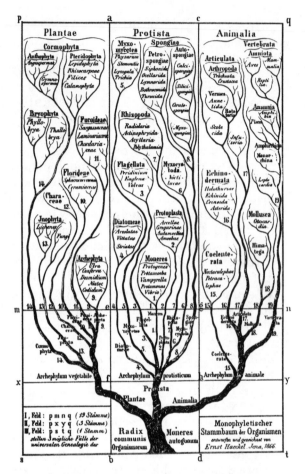

Figure 2.7
The first evolutionary tree or phylogeny (Haeckel*):
"The phylogenetic interpretation has been simply superimposed on the existing classification; a rejection of the former fails to do any violence to the latter" (Mayr*)

2.7 The Comparative Discontinuity Argument: Empirical Evidence from Classification, Comparative Anatomy, and Comparative Biochemistry

The comparative discontinuity argument involves further evidence for distinct ancestry (biological abrupt appearance) rather than common ancestry (biological evolution) of natural groups of organisms. That empirical evidence consists of widespread anomalies in the comparative fields of (a) classification, (b) anatomy, and (c) biochemistry and other areas. (Systematics,[308] comparative anatomy,[309] and comparative biochemistry[310] are three major arguments generally offered in favor of biological evolution.) The anomalies are so widespread, according to many discontinuitist scientists, that these methods of comparative analysis better support biological abrupt appearance than macroevolution or Darwinism.

a. Classification and Discontinuous Ancestry

The data of classification support the distinct ancestry better than the postulated common ancestry of natural groups[311] of organisms, in the view of discontinuitist scientists, for several reasons that are conceded by many evolutionist scientists. As a preliminary consideration, similarities between organisms, which cause them to be grouped together, only "imply shared characteristics . . . rather than common ancestry," as Patterson* points out.[312] "[T]here exists no a priori relation between the appearance of two structures and their relatedness," in the words of Schwabe* and Warr*.[313]

Failure to exercise caution in inferring relatedness from similarity has led to "highly speculative" ventures at classification based on evolutionary assumptions (Huxley*),[314] to "many works on phylogeny [that] read like imaginative literature rather than science" and that "fill gaps in the data with speculations" (Ghiselin*),[315] and to phylogenies in textbooks that "are, as a rule, a festering mass of unsupported assertions" (Bonner*).[316]

First, of the "three prevailing systems of classification,"[317] half of one school (cladistics) and a large part of another school (phenetics) argue that classification is irrelevant to evolution. (The third school is evolutionary systematics.) Within the transformed cladistic school, "evolution is deliberately ignored, being considered unproven and possibly unprovable," according to Charig*[318] and others.[319] Patterson*, a leading cladist and senior paleontologist at the British Museum, writes that

cladistics is theoretically neutral so far as evolution is concerned. It has nothing to say about evolution. You *don't need* to know about evolution, *or believe in it,* to do cladistic analysis.[320]

Benton*, at the Museum of the University of Oxford, concurs that transformed cladists perform classification "without any prior assumptions that evolution has taken place" and claim that classification "does not depend on the theory of evolution."[321] Ridley*, a critic and zoology professor at Oxford, notes that transformed cladists assert "that they can do cladism without evolution, and what they can do, they will."[322] Many others have noted, sometimes in rage, the nonevolutionary nature of transformed cladistics,[323] as discussed later (Sections 3.2(e) and 3.4(b)). Within the phenetics school, "some more radical numerical taxonomists have abandoned the goal of building a taxonomy that reflects evolutionary descent."[324] In place of evolution, transformed cladists and nonevolutionary pheneticists base classification on "natural groups."[325]

That means that classification is not an evidence for biological evolution, but is an area of biology that is independent of evolution, as Darwin* himself evidently believed and as Brady* notes:

> Since Darwin took these relations [common plan, homology, ontogenetic parallelism, and the hierarchy of groups] to be established by previous biology, and used them as evidence for the explanatory power of his theory, he was clearly of the opinion that they were *independent of that theory*. Although several modern figures have argued to the contrary, it seems that Darwin was right. *The patterns listed above are recoverable from observation without reference to evolutionary theory*, which theory may then be applied to provide an account of the process by which they may have come about. That aspect of systematics concerned with the *identification of the empirical patterns* evidently constitutes a study prior to and *independent* of theories of process.[326]

In fact, Mayr* of Harvard concedes that all forms of classification are "based on a study of 'natural groups' found in nature," rather than on phylogeny (evolutionary descent).[327] Crowson*, a zoologist at Glasgow University, agrees that "a perfectly natural classification of plants and animals might even be considered as objectively existing."[328] But the question remains why natural groups exist at all.

Second, the very existence of natural groups is a "massive empirical evidence for the typological view of nature," as biologist Denton* acknowledges:

> [I]t can hardly be denied that there has always been massive empirical evidence for the typological model of nature within the existing realm of life. . . .
>
> The reason for the distinctness of each class and the absence of sequential arrangements, whereby classes can be approached gradually through a series of transitional forms, is precisely as typology implied because each class of organism (just list a class of geometric figures) possesses a number of unique defining characteristics which occur in fundamentally invariant form in all the species of that class but which are not found even in a rudimentary form in any species outside that class. . . .[329]

That typological view embodies the concept of distinct ancestry of natural groups that is part of the biological theory of abrupt appearance, and opposes the concept of common ancestry that is part of the theory of macroevolution, as the history of the typological view shows. Natural groups exist, according to abrupt appearance, because of distinct or discontinuous ancestry, which results in systematic gaps and systematic absences of transitional forms, in both fossil and living organisms.[330] Furthermore, classification is possible because life is an array of natural groups separated by gaps.

Third, from the history of classification, the system of classification was developed by Linnaeus on a creationist basis rather than an evolutionary basis,[331] and "the classification of organisms that existed before the advent of evolutionary theories has undergone surprisingly little change in the times following it," according to Mayr*:

> The fact is that the classification of organisms that existed before the advent of evolutionary theories has undergone surprisingly little change in the times following it, and such changes as have been made have depended only to a trifling extent on the elucidation of the actual phylogenetic relationships through paleontological evidence. The *phylogenetic interpretation* has been *simply superimposed* on the existing classification; a rejection of the former fails to do any violence to the latter. The subdivisions of the animal and plant kingdoms established by *Linnaeus are, with few exceptions, retained* in the modern classification, and this despite the enormous number of new forms discovered since then. The new forms were either included in the Linnaean groups, or new groups have been created to accommodate them. There has been *no necessity for a basic change* in the classification.[332]

Evolutionists of all schools agree, such as Blackwelder*[333] and Simpson*,[334] although some still try to claim classification as an evolutionary argument.[335] The creationist origin and early history of classification indicates that classification is more naturally explained by a theory of abrupt appearance than a theory of evolution.

Fourth, of the two major sources of data considered in classification (phenotype and branching), "these two sources of information are often contradictory."[336] The contradictions would be greater if it were not true that, on the part of evolutionary taxonomists, "classifications are designed primarily, we are too often told, to 'state,' or 'reflect,' or 'be consistent with,' evolutionary and genetic relationships."[337] (That approach is circular, according to Thomson*.[338]) Those widespread anomalies point to distinct ancestry rather than common ancestry of the various natural groups of organisms, and empirical evidence for distinct ancestry is scientific evidence that affirmatively supports the theory of abrupt appearance.

b. Comparative Anatomy and Discontinuous Ancestry

The data of comparative anatomy support the distinct ancestry of natural groups of organisms better than their postulated common ancestry, in the estimation of discontinuitist scientists, because of several considerations with which many evolutionists agree. To begin, as with classification, similar anatomy does not necessarily indicate common ancestry or relatedness, as Boyden* notes:

> Such *general resemblances* in protoplasmic systems as we find in *all* living organisms *do not necessarily mean genetic relationship.* Rather, such resemblances may be fundamentally *convergent,* and represent only the *minimum requirements or "conditions of existence"* which all living systems must possess.[339]

The same point is made by Denton*[340] and Patterson*.[341] That disjunction between similarity and ancestry is reflected in the dissimilar genes that produce similar anatomies, as well as in the dissimilar organisms that have convergent traits and other anatomical anomalies.

First, the general absence of homologous (similar)[342] genes for homologous structures (i.e., the general presence of nonhomologous genes) indicates unrelatedness rather than relatedness of different natural groups of organisms. That was noted by Sir Gavin de Beer*, former director of the British Museum of Natural History and embryology professor at University College of London, in his book entitled *Homology, An Unsolved Problem*:

> Therefore, *homologous structures need not be controlled by identical genes, and homology of phenotypes does not imply similarity of genotypes.*[343]
>
> . . ..
>
> . . .It is now clear that the pride with which it was assumed that the inheritance of *homologous* structures from a common ancestor explained homology was *misplaced*; for such inheritance *cannot be ascribed to identity of genes.* The attempt to find 'homologous' genes, except in closely related species, has been given up as *hopeless.* . . .
>
> . . .[W]hat mechanism can it be that results in the production of homologous organs, the same 'patterns', in spite of their *not* being controlled by the same genes? I asked this question in 1938, and it has not been answered.
>
> It is *useless to speculate* on any explanation in the absence of facts. . . .[343]

Markedly different genes support discontinuous ancestry, regardless of the outwardly similar nature of particular traits.

Indeed, the general rule is nonhomologous genes for similar traits, because of pleiotropy, which Denton* defines and describes*:

The evolutionary basis of homology is perhaps even more severely damaged by the discovery that *apparently homologous structures are specified by quite different genes* in different species. The effects of genes on development are often surprisingly diverse. In the house mouse, nearly every coat-colour gene has some effect on body size. Out of seventeen x-ray induced eye colour mutations in the fruit fly *Drosophila melanogaster*, fourteen affected the shape of the sex organs of the female, a characteristic that one would have thought was quite unrelated to eye colour. *Almost every gene* that has been studied in higher organisms has been found to affect more than one organ system, a multiple effect which is known as pleiotropy. As Mayr argues in *Populations, Species and Evolution:*

> It is doubtful whether any genes that are not pleiotropic exist in higher organisms. Since the primary gene action in multicellular organisms is usually several steps removed from the peripheral phenotypic character, it is obvious that non-pleiotropic genes must be rare if they exist at all.

Not only are *most genes* in higher organisms pleiotropic in their influence on development but, as is clear from a wide variety of studies of mutational patterns in different species, the pleiotropic effects are invariably *species specific.*[344]

Second, anomalies are so widespread, in the form of similarities between groups that evolutionists believe are not closely related, that comparative anatomy supports discontinuous ancestry as well as it supports common ancestry of various natural groups of organisms. Evolutionists term these similarities "convergences," "parallelisms," "iterations," "analogies," etc., rather than homologies, simply to reflect the presupposition that the organisms are not closely related.[345] Convergence is so widespread that Patterson* of the British Museum says "convergence is everywhere."[346] Boyden*, of Rutgers notes that "there are few kinds of characters which are not convergent in some groups," such as the following:

> Multicellularity, symmetry, number of germ layers, presence of exoskeletons, paired-jointed appendages, wings, gills, sense organs, four-chambered hearts, constant body temperature, parthenogenesis, metagenesis, presence of hemoglobin, all these and many more characters appear to be convergent in some . . ..[347]

Denton* gives other examples of "the problem of convergence":

> Then there is the *problem of convergence.* Nature abounds in examples of convergence: the similarity in overall shape of whales, ichthyosaurs and fishes; the similarity in the bone structure of the flippers of a whale and an ichthyosaur; the similarity of the forelimbs of a mole and those of the insect, the molecricket; the great similarity in the design of the eye in vertebrates and cephalopods and the profound parallelism between the

cochlea in birds and mammals. In all the above cases, the *similarities, although very striking, do not imply any close biological relationship.*[348]

Gates* says that "parallelisms occur plentifully in whatever direction we look,"[349] and Romer* of Harvard concurs that convergences and parallelisms are "an almost universal phenomenon."[350] Forey* states that there are "repeated similarities between groups considered to be far apart by palaeontologists" that are categorized as "parallelisms, convergences, and so on,"[351] and Dawkins* calls convergences a "bugbear of the taxonomist."[352]

Yet if similarities between related groups are "everywhere" and "repeated," why would similarities provide any evidence at all that the remaining groups are related? Some evolutionists go as far as a zoologist who concedes that similar anatomies have little relevance to common ancestry (phylogeny):

> the comparison of physiological function throughout the animal kingdom leaves one with the impression that animals of all levels possess the physiological *equipment required for their particular modes of life without much reference to the phylogenetic histories* of the groups to which they belong.[353]

And if dissimilarities exist between supposedly related groups, would that not provide equally strong evidence that they actually are unrelated—discontinuous ancestry? Another evolutionist, Denton*, seems to agree:

> In the last analysis the *facts of comparative anatomy provide no evidence for evolution* in the way conceived by Darwin, and even if we were to construe with the eye of faith some "evidence" in the pattern of diversity for the Darwinian model of evolution this could only be seen, at best, as indirect or circumstantial.
>
> . . .
>
> The same deep homologous resemblance which serves to link all the members of one class together into a natural group also serves to distinguish that class unambiguously from all other classes. Similarly, the same hierarchic pattern which may be explained in terms of a theory of common descent, also, by its very nature, implies the existence of deep divisions in the order of nature. The same facts of comparative anatomy which proclaim unity also proclaim division; while resemblance suggests evolution, *division*, especially where it appears profound, *is counter-evidence against the whole notion of transmutation.*[354]

Finally, as with classification, comparative anatomy was established by creationist scientists (Linnaeus etc.), on the basis of discontinuous ancestry rather than common ancestry, as Dobzhansky* acknowledges:

Linnaeus, the father of systematic biology, named some 4,235 animal species and 5,250 plant species known to him. He regarded these species as primordial entities, made by the Creator in about the same state we find them now. Individuals of a species are, of course, not all alike, and *there exist "varieties"* (we would now call them "races") within species. To Linnaeus, varieties seemed unimportant deviations from the basic models of their species. He correctly recognized that man, apes, and monkeys resemble one another in body structures and placed them next to one another in his system of classification. However, he did *not interpret this propinquity as a consequence of common descent.*[355]

The typological approach is described by Patterson*:

> The science of comparative anatomy developed as a means of searching out these ideal plans, or archetypes.[356]

The very term "homology" was introduced by an antievolutionist scientist (Sir Richard Owen*, the first director of the British Museum), in connection with his view of discontinuous ancestry.[357]

The similarities between various natural groups of organisms may reflect "engineering constraints of good form" for unrelated organisms, rather than common ancestry and relatedness. Evolutionist scientists propose that sort of engineered structure as the explanation for convergences and parallelisms,[358] and see such engineering constraints not just at the level of orders, families, and genera, but at the level of phyla and classes.[359] Discontinuitist scientists merely apply the principle more broadly to say that, if engineering constraints of good form are a sufficient explanation of some similar anatomical traits, then they can be a sufficient explanation of the remaining anatomical similarities.[360] Some evolutionist biologists conclude, for similar reasons, that comparative anatomy or physiology is not evidence for evolution but is instead an indication of structure "needed for their particular modes of life," as Ross* says:

> It is an unspoken assumption that the data of comparative physiology must have implications for phylogeny. Is this realistic? . . . I have searched without success for examples in which physiological comparisons have clarified or corrected phylogenetic relationships based on other data. More often than not functional comparisons turned up phylogenetic paradoxes instead of parallels. Similarly, a search for phylogenetic relationships in the distribution of various mechanisms of muscular contraction *shows only* that animals possess the kinds of muscle, slow, fast, tonic, phasic, rhythmic, *needed for their particular modes of life*, apparently without regard to their phylogenies. Without multiplying the examples, one can safely say that the data of comparative physiology have not contributed much to our views about phylogenetic relationships. That is not to say that these data are irrelevant for theories of

evolutionary processes. It means, however, that physiological evolution must have its own patterns and governing principles, a point which comes up again later.

But in general, the comparison of physiological function throughout the animal kingdom leaves one with the impression that animals of all levels possess the physiological *equipment required* for their particular modes of life *without much reference to the phylogenetic histories* of the groups to which they belong.

It seems that most of the stated aims and general objectives of comparative physiology in all its aspects have been *unfulfilled.* "Illusory" may be too strong a word to describe these objectives but, as I hope to show, it is not just that these objectives have been unrealized but *probably that they are unrealizable.*[361]

And if anomalies are "everywhere" or "repeated," then application of their explanation (engineering constraints of good form and discontinuity of ancestry) to every natural group would be the logical approach.

c. Comparative Biochemistry and Discontinuous Ancestry

The data of comparative biochemistry also point away from the common ancestry of natural groups of organisms, many evolutionist biologists believe, and instead point toward distinct ancestry, discontinuitist biologists suggest. Major anomalies exist in nearly every area of study: cytochrome *c*, hemoglobin and myoglobin, hormones, and hereditary material. Biochemical results not only fail to support Darwinian evolution, but better support the "nonevolutionary . . . pattern" of discontinuous ancestry, according to Denton*:

> It is now well established that the pattern of diversity at a *molecular level conforms to a highly ordered hierarchic system.* Each class at a molecular level is unique, isolated and *unlinked by intermediates.* Thus molecules, like fossils, have *failed* to provide the elusive intermediates so long sought by evolutionary biology. Again, the only relationships identified by this new technique are sisterly. At a molecular level, no organism is "ancestral" or "primitive" or "advanced" compared with its relatives. Nature seems to conform to the same *non-evolutionary* and intensely circumferential *pattern* that was long ago perceived by the great comparative anatomists of the nineteenth century.[362]

As with other comparative approaches, similarity does not necessarily reflect common ancestry or relatedness.[363]

Extensive studies of cytochrome *c*, a protein involved in cell respiration, have been made. One study shows two reptiles to differ more from each other than a fish and a bird, than a fish and a mammal, or than an insect and a mammal, according to Jukes* and Holmquist*, even though common ancestry assumes reptiles are closer to each other than those other pairs.[364] These are "anomalies" that produce "incorrect taxonomic placement" in comparison with evolutionary theory.[365] Another cytochrome *c* study shows a bird to differ from other birds more than from a mammal, and a reptile to differ more from other reptiles than from birds, as Ayala* found.[366] Further research proves that closely related bacteria differ more than mammals from insects and than mammals from amphibians, according to Ambler* and Wynn*.[367] These are all serious anomalies, because common ancestry requires that each branch in the evolutionary bush be closest to the next branch (microorganisms to fish to amphibians to reptiles to birds and lower mammals to primates). Another study found "no correlation" between bacterial cytochrome *c* and evolution.[368]

Studies of blood and muscles show the same frequent anomalies. In testing hemoglobin, a reptile and a bird are more closely related than two reptiles are, and as closely related as man and a reptile, although common ancestry requires the opposite.[369] In testing myoglobin, a reptile and a bird again are more closely related than two reptiles are to each other.[370]

Other studies have been done on hormones. They indicate that amphibians are closer to mammals than reptiles or birds are to mammals, and that fish and reptiles are closer than fish and amphibians are, under the findings of King* and Millar*,[371] even though biological evolution postulates the reverse in each case. Research on relaxin reveals that humans are closer to fish than to other mammals,[372] and one mammal is closer to fish than to another mammal, according to Schwabe*:

> It seems *troublesome*, however, that *shark relaxin is no more different from pig relaxin than pig relaxin is from human relaxin ....* What seems truly astonishing is that shark relaxin also widens the pelvic bone of mice and guinea pigs; it acts specifically on structures that developed only millions of years later in different species. More amazing yet is the fact that the *insulin of guinea pigs*, in violation of the principles of panselectionism, *"devolved" away* from the endogenous receptor to the point where in this species the endogenous insulin is less potent than exogenous porcine insulin. What is the mechanism, we must ask, by which *insulin remains nearly constant* within one group of the Mammalia *whereas another group uses a molecule [relaxin] that differs by roughly 40%* of its sequence? What mechanism is there to explain that the

variation between pig and carp or pig and shark is less than the differ-
ence between the pig and hystricomorph rodents, and what allows an
insulin molecule to change to a less effective state when selection is
purportedly improving the fit between hormone and receptor continuously?[373]

Research on insulin A indicates that man is closer to the rat and the
sei whale than to sheep or goats, and that some fish are closer to
mammals than to other fish, under the research of Eck* and Day-
hoff*,[374] as well as of Schwabe* and Warr*,[375] contrary to the
requirements of common ancestry. Other studies indicate that man
is closer to apes than apes are to each other, and similar anomalies,
as Patterson* found.[376] Similarly, a reptile is closer to a bird than to
another reptile, Fitch* and Margoliash* discovered.[377]

Research in hereditary materials shows other widespread anomalies. Human ribosomal RNA is sufficiently distinctive that "human
mitochondria did not originate from recognizable relatives of present day organisms."[378] The number of chromosomes is totally
anomalous in comparison with evolutionary theory: man has 46,
some mammals 48 (Florida mouse), some reptiles 50 (box turtle),
some fish 94 (goldfish), etc.[379] The structure of chromosomes also
leads to anomalies, as for example in primate studies:

> unfortunately both the evidence that they use and the way in which they
> interpret it have varied considerably.... Based entirely on this evidence,
> but emphasizing different aspects of it, Miller (1977) argued that humans
> and gorillas were most closely related, Yunis & Prakash (1982) that
> humans and chimpanzees were most closely related, and Marks (1983)
> that chimpanzees and gorillas were most closely related....[380]

The most common explanation for such anomalies is that proteins
evolved at different rates, so that for instance proteins evolved
slower between fish and lower mammals (producing less difference)
and faster between lower mammals and human beings (producing
more difference). Two difficulties with that explanation are pointed
out by Schwabe*. First, the hypothesis of different rates is "ad hoc"
and explains any results:

> The obvious discrepancy has been called a quirk even though the New
> Synthesis allows for faster and slower rates of evolution in order to
> render data and trees compatible. Unfortunately, the use of such *ad hoc
> arguments* simultaneously *eliminates a paradigm from the roster of
> hypotheses of science.*[381]

Second, different rates should not exist for one protein but not for
another (for example, insulin and relaxin) in the same pair of organ-

isms, but frequently do as quoted above.[382] Third and most importantly, different rates would not explain why man would be more similar to a fish than a sheep (*i.e.*, why the top and bottom of the evolutionary bush were more similar to each other than to the middle of the bush), even though different rates might explain why man was more similar to a sheep than the sheep was to a fish (*i.e.*, why one part of the bush diverged faster than another part). In that example, the first part is the anomaly that is discussed here.

The anomalies are so widespread that biochemical comparisons do not support the common ancestry required by biological evolution, according to Schwabe* [383] and others.[384] Too many assumed close relatives are too different to have common ancestry, and many assumed distant relatives are even similar by comparison:

> Molecular evolution is about to be accepted as a method superior to paleontology for the discovery of evolutionary relationships. As a molecular evolutionist I should be elated. Instead, it seems *disconcerting that many exceptions exist* to the orderly progression of species as determined by molecular homologies; so many in fact that I think *the exception, the quirks, may carry the more important message.*[385]

Instead, the widespread anomalies in comparative biochemistry support discontinuous ancestry over common ancestry, as Denton* (a molecular biologist) concludes:

> One of the most remarkable features of these new biochemical discoveries is undoubtedly the way in which the pattern of molecular diversity seems to correspond to the predictions of typology. With very few exceptions the *members of each defined taxa are always equally divergent whenever an outgroup comparison is made....* [W]hen outgroup comparisons are made the *subgroups of the type stand equidistant from more distantly related groups*, hold[ing] universally throughout the entire realm of nature. This does not mean, of course, that typology is necessarily correct. But if we accept that closeness to empirical reality is the only criterion by which to judge alternative theories, we would, if strictly impartial, *be forced to choose Aristotle and the eidos in favor of Darwin and the theory of natural selection*. There is little doubt that if this molecular evidence had been available one century ago it would have been seized upon with *devastating* effect by the opponents of evolution theory like Agassiz and Owen, and the idea of organic evolution might never have been accepted.[386]

The extensive anomalies in comparative biochemistry lead Sermonti* to a "null hypothesis" that there may be "no substantial affinity among the different Vertebrate classes," and that a genealogical or phylogenetic bush would look "rather like a bush with many branches emerging directly from the root."[387] A similar point is made by Schwabe*, who finds the anomalies to support polyphyletic ancestry:

> It appears that the neo-darwinian hypothesis is insufficient to explain some of the observations that were not available at the time the paradigm took shape. Three of its weaknesses discussed in this paper pertain to the fact that (1) evolutionary trees constructed from different proteins *suggest the existence of different genealogies* instead of a unique one....[388]

This comparative unrelatedness argument is an affirmative evidence for the theory of abrupt appearance, as not just Denton* and Sermonti* but Zihlman* and Lowenstein* acknowledge in reference to the comparative biochemistry evidence, saying that "this constitutes a kind of 'special creation' hypothesis."[389]

Summary. There are serious anomalies in the comparative fields of classification, comparative anatomy, and comparative biochemistry that puzzle many evolutionists. In classification, "cladistics is theoretically neutral so far as evolution is concerned" and "has nothing to say about evolution" (Patterson*[390]), but instead " 'Transformed Cladistics' is—'natural order systematics' " (Charig*[391]). In a second of the three schools of classification, "some more radical numerical taxonomists have abandoned the goal of building a taxonomy that reflects evolutionary descent" (Luria*, Gould* and Singer*[392]). Some evolutionists concede that the existence of natural groups, which transformed cladists and radical numerical taxonomists use, "has always been massive empirical evidence for the typological model of nature" (Denton*[393]), which is the discontinuous view of the theory of abrupt appearance.

In comparative anatomy, anomalies are called convergences or parallelisms, and "convergence is everywhere" (Patterson*[394]), while "parallelisms occur plentifully in whatever direction we look" (Gates*[395]). "[T]here are few kinds of characters which are not convergent in some groups (Boyden*[396]), and there are "repeated similarities between groups considered to be far apart by paleontologists" that are categorized as "parallelisms, convergences, and so on" (Forey*[397]). At the same time, the "attempt to find 'homologous genes' . . . has been given up as hopeless," and it "is useless to speculate on any explanation in the absence of facts" (de Beer*[398]); instead, "apparently homologous structures are specified by quite different genes in different species" (Denton*[399]). Thus, "the facts of comparative anatomy provide no evidence for evolution in the way conceived by Darwin*," and are instead "counter-evidence against the whole notion of transmutation" (Denton*[400]).

In comparative biochemistry, serious anomalies exist with almost every area of study, such as cytochrome *c*, hemoglobin and myoglobin, hormones, and hereditary material. It "seems disconcerting that many exceptions exist to the orderly progression of species as determined by molecular homologies; so many in fact that I think the exception, the quirks, may carry the more important message," which "the neo-darwinian hypothesis is insufficient to explain" in some cases (Schwabe*[401]). For example, one study of hormones indicates that amphibians are closer to mammals than reptiles or birds are to mammals, and that reptiles are nearer to fish than amphibians are to fish (King* and Millar*[402]). "Each class at a molecular level is unique, isolated and unlinked by intermediates," conforming to a "non-evolutionary and intensely circumferential pattern that was long ago perceived by the great comparative anatomists of the nineteenth century" (Denton*[403])—mostly discontinuitists.

Those anomalies are serious: some noncreationists see classification as more consistent with natural groups than with evolutionary assumptions, find comparative anatomy with convergences and parallelisms "everywhere" but homologous genes nowhere, and wonder at comparative biochemistry that regularly finds evolutionary cousins more similar than evolutionary sisters and that regularly sounds like a broken molecular clock of perverse chimes. Those anomalies are so regular that they go beyond weakening the theory of macroevolution, and support the theory of abrupt appearance in the view of discontinuitists, which is precisely how the leading systematists and anatomists at the time of Darwin* interpreted them (Stansfield*[404]). *Totum non teneas aurum quod splendet ut aurum.*

* * *

The biological theory of abrupt appearance is scientific, not religious, and includes at least seven scientific lines of affirmative support. The underlying evidence is conceded by many evolutionist scientists, and the affirmative arguments are framed as follows by many discontinuitist scientists. The paleontology arguments of systematic abrupt appearances and systematic gaps in the fossil record support biological abrupt appearance. The comparative morphology argument of systematic similarity between fossil organisms and their modern counterparts, and of systematic stasis, also points toward biological abrupt appearance. The information content argument similarly shows vast organization, in complex molecules and organs, that is best explained by biological abrupt appearance. The probability argument concerns the higher probability of biological abrupt appearance than biological macroevolution of complex organisms, complex molecules, and symbiotic relationships. The genetics argument focuses on the genetic limits on viable change. Finally, the comparative discontinuity argument shows that classification, anatomy, and biochemistry better support distinct ancestry of natural groups of organisms through biological abrupt appearance.

These arguments affirmatively support the biological theory of abrupt appearance and do not merely identify weaknesses of the biological theory of evolution, as even some evolutionists concede. The arguments are all empirical, and they thereby show that the theory of abrupt appearance is scientific when compared to the theory of evolution.

Notes

[1] C. Darwin*, *The Origin of Species* 482 (1st ed. 1859, repr. 1964).

[2] Section 1.1(b).

[3] Section 2.7(a).

[4] *E.g.*, Patterson*, *Cladistics*, 27 Biologist 234 (1980) (Cladistics "is about—the pattern in nature—groups, hierarchies or nested sets of groups, and characters of groups."); Charig*, *Cladistics: A Different Point of View*, in Evolution Now 121, 121 (J. Maynard Smith* ed. 1982) (" 'Transformed Cladistics' is—'natural order systematics'."); W. Stansfield*, *The Science of Evolution* 510-11 ("natural groupings"); Leith*, *Are the Reports of Darwin's Death Exaggerated?*, 166 Listener 390, 391 (1981) ("The idea of common ancestry is necessarily theoretical, and one can either do taxonomy within that theoretical framework, believing that one is producing groups of common ancestry, or one can do it as it was done before Darwin, in a nonevolutionary framework, and believe one is finding what were then called 'natural groups.' ").

[5] E. Mayr*, *The Growth of Biological Thought* 219 (1982) (he sees natural groups as implying common ancestry).

[6] This book uses the meanings in the *International Code of Zoological Nomenclature* and the *International Code of Botanical Nomenclature*.

[7] *E.g.*, W. Stansfield*, *The Science of Evolution* 510-11 (1977) ("[H]igher

categories (genera, families, orders, classes, phyla, and even kingdoms), though they do represent greater levels of evolutionary divergence, are still artificial groupings made by humans for convenience in taxonomic work. They are not natural groupings the way that species are."); D. Raup* & S. Stanley*, *Principles of Paleontology* 135, 136, 138 (2d ed. 1978) ("The family, on the other hand, has no comparable objective basis. Higher categories are used to express evolutionary relationships but we do not have, in the present state of our understanding, specific rules that can be applied. In other words, there are no thresholds in the transition from genus to family comparable to the threshold between the subspecies and the species (at a single moment in time)."); Richards*, *Book Review*, 167 Science 1477, 1477 (1970) ("I think nearly all biologists must share, the species, is the only taxonomic category that has at least in more favorable examples a completely objective existence. Higher categories are all more or less a matter of opinion."); N. Macbeth*, *Darwin Retried* 19 (1971) (subjectivity). The subjectivity of classification generates the " 'lumpers' and 'splitters' " among systematists. R. Crowson*, *Classification and Biology* 48 (1970).

[8] E. Mayr*, *The Growth of Biological Thought* 251 (1982).

[9] *E.g.*, E. Forbes, *On the Manifestations of Polarity in the Distribution of Organized Beings in Time*, 1 Proc. Royal Institution of Great Britain 428 (1854); D. Hull*, *Darwin and His Critics* 54 (1973).

[10] *E.g.*, 3 L. Agassiz, *Contributions to the Natural History of the United States* (1860) (reprinted in 30 Am. J. Science 142, 149-150, 154 (1860)).

[11] Sedgwick, *Book Review of On the Origin of Species*, The Spectator, Apr. 7, 1860, at 334-35, reprinted in D. Hull*, *Darwin and His Critics* 159, 162 (1973) ("the higher types of life").

[12] E. Shute, *Flaws in the Theory of Evolution* 5 *passim* (1961) (creationist); M. Pitman, *Adam and Evolution* 36 (1984) (creationist) ("One such concept is the 'type.' It is not a new idea, but new emphasis is being placed on its importance as a natural unit . . . .").

[13] *E.g.*, Mayr*, *Evolution*, Scientific Am., Sept. 1978, at 47, 49 ("Origin of higher types"); D. Raup* & S. Stanley*, *Principles of Paleontology* 126, 131 (2d ed. 1978); W. Stansfield*, *The Science of Evolution* 78 *passim* (1977); T. Dobzhansky*, *Evolution, Genetics, and Man* 2 (1955); F. Ayala* & J. Valentine*, *Evolving: The Theory and Processes of Organic Evolution* 266 (1979) ("adaptive types"); E. Russell*, *The Diversity of Animals* 1, 71 *passim* (1962) ("horse types", "major adaptive types", etc.); J. Huxley*, *Evolution: The Modern Synthesis* 562 (1942) ("a new type"); I. Lerner*, *The Genetic Basis of Selection* (1958); M. Simon*, *The Matter of Life: Philosophical Problems of Biology* 166 (1971); A. Clark*, *The New Evolution* 235-36 (1930) ("all other animal types"); A. Romer*, *Vertebrate Paleontology* 15 (3d ed. 1966); P. Teilhard de Chardin*, *The Appearance of Man* 31 (J. Coehn* trans. 1965); *Monotremes*, 12 Encyclopaedia Britannica 384 (15th ed. 1974); Benton*, *Is a dog more like a lizard or a chicken?*, New Scientist, Aug. 16, 1984, at 18, 18 ("Pattern cladism is close to the ideal morphologist's view of nature

in which the chain of life is broken into discrete "types" separated by clear breaks and in which a classification would represent the "real" pattern"); Brady*, *Dogma and doubt*, 17 Biological J. Linnean Society 79, 80, 90 (1982); Martin*, *A Non-Geneticist Looks at Evolution*, 41 Am. Scientist 100, 100 (1953); Manser*, *The Concept of Evolution*, 40 Philosophy 18, 27 (1965); Gliedman*, *Miracle Mutations*, Science Digest, Feb. 1982, at 90, 91 ("every major type of . . . plant and . . . animal"); Stanley*, *A Theory of Evolution above the Species Level*, 72 Proc. National Academy Sciences 646, 646 (1975) ("types of individuals are favored" by natural selection); Biological Sciences Curriculum Study*, *Biological Science: Molecules to Man* 369 *passim* (3d ed. 1973 & 1976). Others refer to basic types or categories. *E.g.*, A. Boyden*, *Perspectives in Zoology* 27 *passim* (1973) ("major types evolved from other major types"); Gould* & Eldredge*, *Punctuated equilibria: The tempo and mode of evolution reconsidered*, 3 Paleobiology 115, 147 (1977) ("basic morphological designs"); E. Mayr*, *The Growth of Biological Thought* 468 (1982) ("the great anatomical designs," "strikingly different functional types").

[14] The generally accepted scientific use of "type" includes "type species," "type genera," "monotypic," "paratypes," "holotype," "lactotype," "syntype," "reotype," "plesiotypes," and "topotype." D. Raup* & S. Stanley*, *Principles of Paleontology* 113, 131 (2d ed. 1978). *See also* General Assembly of International Union of Biological Sciences*, *International Code of Zoological Nomenclature* 115-58 (3d ed. 1985).

[15] A. Thompson*, *Biology, Zoology, and Genetics* 1 (1983).

[16] F. Ayala* & J. Valentine*, *Evolving: The Theory and Processes of Organic Evolution* 1 (1979) (college textbook) (italics added).

[17] S. Luria*, S. Gould* & S. Singer*, *A View of Life* 767 (1981) (college textbook) (italics added).

[18] Section 3.2(a)-(d).

[19] Section 3.2(e)-(f).

[20] Section 3.1(a).

[21] Gould*, *Catastrophe and Steady State Earth*, Natural History, Feb. 1975, at 15, 15-16.

[22] Eldredge* & Gould*, *Punctuated Equilibria: An Alternative to Phyletic Gradualism*, in Models in Paleobiology 82, 96 (J. Schopf* ed. 1972).

[23] *Prof. Agassiz on the Origin of Species*, 30 Am. J. Science 142, 144-54 (1860), excerpted from 3 L. Agassiz, *Contributions to the Natural History of the United States* (1860) (italics added) (creationist scientist). Of course, the specific theories of genetics and information content were developed subsequently, but Agassiz pointed toward the concepts in his references to biological limits and intelligent structure. Modern discontinuitist scientists do not agree with Agassiz that genetic limits apply generally at the species level, but instead place those limits at the genus or family level depending on the organism.

[24] Lipson*, *A Physicist Looks at Evolution*, 31 Physics Bulletin 138, 138 (1980).

[25] Comment*, *Evolution and Creationism in the Public Schools*, 9 J. Contemp. Law 81 (1983) (italics added).

[26] Laudan*, *Commentary: Science at the Bar—Causes for Concern*, Science, Technology & Human Values, Fall 1982, at 16, 17 (italics added).

[27] Gould*, *Genesis vs. Geology*, Atlantic Monthly, Sept. 1982, at 10, 13; Raup*, *The Geological and Paleontological Arguments of Creationism*, in Scientists Confront Creationism 147, 159 (L. Godfrey* ed. 1983).

[28] Leach*, *Men, Bishops, and Apes*, Nature, Sept. 3, 1981, at 19, 20.

[29] The evolutionary argument is discussed in Section 3.4(a).

[30] Gould*, *The Five Kingdoms*, Natural History, June-July 1976, at 30, 37 (italics added).

[31] D. Raup* & S. Stanley*, *Principles of Paleontology* 372 (2d ed. 1978) (italics added).

[32] Gould*, *Evolution's Erratic Pace*, Natural History, May 1977, at 12, 12 (italics added).

[33] G. Simpson*, *The Major Features of Evolution* 360 (1953) (italics added). *See also* Goldschmidt*, *Evolution, as Viewed by One Geneticist*, 40 Am. Scientist 84, 97 (1952) ("When a new phylum, class, or order appears, there follows a quick, explosive (in terms of geological time) diversification so that *practically all orders or families* known *appear suddenly* and *without any apparent transitions.*") (italics added).

[34] Gould*, *G. G. Simpson, Paleontology, and the Modern Synthesis*, in The Evolutionary Synthesis 153, 164 (E. Mayr* & W. Provine* eds. 1980) (italics in original).

[35] Raup*, *Conflicts Between Darwin and Paleontology*, Field Museum of Natural History Bull., Jan. 1979, at 22.

[36] S. Stanley*, *Macroevolution* 1 (1979) (italics added).

[37] Gould* makes similar arguments: "Gradualists usually extract themselves from the dilemma by invoking the extreme imperfection of the fossil record—if only one step in a thousand survives as a fossil, geology will not record continuous change. Although *I reject this argument*...." Gould*, *The Return of Hopeful Monsters*, Natural History, June-July 1977, at 22, 24 (italics added).

[38] They write: "One hundred and twenty years of paleontological research later, it has become abundantly clear that the fossil record will not confirm this part of Darwin's predictions. *Nor is the problem a miserably poor record.* The fossil record simply shows that this prediction was *wrong.*" N. Eldredge* & I. Tattersall*, *The Myths of Human Evolution* 45-46 (1982) (italics added).

[39] He observes: "Darwin also holds out the hope that some of the gaps would be filled as the result of subsequent collecting. But *most of the gaps* were *still there a century later* and *some paleontologists were no longer willing to explain them away geologically.*" Kitts*, *Paleontology and Evolutionary Theory*, 30 J. Paleontology 458, 467 (1974) (italics added).

[40] *See* D. Raup* & S. Stanley*, *Principles of Paleontology* 303 (2d ed. 1978).

[41]   Raup*, *Conflicts Between Darwin and Paleontology*, Field Museum of Natural History Bull., Jan. 1979, at 22, 25.

[42]   *See* A. Romer*, *Vertebrate Paleontology* 347-96 (3d ed. 1966) (U. of Chicago Press) (data compiled), as summarized in M. Denton*, *Evolution: A Theory in Crisis* 190 (1985).

[43]   M. Denton*, *Evolution: A Theory in Crisis* 189 (1985).

[44]   *Id.*, quoting G. Simpson*, *The Major Features of Evolution* 143 (1953).

[45]   Valentine* & Erwin*, *Interpreting Great Development Experiments: The Fossil Record*, in Development as an Evolutionary Process 71, 84 (1987).

[46]   *E.g.*, E. Ambrose*, *The Nature and Origin of the Biological World* 118 (1982) (italics added):

> Professor Hallam of Birmingham carried out a systematic study of bivalve shell fish found in successive layers of strata formed during the Jurassic period at Lyme Regis. These deposits were laid down by a continuous process in the Jurassic seas, so there were no gaps in the record Hallam hoped to demonstrate the operation of natural selection leading to progressive changes in individual species. He ended up with a completely contrary conclusion, that individual species *appear suddenly* with *no intermediate forms*. They persisted for up to ten million years unchanged. Some continued longer, others disappeared, the basic pattern always showing fixity of species. A similar conclusion was reached by Eldredge, working in the American Museum of Natural History, who studies trilobites, the marine organisms which look rather like modern woodlice. Here again species persisted unchanged for millions of years and new species arose suddenly with no apparent linkage to previous forms.

[47]   *E.g.*, F. Ayala* & J. Valentine*, *Evolving: The Theory and Processes of Organic Evolution* 266-67 (1979) (italics added):

> It is *not reasonable to expect these lineages to have small population sizes* (and certainly not to be poorly adapted) *for such a long time.* Furthermore, even a rare lineage, if skeletonized, *should appear in the fossil record sooner or later if it persisted* for such a long period.

Instead, "[t]here seems, over the years, to have arisen in paleontology a notion which, put cynically, claims that wherever in the fossil record one is looking happens to be where rapid phyletic evolution is not recorded"! S. Stanley*, *Macroevolution* 88 (1979).

[48]   Section 3.2(f).

[49]   A. Thompson*, *Biology, Zoology, and Genetics: Evolution Model vs. Creation Model* 2, 76 (1983) (italics added).

[50]   Clark*, *Animal Evolution*, 3 Quarterly Rev. Biology 523, 539 (1928). Dr. Austin Clark* was curator of paleontology at the Smithsonian Institution.

[51]   J. Draper*, *History of the Conflict between Religion and Science* 246-47 (1896).

[52]   Section 15.2(a). *E.g.*, N. Gillespie*, *Charles Darwin and the Problem of Creation* 26 (1979) ("[Cuvier, Owen, Agassiz, Barrande, Falconer, Forbes,

Lyell, Murchison, Sedgwick] were paleontologists or geologists, and special creation . . . was commonly *recognized by them to have strong empirical evidence* in the fossil series which seemed to support the idea that species appeared full-blown suddenly . . ..").

⁵³ Leakey*, *Introduction*, to C. Darwin*, *The Origin of Species* at 14 (R. Leakey* ed. 1979) (italics added). *E.g.*, Sedgwick, *Book Review of On the Origin of Species*, The Spectator, Apr. 7, 1860, at 334, reprinted in D. Hull*, *Darwin and His Critics* 159, 162 (1973).

⁵⁴ C. Darwin*, *The Origin of Species* 302 (1st ed. 1859, repr. 1964).

⁵⁵ Raup*, *Conflicts Between Darwin and Paleontology*, Field Museum of Natural History Bull., Jan. 1979, at 22, 23 (italics added).

⁵⁶ Leach*, *Men, bishops and apes*, Nature, Sept. 3, 1981, at 19, 20.

⁵⁷ D. Futuyma*, *Science on Trial* 170 (1983). His paragraph begins with the question, "Why do biologists consider evolution to be a fact?" *Id.*

⁵⁸ Kitts*, *Paleontology and Evolutionary Theory*, 28 Evolution 458, 458 (1974).

⁵⁹ Gould*, *Evolution's Erratic Pace*, Natural History, May 1977, at 13, 14 (italics added).

⁶⁰ Kemp, *A fresh look at the fossil record*, New Scientist, Dec. 5, 1985, at 66, 66 (italics added).

⁶¹ Raup*, *Conflicts Between Darwin and Paleontology*, Field Museum of Natural History Bull., Jan. 1979, at 22, 23 (italics added).

⁶² Ager*, *The Nature of the Fossil Record*, 87 Proc. Geological Association 131, 133 (1976).

⁶³ F. Ayala* & J. Valentine*, *Evolving: The Theory and Processes of Organic Evolution* 258 (1979) (italics added).

⁶⁴ *Id.* at 266-67 (italics added).

⁶⁵ Erwin* & Valentine*, *"Hopeful monsters," transposons, and Metazoan radiation*, 81 Proc. National Acad. Sciences 5482, 5482 (1984).

⁶⁶ Davis*, *Comparative Anatomy and the Evolution of Vertebrates*, in Genetics, Paleontology, and Evolution at 64, 74 (G. Jepsen*, E. Mayr* & G. Simpson* eds. 2d ed. 1963)(italics added) (Davis* believes that neo-Darwinism adequately explains most evolutionary modes, or subsequent evolution, after the origin of new adaptive types that appear abruptly).

⁶⁷ Gould*, *Evolution: Explosion, Not Ascent*, N. Y. Times, Jan. 22, 1978, §E, at 6 (most fossil species "enter the record *abruptly*"); J. Rifkin*, *Algeny* 131 (1983) ("Plants and animal species show up *suddenly* in the rocks and then remain structurally the same for millions of years, until they become extinct.").

⁶⁸ *E.g.*, S. Stanley*, *Macroevolution* 22 (1979) ("the fossil record seemed often to document sudden origins of higher taxa"); N. Eldredge* & I. Tattersall*, *The Myths of Human Evolution* 8 (1982) ("Their sudden appearance alongside their unchanged ancestors reflects a common pattern in the geography of evolution."); Hanken* & Hall*, *Evolution of the Skeleton*, Natural History, Apr. 1983, at 28, 30 ("all four major skeletal tissue types

appear more or less simultaneously in the fossil record"); Goldschmidt*, *Evolution as Viewed by One Geneticist*, 40 Am. Scientist 84, 97 (1952) ("practically all orders or families known appear suddenly and without any apparent transitions."); O. Schindewolf*, *Grundfragen der Palaontologie* (1950).

[69]   S. Stanley*, *Macroevolution* 67 (1979) (italics added).

[70]   Gould* writes:

About 570 million years ago, our modern fossil record began with the greatest of geological bangs—the *Cambrian explosion. Within a few million years, nearly all major groups of invertebrates* with hard parts made their first appearance in the fossil record. For fully three billion years before, life had been little more than a long sequence of bacteria and blue-green algae.

Gould*, *The Ediacaran Experiment*, Natural History, Feb. 1984, at 14, 14 (italics added) (he sees the Ediacaran fauna as the one exception). *See also* Gould*, *In the Midst of Life . . .*, Natural History, Feb. 1980, at 34, 40; Gliedman*, *Miracle Mutations*, Science Digest, Feb. 1982, at 90, 91.

[71]   Schopf*, *The Age of Microscopic Life*, 34 Endeavor 49, 51, 57 (1975) (italics added).

[72]   *E.g.*, Repetski*, *A Fish from the Upper Cambrian of North America*, 200 Science 529, 529 (1978) ("Anatolegis, interpreted as a heterostracan fish (class Agnatha), have been discovered in the Deadwood Formation of *Late Cambrian* age in northeastern Wyoming. This discovery extends back the age of the earliest known vertebrate fossils by approximately 40 million years. Other occurrences . . . show that these fish had a widespread geographic distribution in Late Cambrian and Early Ordovician marine environments.") (italics added); N. Cygan* & F. Koucky*, *The Cambrian and Ordovician Rocks of the East Flank of the Big Horn Mountains* (1963).

[73]   Contrary to the findings in the preceding footnote, the majority of scientists place the appearance of vertebrate fish in the Ordovician.

[74]   Axelrod*, *Evolution of the Psilophyte Paleoflora*, 13 Evolution 264, 264 (1959) ("The oldest land plants now known are the Early Cambrian of the Baltic region . . . .. Approximately 60 Cambrian spore-genera are now on record . . . .").

[75]   Schopf*, *The Age of Microscopic Life*, 34 Endeavor 49, 51, 53 (1975) (italics added, footnotes omitted).

[76]   W. Stansfield*, *The Science of Evolution* 75 (1977).

[77]   Ager*, *The Nature of the Fossil Record*, 87 Proc. Geological Association 131, 133 (1976).

[78]   F. Ommanney*, *The Fishes* 60 (1964) (italics added). *See also* A. Romer*, *Vertebrate Paleontology* 15 (3d ed. 1966); White*, *Presidential Address: A little on Lung-fishes*, 177 Proc. Linnean Society 1, 8 (1966). In fact, fish probably appeared before the Ordovician in the Cambrian period. Note 72.

[79]   B. Stahl*, *Vertebrate History: Problems in Evolution* 29-30 (1973) (italics added).

80 *Id.* at 92.

81 *See* Patterson*, *Book Review*, 29 Systematic Zoology 216, 217 (1980); notes 30-68.

82 Carroll*, *Origin of Reptiles*, in 1 Biology of the Reptilia 1, 9 (C. Gans*, A. Bellairs* & T. Parsons* eds. 1969).

83 *E.g., see* 1 W. Swinton*, *Biology and Comparative Physiology of Birds* 1 (A. Marshall* ed. 1960); E. Russell*, *The Diversity of Animals* 118 (1962).

84 Ager*, *The Nature of the Fossil Record*, 87 Proc. of Geological Association 131, 133 (1976) (italics added).

85 D. Johansen* & M. Edey*, *Lucy: The Beginnings of Humankind* 363 (1981) (italics added). *See also* N. Eldredge* & I. Tattersall*, *The Myths of Human Evolution* 7-8 (1982) ("The remains of each of these new [hominid] species appear in the fossil record rather *abruptly.*") (italics added).

86 *E.g., see* S. Zuckerman*, *Beyond the Ivory Tower* 64 (1970); Gould*, *Evolution: Explosion, Not Ascent*, N.Y. Times, Jan. 22, 1978, §E, at 6.

87 Ager*, *The Nature of the Fossil Record*, 87 Proc. Geological Association 131, 133 (1976).

88 *E.g.*, Gray* & Boucot*, *Early Silurian Spore Tetrad from New York: Earliest New World Evidence for Vascular Plants?*, 173 Science 918, 920 (1971).

89 R. Good*, *Features of Evolution in the Flowering Plants* 384 (1974) (italics added).

90 Note 32.

91 Note 31.

92 Note 36.

93 Note 63.

94 Note 84.

95 Note 54.

96 Note 49.

97 Simpson*, *The Sudden Appearance of Higher Categories*, in Evolution of Life 149 (S. Tax* ed. 1960). "Phyla, classes, and orders" are general levels of classification below kingdoms and above families, genera, and species.

98 G. Simpson*, *Tempo and Mode in Evolution* 107 (1944) (italics added); G. Simpson*, *The Major Features of Evolution* 360-61 (1953).

99 Kitts*, *Paleontology and Evolutionary Theory*, 28 Evolution 458, 467 (1974) (italics added).

100 F. Ayala* & J. Valentine*, *Evolving: The Theory and Processes of Organic Evolution* 258 (1979) (italics added).

101 Valentine* & Erwin*, *Interpreting Great Developmental Experiments: The Fossil Record*, in Development as an Evolutionary Process 71, 84 (1987) (italics added).

102 He writes: "But there are still *great gaps* in the fossil record. Most of the major groups of animals *(phyla) appear fully fledged* in the early Cambrian rocks (Fig. 43), and we know of *no fossil forms linking them.*" C. Patterson*, *Evolution* 133 (1978) (italics added).

103 E. Russell*, *The Diversity of Animals* 130 (1962); *see* T. Dobzhansky*,

F. Ayala*, G. Stebbins* & J. Valentine*, *Evolution* 325 (1977).
[104]   Gould*, *Evolution's Erratic Pace*, Natural History, May 1977, at 12, 14 (italics added). *See also* Gould*, *The Return of Hopeful Monsters*, Natural History, June-July 1977, at 22, 24 ("All paleontologists know that the fossil record contains *precious little in the way of intermediate forms*; transitions between major groups are characteristically abrupt.") (italics added); Williamson*, *Palaeontological documentation of speciation on Cenozoic molluscs from Turkana Basin*, 293 Nature 437, 440 (1981) ("A persistent problem in evolutionary biology has been the absence of intermediate forms in the fossil record. Long-term gradual transformations in single lineages are rare and generally involve simple size increase or trivial phenotypic effects.").
[105]   Woodruff*, *Evolution: The Paleobiological View*, 208 Science 716, 716 (1980).
[106]   E. Russell*, *The Diversity of Animals* 58 (1962) ("Each of the great *phyla* of animals is built upon a *structural plan quite different from that of the others*. Their origin is unknown; between them there exist *no true connecting links*, and there is no likelihood of the direct transformation of one into another . . . .") (italics added).
[107]   G. Simpson*, *Tempo and Mode in Evolution* 105 (1944) ("On still higher levels, those of what is here called 'mega-evolution,' the inferences might still apply, but caution is enjoined, because here essentially continuous *transitional sequences* are not merely rare, but are *virtually absent.*") (italics added).
[108]   Gould* & Eldredge*, *Punctuated equilibria: the tempo and mode of evolution reconsidered*, 3 Paleobiology 115, 147 (1977) ("At the higher level of evolutionary transition between basic morphological designs, gradualism has always been in trouble, though it remains the 'official' position of most Western evolutionists. *Smooth intermediates* between Bauplane are *almost impossible to construct*, even in thought experiments; there is certainly *no evidence* for them in the fossil record . . . .") (italics added).
[109]   Raup*, *Conflicts Between Darwin and Paleontology*, Field Museum of Natural History Bull., Jan. 1979, at 22, 25 ("we have *even fewer examples of evolutionary transition than we had in Darwin's time*") (italics added).
[110]   Olson*, *The Problem of Missing Links: Today and Yesterday*, 56 Quarterly Rev. Biology 405, 407 (1981) ("The absence of intermediates in the fossil record was well known during the 19th century.").
[111]   Letter from Dr. Colin Patterson* to Luther D. Sunderland (Apr. 10, 1979) (italics added).
[112]   Raup*, *Conflicts Between Darwin and Paleontology*, Field Museum of Natural History Bull., Jan. 1979, at 22, 22-23.
[113]   R. Blackwelder*, *Taxonomy* 446 (1967).
[114]   Kitts*, *Paleontology and Evolutionary Theory*, 30 J. Paleontology 458, 467 (1974) (italics added).
[115]   T. Huxley*, *Three Lectures on Evolution* 619 (1882).

[116]   Moore*, *Science as a Way of Knowing—Evolutionary Biology*, 23 Am. Zoologist 1, 23 (1983).

[117]   N. Gillespie*, *Charles Darwin and the Problem of Creation* 7 (1979) (U. of Chicago Press).

[118]   He wrote:

So that, until this is forthcoming, we cannot but feel that, whilst the theories are in one direction (and made to dovetail into each other), the *great body of facts* is unquestionably on the opposite side. More especially will this apply to that gravest of all objections (as Mr. Darwin frankly admits), the *thorough and complete absence* (both in geological collections, imperfect though they be, and those, extensive and endless as they are, of the Recent Period) of that countless host *of transitional links* which, on the "natural selection" theory must certainly have existed at one period or another of the world's history. They may be forthcoming some day; we cannot tell (and so, truly, may many other things, after the same fashion of reasoning!): but at present it is absolutely certain that we have not so much as a shadow of evidence either that they do exist, or have ever existed. On whichever side we turn we find order and symmetry to be the *law of creation*, instead of confusion and disorder.

Wollaston, *Book Review of The Origin of Species*, 5 Annals & Magazine of Natural History 132-43 (1860), reprinted in D. Hull*, *Darwin and His Critics* 127, 136 (1973) (U. of Chicago Press) (italics added).

[119]   Johnson*, *Creation, Evolution and Historical Geology*, 78 S. African J. Science 264, 267 (1982) (italics added). In fact, discontinuitists focus on the gaps between genera and families rather than between species.

[120]   R. Good*, *Features of Evolution in the Flowering Plants* 383 (1974) (italics added).

[121]   Gould* & Eldredge*, *Punctuated equilibria: the tempo and mode of evolution reconsidered*, 3 Paleobiology 115, 116 (1977).

[122]   *Id.* at 116 (italics added). Gould* adds elsewhere:

i) Gradualism. In this case, we didn't even see the phenomenon in fossil sequences, but assumed that it must have existed, and been obliterated by an imperfect record—and all because we thought that evolutionary theory (as Darwin falsely claimed) required its generality (Eldredge and Gould 1972; Gould and Eldredge 1977). Thus we ignored as no data one of the most interesting and potentially revealing aspects of the history of most species—stasis.

Gould*, *The promise of paleobiology as a nomothetic, evolutionary discipline*, 6 Paleobiology 96, 103 (1980).

[123]   G. Simpson*, *The Meaning of Evolution* 18 (1949). Axelrod* elaborates on this gap:

One of the major unsolved problems of geology and evolution is the occurrence of *diversified, multicellular marine invertebrates in Lower Cambrian rocks on all the continents* and their *absence in rocks of*

greater age. . . . Evolution preceded their appearance in the record. However, when we turn to examine the *Precambrian rocks* for the forerunners of these Early Cambrian fossils, they are *nowhere to be found.* Many thick (over 5,000 feet) sections of sedimentary rock are now known to lie in unbroken succession below strata containing the earliest Cambrian fossils. These sediments apparently were suitable for the preservation of fossils because they often are identical with overlying rocks which are fossiliferous, yet no fossils are found in them.
Axelrod*, *Early Cambrian Marine Fauna,* 128 Science 7, 7 (1958) (italics added). This is significant because more than two billion years are generally postulated by evolutionists as necessary for life to reach that early Cambrian level of complexity, and numerous fossils should have been deposited in such a vast time, even if relatively small numbers of Precambrian fossils exist. On Precambrian fossils, see Section 2.1(b)(2).

[124] T. Dobzhansky*, F. Ayala*, G. Stebbins* & J. Valentine*, *Evolution* 373, 397 (1977) (italics added).

[125] For example:
> *Over ten thousand fossil species of insect* have been identified, *over thirty thousand species of spiders,* and *similar numbers for many sea-living creatures.* Yet so far the evidence for step-by-step changes leading to major evolutionary transitions looks *extremely thin.* The supposed transition from wingless to winged insects still has to be found, as has the transition between the two main types of winged insects, the paleoptera (mayflies, dragonflies) and the neoptera (ordinary flies, beetles, ants, bees).

F. Hoyle, *The Intelligent Universe: A New View of Creation and Evolution* 43 (1983) (italics added) (panspermia advocate).

[126] Ager*, *The Nature of the Fossil Record,* 87 Proc. of Geological Association 131, 132 (1976) (italics added).

[127] S. Stanley*, *Macroevolution* 88 (1979).

[128] F. Ommanney*, *The Fishes* 60 (1964).

[129] A. Romer*, *Vertebrate Paleontology* 15 (3d ed. 1966).

[130] White*, *Presidential address: A little on Lung-fishes,* 177 Proc. Linnean Society 1, 8 (1966) (italics added).

[131] B. Stahl*, *Vertebrate History: Problems in Evolution* 902 (1973) (italics added).

[132] A. Romer*, *Vertebrate Paleontology* 36 (3d ed. 1966).

[133] Romer*, *Book Review of The Origin of Terrestrial Vertebrates,* 162 Science 250, 250 (1968). *See also* Patterson*, *Book Review,* 29 Systematic Zoology 216, 217 (1980).

[134] Swinton*, *The Origin of Birds,* in 1 *Biology and Comparative Physiology of Birds* 1 (A. Marshall* ed. 1960).

[135] Gould* & Eldredge*, *Punctuated equilibria: the tempo and mode of evolution reconsidered,* 3 Paleobiology 115, 147 (1977).

[136] The first bird, which is essentially a modern bird, appears suddenly in

the same Late Jurassic period as *Archaeopteryx*, which is alleged to be a reptile-bird intermediate. *E.g., The Oldest Fossil Bird: A Rival for Archaeopteryx?*, 110 Science 284 (1978); Cracraft*, *Phylogenetic Relationships and Monophyly of Loons, Grebes, and Hesperornithiform Birds*, 31 Systematic Zoology 35, 53 (1982).

[137]   Section 3.5(f).

[138]   E. Russell*, *The Diversity of Animals* 130 (1962) (italics added).

[139]   Section 3.5(g).

[140]   G. Simpson*, *Tempo and Mode in Evolution* 105-06 (1944). *See also* S. Stanley*, *Macroevolution* 82 (1979) ("despite the detailed study of the Pleistocene *mammals* of Europe, *not a single valid example is known of phyletic transition from one genus to another.*") (italics added).

[141]   Simons*, *The Origin and Radiation of the Primates*, 167 Annals of N.Y. Acad. of Sciences 318 (1969).

[142]   A. Kelso*, *Physical Anthropology* 142 (2nd ed. 1974).

[143]   S. Zuckerman*, *Beyond the Ivory Tower* 64 (1970) (italics added).

[144]   Zihlman* & Lowenstein*, *False Start of the Human Parade*, Natural History, Aug. 1979, at 86, 88 (italics added).

[145]   Gribben* & Cherfas*, *Descent of Man—Or Ascent of Apes?*, 91 New Scientist 592, 594 (1981) ("frailty of the conventional history of man and apes"); Gliedman*, *Miracle Mutations*, Science Digest, Feb. 1982, at 90, 90 ("No fossil or other physical evidence directly connects man to ape.").

[146]   Note 104.

[147]   Note 105.

[148]   Note 98.

[149]   Note 99.

[150]   Note 115.

[151]   Note 120.

[152]   Note 122.

[153]   Note 124.

[154]   Note 130.

[155]   Note 132.

[156]   Note 134.

[157]   Note 135.

[158]   Note 138.

[159]   Note 140.

[160]   Note 141.

[161]   Note 143.

[162]   Note 89.

[163]   P. Grassé*, *Evolution of Living Organisms* 84 (trans. 1977) (italics added). *See also* N. Macbeth*, *Darwin Retried* 121 (1971) ("In hundreds of millions of years there must have been changes in climate, changes in the environment, new enemies, new parasites, new diseases. Yet these creatures, without showing any special virtues or abilities, continue unchanged.").

[164] *Living Fossils* (N. Eldredge* & S. Stanley* eds. 1984).

[165] Hutchinson*, *Marginalia*, 58 Am. Scientist 528, 534 (1970).

[166] *E.g.*, Reiser* & Tasch*, *Investigations of the Viability of Osmophile Bacteria of Great Geological Age*, 63 Trans. Kan. Acad. Science 31 (1960); Dombrowski*, *Bacteria from Paleozoic Salt Deposits*, 108 Annals N.Y. Acad. Science 453 (1963) (fossil *Bacillus circulans* identical to modern *Bacillus circulans*).

[167] *E.g.*, F. Hoyle & N. Wickramasinghe, *Evolution from Space* 86, 89 (1981) ("It is particularly remarkable that no forms with the wings at an intermediate stage of development have been found. Where fossil insects have wings at all they are fully functional to serve the purposes of flight, and *often enough in ancient fossils the wings are essentially identical to what can be found today*. Nor are there intermediate forms between the two kinds of wings, those of the Paleoptera held aloft or permanently at the side as in mayflies and dragonflies respectively, and those of the Neoptera with a flexing mechanism enabling the wings to be folded back into a resting position across the abdomen.") (italics added).

[168] Kuisinitz*, *Cockroach: The Ancient Super-Pest*, Science World, Feb. 4, 1983, at 12 (from Dr. Betty Faber, entomologist with American Museum of Natural History).

[169] Gliedman*, *Miracle Mutations*, Science Digest, Feb. 1982, at 90, 92 ("One of the most familiar of these species is the horseshoe crab. Three slightly different ancestral species connect today's horseshoe crab with a nearly identical creature that flourished in warm Triassic seas 225 million years ago.")

[170] Sturmer*, *A small coleoid cephalopod with soft parts from the lower Devonian discovered using radiography*, 318 Nature 53, 53, 55 (1985) (italics added).

[171] Hessler*, *Cephalocarida: Living Fossil Without a Fossil Record*, in Living Fossils at 181 (N. Eldredge* & S. Stanley* eds. 1984).

[172] Batten*, Neopilina, Neomphalus *and* Neritopsis, *Living Fossil Molluscs*, in *id.* at 218.

[173] Houbrick*, *The Giant Creeper . . . Marine Snail*, in *id.* at 232.

[174] Houbrick*, Diastoma melanoides . . . *Snail from South Australia*, in *id.* at 236.

[175] Ward*, *Is Nautilus a Living Fossil?*, in *id.* at 247.

[176] Winston* & Cheetham*, *The Bryozoan* Nellia tenella *as a Living Fossil*, in *id.* at 257.

[177] Colgan* *The Cretaceous Coral* Heliopora . . ., in *id.* at 266.

[178] J. Beerbower*, *Search for the Past* 168 (1960).

[179] S. Stanley*, *The New Evolutionary Timetable* 83-84 (1981).

[180] Wiley* & Schultze*, *Family* Lepisosteidae *(Gars) as Living Fossils*, in Living Fossils at 160, 163 (N. Eldredge* & S. Stanley* eds. 1984).

[181] S. Stanley*, *The New Evolutionary Timetable* 84 (1981).

[182] Patterson*, *Family* Chanidae *and Other Teleostean Fishes as Living*

Fossils, in Living Fossils at 132 (N. Eldredge* & S. Stanley* eds. 1984).

[183] Greenwood*, Denticeps clupeoides *Clausen* . . ., in *id.* at 140.

[184] Greenwood*, Polypterus *and* Erpetoichthys: *Anachronistic Osteichthyans*, in *id.* at 143.

[185] Gardiner*, *Sturgeons as Living Fossils*, in *id.* at 148.

[186] Schultze* & Wiley*, *The Neopterygian* Amia *as a Living Fossil*, in *id.* at 153.

[187] Forey*, *The Coelacanth as a Living Fossil*, in *id.* at 166.

[188] B. Stahl*, *Vertebrate History: Problems in Evolution* 240 (1973) (italics added).

[189] Meyer*, *Crocodilians as Living Fossils*, in Living Fossils at 105, 105 (N. Eldredge* & S. Stanley* eds. 1984).

[190] *E.g.*, Gliedman*, *Miracle Mutations*, Science Digest, Feb. 1982, at 90, 92.

[191] Mayr*, *Discussion*, in Mathematical Challenges to the Neo-Darwinian Interpretation of Evolution 54, 58 (P. Moorhead* & M. Kaplan* eds. 1967). *See also* Jepsen*, *Early Eocene Bat from Wyoming*, 154 Science 1333, 1333 (1966).

[192] *E.g.*, E. Russell*, *The Diversity of Animals* 123 (1962) ("A specially striking example is provided by the Bats. They appeared in the Middle Eocene with their wings fully differentiated, and since that time, some 50-55 million years ago, the Bat's wings have not essentially progressed, though they have become more diversified (Simpson, p. 119). The Bats, we must assume, have evolved, like the other mammalian Orders, from the primitive insectivores of Upper Cretaceous and Paleocene times, but of this great transformation, involving an entirely new mode of life, and a high degree of structural specialisation, we have so far no record.").

[193] Emry* & Thorington*, *The Tree Squirrel* Sciurus . . . *as a Living Fossil*, in Living Fossils 23, 23, 30 (N. Eldredge* & S. Stanley* eds. 1984) (italics added).

[194] Janis*, *Tragulids as Living Fossils*, in *id.* at 87, 93 (italics added).

[195] Novacek*, *Evolutionary Stasis in the Elephant-Shrew*, Rhynchochyon, in *id.* at 4.

[196] Tattersall*, *The Tree-Shrew*, Tupaia: *A "Living Fossil Model" of the Ancestral Primate?*, in *id.* at 32.

[197] Schwartz*, *What Is a Tarsier?*, in *id.* at 38.

[198] Vrba*, *Evolutionary Pattern and Process in the Sister-Group* Alcelaphini-Aepycerotini (Mammalia: Bovidae), in *id.* at 62.

[199] Janis*, *Tapirs as Living Fossils*, in *id.* at 80.

[200] N. Gillespie*, *Charles Darwin and the Problem of Creation* 26 (1979) (U. of Chicago Press) (italics added).

[201] Sedgwick, *Book Review of The Origin of Species*, The Spectator, Apr. 7, 1860, at 334-35, reprinted in D. Hull*, *Darwin and His Critics* 159, 162 (1973) (U. of Chicago Press).

[202] Moore*, *Science as a Way of Knowing—Evolutionary Biology*, 23 Am.

Zoologist 1, 20 (1983).
[203]   Stebbins* & Ayala*, *Is a New Evolutionary Synthesis Necessary?*, 213 Science 967, 970 (1981).
[204]   Gould*, *Evolution's Erratic Pace*, Natural History, May 1977, at 13, 14 (italics added). *See also* Gould*, *The promise of paleobiology as a nomothetic, evolutionary discipline*, 6 Paleobiology 96, 103 (1980).
[205]   N. Eldredge* & I. Tattersall*, *The Myths of Human Evolution* 8 (1982) (italics added). *See also id.* at 8 ("And this picture of stability for long periods, interrupted by abrupt change, is typical of the fossil record of all life.").
[206]   Gould*, *The Five Kingdoms*, Natural History, June-July 1976, at 30, 37.
[207]   G. Taylor*, *The Great Evolution Mystery* 137-38 (1983) (italics added).
[208]   A. Boyden*, *Perspectives in Zoology* 35 (1973):

All the major types of animals likely to leave fossils are represented in the early Paleozoic rocks. This period of evolution is therefore characterized as much by the conservation of change as by the changes themselves. . . . But so far as is known over this long period of time *no insect and no arthropod has evolved any different pattern leading to another phylum.* The evidences relating to the *Age of Stabilization* do lend themselves to interpretation on the Neo-Darwinian basis, all this evolution being *subspeciational* and completely graded in origin, and the gaps between species having been secondarily acquired.

Id. at 35 (italics added).
[209]   Note 163.
[210]   Note 164.
[211]   Note 205.
[212]   Note 204.
[213]   Note 200.
[214]   Ambrose* defines it as follows: "Information theory can be applied to any situation involving messages. It follows therefore that the language of life, the genetic code written along the lengths of DNA molecules in groups of three coding for the various twenty-two amino acids of proteins, can also be expressed in terms of a given amount of information." E. Ambrose*, *The Nature and Origin of the Biological World* 125 (1982).
[215]   D. Brooks* & E. Wiley*, *Evolution as Entropy* x (1986) (U. of Chicago Press) (italics added).
[216]   *Hoyle on evolution*, Nature, Nov. 12, 1981, at 105, 105 (italics added) (panspermia advocate). Hoyle gives a simplified explanation:

In total there are perhaps 2,000 such enzymes, and their structures are basically the same across the whole of the living world—an enzyme from a bacterium can be used in the cell of a man. The *chance of finding each* individual enzyme by stringing together amino acid beads at random is again like the *Rubik cube being solved by a blindfolded person.* Although the chance of finding all the enzymes, 2,000 of them, by random processes is *not nearly as small as the chance of finding the whole 200,000 proteins on which life depends*, the chance is still exceedingly minute. Call it x[$10^{40,000}$] to 1 against. If you started to write x out in longhand form, beginning with the digit 1 and adding zeros, you would have . . . about forty pages, some 40,000 zeros in all.

F. Hoyle, *The Intelligent Universe* 16-17 (1983). *See also* F. Hoyle & N. Wickramasinghe, *Evolution from Space* 129 (1981). The counterargument that enzymes in early life were shorter is not persuasive. *Id.* at 129. (Hoyle and Wickramasinghe describe their scientific views as panspermia views of a nontheistic and nonbiblical sort.)

[217]   R. Dawkins*, *The Blind Watchmaker* 115-16 (1986) (italics added except title.)

[218]   M. Denton*, *Evolution: A Theory in Crisis* 351 (1985) (italics added). Moreover, he notes that "there is a growing likelihood that the genome may contain even more than one hundred thousand million bits of information." *Id.*

[219]   Eigen* *et al.*, *The Origin of Genetic Information*, in Evolution Now 10, 13 (J. Maynard Smith* ed. 1982) (italics added).

[220]   C. Sagan*, *Cosmos* 278 (1980). *See* ch. 4 n. 7.

[221]   A. Wallace*, *Natural Selection and Tropical Nature* 202 (1895).

[222]   2 *The Life and Letters of Charles Darwin* 67 (F. Darwin* ed. 1887).

[223]   C. Darwin*, *The Origin of Species* 186-87 (1st ed. 1859, repr. 1964) (italics added). *See also* E. Mayr*, *Systematics and the Origin of Species* 296 (1942); M. Ghiselin*, *The Triumph of the Darwinian Method* 215-18, 221, 227-29 (1969).

[224]   G. Hardin*, *Nature and Man's Fate* 71-72 (1961) (italics added). *See also* Gould*, *The Return of Hopeful Monsters*, Natural History, June-July 1977, at 22, 24-25. While Darwin*, Hardin*, and some others have suggested that a flawed eye might have evolutionary value over no eye, the vast information content of the eye remains unexplained.

[225]   *E.g.*, 1 S. Duke-Elder*, *System of Ophthalmology* 178 (1976). *See also* H. Neal* & H. Rand*, *Comparative Anatomy* 582 (1943).

[226]   Raup*, *Conflicts Between Darwin and Paleontology*, Field Museum of Natural History Bull., Jan. 1979, at 22, 24 (italics added).

[227]   J. Prince*, *Comparative Anatomy of the Eye* 334 (1956).

[228]   2 *The Life and Letters of Charles Darwin* 296 (F. Darwin* ed. 1887) (italics added). *See also* E. Mayr*, *Systematics and the Origin of Species* 296 (1942) ("it is a *considerable strain on one's credulity* to assume that finely balanced systems such as certain sense organs (the eye of vertebrates, or the bird's feather) *could* be improved by random mutations"); M. Ghiselin*, *The Triumph of the Darwinian Method* 215-16, 218, 221, 227-29 (1969).

[229]   R. Goldschmidt*, *The Material Basis of Evolution* 6-7 (1940). Goldschmidt* attempted to explain these complex structures by his "hopeful monster" hypothesis of huge-scale mutations. Virtually all biologists reject his hypothesis as impossible under genetic laws and information theory.

[230]   E. Russell*, *The Diversity of Animals* (1962).

[231]   A. Hardy*, *The Living Stream* 209-33 (1964).

[232]   F. Hoyle & N. Wickramasinghe, *Evolution from Space* (1981):

Many of these modifications possess an all-or-nothing character which makes it very difficult to understand how natural selection could have produced them. Thus the python's upper jaw is hinged, and this affords an advantage. The python possesses two curved, pointed fangs which sink into the prey and hold it while the python begins to swallow it. However, the teeth are set pointing backwards, so that they would never enter the victim's flesh, were it not for the hinge, which causes them to strike at a more obtuse angle than they otherwise would. This hinge was not of the slightest value until it formed and worked.

Id. at 40 (italics added). Hoyle describes these other examples:

Warning colours
Many animals like this ladybird and eyed hawkmoth use warning colours and false "eyes" to alarm predators, or warn that they are inedible. But how useful would a rudimentary eye-spot or a weak warning colour be? The initial stages would be more of a handicap than an advantage.

. . ..

Bee food dance
This waggling dance performed by worker bees communicates the location of a food source in an extremely precise way. The development of this system of coded messages by a gradual process is difficult to explain given the limited evolutionary time available.

. . ..

A spider's web
Spiders construct a wide variety of webs, some of great complexity, and all by instinct. Yet a rudimentary web consisting of a few random strands is hardly likely to have trapped much food. How could today's precise structures have evolved by natural selection?

F. Hoyle, *The Intelligent Universe* 40 (1983) (emphasis in original). The house construction and food storage of the wasplike *Eumenedes amedi* provides another example. N. Macbeth*, *Darwin Retried* 71-72 (1971).

[233]   Gould*, *The Return of Hopeful Monsters*, Natural History, June-July 1977, at 22, 24-25 (italics added). *See also* J. Rifkin*, *Algeny* 140 (1983) ("In fact, upon close examination, *virtually every fully operational system* that exists within living things works only as an integrative unit, and the individual parts that make it up appear to exhibit absolutely no value on their own in advancing the survival of the individual or the species."). Preadaptation is listed by Taylor* as one of a "dozen areas where the theory of evolution by natural selection seems either inadequate, implausible, or definitely wrong." G. Taylor*, *The Great Evolution Mystery* 138 (1983).

[234]   S. Gould*, *The Panda's Thumb* (1980).

[235]   M. Denton*, *Evolution: A Theory in Crisis* 327 (1985) (italics added).

[236]   C. Darwin*, *The Origin of Species* 189 (1st ed. 1859, repr. 1964) (italics added).

237   F. Hoyle & N. Wickramasinghe, *Evolution from Space* 150 (1981) (italics added). *See also* J. Maynard Smith*, *The Theory of Evolution* 30-31 (1975) (". . . the fact of evolution was not generally accepted until a theory had been put forward to suggest how evolution had occurred, and in particular how organisms could become adapted to their environment; in the absence of such a theory, *adaptation suggested design, and so implied a creator.*") (italics added). By extending Maynard Smith's* analysis, just as complex adaptation suggests design by "creation," vast information content of complex organs suggests an origin of that content by abrupt appearance. His quotation, of course, is not intended to give aid or comfort to the theories of abrupt appearance or creation.

238   Note 218.

239   Note 220.

240   Note 216.

241   Note 236.

242   Note 229.

243   M. Denton*, *Evolution: A Theory in Crisis* 342 (1985).

244   Note 237.

245   Schutzenberger*, *Algorithms and the Neo-Darwinian Theory of Evolution*, in Mathematical Challenges to the Neo-Darwinian Interpretation of Evolution 73, 74-75 (P. Moorhead* & M. Kaplan* eds. 1967) (italics added).

246   Noda*, *Probability of Life, Rareness of Realization in Evolution*, 95 J. Theoretical Biology 145 (1982).

247   Eden*, *Inadequacies of Neo-Darwinian Evolution as a Scientific Theory*, in Mathematical Challenges to the Neo-Darwinian Interpretation of Evolution 109, 109 (P. Moorhead* & M. Kaplan* eds. 1967) (italics added):
   It is our contention that if *"random"* is given a serious and crucial interpretation from a probabilistic point of view, the randomness postulate is *highly implausible* and that an adequate scientific theory of evolution *must await the discovery and elucidation of new natural laws*—physical, physico-chemical and biological.

248   *Id.* (italics added).

249   E. Ambrose*, *The Nature and Origin of the Biological World* 142 (1982) (assuming natural selection did not increase the probability, as discussed in Section 3.3(a)).

250   Section 3.3(b).

251   E. Steele*, *Somatic Selection and Adaptive Evolution* 3 (2d ed. 1981) (U. of Chicago Press) (italics added). Taylor* lists, as one of twelve points rendering biological evolution "inadequate, implausible, or definitely wrong," the "repeated occurrence of changes calling for numerous *coordinated innovations*, both at the level of organs and of complete organisms." G. Taylor*, *The Great Evolution Mystery* 137 (1983).

252   E. Steele*, *Somatic Selection and Adaptive Evolution* 3 (2d ed. 1981) (italics added).

253   Section 4.2.

254   *E.g.*, E. Borel*, *Probabilities and Life* 28 (1962) ("We may be led to set at

10[-50] the value of negligible probabilities on the cosmic scale. When the probability of an event is below this limit, the opposite event may be expected to occur with certainty, whatever the number of occasions present-ing themselves in the entire universe."); G. Salet*, *Chance and Certainty: Evolution in the Light of Modern Biology* (1972), quoted in Lafont*, *Book Review*, Permanences, Nov. 1972, at 8; E. Borel*, *Elements of the Theory of Probability* 57 (1965).

[255]   F. Hoyle, *The Intelligent Universe* 12 (1983) (panspermia advocate).

[256]   Similarly, myoglobin provides oxygen transport in muscle, just as hemoglobin does for blood, and evolutionists generally assume that hemo-globin evolved from myoglobin. Yet that would require many mutations, and the intermediate forms would be "unsatisfactory proteins":

> Such changes cannot happen all at once; they must occur in many stages, over a long period of time. The *intermediate mutational forms*, we would suppose, must be rather *unsatisfactory proteins*, with imperfect tendencies to form loose aggregates of monomers, but *without the advan-tageous cooperative interactions* of haemoglobin as we know it. They would be neither good myoglobin nor good haemoglobin, and the organ-isms that possessed such molecules *would scarcely be expected to do well in the ordeal of natural selection.*

Edsall*, *Thoughts on the Conformation of Proteins in Solution*, in Structu-ral Chemistry and Molecular Biology at 88, 93-94 (A. Rich* & N. Davidson* eds. 1968) (italics added).

[257]   Also, at least 34 of these mutations would require changes in two or three nucleotides of the DNA segment that codes for hemoglobin. Eden*, *Inadequacies of Neo-Darwinian Evolution as a Scientific Theory*, in Mathematical Challenges to the Neo-Darwinian Interpretation of Evolu-tion 5, 7 (P. Moorhead* & M. Kaplan* eds. 1967). Yet the change of a single nucleotide pair usually has lethal or very harmful results; the change of one of the 574 amino acids in hemoglobin causes sickle-cell anemia. *See* Wald*, *Discussion*, in *id.* at 12, 19.

[258]   Lipson*, *A Physicist Looks at Evolution*, 31 Physics Bull. 138, 138 (1980).

[259]   E. Russell*, *The Diversity of Animals* 81 (1962) (italics added).

[260]   Mayr*, *Accident or Design, The Paradox of Evolution*, in The Evolu-tion of Living Organisms 1, 3 (G. Leeper* ed. 1962) (Cambridge U. Press) (Mayr* sees no inconsistency with neo-Darwinism).

[261]   *Id.* at 2 (italics added).

[262]   *E.g.*, M. Ghiselin*, *The Triumph of the Darwinian Method* 215-18, 221, 227-29 (1969); E. Mayr* *Systematics and the Origin of Species* 296 (1942) ("it is a considerable strain on one's credulity to assume that . . . the famous yucca moth case could result from random mutations").

[263]   Mayr*, *Accident or Design, The Paradox of Evolution*, in The Evolu-tion of Living Organisms 1, 2-3 (G. Leeper* ed. 1962) (italics added).

[264]   C. Patterson*, *Evolution* 162-63 (1978).

[265]   F. Hoyle, *The Intelligent Universe* (1983):

The complex life of a parasite
The parasitic flatworm. . ., *Dicrocoelium dendriticum*, lives as a larva in snails and ants, and then matures in sheep. When attacking an ant, the larvae split up into two groups; a small number make for a particular nerve below the ant's mouth, paralyzing its jaws. The ant is then often stranded high up on a grass stem ready to be eaten by a passing sheep—a remarkable process difficult to explain by the haphazard modifications of evolutionary trial-and-error.
Cleaner fish
These brightly striped fish feed on parasites of larger species. Their "clients" do not attack them. How did this partnership evolve? The first cleaner to follow this behaviour would frequently have risked being eaten.
Id. at 40 (italics in original). Each adaptation requires a large number of specific mutations.

[266]   J. Mill*, *Three Essays on Religion* 174 (2d ed. 1874).

[267]   Salisbury*, *Natural Selection and the Complexity of the Gene*, 224 Nature 342, 343 (1969). He states that creation would not suggest experiments.

[268]   F. Hoyle & N. Wickramasinghe, *Evolution from Space* 130 (1981) (italics added).

[269]   Macbeth*, a noncreationist, summarizes the best-in-field fallacy:

Darwinism has had to compete with various rival theories, each of which aimed to be a more or less complete explanation. . . . The Darwinians have shown that none of these theories is any good. . . . Thus the Darwinians are able to say that Darwin made a better try than anyone else, and they find real comfort in this.

Does this mean that Darwinism is correct? No. Sir Julian Huxley says that, once the hypothesis of special creation is ruled out, adaptation can only be ascribed to natural selection, but this is utterly unjustified. He should say only that Darwinism is better than the others. *But when the others are no good, this is faint praise.* Is there any glory in outrunning a cripple in a foot race?

. . ..

It seems that the standards of the evolutionary theorists are relative or *comparative rather than absolute.* If such a theorist makes a suggestion that is better than other suggestions, or better than nothing, he feels that he has accomplished something even if his suggestion will obviously not hold water. He *does not believe that he must meet any objective standards* of logic, reason, or probability.

N. Macbeth*, *Darwin Retried* 77-78 (1971) (italics added). *See also* M. Ghiselin*, *The Triumph of the Darwinian Method* 215-18, 221, 227-29 (1969).

[270]   Note 245.

[271]   Note 247.

[272]   Note 249.

[273]   *See* note 263.

[274] Note 266.

[275] Note 268 (discontinuitist scientists).

[276] This genetics argument is different from a concept of the "fixity of biblical kinds" or the "fixity of species," in that it is based on genetic laws and applies to genera usually rather than "kinds" or "species." However, the concept of fixity is not necessarily religious or nonscientific, as its history shows:

From Plato and Aristotle until Darwin the mainstream of western philosophers explained the orderliness and stability of the biological world by positing an immutable 'nature', 'form', or 'essence' for every organism that naturally breeds true. . . . The high-water mark of this Aristotelian philosophy of nature (though without Aristotle's metaphysical sophistication) was reached in the taxonomic labours of John Ray in the seventeenth century and Carolus Linnaeus in the eighteenth.

J. Moore*, *The Post-Darwinian Controversies* 206 (1979).

[277] Mutations "can be classified in one of two major categories: gene (or point) mutations, which affect only one or a few nucleotides within a gene; and chromosomal mutations (or aberrations), which affect the number of chromosomes, or the number or the arrangement of genes in a chromosome." T. Dobzhansky*, F. Ayala*, G. Stebbins* & J. Valentine*, *Evolution* 57 (1977). *See also* S. Luria*, S. Gould* & S. Singer*, *A View of Life* 778 (1981).

[278] C. Darwin*, *The Origin of Species* 255 (2d ed. 1859, repr. 1967). Modern discontinuitist scientists do not argue that genetic limits necessarily occur generally at the species level, but at the natural group level, which more commonly corresponds to the genus or family level depending on the organism.

[279] Eiseley*, *Charles Darwin, Edward Blyth and the Theory of Natural Selection*, Proc. Am. Philosophical Society, Feb. 1959, at 94.

[280] M. Pitman, *Adam and Evolution* 75-76 (1984) (creationist author).

[281] Agassiz, *Evolution and Permanence of Type*, Atlantic Monthly, Jan. 1874, at 92; Agassiz, *Synopsis of the Ichthyological Flavor of the Pacific Slope*, 19 Am. J. Science & Arts 215 (1855).

[282] A. Boyden*, *Perspectives in Zoology* 27, 35 (1973) (italics added).

[283] Rifkin* notes the genetic "upper and lower limits":

The fruit fly has long been the favorite object of mutation experiments because of its fast gestation period (twelve days). X rays have been used to increase the mutation rate in the fruit fly by 15,000 percent. All in all, scientists have been able to "catalyze the fruit fly evolutionary process such that what has been seen to occur in *Drosophila* (fruit fly) is the equivalent of many millions of years of normal mutations and evolution." Even with this tremendous speedup of mutations, scientists have never been able to come up with anything other than another fruit fly. More important, what all these experiments demonstrate is that the fruit fly can vary within certain upper and lower limits but will never go beyond them. For example, Ernst Mayr reported on two experiments performed on the fruit fly back in 1948. In the first experiment, the fly was selected for a decrease in bristles and, in the second experiment, for an increase in bristles. Starting with a parent stock averaging 36 bristles, it was possible after thirty generations to lower the average to 25 bristles, "but then the line became sterile and died out." In the second experiment, the average number of bristles was increased from 36 to 56; then sterility set in. Mayr concluded with the following observation:

> Obviously any drastic improvement under selection must seriously deplete the store of genetic variability. . . . The most frequent correlated response of one-sided selection is a drop in general fitness. This plagues virtually every breeding experiment.

J. Rifkin*, *Algeny* 134 (1983) (italics added). *See also* N. Macbeth*, *Darwin Retried* 35 (1971) ("Genetic homeostasis makes even micro changes look difficult, and seems to be a fatal obstacle to macroevolution.").

[284] P. Grassé*, *The Evolution of Living Organisms* 87, 88 (trans. 1977) (italics added).

[285] E. Russell*, *The Diversity of Animals* 123 (1962) (italics added). *See also* McDonald*, *The Molecular Basis of Adaptation: A Critical Review of Relevant Ideas and Observations*, 14 Annual Rev. Ecology & Systematics 77, 97 (1983).

[286] E. Ambrose*, *The Nature and Origin of the Biological World* 123-24 (1982) (italics added).

[287] L. Burbank*, *Partner of Nature* 98-99 (W. Hall* ed. 1939) (italics added).

[288] Deevey*, *The Reply: Letter from Birnam Wood*, 61 Yale Rev. 631, 636 (1967) ("Some remarkable things have been done by crossbreeding and selection inside the species barrier, or within a larger circle of closely related species, such as the wheats. But wheat is still wheat, and not, for instance, grapefruit; and we can no more grow wings on pigs than hens can make cylindrical eggs.").

[289] L. Eiseley*, *The Immense Journey* 223 (1958) ("It would appear that careful domestic breeding, whatever it may do to improve the quality of race horses or cabbages, is not actually in itself the road to the endless biological deviation which is evolution.").

[290] D. Falcone*, *Introduction to Quantitative Genetics* 186 (1960) ("the improvements that have been made by selection in these [domesticated breeds] have clearly been accompanied by a reduction of fitness for life under natural conditions and only the fact that domesticated animals and plants do not live under natural conditions has allowed these improvements to be made.").

[291] Erwin* & Valentine*, *"Hopeful Monsters," transposons, and Metazoan radiation*, 81 Proc. National Acad. Sciences 5482, 5482 (1984) (italics added).

[292] F. Hoyle, *The Intelligent Universe* 35 (1983) (italics added) (panspermia advocate).

[293]   E. Ambrose*, *The Nature and Origin of the Biological World* 120 (1982).
[294]   J. Huxley*, *Evolution in Action* 41 (1953) (proportion of beneficial mutations is less than 1 in 1000).
[295]   J. Kendrew*, *The Thread of Life* 106-07 (1966).
[296]   E. Ambrose*, *The Nature and Origin of the Biological World* 120 (1982) (italics added).
[297]   *Id.* at 120-21 (italics added).
[298]   Wald*, *Discussion*, in Mathematical Challenges to the Neo-Darwinian Interpretation of Evolution 12, 19 (P. Moorhead* & M. Kaplan* eds. 1967).
[299]   E. Dodson*, *Evolution: Process and Product* 225 (1960).
[300]   Note 282.
[301]   Note 284.
[302]   Note 285.
[303]   Note 286.
[304]   Note 296.
[305]   Note 298.
[306]   Letter from A. Wallace to A. Reid* (Dec. 28, 1909), in *Alfred Russel Wallace, Letters and Reminiscences* 340 (J. Marchant* ed. 1916).
[307]   Note 280.
[308]   "Classification" or "taxonomy" is "the theory and practice of naming, describing, and classifying organisms." W. Stansfield*, *The Science of Evolution* 98 (1977). The evolutionary argument is discussed at Section 3.4(c).
[309]   "Comparative anatomy" is the study of "genetic affinities as expressed in adult structures." *Id.* at 116. The evolutionary argument is discussed at Section 3.4(d).
[310]   "Comparative biochemistry" (or "molecular homology") is the study of similarities or "homologies at the molecular level," such as hemoglobin, cytochrome *c*, and insulin. *Id.* at 125. The evolutionary argument is discussed in Section 3.4(f).
[311]   "Natural groups" were defined in the introduction to Chapter 2.
[312]   He states in full:

> But *it is possible* to look at diagrams like Figure 3, and at the definitions Hennig associated with them, in a more general framework, one which has *no evolutionary implications*. Branching diagrams can be seen not as evolutionary trees, but as cladograms in which there is no time scale and the *nodes imply shared characters (synapomorphies) rather than common ancestry.*

Patterson*, *Cladistics and Classification*, 94 New Scientist 303, 304 (1982) (italics added). Thompson, the late Director of the Commonwealth Institute of Biological Control of Canada and a creationist scientist (Ph.D. in entomology), made this point with a good analogy in his Introduction to the 1956 edition of Darwin's* *Origin of Species*:

> But not all the things that can be classified are connected by generation. The arrangement of the chemical elements and their compounds is a true

classification and so is the arrangement of geometric forms; yet no genealogical considerations are involved. . . . If we wish to erect a genealogical classification we cannot do so with a collection of abstractions drawn from our arrangement of existing organisms—we must discover through what forms the existing organisms have actually descended. If these historical facts cannot be ascertained, then it is useless to seek for substitutes, and from the fact that a classification is possible we certainly cannot infer that it is genealogical and is in any sense a proof of evolution.
Thompson, *Introduction*, to C. Darwin*, *The Origin of Species* at xvii (1956).

[313] Schwabe* & Warr*, *A Polyphyletic View of Evolution: The Genetic Potential Hypothesis*, 27 Perspectives in Biology & Medicine 465, 468 (1984).

[314] J. Huxley*, *Evolution: The Modern Synthesis* 394-95 (1942).

[315] Ghiselin*, *Models in Phylogeny*, in Models in Paleobiology 130, 131 (T. Schopf* ed. 1972).

[316] Bonner*, *Book Review*, 49 Am. Scientist 240 (1961).

[317] T. Dobzhansky*, F. Ayala*, G. Stebbins* & J. Valentine*, *Evolution* 262 (1977). *See also* S. Luria*, S. Gould* & S. Singer*, *A View of Life* 684 (1981); Ridley*, *Can classification do without evolution?*, New Scientist, Dec. 1, 1983, at 647, 648.

[318] Charig*, *Cladistics: A Different Point of View*, in Evolution Now 121, 121 (J. Maynard Smith* 1982).

[319] Platnick*, *Philosophy and the Transformation of Cladistics*, 28 Systematic Zoology 537, 537 (1979) ("neither the value nor the success of the methods is limited by the value or success of that evolutionary model").

[320] C. Patterson*, *The Goals, Uses, and Assumptions of Cladistic Analysis* (1981), quoted in Beatty*, *Classes and Clades*, 31 Systematic Zoology 25, 31 (1982) (italics added). *See also* Patterson*, *Cladistics and Classification*, 94 New Scientist 303, 304, 306 (1982) ("Thus cladistics calls into question much of conventional evolutionary history."); Patterson*, *Cladistics*, 27 Biologist 234 (1980) ("the evolutionary framework is inessential, and may be dropped").

[321] Benton*, *Is a dog more like a lizard or a chicken?*, New Scientist, Aug. 16, 1984, at 18, 18.

[322] Ridley*, *Can classification do without evolution?*, New Scientist, Dec. 1, 1983, at 647, 651.

[323] Ball*, *On Groups, Existence and the Ordering of Nature*, 32 Systematic Zoology 446, 446 (1983) (transformed cladists are "neutral or opposed to evolutionary theorizing of any kind," and "operate in a non-evolutionary domain"); Beatty*, *Classes and Cladists*, 31 Systematic Zoology 25, 29, 31 (1982) ("cladists have taken more or less extreme measures to sever their ties" to evolutionary biology, and are "at odds with evolutionary thinking").

[324] S. Luria*, S. Gould* & S. Singer*, *A View of Life* 676 (1981).

[325] Note 4.

[326] Brady*, *On the Independence of Systematics*, 1 Cladistics 113, 113

(1985) (italics added).

[327] E. Mayr*, *The Growth of Biological Thought* 219 (1982) (Harvard U. Press).

[328] R. Crowson*, *Classification and Biology* 276 (1970).

[329] M. Denton*, *Evolution: A Theory in Crisis* 105 (1985).

[330] Dr. W. R. Thompson wrote that, "taking the *taxonomic system as a whole*, it appears as an orderly arrangement of clear-cut entities which are *clear-cut because they are separated by gaps*. These gaps Darwin explained by the hypothesis that the intermediates are constantly eliminated by natural selection. I do not think we can be expected to accept this unproved supposition as an argument for Darwinism. But in any case it has no bearing on the persistence throughout geological time, in spite of the fortuitous variation and natural selection, on the *persistence* of the fundamental anatomical plans exhibited by the great groups." Thompson, *Introduction*, to C. Darwin*, *The Origin of Species* at xvi-xvii (1956) (italics added).

[331] W. Stansfield*, *The Science of Evolution* 99 (1977). *See also* Dobzhansky*, *Evolution*, in 10 Encyclopedia Americana 734, 734 (1982) ("he did not interpret this propinquity as a consequence of common descent").

[332] E. Mayr*, *Systematics and the Origin of Species* 276 (1942) (italics added).

[333] Blackwelder*, *Twenty-Five Years of Taxonomy*, 26 Systematic Zoology 107, 134 (1977) ("Evolutionary taxonomy never has been really different from classical taxonomy, in spite of all the fireworks.").

[334] Simpson*, *The Principles of Classification and the Classification of Mammals*, 85 Bull. Am. Museum Natural History 4 (1945) ("By substituting 'common ancestor' for 'archetype' the *same classification could be considered phylogenetic or not*, at will. The common ancestor was at first, and in most cases, just as hypothetical as the archetype, and the methods of inference were much the same for both, so that *classification continued to develop with no immediate evidence of revolution in principles*.") (italics added). *See also* N. Macbeth*, *Darwin Retried* 20 (1971).

[335] Section 3.4(c).

[336] S. Luria*, S. Gould* & S. Singer*, *A View of Life* 763-64 (1981).

[337] Kitts*, *Karl Popper, Verifiability and Systematic Zoology*, 26 Systematic Zoology 185, 190 (1977). *See also* S. Gould*, *Hen's Teeth and Horse's Toes* 355 (1983).

[338] Thomson*, an evolutionist, writes: "In fact, there is *circularity* in the approach that *first assumes some sort of evolutionary relatedness and then assembles a pattern of relations* from which to argue that relatedness must be true. This interplay of data and interpretation is the Achilles' heel of the second meaning of evolution." Thomson*, *Marginalia: The Meanings of Evolution*, 70 Am. Scientist 529, 529-30 (1982) (italics added).

[339] A. Boyden*, *Perspectives in Zoology* 27 (1973) (italics added).

[340] M. Denton*, *Evolution: A Theory in Crisis* 178 (1985) ("similarities, although very striking, *do not imply any close biological relationship*")

(italics in original).

341 Patterson*, *Significance of Fossils in Determining Evolutionary Relationships*, 12 Ann. Rev. Ecology & Systematics 195, 217 (1981) ("Such hypotheses are untestable by *morphology* alone, which *cannot discriminate descent from common ancestry, or from non-evolutionary relationship.* Other assumptions (fossil record complete; evolution irreversible) are necessary to justify the hypothesis of descent, and may immunize it from direct test.").

342 "Homology is uniquely evolved structural similarity in different organisms." A. Kluge*, *Chordate Structure and Function* 12 (2d ed. 1977) (italics added).

343 *See* G. de Beer*, *Homology: An Unsolved Problem* 15-16 (1971) (italics added) (he does not argue that the absence of homologous genes indicates unrelatedness but merely the limited relevance of homologous anatomical features). *See also* Patterson*, *Significance of Fossils in Determining Evolutionary Relationships*, 12 Ann. Rev. Ecology & Systematics 195, 208 (1981) (arguing that similar features (synapomorphies) "need have no evolutionary implications," according to transformed cladistics).

344 M. Denton*, *Evolution: A Theory in Crisis* 149 (1985) (most italics added).

345 Ayala* and Valentine* define these terms:

On the other hand, some lineages that are only distantly related and that begin quite distinct morphologically may evolve so as to resemble each other closely. This is *convergence* and indicates that the separate lineages are becoming adapted to similar modes of life, usually in similar environments.

Other patterns of resemblance between different lineages include *parallelism*, when two or more independent lineages change in similar ways so that their degree of resemblance remains about the same (Fig. 7.4); and *iteration*, when a given trait appears a number of separate times.

. . ..

When comparing different taxa of organisms, it has proven useful to distinguish between characters that resemble each other because they are descended from a common ancestor, called *homologous* characters, and those that resemble each other because they have similar functions, called *analogous* characters.

F. Ayala* & J. Valentine*, *Evolving: The Theory and Processes of Organic Evolution* 232 (1979) (italics added). *See also* S. Luria*, S. Gould* & S. Singer*, *A View of Life* 645, 670-71 (1981).

346 Address of Dr. Colin Patterson* at the American Museum of Natural History, tr. at 9 (Nov. 5, 1981).

347 A. Boyden*, *Perspectives in Zoology* 27 (1973).

348 M. Denton*, *Evolution: A Theory in Crisis* 178 (1985) (italics added).

349 R. Gates*, *Human Ancestry from a Genetical Point of View* 3 (1948) (Harvard U. Press).

[350] A. Romer*, *Man and the Vertebrates* 139 (1941) (U. of Chicago Press).

[351] Forey*, *Neontological Analysis Versus Palaeontological Stories*, in Problems of Phylogenetic Reconstruction 119, 149 (K. Joysey* & A. Friday* eds. 1982) (he is focusing on Recent vertebrates).

[352] R. Dawkins*, *The Blind Watchmaker* 269 (1986).

[353] Ross*, *Illusion and reality in comparative physiology*, 59 Canadian J. Zoology 2151, 2154 (1981) (italics added).

[354] M. Denton*, *Evolution: A Theory in Crisis* 155 (1985) (italics added).

[355] Dobzhansky*, *Evolution*, in 10 Encyclopedia Americana 734, 734 (1982) (italics added).

[356] C. Patterson*, *Evolution* 121-22 (1978). *See also* Patterson*, *Cladistics and Classification*, 94 New Scientist 303, 303 (1982).

[357] Owen*, *Report on the Archetype and Homologies of the Vertebrate Skeleton*, Reports of the British Ass'n for the Advancement of Science 169, 175 (1847).

[358] S. Luria*, S. Gould* & S. Singer*, *A View of Life* 645 (1981). *See also* Gould*, *Darwin's Untimely Burial*, Natural History, Oct. 1986, at 24. The concept of "basic designs" is also acknowledged by evolutionists. *E.g.*, Gould*, *The Ediacaran Experiment*, Natural History, Feb. 1984, at 14, 22 ("in honest moments we must admit that the history of complex life is more a story of multifarious variation about a set of basic designs than a saga of accumulating excellence"); A. Boyden*, *Perspectives in Zoology* 27 (1973) ("the minimum requirements or 'conditions of existence' which all living systems must possess").

[359] *E.g.*, A. Boyden*, *Perspectives in Zoology* 27 (1973); E. Russell*, *The Diversity of Animals* 58 (1962). Russell* states:

Diversity of type meets us at the very outset. Each of the great phyla of animals is built upon a structural plan quite different from that of the others. Their origin is unknown; between them there exist no true connecting links, and there is no likelihood of the direct transformation of one into another, as Vialleton in particular has so clearly pointed out (1929). They represent quite distinct modes of organisation, quite different solutions of the problems of moving, feeding and breathing.

Id.

[360] For example, Agassiz stated in 1860:

Far from agreeing with these views [of Darwin], I have, on the contrary, taken the ground that *all the natural divisions in the animal kingdom are primarily distinct*, founded upon different categories of characters, and that all exist in the same way, that is as categories of thought, embodied in individual living forms. I have attempted to show that *branches in the animal kingdom are founded upon different plans of structure*, and for that very reason have embraced from the beginning representatives . . . *that exclude, as much as all the preceding distinctions, the idea of a common descent.*

3 L. Agassiz, *Contributions to the Natural History of the United States*

(1860) (reprinted in 30 Am. J. Science 142, 143 (1860)) (italics added) (modern discontinuitist scientists do not follow his Platonic approach). Thompson (Ph.D. in entomology and former Director of the Commonwealth Institute of Biological Control of Canada) similarly explains:

What such cases like those of anatomical 'convergence' and general homology actually demonstrate is that there are large numbers of organisms, differing considerably in the details of structure but constructed on the *same fundamental plan*. However, this is *no proof of descent* from one original ancestor of this anatomical type.

. . ..

. . .Therefore, the *last thing we should expect on Darwinian principles is the persistence of a few common fundamental structural plans. Yet this is what we find.* The animal world, for example, can be divided into some ten great groups or phyla, all of which are not morphologically as coherent and clear-cut as we might wish for convenience in classification, but nevertheless are stable and definable entities from the taxonomic standpoint. All identifiable animals that ever have existed can be placed in these groups. Generally speaking, the subordinate groups are equally well defined.

Thompson, *Introduction*, to C. Darwin*, The Origin of Species xvi-xvii (1956) (italics added). *See also* Kenyon, *The creationist view of biologic origins*, NEXA Journal, Spring 1984, at 28, 33 (a creationist scientist, Ph.D. from Stanford in biophysics).

[361] Ross*, *Illusion and reality in comparative physiology*, 59 Canadian J. Zoology 2151, 2153-54 (1981) (italics added).

[362] M. Denton*, *Evolution: A Theory in Crisis* 290 (1985) (italics added).

[363] G. de Beer*, *Homology: An Unsolved Problem* 15 (1971); notes 312-13 & 339.

[364] Jukes* & Holmquist*, *Evolutionary Clock: Nonconstancy of Rate in Different Species*, 177 Science 530, 532 (1972) (the organisms were rattlesnake and turtle, lamprey and chicken, dogfish and horse, screw worm fly and dog). The authors see overall support of molecular biology for evolution.

[365] *Id.* at 530 ("However, the difference between *turtle* and *rattlesnake* of 21 amino acid residues per 100 codons is notably *larger than* many differences between representatives of widely separated classes, for example, 17 between *chicken and lamprey*, or 16 between *horse and dogfish*, or even 15 between *dog and screw worm fly* in two different phyla") (italics added).

[366] *See also* Ayala*, *The Mechanisms of Evolution*, Scientific Am., Sept. 1978, at 56, 68 ("The cytochrome c phylogeny disagrees with the traditional one in several instances, including the following: the *chicken* appears to be related more closely to the penguin than to ducks and pigeons; the *turtle*, a reptile, appears to be related more closely to birds than to the rattlesnake, and *man* and monkeys diverge from the mammals before the marsupial kangaroo separates from the placental mammals.") (italics added).

[367] Ambler* & Wynn*, *The Amino Acid Sequences of Cytochromes c-551*

from Three Species of Pseudomonas, 131 Biochemical J. 485 (1973) (*Pseudomonas* bacteria).

[368]	Ambler* *et al.*, *Cytochrome c2 Sequence Variation Among the Recognized Species of Purple Nonsulphur Photosynthetic Bacteria*, 278 Nature 659, 659 (1979).

[369]	Address of Dr. Colin Patterson* at American Museum of Natural History, tr. at 7-9 (Nov. 5, 1981).

[370]	*Id.* at 7-8.

[371]	King* & Millar*, *Heterogeneity of Vertebrate Lutenizing Hormone-Releasing Hormone*, 206 Science 67, 67 (1979) (the fish was a teleost).

[372]	Schwabe*, *On the validity of molecular evolution*, 11 Trends in Biochemical Science 280, 280-81 (1986) (italics added) (human differs from sharks 50% and 52% and from pig and rat 54% each).

[373]	*Id. See also* Schwabe* & Warr*, *A Polyphyletic View of Evolution: The Genetic Potential Hypothesis*, 27 Perspectives in Biology & Medicine 465, 469-74 (1984) (anomalies in relaxin).

[374]	R. Eck* & M. Dayhoff*, *Atlas of Protein Sequence and Structure* 110 (1966). Similar conclusions result from study of insulin B. *Id.* at 111.

[375]	Different research with insulin shows vast anomalies. *See also* Schwabe* & Warr*, *A Polyphyletic View of Evolution: The Genetic Potential Hypothesis*, 27 Perspectives in Biology & Medicine 465, 471-74 (1984) (arguing for polyphyletic ancestry).

[376]	Address of Dr. Colin Patterson* at American Museum of Natural History, tr. at 12-13 (Nov. 5, 1981) (man, chimp, gorilla, orangutan, and gibbon).

[377]	Fitch* & Margoliash*, *Construction of Phylogenetic Trees*, 155 Science 279 (1967) (turtle, bird, rattlesnake).

[378]	Eperon*, Anderson* & Nierlich*, *Distinctive sequence of human mitochondrial ribosomal RNA genes*, 286 Nature 460, 460 (1980) (human ribosomal RNA is sufficiently distinctive that "human mitochondria did not originate from recognizable relatives of present day organisms").

[379]	*See* K. Campbell* & M. Day*, *Rates of Evolution* 267 (1987).

[380]	Andrews*, *Aspects of hominoid phylogeny*, in Molecules and morphology in evolution: conflict or compromise? 25, 27 (C. Patterson* ed. 1987).

[381]	Schwabe*, *On the validity of molecular evolution*, 11 Trends in Biochemical Sciences 280, 280 (1986) (italics added).

[382]	Note 373.

[383]	Schwabe* & Warr*, *A Polyphyletic View of Evolution: The Genetic Potential Hypothesis*, 27 Perspectives in Biology & Medicine 465, 467-74 (1984) (arguing for polyphyletic ancestry).

[384]	F. Hoyle & N. Wickramasinghe, *Evolution from Space* 82-84 (1981) (panspermia advocate scientists).

[385]	Schwabe*, *On the validity of molecular evolution*, 11 Trends in Biochemical Sciences 280, 280 (1986) (italics added).

[386]	M. Denton*, *Evolution: A Theory in Crisis* 290-91 (1985) (italics added).

[387] Sermonti* & Sermonti*, *The null hypothesis in vertebrate evolution*, 80 Rivista di Biologia (Biology Forum) 55, 56, 55 (1987).

[388] Schwabe*, *On the validity of molecular evolution*, 11 Trends in Biochemical Sciences 280, 280 (1986) (italics added).

[389] Zihlman* & Lowenstein*, *False Start of the Human Parade*, Natural History, Aug. 1979, at 86, 90.

[390] Note 320.

[391] Note 4.

[392] Note 324.

[393] Note 329.

[394] Note 346.

[395] Note 349.

[396] Note 347.

[397] Note 351.

[398] Note 343.

[399] Note 344.

[400] Note 354.

[401] Note 385.

[402] *See* note 371.

[403] Note 362.

[404] *See* note 331.

CHAPTER 3

Evolution as Theory and Conjecture: Biological Evolution (Macroevolution) of Living Organisms

Any teacher who teaches the boys or the girls of today an incredible theory—we need not worry about those children of this generation paying much attention to it. The children of this generation are pretty wise. People, as a matter of fact I feel that the children of this generation are probably much wiser than many of their elders. The least that this generation can do, your honor, is to give the next generation all the facts, all the available theories, all the information that learn-

---

*Scientists cited in this chapter, unless otherwise indicated, are not proponents of, and their quoted statements are not intended as endorsements of, either the theory of abrupt appearance or the theory of creation. However, their quoted statements are acknowledging data that involve weaknesses of the theory of evolution.

*ing, that study, that observation has pro-
duced, give it to the children in the hope of
heaven that they will make a better world
of this than we have been able to make it.
We have just had a war with twenty-
million dead. Civilization is not so proud
of the work of the adults. Civilization need
not be so proud of what the grown ups
have done. For God's sake, let the children
have their minds kept open—close no
doors to their knowledge; shut no door
from them. . . .*
—Dudley Field Malone*,
attorney for John Scopes,
during the *Scopes* trial[1]

"Biological evolution" describes the origin of all living organisms through ultimately progressive change "from primordial life, through unicellular and multicellular organisms, invertebrate and vertebrate animals, to man . . .," in the words of Theodosius Dobzhansky*.[2] It postulates that all fish, amphibians, reptiles, birds, lower mammals, apes, and man evolved from a "common ancestor," as described by Ayala* and Gould*:

The millions of diverse living species we find around us in the modern world are all descended from a *common ancestor* that lived in the remote past. The processes that have brought this diversity about are collectively called evolution.[3]

evolution[:] The process by which all organisms have arisen by descent from a *common ancestor*.[4]

This definition of biological evolution, which includes evolutionary descent of all organisms from common ancestry (macroevolution), is put forth in typical textbooks in public schools,[5] and is the generally accepted definition.[6]

This chapter assesses the scientific support for macroevolution and Darwinism. Its point is not whether biological macroevolution and Darwinism are right or wrong, but whether they are so compellingly established that no scientific alternative can coexist.

Anti-Darwinism and Anti-Evolutionism. Rejection of macroevolution or Darwinism, and skepticism toward them, are widespread among noncreationist scientists as well as among discontinuitist scientists. In fact, "scientists who utterly reject evolution may be one of our fastest-growing controversial minorities," Hatfield* writes.[7] There are "some among the biologists who feel that much of the fabric of [macroevolutionary] theory accepted by the majority today is actually false," and "a generally silent group of students engaged in biological pursuits who tend to disagree with much of the current thought," Olson* acknowledges.[8]

Transformed cladists generally "question much of conventional evolutionary history" and are "at odds with evolutionary thinking," as described further below.[9] Structuralists "abandon the system of concepts which we call the 'evolutionary paradigm' and attempt to construct what seems to us a more satisfactory conceptual structure," because they believe "the current theory of evolutionary transformation remains, at best, incomplete and unsatisfactory."[10] Other such schools of thought are described in Section 3.2(e)-(f).

Grassé*, "the most distinguished of French zoologists" according to Dobzhansky*,[11] has concluded that "the explanatory doctrines of biological evolution do not stand up to an in-depth criticism":[12]

> The book of Pierre P. Grassé is a *frontal attack on all kinds of "Darwinism."* Its purpose is "to destroy the myth of evolution as a simple, understood, and explained phenomenon," and to show that evolution is a *mystery* about which little is, and perhaps can be, known. Now, one can disagree with Grassé but not ignore him. He is the *most distinguished of French zoologists*, the editor of the 28 volumes of "Traité de Zoologie," author of numerous original investigations, and ex-president of the Academie des Sciences. His knowledge of the living world is *encyclopedic*, and his book is replete with interesting facts that any biologist would profit by knowing. Unfortunately, the theoretical interpretations of these facts leaves [sic] one dissatisfied, and occasionally exasperated.[13]

Macroevolution or Darwinism or both similarly have been rejected or severely criticized by such other noncreationist scientists as Soren Løvtrup*, the author of *Darwinism: The Refutation of a Myth*;[14] Michael Denton*, the author of *Evolution: A Theory in Crisis*;[15] E. C. Ambrose*, the author of *The Nature and Origin of the Biological World*;[16] Giuseppe Sermonti* and Roberto Fondi*, the authors of *Dopo Darwin: Critica all'Evoluzionismo*;[17] G. A. Kerkut*, the author of *Implications of Evolution*;[18] M. Vernet*, the author of *Revolution en Biologie*;[19] and Paul Lemoine*, the editor of the *Encyclopedie Française*.[20] The same approach is taken by such recent noncreationists as Hitching*,[21] Taylor*,[22] Macbeth*,[23] and Himmelfarb*.[24] Koestler* concludes that the macroevolutionary "citadel they are defending lies in ruins";[25] Rifkin* calls it "little more than an imaginary trip";[26] and Bethell* sees "Darwin's theory. . . on the verge of collapse."[27]

Among high school teachers, "a significant minority of them simply do not believe a word of it."[28] In fact, a recent scientific survey shows that "significant minority" to be 42.3% of public school biology teachers that choose "creation" or "some strong combination of evolution and creation" over just "evolution."[29] In general public, the percentage is much higher.

Evolution "in Crisis." In summary, "evolutionary theory is in crisis," in the words of Saunders* and Ho*:

> Today, however, the picture is entirely different. *More and more workers* are showing signs of *dissatisfaction with the synthetic theory.* Some are attacking its philosophical foundations, arguing that the reason that it has been so amply confirmed is simply that *it is unfalsifiable; with a little ingenuity any observation can be made to appear consistent with it.* Others have been deliberately setting out to work in just those areas in which neo-Darwinism is least comfortable, like the problem of the gaps in the fossil record or the mechanisms of non-Mendelian inheritance. Still others, notably some systematists, have decided to *ignore the theory altogether,* and to carry on their research without an a priori assumption about how evolution has occurred. Perhaps most significantly of all, there is now appearing a stream of articles and books defending the synthetic theory. It is not so long ago that hardly anyone thought this was necessary.
>
> All the signs are that *evolution theory is in crisis,* and that a change is on the way.[30]

Denton* agrees and subtitles his book "A Theory in Crisis."[31]

The following sections discuss the following aspects of biological macroevolution and Darwinism:

3.1 The meanings of biological evolution
3.2 The approaches to macroevolution
3.3 The postulated mechanisms of macroevolution
3.4 The postulated evidence for macroevolution and Darwinism
3.5 The postulated stages of macroevolution and Darwinism.

The purpose is to summarize, rather than to cover comprehensively, the problems with biological evolution that many nondiscontinuitist scientists recognize.

Section 3.1 discusses the microevolutionary, macroevolutionary, and Darwinian components of biological evolution, and their status as fact, partly demonstrated theory, or working hypothesis. Section 3.2 summarizes current approaches to macroevolution: classical Darwinian evolution, the neo-Darwinian synthesis, punctuated equilibria, non-Darwinian approaches, transformed cladistics, and various anti-evolutionist approaches. Section 3.3 analyzes the alleged mechanism of macroevolution, which involves the "three main processes—mutation, genetic recombination, and natural selection"[32]—in conjunction with other factors or alternatively the main process of species selection. Section 3.4 discusses the alleged evidence for macroevolution: the paleontology argument, the phylogeny argument, the classification argument, the comparative anatomy argument, the comparative embryology argument, the comparative biochemistry argument, the population genetics argument, and the artificial selection argument. Finally, Section 3.5 scrutinizes the alleged stages of macroevolution: from prokaryotes to eukaryotes, to plants and to invertebrates, to vertebrate fish, to amphibians, to reptiles, to birds and to lower mammals, to primates, and finally to man. All citations in these sections are to *evolutionists* and *noncreationists*, including the citations that acknowledge severe problems with biological macroevolution or with Darwinism. Biological macroevolution and Darwinism are far from compellingly established; they are "in crisis" in the words of Saunders* and Ho* as well as Denton*.

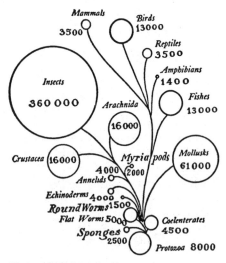

Figure 3.1
*Macroevolution as part of evolution: as pictured in the biology text used by Scopes**

The evolutionary tree.

3.1 The Meanings of Biological Evolution: Macroevolution and Darwinism and Fact

The term "biological evolution" is a generally accepted term among scientists.[33] It is often used synonymously with "organic evolution," with (a) "macroevolution," which is discussed next, with (b) "Darwinism," and with (c) "microevolution" or other "facts."

a. Macroevolution and Microevolution

"It is traditional to divide the study of [biological] evolution into two areas which can loosely be called macroevolution and microevolution," Riddiford* and Penny* note.[34] These terms are defined by Gould* as follows:

> macroevolution[:] Evolutionary change *above the species level*: e.g., long-term trends within lineages and mass extinctions.
>
> . . ..
>
> microevolution[:] Evolutionary change within local populations, *up to the origin of new species*.[35]

Similar definitions are given by other evolutionist scientists such as Mayr*,[36] Stanley*,[37] Simpson*,[38] and others,[39] and the terms macroevolution and microevolution are generally accepted terms.[40]

The core of macroevolution is the "descent from a common ancestor" that is described above. Mayr* describes as "the first Darwinian revolution . . . the theory of common descent . . . ."[41] Kluge* points out under "evolutionary and speciational theories that each and every species, living and dead, is linked by genealogical descent and common ancestry."[42] The implications of descent from common ancestry were stated earlier by Dobzhansky*,[43] and are spelled out by Simpson*:

> In the world of Darwin man has no special status other than his definition as a distinct species of animal. He is in the fullest sense a part of nature and not apart from it. He is *akin*, not figuratively but literally, *to every living thing, be it an ameba, a tapeworm, a flea, a seaweed, an oak tree, or a monkey*—even though the degrees of relationship are different and we may feel less empathy for forty-second cousins like the tapeworms than for, comparatively speaking, brothers like the monkeys. . . .[44]

The same common descent " 'from amoeba to man' " is described by Hardin*,[45] Stebbins*,[46] and others.[47] This "transformism," or macroevolution, "is the essential part of the concept of organic evolution."[48]

Microevolution is not disputed, by contrast. All discontinuitist scientists agree that microevolution has occurred and does occur,[49] although they generally prefer to use another term for it.[50]

This makes clear that evolution is not merely change, as discussed earlier (Section 1.1(a)). Instead, it refers to the large-scale change of macroevolution that amounts to transformism or transmutation, the smaller-scale change of microevolution, and the mechanism for macroevolution proposed by Darwin*.

b. Darwinism and Evolution

"[A]lthough it is now a truism that evolution and Darwinism are not synonymous, it may be doubted whether this distinction was appreciated in the earlier days," as noted by Good*.[51] In fact, the distinction is being forgotten again, it is lamented by O'Grady*, a zoologist at University of British Columbia:

> Descent with modification is *one* process postulated to be capable of producing that hierarchy, and natural selection is *one* process postulated to be capable of producing descent with modification. I feel that the undesirable has happened: *the model developed to explain evolution has come to be seen as evolution itself.*[52]

The distinction between macroevolution, microevolution, and Darwinism is diagrammed by Riddiford* and Penny*, zoologists and botanists at Massey University:

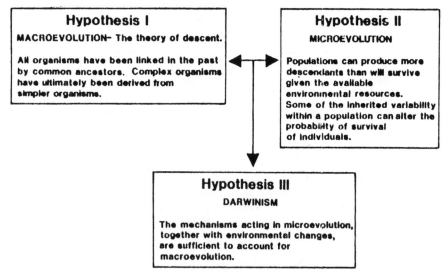

Figure 1. The three main hypotheses of the synthetic theory. They are shown with arrows in each direction because they are mutually supporting in that, for example, the theory of descent is supported by the existence of a mechanism that could lead to species modification and divergence; but the theory of descent has also led to a search for a mechanism that could result in descent with modification.

> *Hypothesis I. The theory of descent* (macroevolution, the fact of evolution,
> evolution, historical reconstruction of evolution).
> *Hypothesis II. Microevolution* (natural selection and chance). . . .
> *Hypothesis III. Darwinism.* Microevolution is sufficient to account for
> macroevolution.

Mayr* concurs by distinguishing the "first Darwinian revolution, that is, the theory of common descent" from the "second Darwinian revolution, the acceptance by [neo-Darwinist] biologists of natural selection as the only direction-giving factor in evolution."[54]

c. "Fact," "Partly Demonstrated Theory," and "Working Hypothesis"

The statement is often made that *"evolution is a fact,"* in the words of Sagan* in *Cosmos*[55] and many others.[56] Although *microevolution* is indeed a fact (concurred in by discontinuitist scientists), Darwinism is *not* a fact but only a "partly demonstrated theory," in the words of leading evolutionists Dobzhansky*, Ayala*, Stebbins*, and Valentine*:

> evolution at the *subspecific level* by means of recognized processes is now
> regarded by most biologists as an experimentally demonstrated fact. On
> the other hand, *some doubt the ability of these processes*, by themselves,
> to give rise to genera, families, or any groups of organisms having "new"
> characteristics. *"Transspecific evolution"* [*macroevolution*] is generally
> recognized as a reality, but its explanation on the basis of recognized
> processes is still in the stage of *partly demonstrated theory* or, in the case
> of the origin and early differentiation of the *first cellular organisms*, a
> *working hypothesis*.[57]

(In fact, not only is that book one of the "[t]wo textbooks of evolution that now dominate the field," but Dobzhansky* is "the greatest evolutionist of our century," according to Gould*.[58])

Darwinism and other theories of macroevolution "are, more accurately, only working hypotheses," in the words of botanist Good*:

> The fundamental inherent difficulty in the study of evolution is, that
> this great natural process involves time dimensions of a magnitude quite
> out of proportion to the duration of human life or even to the sum of
> human experience, and the observer has therefore to *rely on indirect, or
> circumstantial evidence*. Hence beliefs that are often referred to as *theo-
> ries of evolution* are, *more accurately, only working hypotheses*. This is a
> very important matter because the essence of a *hypothesis* is that it is an
> opinion suggested by the available evidence, but *not one which precludes
> the possibility of some alternative*. A hypothesis may well be substan-
> tiated when more corroborative details are forthcoming, but until then
> there is *no logical reason for excluding the consideration of some other
> explanation of the facts*. So, while it may be justifiable to believe that

evolution affords a reasonable explanation of the facts of nature, it is *not justifiable to maintain that no other explanation is possible or permissible.*[59]

(The hypothetical nature of neo-Darwinism is why "alternative explanations" are possible, such as structuralism, macromutationism, non-Darwinian evolution, and perhaps abrupt appearance.) The status of Darwinism as only "a highly speculative hypothesis" is the view of Denton* as well:

The overriding supremacy of the *myth* has created a widespread *illusion that the theory of evolution was all but proved one hundred years ago and that all subsequent biological research*—paleontological, zoological and in the newer branches of genetics and molecular biology— *has provided ever-increasing evidence for Darwinian ideas. Nothing could be further from the truth.* The fact is that the evidence was so patchy one hundred years ago that even Darwin himself had increasing doubts as to the validity of his views, and the only aspect of his theory which has received any support over the past century is where it applies to microevolutionary phenomena. His general theory, that all life on earth had originated and evolved by a gradual successive accumulation of fortuitous mutations, is still, as it was in Darwin's time, *a highly speculative hypothesis* entirely without direct factual support and very far from that self-evident axiom some of its more aggressive advocates would have us believe.[60]

Many ardent Darwinians claim no more than that Darwinism is theory, although generally contending that macroevolution is fact. Ayala*, a genetics professor at University of California at Davis, calls it the "*theory* of evolution [that] explains, on the basis of scientific evidence, how evolution happened," while characterizing macroevolution as "fact."[61] Futuyma*, an ecology and evolution professor at State University of New York, makes the same distinction:

It is important here to recognize the *distinction* between the proposition that *evolution has occurred* and the *theory that describes the causes of evolutionary change.* That evolution has occurred—that diverse organisms have descended from *common ancestors* by a history of modification and divergences—is accepted as *fact* by virtually all biologists. . . .

The *theory* of evolution, on the other hand, like the atomic theory of chemistry, is a complex, ever-growing body of statements intended to describe *mechanisms*—of chemical reactions in the case of chemistry, of evolutionary change in the case of biology. . . .[62]

Others characterize neo-Darwinism as "a relatively complete *theory* of proximal cause in biology."[63]

Macroevolution, as well as Darwinism, is not fact but theory.

Kerkut* finds the evidence weak enough that he terms macroevolution only "a working hypothesis":

> On the other hand there is the theory that all the living forms in the world have arisen from a single source which itself came from an inorganic form. This theory can be called the "General Theory of Evolution" [macroevolution] and the *evidence that supports it is not sufficiently strong* to allow us to consider it as anything more than *a working hypothesis.* . . .[64]

Eldredge*, a leader of the punctuated equilibria camp, on that point agrees with many spokesmen for the neo-Darwinian synthesis:

> But theories in science are merely ideas: a theory may be a single, simple idea or, more usually, a complex set of ideas. Some are good and have withstood the test of time well. Evolution—specifically, the notion that all organisms past and present are interrelated by a process of *ancestry and descent*—is such a *theory*.[65]

The claim of Huxley* and others, that either macroevolution or "Darwinian theory . . . is no longer a theory but a fact," is "simply nonsense," in the assessment of Denton*:

> Now of course such claims are *simply nonsense*. For Darwin's model of evolution is still *very much a theory* and still *very much in doubt when it comes to macroevolutionary phenomena*. Furthermore being basically a theory of historical reconstruction, it is impossible to verify by experiment or direct observation as is normal in science.[66]

Macroevolution is merely an "assumption," according to Boyden*, a Rutgers zoologist:

> Actually we shall never be able to prove the common ancestry of all animals, and therefore we have no right to state as a fundamental principle what must always remain an assumption.[67]

Summary. Biological evolution includes both microevolution, which discontinuitists accept, and macroevolution, which is the more controversial postulate that all plants and animals "have arisen by descent from a common ancestor" (Gould*[68]), so that macroevolution proceeded "from primordial life, through unicellular and multicellular organisms, invertebrate and vertebrate animals, to man" (Dobzhansky*[69]). Biological evolution also includes Darwinism, which is the "hypothesis" that "[m]icroevolution is sufficient to account for macroevolution" (Riddiford* and Penny*[70]); "evolution and Darwinism are not synonymous" (Good*[71]). While microevolution is an undisputed fact, macroevolution or " '[t]rans-specific evolution' is generally recognized as a reality, but its explanation on the basis of recognized processes is still in the stage of partly demonstrated theory" in the form of Darwinism (Dobz-

hansky*, Ayala*, Stebbins*, and Valentine*[72]). *Ex pede Herculem?*
Macroevolution itself "must always remain an assumption" that
cannot be proved (Boyden*[73]), and is properly called "a theory"
(Eldredge*[74]). Thus, White*, in his presidential address to the pres-
tigious Linnean Society, said that "I have often thought how little I
should like to prove organic evolution in a court of law."[75]

Figure 3.2
The anti-Darwinian and
Darwinian approaches:
Agassiz (1863) and Dar-
win (1854)*

3.2 The Approaches to Macroevolution: Darwinian, Anti-Darwinian, and Anti-Evolutionist Schools

There are at least six significant approaches to macroevolution.
These are (a) classical Darwinian evolution, which has been effectively abandoned; (b) the neo-Darwinian synthesis, which is the
majority viewpoint; (c) punctuated equilibria, the growing minority
viewpoint; (d) non-Darwinian evolution, such as nonequilibrium
evolution, structuralism, and anti-Darwinian approaches; (e) transformed cladistics, also a growing approach whose proponents refuse
to use and in some cases reject macroevolution entirely; and (f)
antievolutionist approaches (other than the theory of abrupt
appearance). The existence of widespread dissent strengthens the
point made by Stonehouse* of Cambridge, an evolutionist:

> [S]ome fundamental truths about evolution have so far eluded us all, and
> that *uncritical acceptance of Darwinism may be counterproductive* as
> well as expedient. Far from ignoring or ridiculing the groundswell of

opposition to Darwinism that is growing, for example, in the United States, we should *welcome it as an opportunity to re-examine our sacred cow* more closely. . . .[76]

a. Classical Darwinian Evolution

"Classical Darwinian evolution" is the viewpoint proposed by Darwin* in *The Origin of Species*. Modern evolutionist scientists, while generally not forthrightly announcing that it is dead, have stated that classical Darwinism is wrong in many critical areas.

Virtually all agree that Darwin* simply "was wrong" that fossil discoveries would fill the gaps:

> *He prophesied that future generations of paleontologists would fill in these gaps* by diligent search and then his major thesis—that evolutionary change is gradual and progressive—would be vindicated. One hundred and twenty years of paleontological research later, it has become abundantly clear that the fossil record will not confirm this part of Darwin's predictions. Nor is the problem a miserably poor record. *The fossil record simply shows that this prediction was wrong.*[77]

All evolutionists agree that "Darwin's work was plagued by ignorance and misinformation concerning the laws of heredity," and that he erred in his theorizing about pangenesis and gemmules,[78] and in his view of natural selection as differential mortality.[79] A growing number of scientists have rejected Darwin's* postulate of gradualism and its corollary of graded intermediate forms, such as Gould* of Harvard:

> The evolutionary trees that adorn our textbooks have data only at the tips and nodes of their branches; the rest is inference, however reasonable, not the evidence of fossils. Yet Darwin was *so wedded to gradualism* that he *wagered his entire theory on a denial of this literal record*:
>
> > [Darwin wrote:] The geological record is extremely imperfect and this fact will to a large extent explain why we do not find interminable varieties, connecting together all the extinct and existing forms of life by the finest graduated steps. He who rejects these views on the nature of the geological record, will rightly reject my whole theory.[80]

A brilliant book by a noncreationist, Macbeth*, carefully establishes that classical Darwinism is "sadly decayed" and invalid:

> I assert only that the *mechanism* of evolution suggested by Charles Darwin has been found *inadequate* by the professionals, and that they have moved on to other views and problems. In brief, *classical Darwinism is no longer considered valid by qualified biologists.*
>
> . . ..
>
> In examining the single parts of classical Darwinism, I concluded that they were all sadly decayed.[81]

b. Neo-Darwinian Evolutionary Synthesis

The "neo-Darwinian synthesis," often called the "modern evolutionary synthesis" or "phyletic gradualism," is defined by Ernst Mayr* (a leading proponent) as involving

> two conclusions: gradual evolution can be explained in terms of small genetic changes ('mutations') and recombination, and the ordering of this genetic variation by natural selection; and . . . macroevolutionary processes and speciation, can be explained in a manner that is consistent with the known genetic mechanisms.[82]

Other authors concur.[83] As the quotation indicates, essential parts of the neo-Darwinian synthesis are gradualism,[84] the mechanism of mutation and recombination added to the "overwhelming importance of natural selection," and extrapolation from microevolutionary processes to macroevolutionary processes.[85]

That neo-Darwinian synthesis has been described as "effectively dead, despite its persistence as textbook orthodoxy," and as "breaking down," by Gould* (who advocates punctuated equilibria).[86] Its "explanation of macroevolution" is "very flimsy" in the estimation of Saunders*,[87] its "obituary" has been written according to Platnick*, and it is "dead" in the view of Macbeth*.[88] Neo-Darwinism is "incoherent" as well as "dead," according to Cracraft*:

> In summary, some chapters of this book should be read by anyone interested in evolutionary theory. If nothing else, they demonstrate that current neo-Darwinism is little more than an incoherent collection of theoretical and quasi-theoretical statements, many seemingly without much generality. . . .
>
> . . . .
>
> These chapters demonstrate the dearth of our knowledge about the interface between genetics and development. These critics are surely correct that the *traditional Darwinian view*—that phenotypic evolution is reducible to gene change—*is dead*. Yet at the same time, they seem to forget that many neo-Darwinians have rejected that view themselves.[89]

The gradualism of macroevolutionary change, which most neo-Darwinists insist upon, has been severely attacked as "a myth" (Eldredge* and Tattersall*),[90] as "untenable in light of fossil evidence" (Stanley*),[91] as having "broken down on both its fundamental claims" and as having "no support" in the "fossil record" (Gould*),[92] and as known to be wrong by paleontologists "privately . . . for over a hundred years" (Eldredge*).[93] Eldredge*, a paleontologist at the American Museum of Natural History, describes gradualism as "akin to the 'Emperor's new clothes' ":

> It is, indeed, a very curious state of affairs, I think, that paleontologists

have been insisting that their record is consistent with slow, steady, gradual evolution where I think that *privately, they've known for over a hundred years* that such is not the case. I view stasis and the trumpeting of stasis to the whole world that the fossil record shows slow, steady, continuous change (as opposed to herky jerky patterns of change) as something *akin to the "Emperor's new clothes." Paleontologists have known this for over a hundred years.*[94]

Stanley* says that there is not even "a single example" of gradual macroevolutionary steps:

> The known *fossil record fails to document* a single example of phyletic evolution accomplishing a major morphologic transition and hence offers no evidence that the gradualistic model can be valid.[95]

The "overwhelming importance of natural selection" has also been savagely attacked as wrong, and the extrapolation of micro-evolution to explain macroevolution (Mayr's* second point) has been similarly ravaged, as discussed below.[96]

c. Punctuated Equilibria

The "punctuated equilibria" approach is defined by Raup* and Stanley* as follows:

> The idea that considerably more than 50 percent of evolution occurs through the proliferation of species has been termed the *punctuated equilibrium model* of evolution or the *punctuational model.* The name refers to the step-like or "punctuated" nature of the phylogenetic model.... The opposing idea, that considerably more than 50 percent of evolution occurs as phyletic change within established species, has been termed *phyletic gradualism* or the *gradualistic model* [or Neo-Darwinism].[97]

Similar definitions are given by others.[98] Punctuated equilibria explains macroevolution by "very rapid events of speciation" (species formation), "the differential success of certain species" in relation to other species (species selection and extinction), and non-change of "most species" (stasis), so that "most species ... either do not change in any appreciable way, or else they fluctuate mildly in morphology, with no apparent direction."[99] Punctuated equilibria acknowledges the existence of most of the abrupt appearances of complex organisms in the fossil record, of most of the systematic gaps between fossil categories (the "trade secret of paleontology"), and of most of the stasis that the theory of abrupt appearance identifies (although punctuated equilibria interprets these phenomena very differently).[100] The punctuated equilibria approach views this non-gradual fossil record and other factors as fatal to the modern evolutionary synthesis, and sees punctuated equilibria as the successor theory of macroevolution.[101]

Punctuated equilibria has not been without critics, and they point out some key difficulties. The basic criticism is that "[s]pecies selection may happen, but it doesn't seem to *do* anything,"[102] that is, it is not "an important explanation for the evolution of complex adaptations" or for macroevolution, in the words of Dawkins*.[103] Other criticisms are described later: that it conveniently assumes that speciation only occurs where fossils are not left, that its assumption that speciation occurs normally in small populations is contrary to the evidence, and that species selection is meaningless because only individuals have traits that are the subjects of selection.[104] Some such criticisms are made by Schopf*,[105] Maynard Smith*,[106] Hoffman* and Hecht*,[107] Arthur*,[108] Levinton* and Simon*,[109] Charlesworth*, Lande*, and Slatkin*,[110] and Valentine* and Erwin*.[111]

d. Non-Darwinian Evolution
and Anti-Darwinian Approaches

"Non-Darwinian" approaches to macroevolution are taken by "a generally silent group of students engaged in biological pursuits who tend to disagree with much of the current thought,"[112] and by many leading scientists such as Nobel laureate Szent-Gyorgyi*, the late geneticist Goldschmidt* of Berkeley, and the famous late geneticist de Vries* of University of Amsterdam. In fact,

> throughout the past century there has *always existed a significant minority of first-rate biologists who have never been able to bring themselves to accept the validity of Darwinian claims.* In fact, the number of biologists who have expressed some degree of disillusionment is practically endless. When Arthur Koestler organized the Alpbach Symposium in 1969 called "Beyond Reductionism", for the express purpose of bringing together biologists critical of orthodox Darwinism, he was able to include in the list of participants many authorities of world stature, such as Swedish neurobiologist Holgar Hyden, zoologists Paul Weiss and W.H. Thorpe, linguist David McNeil and child psychologist Jean Piaget. Koestler had this to say in his opening remarks: ". . . invitations were confined to personalities in academic life with undisputed authority in their respective fields, who nevertheless share that holy discontent."
>
> At the Wistar Institute Symposium in 1966, which brought together mathematicians and biologists of impeccable academic credentials, Sir Peter Medawar acknowledged in his introductory address the existence of a widespread feeling of scepticism over the role of chance in evolution, a feeling in his own words that: ". . . something is missing from orthodox theory."[113]

Darwinism has been so "severely criticized" from the scientific and philosophic communities that "the scientific status of the theory has become a subject of contention."[114]

Evolutionary saltationists, such as famed geneticists de Vries*[115] and Goldschmidt*,[116] paleontologists Schindewolf*[117] and Spath*,[118] and neontologist Clark*,[119] rejected Darwinism and proposed a "hopeful monster" approach or macromutations. Some modern evolutionary saltationists follow suit, such as Grant*[120] and Wolsky*.[121]

Neutral selectionists fall back on "a population genetics view," such as Kimura*, Crow*, Ohta*, Thoday*, and Ewens*.[122] Their challenge is directly against Darwinism, as Grene* perceives:

> Of the many lines of debate now current, however, it seems to me, only two, or perhaps better three, constitute such fundamental challenges [to Darwinism]: (1) neutral mutation theory, (2) cladism, and (3) a protest from the perspective of ontogenesis and sometimes also of morphology. . . . That mutations are random even the most fervent selectionist admits: indeed, it is necessary to the structure of a neo-Darwinian, non-Lamarckian account that this be so (see Rensch's essay, for example). But that alleles wholly unconnected with fitness should persist for long periods and in great numbers is a thesis that selectionists find difficult to accept. Yet despite selectionist arguments to the contrary, the view persists (Kimura, 1976; King and Jukes, 1969). . . .[123]

Structuralists reject Darwinian functionalist explanations in favor of structural explanations of the various morphologies that can be classified hierarchically.[124] Their general anti-Darwinian view is summarized by Webster* and Goodwin*, biologists at University of Sussex, as follows:

> the only way of achieving clarification was to abandon *the system of concepts which we call the 'evolutionary paradigm'* and attempt to construct what seems to us a more satisfactory conceptual structure. . . .
>
> In this paper *we question the adequacy of the evolutionary paradigm* in relation to its failure to provide any satisfactory theory of the production and re-production of biological form. We do not believe that this failure is a result of the supposed difficulty of the problem, but rather that it is a consequence of the intrinsic inadequacy of the current system of concepts; we contend that, without a change in the system, no progress can be expected in this crucial area. It follows inevitably from the absence of any coherent account of morphology or morphogenesis that the *current theory of evolutionary transformations* remains, at best, *incomplete and unsatisfactory.*
>
> . . ..
>
> . . .It will be apparent that *we regard the theory of evolution, and in particular neo-Darwinism,* as having *extremely limited explanatory power* with respect to the problem of form to which it was originally

addressed. This limitation arises as a consequence of the absence of any adequate theory of the means of production of 'typical forms' and is such, we would maintain, as to *render debatable the claim that neo-Darwinism is 'the unifying theory in biology'* (Maynard Smith, 1975).... The structuralist position we adopt is perfectly consistent with a theory of historical descent (though *not dependent upon it*) and, by providing a conceptual framework within which a theory of transformations can be produced, both clarifies some of the issues raised by such a theory and provides a picture of the evolutionary process which is somewhat different to that of the neo-Darwinists.[125]

Hughes* and Lambert* concur that, in contrast to their structuralist view, functionalist "neo-Darwinism is like a cosmological theory in physics without the context of physical law."[126]

Nonequilibrium thermodynamics rejects Darwinism while holding to macroevolution, as Brooks* and Wiley*, its leading American proponents, indicate:

In this book we will develop the idea that evolution is an axiomatic consequence of organismic information and cohesion systems obeying the second law of thermodynamics in a manner analogous to, but not identical with, the consequences of the second law's usual application in physical and chemical systems. By "axiomatic" we mean that the results are necessary consequences or outcomes. . . .

If evolution is an axiomatic consequence of certain biological processes following the second law, then current theories of the evolutionary process must necessarily be incomplete because they are theories of proximal cause.... In a real sense Darwin produced a theory of proximal cause, evolution by natural selection . . . .[127]

Szent-Gyorgyi* rejects the neo-Darwinian approach and casts aside "the usual answer . . . that there was plenty of time to try everything."[128]

Many other viewpoints are anti-Darwinian although macro-evolutionist. The prominent biologist Løvtrup*, professor of zoophysiology at University of Umea (Sweden), poses a new theory while brilliantly repudiating Darwin*, with the provocative title *Darwinism: The Refutation of a Myth*:

After this step-wise elimination, *only one possibility remains: the Darwinian theory of natural selection, whether or not coupled with Mendelism, is false.* I have already shown that the arguments advanced by the early champions were not very compelling, and that there are now considerable numbers of empirical facts which do not fit with the theory. Hence, to all intents and purposes the theory has been *falsified*, so why has it not been abandoned?

I think the answer to this question is that current Evolutionists follow Darwin's example—they refuse to accept falsifying evidence. . . .[129]

The noted biochemist Fox* of University of Miami, with Ho* of Open University and Saunders* of King's College at London, have proposed a new model in place of Darwinism*.[130] Polyphyletists such as Schwabe* say that "neo-Darwinism is or rather should be... disputed," and replace it with life having "countless origins."[131] Hsü*, a prominent geologist at the Geological Institute E.T.H. at Zurich, argues that Darwin* misunderstood geology, and concludes, "We have had enough of the Darwinian fallacy. It is time that we cry: 'The emperor has no clothes.' "[132] von Eisenstein* similarly discards Darwinism for other mechanisms.[133]

Many anti-Darwinians find no explanation satisfactory for macroevolution, such as Grassé*,[134] Lemoine*,[135] Macbeth*,[136] Ambrose*,[137] Russell*,[138] and Martin*.[139] For example, Grassé*, who was cited earlier in this chapter, reached the following anti-Darwinian conclusion:

> Their success among certain biologists, philosophers, and sociologists notwithstanding, the explanatory doctrines of biological evolution do not stand up to an objective, in-depth criticism. They prove to be either in conflict with reality or else incapable of solving the major problems involved.[140]

Lemoine*, a president of the Geological Society of France, director of the Natural History Museum in Paris, and the editor of the *Encyclopedie Française*, writes:

> The theories of *evolution*, with which our studious youth have been *deceived*, constitute actually a *dogma* that all the world continues to teach: but each, in his specialty, the zoologist or the botanist, ascertains that *none of the explanations furnished is adequate*....[I]t results from this summary, that the theory of evolution, is *impossible*.[141]

Similarly, Good*, formerly a botany professor at University of Hull, finds that the macroevolutionary literature often has "mirage"-like clarity:

> All this being so it might be expected that there would be an essential unanimity of opinion about the probable means by which evolution has been effected and that writings on the subject would be distinguished by the highest standards of scientific dialectic, but *in neither case can this be claimed*. There are still deep divergences of opinion about the nature of evolutionary processes, while it is the experience of many that *increased acquaintance with the literature brings more rather than less uncertainty* together with a conviction that however much may already have been said there is even more still to be learned. Moreover, much of this literature has something of the alluring but elusive quality of a mirage, in which the scene, at first apparently so sharply etched, gradually dissolves as it is more closely approached until it loses much of its earlier certainty of outline.[142]

Erbrich* concludes that "the explaining mechanism is fundamentally inadequate" for evolution, and suspects that "there is no alternative whatsoever which could explain the fact of universal evolution . . . within the framework of natural science."[143]

Some popular writers have launched attacks on Darwinism and all explanations of macroevolution, such as Hitching*,[144] Taylor* ("inadequate, implausible, or definitely wrong"),[145] Rifkin*,[146] Himmelfarb*,[147] and Koestler*,[148] who were quoted earlier. All the authors cited in this subsection, while rejecting the theory of abrupt appearance, also reject Darwinian explanations of both major schools (the neo-Darwinian synthesis and punctuated equilibria).

e. Transformed Cladistics

The "transformed cladist" approach is a major part of one of the three major schools of classifying organisms,[149] and is "neutral or opposed to evolutionary theorizing of any kind in systematics," operating instead "in a non-evolutionary domain," according to Ball*.[150] It is "at odds with evolutionary thinking" rather than "evolutionarily neutral," Beatty* observes,[151] and concededly "calls into question much of conventional evolutionary history."[152] Transformed cladistics "is fundamentally a non-evolutionary classification," Oldroyd* notes,[153] and "is not only anti-Darwinian" but "against evolution itself," Gene* says.[154] The word "transformed" refers to a "transformation away from dependence on evolutionary theory."[155]

For example, Patterson* has serious doubts about macroevolution:
It's true that for the last eighteen months or so I've been kicking around *non-evolutionary or even anti-evolutionary* ideas . . ..
. . ..
. . .So that is my first theme: that evolution and creation seem to be sharing *remarkable parallels* that are increasingly hard to tell apart. The second theme is that evolution not only conveys no knowledge but it seems somehow to convey *anti-knowledge*.[156]

Cracraft*, another leading cladist, says that "neo-Darwinism is coming apart at the seams" and has "yielded a healthy amount of mindless pap."[157] Nelson* and Platnick*, other leaders, conclude that "Darwinism . . . is, in short, a theory that has been put to the test and found false," and that the "Darwinian theory of systematics . . . has been falsified."[158] The nonevolutionary and antievolutionary approaches of the transformed cladists are described in further detail in Section 3.4(c).

f. Anti-Evolutionary Approaches

An antievolutionist approach is taken by many noncreationist scientists. Olson* reports that there are "some among the biologists who feel that much of the [macroevolutionary] theory accepted by the majority today is actually false."[159]

Kerkut*, a leading biochemist who has edited a significant series of books on physiology and teaches at the University of Southampton, systematically assesses the evidence for macroevolution and finds it weak:

> What conclusions, then, can one come to concerning the validity of the various implications of the theory of evolution? If we go back to our initial assumptions it will be seen that the *evidence is still lacking* for most of them.[160]

Lipson*, a British physicist and Fellow of the Royal Society, rejects macroevolution based on his scientific analysis of it:

> I have always been slightly suspicious of the theory of evolution because of its ability to account for any property of living beings (the long neck of the giraffe, for example). I have therefore tried to see whether biological discoveries over the last thirty years or so fit in with Darwin's theory. *I do not think that they do.*
>
> . . ..
>
> To my mind, the theory does *not stand up* at all.[161]

Denton*, an Australian molecular biologist, discards Darwinism and macroevolution based on his assessment of the evidence:

> In this book I have adopted the radical approach. By presenting a *systematic critique of the current Darwinian model*, ranging from paleontology to molecular biology, I have tried to show why I believe that the *problems are too severe* and too intractable to offer any hope of *resolution in terms of the orthodox Darwinian framework*, and that consequently the conservative view is no longer tenable.
>
> . . ..
>
> The *anti-evolutionary thesis* argued in this book, the idea that life might be fundamentally a discontinuous phenomenon, runs counter to the whole thrust of modern biological thought.[162]

Sermonti*, the senior editor of *Rivista di Biologia* (*Biology Forum*), professor of genetics at University of Perugia, and former director of the Genetics Institute of University of Palermo (Italy), and Fondi*, professor of paleontology at University of Siena, reject macroevolution because of its scientific weakness.[163] Vernet* in France reaches a similar conclusion.[164]

Historically, most of the leading scientists at the time of Darwin* rejected and continued to reject macroevolution, as described in a later section.[165] Hull* acknowledges that their reasons were mostly honest scientific considerations rather than religious bigotry.[166] In the early 1900s, Fleischmann* was a "competent zoologist" who called the [macroevolutionary] theory a beautiful myth not substantiated by any factual foundation," according to Mayr*.[167] Today, many agree.[168]

Summary. Of six scientific approaches to macroevolution besides the theory of abrupt appearance, classical Darwinism is "wrong" on key issues, neo-Darwinism and punctuated equilibria cancel each other by denying the sufficiency of the other's mechanism, and three approaches are anti-Darwinian with one opposing and a second being agnostic toward macroevolution. Classical Darwinism "was wrong" that fossils "would fill in these gaps" (Eldredge* and Tattersall*[169]), that gradualism could explain the "extreme rarity of transitional forms" (Gould*[170]), and that acquired traits could be inherited by a "pangenesis theory" (Rosen*[171]). Neo-Darwinism is also "effectively dead, despite its persistence as textbook orthodoxy" (Gould*[172]), has had its "obituary" written (Platnick*[173]), is "very flimsy" in its "explanation of macroevolution" (Saunders*[174]), and is "incoherent" (Cracraft*[175]), according to punctuated equilibria proponents and others. Punctuated equilibria in turn is not "an important explanation for the evolution of complex adaptations" or macroevolution (Dawkins*[176]), neo-Darwinians reply.

Anti-Darwinians consist of "a significant minority of first-rate biologists who have never been able to bring themselves to accept the validity of Darwinian claims" (Denton*[177]), such as evolutionary saltationists, neutral selectionists, structuralists, nonequilibrium thermodynamics advocates, and others. Examples are Løvtrup's recent *Darwinism: The Refutation of a Myth* (1987), Ho's* and Saunders'* *Beyond Neo-Darwinism* (1984), Ambrose's* *The Nature and Origin of the Biological World* (1982), and Grassé's* *The Evolution of Living Organisms* (trans. 1977). Transformed cladists operate "in a non-evolutionary domain" and are "neutral or opposed to evolutionary theorizing" (Ball*[178]), such as Patterson* who has "been kicking around non-evolutionary or even anti-evolutionary ideas" while concluding that macroevolution "seems somehow to convey anti-knowledge" (Patterson*[179]).

Anti-evolutionists include Denton's* *Evolution: A Theory in Crisis* (1985) with its "anti-evolutionary thesis" (Denton*[180]), Sermonti's* and Fondi's* *Dopo Darwin: Critica all' Evoluzionismo* (1980), and others who find that "the evidence is still lacking" for most macroevolutionary postulates (Kerkut*[181]). In such a climate of scientific dispute, it is clear to all but the blinded zealots that Darwinism and macroevolution are not compellingly established or immune to criticism. *Non consensus omnium.*

Figure 3.3
Natural selection in "the most striking evolutionary change ever witnessed by man" (Kettlewell): the peppered moths "either have nothing to do with evolution or are insignificant" (Grassé*)*

3.3 The Postulated Mechanisms of Macroevolution: Natural Selection, Species Selection, and Other Factors

Macroevolution may legitimately be regarded as noncompelling if no plausible mechanism is offered to show that it can occur. Evolutionists are fond of saying that all agree on the "fact" of evolution, and are "merely" disagreeing on the mechanism. That is as odd as a trial, not on the assumed "fact" of the accused's guilt, but only on the "mechanism" of his assumed crime. Because macroevolution is not a "fact," as discussed in Section 3.1(c), and assertedly occurred by solely naturalistic processes, the mechanism remains vitally important. Every proposed mechanism comes with severe difficulties, in the estimation of many evolutionist scientists. The point of this section is not that Darwinian mechanisms for macroevolution are wrong, but that they are not compellingly established and do not preclude scientific alternatives.

Factors. In the neo-Darwinian view, the three primary factors in a mechanism for macroevolution are (a) natural selection, (b) mutation, and (c) genetic recombination, as described by leading evolutionists Dobzhansky*, Ayala*, Stebbins*, and Valentine*:

three main processes—mutation, genetic recombination, and *natural selection* . . . .[182]

. . . .

. . .In a nutshell, the [neo-Darwinian synthesis] theory maintains that *mutation* and sexual *recombination* furnish the raw materials; that *natural selection* fashions from these materials genotypes and gene pools; and that, in sexually reproducing forms, the arrays of adaptively coherent genotypes are protected from disintegration by *reproductive isolating* mechanisms.[183]

This is the standard view[184] as espoused by Mayr* and others.[185] Other factors frequently mentioned are (d) migration and isolation, and (e) genetic drift.[186]

Advocates of punctuated equilibria agree that the preceding factors exist, but hold that those factors only produce microevolution or phyletic evolution.[187] They list (f) species selection, including speciation and extinction, instead as the mechanism of macroevolution.[188] Darwinians and advocates of non-Darwinian approaches offer (g) various other factors.

Each school of Darwinian macroevolution (neo-Darwinian synthesis and punctuated equilibria) offers a set of factors as almost totally explaining the mechanism of macroevolution that the other school regards as fairly insignificant.[189] A hundred and fifty leading macroevolutionists of both schools met in Chicago in 1980 to discuss the mechanism of macroevolution, and came away without any agreement on any viable mechanism to explain how macroevolution could occur.[190] This section summarizes the conclusions of various evolutionists that natural selection and each of these other factors fail to provide all or a substantial part of a workable mechanism for macroevolution.

Extrapolation. The choice of mechanism depends on the question of whether microevolutionary change can be assumed ultimately to produce macroevolutionary change ("extrapolation" from microevolution to macroevolution), and this is a critical point of disagreement. Neo-Darwinians answer yes, and identify microevolution (factors (a)-(c)) as the mechanism for macroevolution, as exemplified by Dobzhansky* *et al.*:

Subspecific evolution and transspecific evolution are not different phenomena or processes: they are *two aspects* of the same series of processes and phenomena. . . . They *extrapolate to the transspecific level* by comparing individuals or populations that have evolved over time spans measured in terms of millions of generations or years. Findings at the subspecific level *can be applied* to the transspecific level if one grants that the processes that promote evolutionary change in modern populations have been active throughout the millions of years during which organisms have existed. *Extrapolation* from the present to the past is therefore possible. . . .[191]

Mayr* and others similarly argue for extrapolation.[192]

Punctuated equilibria advocates answer no, attacking the "fallacy of direct extrapolation,"[193] and identify species selection (factor (f)) as the mechanism for macroevolution. For example, Eldredge* and Tattersall* write:

> What is wrong with the synthesis is not the core neo-Darwinian formulations of mechanics (natural selection working on variation within species to effect gradual change). *What is wrong* is the wholesale, uncritical—and unwarranted—*extrapolation* of these mechanisms via metaphors such as the adaptive landscape to embrace the evolution and diversification of all life.[194]

Gould* makes the same argument,[195] and Stanley* and others conclude that "macroevolution is decoupled from microevolution."[196]

The Chicago conference in 1980 addressed extrapolation as its central question, and the answer was "a clear No" according to *Science* reporter Lewin*.[197] Discontinuitist scientists also answer no, and suggest that all of the neo-Darwinian and punctuationist factors are insufficient to produce macroevolution.

There is "no evidence" for extrapolation, according to not only punctuationists but also a number of nonpunctuationist biologists, such as Saunders* and Ho*:

> The real question, however, and this is what the claim to sufficiency is all about, is whether all of evolution can be explained as an *extrapolation* from these examples, i.e., as arising from the natural selection of many small random variations. Is evolution nothing more than industrial melanism writ large? On this—the crucial issue—there is *no evidence in favor* of the synthetic theory. From the claims that are made for neo-Darwinism one could easily get the impression that it has made great progress towards explaining evolution, leaving mostly details to be cleared up. In fact, quite the reverse is true. Neo-Darwinism can account for some of the details, but the *major problems remain unsolved*. Samuel Butler's (1911) complaint that Darwin had given us "an *Origin of the Species* with the 'Origin' cut out" is as true today as when he wrote it.[198]

Similarly, the Cambrian explosion is inconsistent with extrapolation, according to geologists Erwin* and Valentine*:

> These problems of viable "hopeful monsters" are exacerbated when considering evolution near the Precambrian-Cambrian boundary, when new higher taxa appeared at such a rate that we have estimated that 1 in 40 or so species represented a new class. This figure is arguable, but it is

clear that the process causing evolutionary novelty could not have depended on exceedingly rare events [viable mutations with major morphological or physiological effects]. *Explanations for the Cambrian radiation* of invertebrate marine phyla and classes have focused on *species selection or traditional microevolutionary processes.* The rapidity of and low species numbers during the radiation render these explanations *untenable.*[199]

Many non-Darwinians also reject extrapolation and denounce "the faith . . . that macroevolution can be accounted for in principle by the same factors that bring about microevolution," in the words of Russell*,[200] such as Kerkut*,[201] Goldschmidt*,[202] Grant*,[203] Kitts*,[204] Ricklefs*,[205] Wolsky*,[206] and others.[207] Grassé echoes the view of many scientists:

> How does the Darwinian mutational interpretation of evolution account for the fact that the *species that have been the most stable*—some of them for the last hundreds of millions of years—*have mutated as much as the others do?* . . . Once one has noticed microvariations (on the one hand) and specific stability (on the other), it seems very *difficult to conclude that the former* (microvariation) *comes into play in the evolutionary process.*[208]

Løvtrup concurs that "neither in Nature nor under experimental conditions have any substantial effects ever been obtained through the systematic accumulation of micromutations."[209]

a. Natural Selection as a Mechanism and Its Difficulties

Natural selection is the process "whereby organisms best adapted to local environments leave more surviving offspring and spread their favored traits through populations."[210] It is "the fundamental process directing evolutionary change" and "the main process responsible for the adaptations of organisms," according to gradualists Dobzhansky*, Ayala*, Stebbins*, Valentine*,[211] and Mayr*.[212] In the neo-Darwinian view, it is not just a negative force but a creative force, Mayr* states:

> An understanding of the working of natural selection is the *key* to the synthetic theory of evolution. I know of no other scientific theory that has been *misunderstood and misrepresented* as greatly as the theory of natural selection. First of all *it is usually represented as strictly negative,* as a force that eliminates, a force that kills and destroys. Yet Darwin, by his choice of the name selection, had clearly emphasized the *positive aspects* of this force. Indeed, we now know that one can go even further and call natural selection a creative force.[213]

However, many evolutionist biologists and philosophers of science attack natural selection as being insufficient to act as a significant factor in macroevolution:

In spite of the reverence that many systematists hold for neo-Darwinian evolution and natural selection, *some biologists (Løvtrup, 1974; Rosen and Buth, 1980) doubt its merits,* and *philosophers have questioned* the value of the theory of natural selection (Barker, 1969; Brady, 1979; Grene, 1974; Smart, 1963).[214]

Those biologists include Forey*,[215] Gruner*,[216] Rosen*,[217] possibly Simpson*,[218] and others.[219] For example, Stanley* writes that "natural selection, long viewed as the process guiding evolutionary change, cannot play a significant role in determining the overall course of evolution."[220]

(1) Inadequacy for Macroevolution. The problem with natural selection that biologists have attacked is that it cannot be extrapolated from microevolution (which it does cause) to macroevolution, as discussed earlier in this section. Thus, it does not provide an adequate mechanism to bring about macroevolution ultimately from one or more first living cells to all existing life.

The different attack on natural selection by several dozen philosophers and biologists, in published articles, is that it is unfalsifiable,[221] untestable,[222] tautologous or nonexplanatory,[223] or all three, as discussed in full later. For example, Brady*, a philosopher of science at College of New Jersey, finds natural selection unfalsifiable and thus not a sufficient mechanism or part of a mechanism at all:

> [M]ost recent critics have already understood this and are actually arguing that the theory is *not falsifiable* in its operational form. Under examination, the operational forms of the concepts of adaptation and fitness turn out to be *too indeterminate to be seriously tested,* for they are protected by ad hoc additions drawn from an indeterminate realm.[224]

Similarly, Waddington* of University of Edinburgh concludes that natural selection is a tautology:

> Natural selection . . . turns out on closer inspection to be a *tautology,* a statement of an inevitable although previously unrecognized relation. It states that the fittest individuals in a population (defined as those which leave the most offspring) will leave most offspring.[225]

Bradie* does not agree with Waddington* that natural selection technically is a tautology, but does suggest that to "identify natural selection with the differential survival and reproduction of organisms is to render the principle vacuous."[226] As a final example, Hughes* and Lambert*, zoologists at University of Auckland, suggest that natural selection is nonexplanatory, in the sense that it provides only a description and not a cause:

> By the application of fairly simple mathematical procedures to one and two locus systems R.A. Fisher, in particular, was able to convince biolo-

gists that he had provided an empirical verification of natural selection. This is clearly *not correct*. Fisher merely made the selectionist "way of seeing" numerate. As Løvtrup (1979) acidly remarked: "...Fisher (1930) *demonstrated* nothing, he made some calculations" (see Lambert (1984) for a critical analysis of the logical structure of population genetics). We should remember that *natural selection is not necessarily real* (*sensu* Thom, 1972; Bhaskar, 1978) *just because biologists and mathematicians have been talking about it for over 100 years*. As Lewontin (1976) commented: "It cannot be assumed that any behaviour or institution to which a name can be given necessarily has an existence as a real thing subject to the laws of nature".

. . ..

In essence, we contend that *neo-Darwinism is a theory of differential survival and not one of origin.* . . .

. . ..

We are certainly not arguing here that differential survival of whole organisms does not occur. This must inevitably happen. The question that we must ask is, does this represent the controlling dynamic of organic evolution (Hailman, 1982)? *Cannot a similar argument be equally well constructed to "explain" any frequency distribution?* For example, consider rocks which vary in hardness and also persist through time. Clearly the harder rocks are better "adapted" to survive harsh climatic conditions. As Lewontin (1976) points out, a similar story can be told about political parties, rumours, jokes, stars and discarded soft drink containers.[227]

Those philosophy arguments are extensively discussed in Chapter 10.

In response to those and other criticisms, natural selection has been drastically redefined, yet not openly but by "subterfuge", according to Rosen*:

If the theory of natural selection, as formulated by Darwin is tautological, and if the neo-Darwinists have retreated from the criticism of this tautology by *redefining* natural selection in more esoteric terms (population genetics or ecological genetics)—even though it still does not explain either the appearance of evolutionary novelties or evolutionary diversity—then biologists might appear to an onlooker to have rejected modern synthetic evolutionary theory but *practiced a subterfuge to retain it as the orthodox position*.[228]

(2) Inadequacy of Empirical Examples. Many biologists also argue that natural selection is not supported by any persuasive examples or evidence relevant to macroevolution, even though a few examples involve microevolution. That is the point of the arguments against extrapolation that are cited above. Cracraft* suggests that natural selection does not apply to the species level or higher levels, and that such extrapolations "confuse" analysis:

Moreover, it is clear that statements about *natural selection should be restricted to the intrapopulational level* of analysis; extending natural selection to *specific* and *supraspecific levels*, as do nearly all of the above cited studies, further *confuses* the issue of process analysis (Eldredge and Cracraft, 1980).[229]

Patterson* concurs that "[n]o one has ever produced a new species by means of natural selection":

There's no doubt at all that natural selection works—it's been repeatedly demonstrated by experiment. But the question of *whether it produces new species is quite another matter. No one has ever produced* a new species by means of natural selection, *no one has ever got near it*, and most of the current argument in neo-Darwinism is about this question. . . .[230]

That inapplicability of natural selection to speciation leads Grene* to say that Darwin's* *The Origin of Species* "simply is not about the origin of species, let alone of the great orders and classes and phyla."[231]

Other biologists carry the point further to deny that natural selection is supported by any evidence at all, whether at the macroevolutionary or even microevolutionary level. Grassé*, whose "knowledge of the living world is encyclopedic" according to Dobzhansky*,[232] simply finds "not one single sure datum":

The role assigned to *natural selection* in establishing adaptation, while speciously probable, is based on *not one single sure datum*. Paleontology (cf. the case of the transformation of the mandibular skeleton of the theriodont reptiles) does not support it; direct observation here and now of the genesis of a hereditary adaptation is nonexistent, except, as we have stated, in the case of bacteria and insects preadapted to resist viruses or drugs.[233]

Manly* surveys the statistical research on natural selection among animals, and concludes that in "most cases . . . there also seem to be alternative, non-selective explanations" for the alleged evidence:

The purpose of this paper is to provide a broad overview of statistical aspects of studies designed to detect and measure natural selection on animal populations.

. . ..

The main body of the paper consists of a review of five different approaches that have been used to study selection: (a) the comparison of survival rates of different types of individuals over one stage in a life cycle; (b) searching for correlations either between the distribution of a species and environmental variables, or between the distributions of two related species; (c) studies on specific genetic loci, concerned with temporal changes in gene frequencies, or with the question of whether gene distributions are consistent with models of no selection; (d) studying changes over many generations in the mean of a character in a population; and (e) methods for studying selection in relationship to mating.

From the review it becomes obvious that *it has proved to be very difficult to obtain unequivocal evidence of natural selection.* In most cases where evidence has been found, *there also seem to be alternative, non-selective explanations.* Although it is now over 125 years since Darwin and Wallace put forward the argument that selection is a primary cause of evolutionary change, it is *still not clear whether or not they were correct.*

. . ..

One thing that emerges clearly from this review is how *difficult it has been to get unequivocal evidence of selection* in natural populations. Indeed, although it is now more than 125 years since Darwin and Wallace put forward the argument that selection is a primary cause of evolutionary change, *it is still not obvious how important selection is.*

The review has indicated several reasons for this state of affairs. There is a *size-biased sampling problem*: the more selection occurring in a particular situation, the more liable that situation is to be noticed. This effect is reinforced by the large sample sizes that may be needed to detect small or moderate amounts of selection. Also, much "evidence" for selection is simply a significant *deviation from randomness* which can be *explained equally well by migration, historical events or even by non-random sampling.* . . .[234]

Good*, in his full book on flowering plants, finds that there is "no evidence that natural selection has played an important part in their evolution":

As regards *natural selection* it can only be said that it is difficult to avoid the conclusion that the circumstances exhibited by the Flowering Plants, and especially such of them as have been noticed in this book, are *in many important respects inexplicable* on this theory.

The conclusions with regard to the bearing of the Flowering Plants on these various hypotheses are, therefore, that these plants, though providing little positive evidence in favour of orthogenesis, show even fewer indications of evidence against it; that they reveal *no evidence that natural selection has played an important part in their evolution*, though they provide *many indications that this has not, in fact, been the case*; and that they suggest that mutation, on a comparatively large scale, has been a frequent and potent factor in their history.[235]

The "most famous, strongly documented case" of natural selection is that of "the replacement of light-colored by dark-colored moths in industrial areas of England after trees were coated with soot," so that birds picked off the more visible light-colored moths and caused the dark-colored moths to become more prevalent.[236] Grassé* and others note that this is not macroevolution but only "insignificant" microevolution:

At best, present evolutionary phenomena are simply slight changes of genotypes within populations, or substitution of an allele by a new one. For example, the mutant carbonaria of the birch moth, *Biston betularia*, replaces the regular butterfly in polluted industrial areas (Haldane, 1956; Ford, 1971).... Some biologists maintain that they cannot only observe it but also describe it in action; the *facts that they describe, however, either have nothing to do with evolution or are insignificant.*[237]

This example simply does "not show evolution in progress," Mathews* concedes:

> *they do not show evolution* in progress, for, however the populations may alter in their content of light, intermediate or dark forms, *all the moths remain from beginning to end Biston betularia.*[238]

Many other biologists and philosophers concur, such as Saunders* and Ho*,[239] Brady,[240] and Millar*, Hughes*, and Jones*.[241]

The same is true of Darwin's* example of Galapagos finches, which are "minutiae" of microevolution.[242] The best explanation is that "most of the speciations are the result of the multiple invasions mechanism," zoologist Harper* concludes:

> Perhaps the most telling indicator of the external influences guiding biological thought in this area is the extraordinary history of Darwin-finch taxonomy. At one extreme Swarth (1929) raised the taxon to family status, the Geospizidae, which was also recognized by Mayr (1942). Later, Lack (1945, pp. 6-7) realized that the group did not merit even subfamily status, but used the term 'Geospizinae' for convenience. And now not only are the Darwin finches generally denied subfamily status, there is also support, on much the same kind of evidence as was available to Swarth, for the idea that they are all congeneric with a mainland species, as mentioned above....[242A]

The examples of sickle cell anemia and insecticide resistance are similarly "minor" and below the species level:

> Neo-Darwinist textbooks on evolution keep citing the same comparatively *few* examples: industrial melanism, sickle cell anaemia, DDT resistance. All are comparatively *minor* evolutionary changes; all involve *variations* in which a large and obvious selective advantage can be obtained by a *single allele substitution.*[243]

Another frequent example is breeding experiments, which similarly show nothing about macroevolution, but instead are human-directed and do not generate new species (or higher categories of organisms), as discussed below.[244]

(3) Inadequacy for Explaining Other Data. Other problems with natural selection are numerous. Raup* and most punctuationists see natural selection as inconsistent with mass extinctions:

> The best clincher is *extinction.* For every species now in existence, roughly ninety-nine have become extinct. The question of *why* they

have become extinct is of enormous importance to evolutionists. It has been studied by many men, but a *convincing answer has not been found*. It remains unclear why any given species has disappeared. The discussion of survival of the fittest showed that the phrase led to *circular reasoning*; you survive because you are fit and you are fit because you survive. Discussion of extinction is beset by a similar danger. It is all too easy to say that a species *becomes extinct because it fails to adapt*, while establishing its failure to adapt only by its becoming extinct: in other words, you die because you are unfit and you are unfit because you die.[245]

Others note that the net trend from natural selection, if effective, would be to downward evolution rather than upward evolution:

> The situation as it turns out mathematically is a tussle between the eradicative effect of *natural selection* on the one hand and the *frequency with which small damaging mutations* arise on the other, with many small mutations adding up to produce serious *disadaptation* to the environment. Nor does it turn out that natural selection always adds up the much rarer cases in which mutations happen to be good. Indeed for *good mutations* that are small the adding up process which should spread the mutations is *exceedingly weak*. Natural selection works, in short, only when the variations on which it operates are *large*, and quite likely it is this situation which supporters of the Darwinian theory have constantly at the back of their minds.
>
> The Darwinian theory is wrong because *random variations tend to worsen performance*, as indeed common sense suggests they must do.[246]

Moreover, natural selection does not adequately explain the vast variety in nature that is neutral rather than adaptive or beneficial,[247] as Darwin* himself noted:

> I did not formerly consider sufficiently the existence of *structures* which, as far as we can . . . judge, are *neither beneficial nor injurious*, and this I believe to be one of the greatest *oversights* as yet detected in my work. This led to my tacit assumption that every detail of structure was of some special though unrecognized service.[248]

The problem is still not solved, in the eyes of Russell* and others.[249] Gould* calls the conjectures about how adaptations occurred and how the intermediate stages were beneficial "little more than plausible 'just-so' stories," and cautions that "[s]cience is tested evidence, not tall tales."[250] He elsewhere calls the "silly pan-selectionism that views all structures as adaptations" a "caricature of proper science" that "make[s] up a story."[251]

These various reasons cause many scientists to deny that natural selection is a significant factor in evolution. And they explain why the "theory of natural selection . . . never enjoyed majority support" in Darwin's* lifetime, and "never, to this day, in France or Germany" became an orthodoxy.[252] These difficulties may even explain why Darwin* himself made a "relative retreat from natural selection" in his later book, *The Descent of Man*.[253]

b. Mutation and Its Significance

Mutation[254] is also one of the "three main processes" of "organic evolution," and in fact "the mutation process is the ultimate source of this variability," according to Dobzhansky*, Ayala*, Stebbins*, and Valentine*.[255] Mutations "are the only raw material of evolution," according to neo-Darwinists such as Mayr*,[256] and "the ultimate source of new genetic variability," according to punctuationists such as Gould*.[257]

(1) Inadequacy of Scope of Mutations. While there is no question that mutations occur, one problem is the insignificant scope of nonharmful mutations, which Grassé* finds to prevent any contribution to macroevolution:

> In sum, the mutations of bacteria and viruses are merely hereditary fluctuations around a median position; a swing to the right, a swing to the left, but no final evolutionary effect. . . .
>
> . . ..
>
> . . .No matter how numerous they may be, mutations do not produce any kind of evolution.[258]

Russell* and others agree that mutations "seem quite incapable of giving rise to the major divergences of structuro-functional organisation,"[259] and advocates of punctuated equilibria generally disparage the effect of point mutations.[260] The need for multiple mutations to generate almost any noticeable new trait is discussed after the next paragraph.

The difficulty is compounded by the loss of many mutations from the gene pool, and the occurrence of back mutation, in the words of Byles*:

> [N]onrecurrent mutations have a very low probability of remaining in the gene pool at all . . . .. [T]he *odds against a recurrent mutation being retained in the gene pool* for any significant number of generations are very high . . . . As numerous workers have pointed out, *most recurrent mutations have been observed to retain the potential for back mutation*, a mutation which transforms the mutant form back into the wild type of gene . . . ..
>
> . . .Thus, the power of the PME [probable mutation effect] depends on a low value for v [the back mutation rate], which is precisely the meaning of limiting condition number three.[261]

Some scientists question whether any mutations at all are beneficial.[262] Darwin* himself conceded that he had no proof of beneficial changes:

When we descend to details, we can prove that no species has changed (i.e., we cannot prove that a single species has changed); nor can we prove that the supposed changes are beneficial, which is the groundwork of the theory.[263]

(2) Inadequacy of Frequency of Mutations. Another problem is the extreme infrequency of nonharmful mutations.[264]

Viable mutations with major morphological or physiological effects *are exceedingly rare and usually infertile*; the chance of two identical rare mutant individuals arising in sufficient propinquity to produce offspring seems too small to consider as a significant evolutionary event. . . .[265]

A mutation to produce a "correct" trait is "an extremely rare event," and "the most likely result of a random mutation process will be the production of 'abnormal,' and probably 'unfit', phenotypes," Steele* adds.[266] This low mutation rate "has long been considered one of the major stumbling blocks to the PME [probable mutation effect]," Byles* notes.[267] The difficulty is that "point mutations occur on average only once in each complete copying of the whole 200,000 chains" of DNA,[268] and of these "the frequency with which a single non-harmful mutation is known to occur is about 1 in 1000."[269] Then several mutations are necessary to generate almost any significant trait, and must be combined in the same organism.[270] For example,

Suppose that an important adaptive process in a multicellular species requires the parallel occurrence *within* an individual of three new dominant germline genes: if the chance for each to occur is (say) 10^{-5} per gene per generation, then the probability of their mutual occurrence is very unlikely (10^{-15}). . . .[271]

Moreover, mutations may take about 10,000,000 years to become established in a population.[272] The chance is "infinitesimally small" that the new trait will arise coincident with a major environmental change:

[Mutation] is the only apparent source of the major regulatory changes seemingly associated with major adaptive shifts. One possible objection to this view is that the *waiting time* for such "*hopeful mutations*" may be *prohibitively long*. Moreover, the *probability that the occurrence of such a mutation will coincide with a major environmental shift* requiring an appropriate adaptive response seems *infinitesimally small*. . . .[273]

The experimental evidence on mutation raises another interesting difficulty:

The problem for the Darwinian view, however, is that there has not been any variation observed within natural populations in those regulatory loci set deep within the control network. . . . In other words, the results of the last 20 years of research on the genetic basis of adaptation has led us to a great Darwinian paradox. *Those loci that are obviously variable within natural populations do not seem to lie at the basis of many major adaptive changes, while those loci that seemingly do constitute the foundation of many, if not most, major adaptive changes apparently are not variable within natural populations.*[274]

These difficulties, which were further discussed earlier,[275] leave it improbable that mutations (even if natural selection were effective) could be a sufficient factor in significant macroevolution.

c. Genetic Recombination and Its Significance

Genetic recombination, along with natural selection and mutation, is also one of the "three main processes" of organic evolution.[276] It involves the combination of genes of both parents in an offspring through sexual reproduction.[277] As the phrase implies, recombination only rearranges the "raw material" for natural selection. Thus, Savage* observes, "[r]ecombination acts to enhance the effects of mutation by assembling a broad spectrum of gene combinations..., but *cannot be regarded as an evolutionary force*, since it never changes gene frequencies."[278]

That rearrangement does sometimes produce split genes that contain "introns that are initially transcribed into the nascent mRNA" (messenger RNA). However, those introns "are then excised prior to mRNA translation," and "an intron-containing gene and an intron-lacking gene both cod[e] for the same protein."[279] Thus, "in no case" have chromosomal rearrangements produced evolutionarily significant morphological change, according to Miklos* and John*:

> The conclusions that flow from these and similar examples are that the genome can be mercilessly modified by gross karyotypic rearrangements and still produce equivalent phenotypes. Indeed, in no case has it been demonstrated that an evolutionarily significant morphological change has been the direct consequence of any *chromosomal rearrangement*, as opposed to a point mutation in a gene or its controlling sequences, or gene inactivation stemming from the *mobile sequences* that often abound in a genome.[280]

d. Migration and Isolation and Their Significance

Migration is defined as "gene flow...from one to another population."[281] It can "help maintain high levels of genetic variation in natural populations."[282] However, like recombination, it only rearranges existing genes, and does not generate any new genes necessary for macroevolution.

e. Genetic Drift and Its Significance

Genetic drift has been defined as "directional change in gene frequency that arises by chance but that persists without being favored by natural selection."[283] That "random drift can diversify an array of genetically identical but isolated populations . . . without intervention of natural selection," but only in the sense of changing the relative frequency of particular genes that already are present in the various populations.[284] Again, although gene frequencies within a population certainly can shift, that only explains changes of the proportion of a population with preexisting genes and does not generate the new genes necessary to macroevolution.

f. Species Selection as a Mechanism and Its Difficulties

While advocates of the neo-Darwinian synthesis generally believe that the preceding five factors are a sufficient mechanism for macroevolution, advocates of punctuated equilibria generally believe that those five factors are insufficient. Punctuationists such as Stanley* instead point to speciation in generating new species, extinction in eliminating them, and species selection from differing rates of speciation and extinction, as the only sufficient mechanisms for macroevolution:

> How, then, do large-scale evolutionary trends (macroevolutionary trends) develop? . . . There are three ways in which such change is accomplished. 1. By *phyletic evolution*— . . . this mode of change amounts to *little more than fine tuning*. 2. By *speciation*—by the addition of new species. I have concluded that speciation events are *largely responsible for the origin of higher taxa*. 3. By *extinction*—by the loss of species from the higher taxa. Extinction obviously *cannot produce a new higher taxon*, but it does automatically modify the properties of existing higher taxa. . . .
> . . .Species selection. This is a change in the composition of a segment of phylogeny resulting from some combination of *differential rates of speciation* and *differential rates of extinction among species*.[285]

Other proponents of punctuated equilibria give similar descriptions.[286]

Species selection to punctuationists is the predominant factor in macroevolution: "species selection . . . must largely determine the overall course of evolution" according to Stanley*,[287] and is the cause of "macroevolutionary changes" according to Gould*.[288] It is said to be "analogous to natural selection but acts upon species within higher taxa rather than upon individuals in populations."[289]

While the microevolutionary development of new species and the extinction of old ones is not questioned, neo-Darwinian scientists and discontinuitist scientists both question whether punctuated equilibria provides a sufficient mechanism for macroevolution. They identify a number of problems: (1) that no macroevolution results from species selection; (2) that no species-level selection occurs at all; (3) that no speciation mechanism is provided, nor is there a plausible reason why fossils should not be left sometimes; and (4) that extinction cannot produce macroevolutionary change. In addition, neo-Darwinians question the aspects of punctuated equilibria that discontinuitist scientists accept, such as nongradualism (punctuations) and stasis (equilibria).[290] As Schopf* contends, "[g]radualism is not without its problems, but punctuated equilibria doesn't seem to be one of them."[291]

(1) No Macroevolution from Species Selection. The most important objection is that punctuated equilibria does not embody a mechanism sufficient to produce any macroevolution or complex adaptation, as Dawkins* of Oxford suggests:

> The species selection, such as it is, is simple single-step selection, *choosing between only two traits*, asexuality versus sexuality, slow evolution versus fast evolution. The machinery of sexuality, sex organs, sexual behaviour, the cellular machinery of sexual cell division, all these must have been put together by standard, low-level Darwinian cumulative selection, not by species selection. . . .
>
> To conclude the discussion of species selection, it could account for the pattern of species existing in the world at any particular time. It follows that it could also account for changing patterns of species as geological ages give way to later ages, that is, for changing patterns in the fossil record. But it is not a significant force in the evolution of the complex machinery of life. *The most it can do is to choose* between various alternative complex machineries, *given that those complex machineries have already been put together* by true Darwinian selection. As I have put it before, *species selection may occur but it doesn't seem to do anything much!* . . .[292]

The macroevolutionary events that remain unexplained are summarized by Denton*, who actually accepts punctuated equilibria as a cause of microevolutionary changes while rejecting Dawkins'* faith in Darwinian natural selection:

> While Eldr[e]dge and Gould's model is a perfectly reasonable explanation of the gaps between species (and, in my view, correct) *it is doubtful if it can be extended to explain the larger systematic gaps.* The gaps which separate species: dog/fox, rat/mouse, etc[.] are utterly *trivial* compared

with, say, that between a primitive terrestrial mammal and a whale or a primitive terrestrial reptile and an Ichthyosaur; and even these relatively major discontinuities are trivial alongside those which divide major phyla such as molluscs and arthropods. *Such major discontinuities simply could not, unless we are to believe in miracles, have been crossed in geologically short periods of time* through one or two transitional species occupying restricted geographical areas. Surely, such transitions must have involved long lineages including many collateral lines of hundreds or probably thousands of transitional species . . ..[293]

Along with others,[294] Kerkut* concurs that "[i]t is not clear whether the changes that bring about speciation are of the same nature as those that brought about the development of new phyla."[295] Valentine* and Erwin* agree that punctuated equilibria does not "seem applicable to the origin of new body plans."[296] And Arthur* joins in that punctuated equilibria "cannot explain the origin of evolutionary novelty—only the proliferation of species already possessing some novel characteristic."[297]

(2) No Species-Level Selection of Any Consequence. Another major objection is that no consequential selection occurs at the species level, for several reasons.

First, almost all traits belong to individuals rather than species, as Maynard Smith* points out:

> The graver difficulty, however, is the logical one. *Species do not* chew or gallop or keep warm or bear their young alive: *Individual animals do* these things. Hence, if I am right in thinking that the secondary palate evolved because it enables an animal to chew and breathe at the same time, there is no way in which "species selection" could be responsible for its evolution, except insofar as *species survive if and only if the individuals who compose them survive.*[298]

Thus, natural selection may result from survival differences of individuals, but species selection could not result from nonexistent survival differences of species, as Dawkins* observes:

> But, as I said, nobody wants to say that species selection is an important explanation for the evolution of complex adaptations. Here is why.
>
> Complex adaptations are in most cases not *properties of species*, they are *properties of individuals*. Species don't have eyes and hearts, the individuals in them do. If a species goes extinct because of poor eyesight, this presumably means that every individual in that species died because of poor eyesight. Quality of eyesight is a property of individual animals. What kinds of traits can *species* be said to have? . . . this is pretty unconvincing. *It is hard to think of reasons why species survivability should be decoupled from the sum of the survivabilities of the individual members of the species.*[299]

Grene*[300] and Hoffman* concur.[301] The only trait that is arguably a species-level trait is sex, but "the modern consensus is against the old theory that sexuality is maintained by some kind of group level or species level selection."[302] Otherwise, "no other species-level properties have been identified that would not be reducible to individually advantageous characteristics of individual organisms," Hoffman* states,[303] and logical tests for such properties have not been met.[304]

Second, no persuasive examples of species selection exist, as Hoffman* points out:

> Thus, evidence is still lacking for species selection as a causal process involving differential rates of speciation.
>
> In principle, then, it is possible to understand how the causal process of species selection can operate, but it is difficult to envisage a process of this grandeur that is lacking in unquestionable examples.[305]

He questions the applicability of the alleged examples provided by volutid snails[306] and Hawaiian Drosophila.[307] The tests of punctuated equilibria similarly have failed to support it significantly, according to Schopf* (until lately of University of Chicago):

> Finally, the *two major attempts to test* statistically for the presence of punctuated equilibria (Bookstein et al., 1978; Raup and Crick, 1981) *either argue that it is an uncommon event, or that no conclusion can be drawn*. A view of hierarchy in the biological world is quite reasonable, but the hierarchical view is not dependent on punctuated equilibria, *whose existence is doubted*.[308]

Third, even if there were species-level traits and empirical examples, species selection apparently is not a causal process but only a description:

> As explained at great length by Sober, a necessary condition for this to happen is that species A and B differ in some biological property that is a positive causal factor on differential success of their constituent organisms (if individual organisms are the only "benchmark of selection"), or on differential frequency of character states in, or differential speciosity of, their descendant clades (if species are also a "benchmark of selection"). If no such property can be identified, there may well be accidental species selection of something but not causal species selection *for* anything.
>
> In other words, determination of selection of some units is equivalent to *description, but not explanation*, of phenomena.[309]

Levinton* and Simon* concur that punctuated equilibria lacks a mechanism (other than natural selection and gradualistic processes) for species selection.[310]

Fourth, in any event, the species selection process is "too slow," according to Charlesworth*, Lande*, and Slatkin*.

[I]f the changes during speciation are random for each genetically independent combination of characters, then the time scale for *species selection* seems too slow to explain the rapid origin of complex adaptations which require mutual adjustments of numerous parts that vary in many independent dimensions.[311]

Valentine* and Erwin* pose the dilemma:

The required rapidity of the change implies either a few large steps or many and exceedingly rapid smaller ones. Large steps are tantamount to saltations and raise the problems of fitness barriers; small steps must be numerous and entail the problems discussed under microevolution [including the problem of "extrapolation of microevolutionary rates to explain the origin of new body plans"].[312]

Futuyma* approaches the problem from another direction by agreeing with Dawkins* "that punctuationists are just as gradualist as Darwin."[313]

(3) No Speciation Mechanism or Plausible Explanation of Missing Fossils. Punctuationists define speciation in inconsistent ways,[314] but seem to mean "when a small subpopulation branches off from its parental population and diverges to become a new species" (Gould's* textbook definition).[315] Critics of punctuated equilibria identify problems with its concept of speciation as well as with its concept of species selection.

First, they note that no mechanism is offered for speciation other than the gradualist mechanism, as noted above. In either case, scientists "have absolutely no idea what happens genetically during speciation"; this was the conclusion of "an international conference in Rome in 1981 on the mechanisms of speciation . . . attended by many of the leading botanists, zoologists, paleontologists, geneticists, cytologists, and biologists."[316] Thus, Bush* suggests that "our models of speciation must remain little more than speculation based on the subjective interpretation of equivocal data."[317]

Second, the convenient assumption of punctuated equilibria, that speciation occurs in small peripheral populations and therefore almost never leaves fossils, amounts to the assumption that speciation only occurs where it cannot leave fossil evidence. Stanley* makes a comment about Darwin's* claims that applies directly to punctuationists' claims:

Certainly, also, the claim of a deficient fossil record represented a comfortable refuge for the fragile new theory if the alternative was a contention that extinct species commonly appeared rapidly and thereafter evolved so slowly that it was difficult to detect substantial modification of their form before extinction. *Any claim that natural selection operated with greatest effect exactly where it was least likely to be documented—*

in small, localized, transitory populations—would have seemed to render Darwin's new theory *untestable* against special creation, and perhaps *almost preposterous* as a scientific proposition. . . .[318]

Even if speciation sometimes occurs rapidly in small populations without leaving fossil traces, as punctuated equilibria hypothesizes, it should occur at intermediate rates in intermediate populations and should leave some fossil evidence if it progressed to macroevolutionary steps.[319] As Valentine* and Erwin* note:

> The periods of stasis . . . raise the *probability that the lineage would enter the fossil record,* and we reiterate that we can identify *none of the postulated intermediate forms.* Finally, the large numbers of species that must be generated so as to form a pool from which the successful lineage is selected are *nowhere to be found.* . . .
>
> . . .*The populations must remain small (and undetected) and evolve steadily* and consistently toward the body plan that comprises the basis of a new phylum (or class). *This is asking a lot.* Deleterious mutations would tend to accumulate in small populations to form *genetic loads* that selection might not be able to handle. Stable intermediate adaptive modes cannot be invoked as a regular feature, since we are then again faced with the problem of just where their remains are. . . .[320]

Third, studies do "not support Eldredge and Gould's claim that speciating populations are small," and give reason to question "whether evolution is rapid in small populations," according to Ridley* of Oxford.[321] Instead, speciation logically need not occur in peripheral isolated populations, Levinton* and Simon* argue.[322] Moreover, most change need not occur at speciation as opposed to before and after speciation.[323]

(4) No Macroevolution from Extinction. As for extinction, "extinction obviously cannot produce a new higher taxon" (or new genes), Stanley* concedes, but can only contract or eliminate existing ones.[324] Differential extinction similarly cannot produce positive change (speciation) but can only negatively eliminate species (despeciation, perhaps), as Hoffman* observes:

> On the other hand, examples of *species selection by differential extinction are even more difficult to imagine.* For although a catastrophic extinction by instantaneous habitat destruction or rapid environmental change beyond the capacity of species to adapt is a process that cannot be interpreted as being under the control of natural selection, it clearly belongs to the class of "selection of" rather than "selection for" processes. And while Gilinsky mentions the possibility of "an extinction mechanism that extirpates species as single integrated systems" instead of wiping out all organisms as individuals, he does not exemplify how this vague concept can produce speciose clades.[325]

Overall, it appears that most of the criticisms of the neo-Darwinian synthesis and natural selection apply in slightly different ways to punctuated equilibria and species selection.[326] Moreover, it seems that the general view that punctuated equilibria is merely a sub-model of neo-Darwinism, along with gradualism or the synthetic view, shows that neo-Darwinism has "failed as a rigorous theory" and has "few hard-core theoretical statements," perhaps rendering it nonscientific, as Cracraft* observes:

> For example, Ho and Saunders identify neutral mutation theory and the challenge to Darwinian gradualism by "punctuated equilibrium" as seminal contributions to the erosion of neo-Darwinism, yet *both have been interpreted as entirely consistent with that view* (not only by the defenders of neo-Darwinism itself but also by some of the chief advocates of neutralism and punctuated equilibrium). This points up the *difficulty of chipping away at a theory having few hard-core theoretical statements* and *allowing virtually any observation within its conceptual purview.* If the critics are correct to spurn this state-of-affairs, and I think they are, then they would do well to rid themselves of one of the primary attributes of this new "emerging paradigm of evolution," which according to Ho and Saunders is its "pluralism." To them, evolution is a complex phenomenon, with a variety of processes operating at different hierarchical levels, and thus a pluralistic viewpoint is not only necessary but "leads to a fundamentally different approach" (pp. x, 5). *"Pluralism"—or virtually anything goes—is a predicament for neo-Darwinism* and, as far as I can see, will not serve any competing world-view well. The goal of a general theory of evolution should not be to account for any and all observations; that is too much to demand. Such a theory must describe, in contrast, what generally is the rule. *Neo-Darwinism,* as usually conceived by most contemporary biologists, has *failed as a rigorous theory* because it does not present us with a narrow, precise set of statements about how most of the world is organized. Instead, it tries to tell us how all the world is consistent with a "pluralistic" worldview called neo-Darwinism. *Old-fashioned Darwinism, in contrast to our present mutation of it, would find difficulty reconciling* neutralism and pervasive morphological stasis through time with the notion of directional natural selection relentlessly sculpturing the phenotype along the path of environmental change. A "pluralistic" philosophy toward the structure of scientific theories *inevitably results in accepting virtually any data as being "consistent"* with the theory. . . .[327]

Rather than being consistent with Darwinism, punctuated equilibria may really be post-Darwinian.

g. *Other Factors and Their Significance*

Some evolutionist scientists point to other factors as all or part of the mechanism of macroevolution, such as (1) adaptation, (2) regulatory genes, (3) selfish genes, (4) paedomorphosis and epigenesis, (5) systemic mutations, and (6) nonequilibrium thermodynamics.

(1) Adaptation. Adaptation (a "feature . . . that fits an organism for life in its local environment"[328]) is called "almost tautological" by Sir Karl Popper* because it is another way of saying "selected" by natural selection:

> To say that a species now living is adapted to its environment is, in fact, *almost tautological.* Indeed, we use the terms 'adaptation' and 'selection' in such a way that we can say that, if a species were not adapted it would have been eliminated by natural selection. Similarly, if a species has been eliminated it must have been ill adapted to the conditions.[329]

Brady* sees a similar "danger of tautology":

> If we substitute "adaptive complexity" for "fitness" we are indeed in *danger of tautology*, since the term "adaptive," by presuming some sort of positive adaptation to fit the environment, already means "fit," and thus it has no explanatory value here.[330]

Others agree that identification of "adaptations" is notoriously fallible, such as Simpson*:

> The *fallibility of personal judgments as to the adaptive value* of particular characters, most especially when these occur in animals quite unlike any now living, is notorious.[331]

Grene* refers to "the just-so aspect of adaptationist explanation" that "tells what tales it likes of any and every trait."[332] In effect, no one can accurately say that any trait is nonadaptive unless the organism dies, which is something that all organisms tend to do.

(2) Regulatory Genes. Regulatory genes, which allegedly "switch on and off batteries of protein-producing genes," are an area where "speculation is free, for we know nothing about these regulatory master genes, and that they exist is only an informed guess."[333] Charlesworth*, Lande*, and Slatkin* note the lack of substantial empirical support:

> The suggestion that morphological evolution depends on changes in gene regulation rather than in structural genes . . . *lacks strong empirical support.* . . . In the absence of detailed molecular and developmental studies, any interpretations of interspecific differences involving gene regulation are strictly hypothetical.[334]

Miklos* and John* agree with that conclusion, and add "that no single compelling observation was responsible for this spotlighting of the putatively significant evolutionary role of regulatory genes."[335]

McDonald* points out that the only observed regulatory gene variation in natural populations is in those regulatory genes that cannot produce major changes—a "great Darwinian paradox":

> [T]here has not been any variation observed within natural populations in those regulatory loci set deep within the control network . . . . Those loci that are obviously variable within natural populations do not seem to lie at the basis of many major adaptive changes, while those loci that seemingly do constitute the foundation of many, if not most, major adaptive changes apparently are not variable within natural populations.[336]

(3) Selfish Genes. Selfish genes are postulated as a "self-replicating molecular assembly" with a selective advantage. The concept is "tautologous" and only hypothetical, according to Ambrose*:

> The "selfish gene" is *defined as a self-replicating molecular assembly which in any given situation has a selective advantage over other self-replicating systems.* It will therefore survive. No argument about such a definition is possible. It is of the type criticised by Popper [as tautologous]. The emergence of all living organisms and of surviving populations is then explained in terms of the "selfish gene."[337]

Ho* and Saunders* call the selfish gene concept the "reductio ad absurdum" of "the neo-Darwinian framework" and "a fundamental weakness in the theory."[338]

(4) Paedomorphosis and Epigenesis. Paedomorphosis is changes in the developmental rates of features already present,[339] and epigenesis is a "[d]evelopmental pattern arising by gradual unfolding of the genetic program."[340] In particular, some punctuationists appeal to these processes as major factors in punctuational changes.[341] The primary problem with both paedomorphosis and epigenesis is that, although they correctly describe occasional changes in an individual's development rate and rare monstrosities in individual features, they generally do not involve inheritable traits that are necessary for any evolutionary significance, as Cracraft* intimates:

> Løvtrup calls for an epigenetic theory of evolutionary mechanisms. What this might mean is never made entirely clear. He certainly does not reject the notion that developmental pathways have a component of genetic heritability. Even neo-Darwinians agree that epigenetic influences are important, but *unless those influences are eventually incorporated into pathways of inheritance, what is the link between ontogeny and phylogeny?*[342]

(5) Systemic Mutations. Evolutionary saltation, or evolution by vast "systemic mutations," is based on postulated mutations that "have never appeared."[343] Stebbins* and Ayala* call it disproved:

The specific solution postulated by Goldschmidt, that is, the occurrence of systemic mutations, yielding hopeful monsters, can be excluded in view of current genetic knowledge . . ..[344]

Mayr* says that such "hopeful monsters" are really "hopeless monsters" because they necessarily will be eliminated by natural selection:

> The occurrence of genetic monstrosities by mutation . . . is well substantiated, but they are such evident freaks that these monsters can be designated only as "hopeless". They are so utterly unbalanced that *they would not have the slightest chance of escaping elimination through selection*. Giving a thrush the wings of a falcon does not make it a better flyer. Indeed, having all the other equipment of a thrush, it would probably hardly be able to fly at all. . . . To believe that such a drastic mutation would *produce a viable new type*, capable of occupying a new adaptive zone, *is equivalent to believing in miracles*.[345]

Maynard Smith* concurs that such mutations could not "giv[e] rise in a single step to a new species or higher taxonomic group," and that such a belief involves "postulating a miracle."[346] Nearly all biologists, such as Wright*,[347] Lande*,[348] and Denton*,[349] join in that conclusion.

(6) Nonequilibrium Thermodynamics. Brooks* and Wiley*, and their allies, suggest "that a deeper understanding of evolution lies in understanding the nature of entropy production, or entropy increases, in nonequilibrium systems." Thus, the "expected outcome of historical constraints on the action of the second law in biological systems is self-organization."[350] Most biologists disagree that self-organizing occurs naturally in biological systems, and distinguish organizing events such as growth that are guided by incredibly complex DNA that itself could not be self-organized.[351]

Summary. Thus, *macro*evolution at present lacks any persuasive Darwinian mechanism (although there is no question that *micro*evolution has occurred and is occurring). In fact, each major school of evolutionists denies the sufficiency of the mechanism for macroevolution proposed by the other school, and then confronts additional problems as well. Natural selection, the "fundamental process directing evolutionary change" according to the neo-Darwinian synthesis (Dobzhansky*, Ayala*, Stebbins*, and Valentine*[352]), is tautologous or nonexplanatory (Section 10.2), or nontestable or unfalsifiable (Sections 10.3-10.4), according to scores of biologists and philosophers of science; "is based on not one sure datum" (Grassé[353]); and "inevitably results in accepting virtually any data as being 'consistent' with the theory," and thus "has failed as a

rigorous theory"(Cracraft*[354]). Species selection, which "must largely determine the overall course of evolution" under the punctuated
equilibria model (Stanley*[355]), "doesn't seem to do anything much"
toward macroevolutionary change (Schopf*[356]), does not explain
what traits are species-level traits rather than individual traits on
which selection can act (various authors[357]), has the problem that
"the evidence is still lacking for species selection" (Hoffman* and
Hecht*[358]), and is "not causal" but merely a "description"(id.[359]).
Without a credible mechanism, macroevolution is not compellingly
established, particularly in view of the noncompelling evidence that
macroevolution has occurred at all. *Cadit quaestio?*

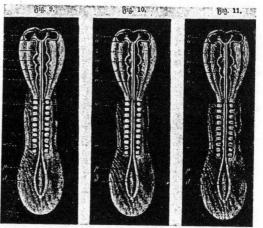

*Figure 3.4
The embryological
argument of Ernst
Haeckel*: examples of
his "faked" drawings
in a figure supposedly
showing similarities of
dog, chicken, and tur-
tle embryos for which
actually "Haeckel used
the same printing
stock" (Rager*)*

3.4 The Postulated Evidence for Macroevolution and Darwinism: Darwinian Arguments and the Disintegrating Neo-Darwinian Synthesis

The major arguments for macroevolution are described by Stansfield* as follows:

> Two of the major lines of evidence supporting the evolutionary theory,
> namely *paleontology* and *biogeography*, were presented in the last chap-
> ter. This chapter presents further supporting evidence drawn from the
> disciplines of *taxonomy, comparative embryology, comparative anat-
> omy, comparative biochemistry*, and *physiology*.[360]

Those "evidences for evolution" are similarly summarized by
Good*[361] and Gould*.[362] The arguments for Darwinian evolution are
discussed as follows: (a) the paleontology argument, (b) the phylog-

eny argument, (c) the classification (taxonomy) argument, (d) the comparative anatomy and physiology argument, (e) the comparative embryology argument, (f) the comparative biochemistry argument, (g) the population genetics argument, and (h) the artificial selection argument.

These postulated evidences for macroevolution are viewed with great cynicism by Grassé:

> Through use and abuse of hidden postulates, of *bold, often ill-founded extrapolations*, a *pseudoscience* has been created. It is taking root in the very heart of biology and is *leading astray* many biochemists and biologists, who sincerely believe that the accuracy of fundamental concepts has been demonstrated, which is not the case.[363]

The same skepticism is held by Kerkut* and many other noncreationist scientists:

> The attempt to explain all living forms in terms of an *evolution from a unique source*, though a brave and valid attempt, is one that is premature and *not satisfactorily supported* by present-day evidence.[364]

In fact, classification, comparative anatomy, comparative embryology, population genetics, and artificial selection data can "be accounted for on some different hypothesis" besides evolution, although paleontology cannot, Good* concludes.[365]

a. Paleontology Argument and Difficulties

The paleontology argument for macroevolution is based on the fossil record; paleontology is "the study of fossils."[366] "Direct study of macroevolutionary patterns is only possible in the fossil record,"[367] Valentine* notes, and this fossil record "forms our most direct evidence . . . of the course of biological evolution," Dobzhansky* *et al.* conclude.[368] Yet the fossil record is characterized by systematic abrupt appearances of groups of organisms and systematic gaps between groups, rather than by a generally progressive emergence of one group from another (as discussed earlier[369]).

Consequently, even though the fossil record is the "most direct evidence" of macroevolution, Ridley* (a biologist at Oxford) states that "no real evolutionist, whether gradualist or punctuationist, uses the fossil record as evidence in favour of the theory of evolution as opposed to special creation."[370] Thus far, according to Hoffman* (a geologist formerly at University of Tübingen), paleontology has added "nothing to evolutionary biology":

> All the recent paleobiological debates have, in my opinion, contributed much to the conceptualization of paleobiological research itself, but nothing to evolutionary biology. This is not to say that paleobiologists

cannot contribute to evolutionary biology. I contend only that they have not done so. . . .[371]

Patterson* concludes that the concept that fossils are the best evidence for evolution is a "myth":

> I conclude that *instances of fossils overturning theories of relationship* based on Recent organisms are *very rare*, and *may be nonexistent*. It follows that the *widespread belief that fossils are the only or best means of determining evolutionary relationships is a myth*. Tracing how this myth came to be an article of faith among biologists [an "Idol of the Academy"] should be an interesting study in the sociology of science; it seems to have followed, as an unquestioned corollary, from acceptance of evolution.[372]

(1) Abrupt Appearances and Gaps. The overwhelming problem that the fossil record poses for macroevolution thus is that the record is characterized by abrupt appearances and systematic gaps, as paleontologist Gould* acknowledges:

> Increasing diversity and multiple transitions seem to reflect a determined and inexorable progression toward higher things. But the *paleontological record supports no such interpretation*. There has been *no steady progress* in the higher development of organic design. We have had, instead, vast stretches of *little or no change* and one evolutionary *burst* that created the entire system.[373]

> *New species* almost always *appeared suddenly* in the fossil record with *no intermediate links* to ancestors in older rocks of the same region.[374]

The systematic gaps are actually "the *trade secret* of paleontology":

> The *extreme rarity of transitional forms* in the fossil record persists as the *trade secret of paleontology*. The evolutionary trees that adorn our textbooks have *data only at the tips* and nodes of their branches; the rest is inference, however reasonable, not the evidence of fossils.[375]

That trade secret is being let out by more and more scientists, such as Grassé[376] and Boyden*[377] for the origin of phyla, George*[378] and Simpson*[379] for the origin of genera and families, and many others quoted in Sections 2.1 and 2.2.

The alleged evolutionary trees are not just mostly "inference" rather than "data," but are "highly conjectural" and either do not support or actually "deny" macroevolution.[380] The alleged transitional forms are such that now "we have even fewer examples of evolutionary transition than we had in Darwin's time,"[381] and "there is not one such fossil for which one could make a watertight case,"[382] according to geologist Raup* and paleontologist Patterson*. These few alleged transitional forms are not statistically significant enough to lend support to macroevolution or Darwinian mechanisms, as biologist Denton* points out:

Even if a number of species were known to biology which were indeed perfectly intermediate, possessing organ systems that were unarguably transitional in the sense required by evolution, this *would certainly not be sufficient to validate the evolutionary model* of nature. To refute typology and securely validate evolutionary claims *would necessitate hundreds or even thousands of different species, all unambiguously intermediate* in terms of their overall biology and the physiology and anatomy of all their organ systems.[383]

That statistical insignificance is evident in view of the 250,000 fossil species that have been catalogued,[384] which represent thousands of orders, families, and genera; and the 1,071,500 animal species and 368,715 plant species alive today.[385] Moreover, many of the unbridged gaps are such that one cannot even "invent a reasonable sequence of intermediate forms," Gould* concedes.[386] The few alleged transitional fossils are discussed later.[387]

These abrupt appearances and systematic gaps pose critical if not fatal problems for macroevolution. "[I]t *should* be possible to find some 'connecting links'," because "higher categories become distinct entities through extinction of intermediate related groups."[388] Darwin* saw the "fatal" significance of abrupt appearances:

On the *sudden appearance* of whole groups of Allied Species. . . . If numerous species, belonging to the same genera or families, have really started into life all at once, the fact would be *fatal* to the theory of descent with slow modification through natural selection.[389]

Darwin* also recognized the fatal significance of the problem posed by systematic gaps:

Why then is not every geological formation and every stratum full of such *intermediate links*? Geology assuredly does not reveal any such finely graduated organic chain; and this, perhaps, is the *most obvious and gravest objection which can be urged against my theory.* The explanation lies, as I believe, in the extreme imperfection of the geological record.[390]

T. H. Huxley*, probably his chief advocate, conceded that "if it could be shown that this fact had always existed, the fact would be fatal to the doctrine of evolution."[391] Biological macroevolutionists have proposed two major solutions.

(2) Adequacy of the Fossil Record. One defense raised by Darwin* and many macroevolutionists is an "extreme imperfection of the geological record."[392] In fact, Darwin* staked his case on imperfection being an accurate portrayal of the record: "He who rejects these views on the nature of the geological record, will rightly reject my whole theory."[393]

However, now that 200 million fossil specimens have been catalogued of over 250,000 fossil species,[394] the fossil record cannot really be called inadequate, as paleontologist Stanley* argues:

> In part, the role of paleontology in evolutionary research has been defined narrowly because of a false belief, tracing back to Darwin and his early followers, that the fossil record is woefully incomplete. Actually, the record is of *sufficiently high quality* to allow us to undertake certain kinds of analysis meaningfully at the level of the species.[395]

The fossil "data for genera and families are numerous enough to allow for meaningful analysis," Raup* states,[396] and for mammals the "geological history is comparatively well documented."[397] The fossil record, particularly for marine life, is quite good, Hsü adds:

> We now know that Darwin and Lyell were *wrong* in their insistence on the imperfection of the geologic record. The unconformity between the Late Cretaceous and the early Tertiary cannot possibly span 100 m.y. The record of marine life is, in terms of geologic chronology, continuous in the deep sea. The Cretaceous/Tertiary boundary falls within magnetostratigraphic Chron C29R, which was less than 0.5 m.y. in duration (Kent, 1977). The boundary is recorded by *precision stratigraphy*, which has a *resolution power to recognize events thousands, if not hundreds, of years in duration* . . . .[397A]

The "beating [of] the drums and chanting [of] the imperfection of the geologic record" simply "is not relevant. The key question is, Does the imperfection tell lies?" Hsü finds that it does not.[397B] The only sense in which the fossil record is imperfect may be that it does not contain the numerous "intermediate links" expected by Darwin*:

> As an aside, one is led to ask *to what degree the "imperfect" geological record was viewed as such by Darwin simply because there were no observed transitional links.* There can be no doubt that Darwin had empirical reason to believe in an imperfect record, but was his emphasis based partly on his biological expectations? In any case, there is no question that Darwin expected those finely graded transitions. He firmly believed that transitions must have existed and struggled to rationalize their absence . . . .
>
> Darwin's expectations and theorizations were clearly at variance with his observations of nature. . . .[398]

(3) Insufficiency of Assumed "Ancestral Groups." Another defensive approach taken by many macroevolutionists is to identify purported common "ancestral groups," a fall-back position resulting from the absence of actual fossils of common ancestors or transitional forms. However, postulations about "such groups are inconsistent with evolutionary theory," according to Patterson*.[399] There are several problems.

First, talk about ancestral groups is highly conjectural,[400] and may be imagining a relationship between what may be totally unrelated groups, as Rosen* *et al.* note:

> The search for fossils has produced *superficially acceptable sequences,* as it was bound to, for *few transformations, however fantastic, are forbidden by the Darwinian* or Neo-Darwinian picture of the evolutionary process. Yet the sequences consist of nothing more than abstractions from paraphyletic groups such as rhipidistians, osteolepiforms, and labyrinthodonts.[401]

Those conjectures are no different from the pre-Darwinian conjectures about archetypes, Brady* adds:

> Patterson (1982) reviews the Owen version of an archetype and notes that the real problem is the notion of general homology, by which "an idealization" is homologized with actual features through "abstract transformations." He then argues that the same strategy can be found in the contemporary practice of homologizing dissimilar organs on the basis of the homology of each with the primitive version of the organ in a hypothesized progenitor. Due to the use of such a strategy in contemporary works, Patterson concludes that *"archetypes are by no means extinct," but live on in the form of speculative progenitors.* These modern versions are Darwinian, of course, but however far they appear to be from Owen's idealistic schema, they result in the *same difficulties.*[402]

Such "speculations" are not persuasive even if the postulated sequence is somewhat similar, Denton* points out:

> It is possible to allude to a number of species and groups such as *Archeopteryx,* or the rhipidistian fish, which appear to be to some extent intermediate. But even if such were intermediate to some degree, there is no evidence that they are any more intermediate than groups such as the living lungfish or monotremes which, as we have seen, are not only tremendously isolated from their nearest cousins, but which have individual organ systems that are not strictly transitional at all. As evidence for the existence of natural links between the great divisions of nature, *they are only convincing to someone already convinced of the reality of organic evolution.*[403]

For example, some rocks resemble each other and can be lined up in an evolutionary sequence, but that does not prove that one evolved into the others.[404] "Fossils may tell us many things, but one thing they can never disclose is whether they were ancestors of anything else," as Patterson*,[405] Oldroyd*,[406] and Good*[407] emphasize.

Second, the concept of "the hypothetical ancestor . . . is equally without empirical foundation," and is untestable and thus "vacuous," which is the reason why it is speculative, according to Brady*:

A similar problem arises with regard to the hypothetical ancestor, for *this invention is equally without empirical foundation*, and occupies a space in our reflections that should be reserved for actual observation. If we can invent one ancestral form, *we can invent many*, and lacking the evidence for which they substitute, there is no way to determine which form, if any, is correct.

We must remember, while reviewing these problems, that the mediating form was hypothesized because the data was inconclusive without it. It becomes, therefore, an interpretive tool by which the data can be given definition. The known forms are now interpreted by the hypothesized ancestor (or intermediate), and what the existent organisms do or do not possess will now depend upon what the hypothesized ancestor (or intermediate) says they possess. *If the empirical forms must submit to interpretation by the hypothesis, they cannot be used to test that hypothesis.* For these reasons Patterson calls general homology *"vacuous,"* and I must concur. *Speculative* construction of general forms and the paths of transformation that they suggest may hold a certain fascination for the imagination, but the practice is *merely guesswork* and can tell us nothing about the actual paths of transformation. 'General homology' is not actual homology.[408]

Third, statistically there should be a large number of actual fossils of common ancestors or intermediate forms, given the quarter billion catalogued fossils of a quarter million fossil species, as discussed above. Darwin* and Huxley* conceded that that must be the case if macroevolution were true, and that should be the case even if macroevolution occurs in punctuated bursts (Section 3.3(f)(3)).

Fourth, even if the search for actual ancestors or intermediates is abandoned for a search for roughly ancestral groups, there is the problem that no even rough ancestral groups exist for most major categories. There are no such ancestral groups for any of the twenty-five phyla of the animal kingdom, because there are "no extinct fossil groups known that are the common ancestors of two or more living phyla" and there are absences of intermediate forms between "all" twenty-five phyla, according to Ayala* and Valentine*.[409] The same is true for many other higher categories, and for every taxon where an abrupt appearance occurs.[410] Transformed cladists, such as Patterson*, criticize "the textbook stories [that] are replete with phantoms—extinct, uncharacterizable groups giving rise one to another."[411] It is not enough for a small handful of rough ancestral groups to be found, as Denton* stresses:

> To demonstrate that the great divisions of nature were really bridged by transitional forms in the past, *it is not sufficient to find in the fossil*

record one or two types of organisms of doubtful affinity which might be
placed on skeletal grounds in a relatively intermediate position between
other groups....[412]

A number of rejoinders by defenders of the "ancestral group"
approach are addressed by Patterson*:

> Evolutionary paleontologists have offered three responses to criti-
> cisms of ancestral groups. First, that grouping by phenetic similarity (as
> in forming paraphyletic groups) reflects genotypic similarity, and is
> therefore a valid reflection of evolutionary relationships. This argument
> has been refuted above. Second, that ancestral groups are approxima-
> tions, "with the admission that evidence available at present is insuffi-
> cient to make a more specific statement"; the rank assigned to such
> groups "symbolizes the degree of confidence which one has in a hypothe-
> sis about phylogeny." This response seems to reflect only the inductivist
> view so long prevalent among paleontologists—"we need more fossils
> before we shall know the answer." Third, paraphyletic groups are "adap-
> tively unified." While this may be true of some such groups (as some may
> be "phenetically" unified), it cannot serve as a general justification. No
> one can argue that Invertebrata (a paraphyletic group) are adaptively
> unified.[413]

For ancestral groups as for adaptations, "a plausible story is not
necessarily a true one."[414]

(4) Nonprobativeness of the Geological Column. Many macroevolutionists suggest that, even if the specific fossil record for particular organisms does not compel or support belief in biological macroevolution or Darwinism, the general fossil sequence for all organisms
does prove macroevolution and a Darwinian mechanism. Whatever
their interpretation of the geological column, however, modern discontinuitist scientists disagree on powerful historical grounds that
the fossil sequence requires either macroevolution or Darwinism.

Those historical grounds, as many evolutionists concede such as
Glenister* and Witzke*, are that "[b]oth the stratigraphic column
and our general understanding were thus developed empirically and
without any reference to evolutionary assumption," by scientists
who nearly all found the geological record consistent with the theory of creation and nonsupportive of the theory of evolution:

> With the exception of the Ordovician (established later to resolve a
> dispute over the boundary between Cambrian and Silurian), *all intervals*
> *were proposed prior to publication of Darwin's Origin of Species in 1859.*
> The Tertiary preceded the *Origin* by a full century. Components of the
> time scale were established on the basis of objective data, primarily
> superposition (observed stratigraphic succession) and fossil content. The

"wonderful order and regularity with which nature has disposed of these singular productions (fossils) and assigned to each its class and peculiar stratum" were *recognized as early as 1796*

DATES WHEN GEOLOGICAL TIME SCALES
WERE FIRST PROPOSED

Period	Date	Era	Date
Quaternary	1829		
Tertiary	1759	Cenozoic	1841
Cretaceous	1822		
Jurassic	1795	Mesozoic	1841
Triassic	1834		
Permian	1841		
Carboniferous	1822		
Devonian	1837		
Silurian	1835	Paleozoic	1838
Ordovician	1879		
Cambrian	1835		

by William Smith, the father of stratigraphy. At about the same time, the noted French biologists Georges Cuvier and Alexandre Brongniart arrived independently at comparable conclusions. Cuvier noted that "these fossils are generally the same in corresponding beds, and present tolerably marked differences of species from one group of beds to another. It is a method of recognition which up to the present time has never deceived us."

Both the stratigraphic column and our general understanding of fossil successions were thus developed empirically and without any reference to evolutionary assumption. In fact, *Cuvier* was a leading catastrophist who *emphatically denied that evolution had occurred.* The sequence of geologic periods was reasonably well established in 1841. It was not until several decades later that scientists rather suddenly began to recognize the evolutionary thread connecting successive assemblages of fossils.[415] Sermonti* and Sermonti* conclude that the "successive emergence is more folklore than the actual outcome of paleontological data," for the "emergence of Agnates—Fish—Amphibia—Reptiles—Mammals and Birds . . .."[415A]

Thus, the paleontology argument for biological macroevolution and Darwinism is weak if not subversive, in the view of many Darwinians as well as nonevolutionist scientists. That is why Ridley* of Oxford stated that "no real evolutionist, whether gradualist or punctuationist, uses the fossil record as evidence in favour of the theory of evolution as opposed to special creation."[416]

b. Phylogeny Argument and Difficulties

The phylogeny argument for macroevolution is based on "phylogenetic trees" of assumed evolutionary descent.[417] (A phylogeny is a "sequence of ancestor-descendant forms."[418]) This phylogeny field of systematics "is the very cornerstone of evolutionary analysis."[420] Yet it is a weak cornerstone, according to a number of evolutionist as well as nonevolutionist biologists.

One problem with the phylogeny argument is that reconstruction of phylogenies is *impossible* in the professional opinion of many evolutionists such as Hull*, a philosopher of science at Northwestern University:

> The chief question with respect to phylogenetic reconstruction has always been its *feasibility*. Throughout the history of "Systematic Zoology," a *series of objections* have been raised to it, starting with Blackwelder, Bigelow, Boyden, and Borgmeier, continuing with the pheneticists, and culminating with at least some cladists.[420]

For example, the cladist objection to phylogenies begins with the point that "common ancestral species are necessarily hypothetical, and . . . will forever remain unknown and unknowable in a directly empirical sense," Nelson* states.[421] Consequently, rough ancestral groups must be used instead, and they are "flawed artefacts" with questionable assumptions, Patterson* contends:

> Because of all these problems, it is *rare to find palaeontologists offering ancestral species*, or doing so with any conviction. Instead, they usually *propose "ancestral groups"*, as approximations to the truth, with the claim that the true ancestor, if found, would fall within the group. . . .
> Yet these *flawed artefacts* play a *central role in phylogenies*—accounts of the evolutionary descent of lineages. This raises yet another problem, for *groups cannot evolve*—species are the largest units capable of change. Thus *cladistics calls into question much of conventional evolutionary history*.[422]

The rejection of phylogenies—and of macroevolution itself—by many pheneticists and cladists is discussed in the next subsection.[423]

Another serious difficulty, related to the first, is that phylogenies are almost *totally speculative*. Bonner* says that those in textbooks "are, as a rule, a festering mass of unsupported assertions."[424] Ghiselin* concludes that many "read like imaginative literature" and "fill gaps in the data with speculations."[425] Boyden* observes that "phylogenies grew up like weeds" for "even organisms with no fossils available,"[426] and Good* notes that such "studies in plant evolution are generally no more than the raw materials of phylogenetic speculation."[427] Charig* calls some "meaningless waffle,"[428]

Turrill* calls most "extremely doubtful approximations,"[429] and Sokal* calls many "utter rubbish."[430] The gross subjectivity of postulated phylogenies is evident in the treatment of the fossil record as inadequate when the fossils do not fit the phylogenetic hypotheses, but as adequate when the fossils can be interpreted to support the phylogenetic hypotheses:

> But *when a new fossil is found and is inconsistent* with the phylogeny (like *Ichthyostega*), the stratopheneticist's answer is that this *test has shown that the fossil record was insufficiently dense* and continuous for the method to work. And *when a new fossil is consistent* with the phylogeny, the record *was sufficiently dense and continuous*. Plainly, the method is hard to fault, for the fossil record, rather than the phylogeny, is under test (cf. Nelson, 1978). . . .[431]

Forey* concurs in that objection,[432] and Kitts* provides part of the reason in noting that "paleontological phylogeny construction has not been provided with a solid theoretical foundation."[433]

A further problem, closely related to the preceding ones, is that phylogenies are used to support macroevolution through *circular reasoning*, as Thomson* notes:

> any reasonably graded series of forms can be thought to have legitimacy. In fact, there is *circularity* in the approach that first assumes some sort of evolutionary relatedness and then assembles a pattern of relations from which to argue that relatedness must be true. This interplay of data and interpretation is the *Achilles' heel* of the second meaning of evolution.[434]

Forey*,[435] Cartmill*, [436] and Kitts*[437] reaffirm the presence of circular reasoning.

A crowning problem is that the quest for phylogenies has *"failed"* utterly, according to Saiff* and Macbeth*:

> A. *The Commitment in Theory.* Darwinian theory asserts that physical descent with modification has been universal, which means that every modern species is the latest link in a phylogeny. There must therefore have been hundreds of thousands of phylogenies, and it was Darwin's expectation that these would be found. His followers, sharing his expectation, felt a duty to seek and find the phylogenies.
>
> . . ..
>
> B. *Another Miserable Failure.* The expectations were vain. The zeal came to naught. In the 125 years since the *Origin* was published, nothing has been accomplished. *No phylogenies have been established* and the pursuit of them has fallen into disrepute. The following authorities attest to this.[438]

Mayr* finds the "futile attempts" to be "depressing":

> The *futile attempts* to establish the relationship of the major phyla of animals induced at least one competent zoologist at the turn of the century to deny common descent. Fleischmann (1901) called the theory a

beautiful myth not substantiated by any factual foundation. Kerkut, fifty years later, does not draw such an extreme conclusion but he is almost equally pessimistic about ever achieving an understanding of the relationship of the higher animal taxa. Honesty compels us to admit that *our ignorance concerning these relationships is still great, not to say overwhelming*. This is a depressing state of affairs considering that more than one hundred years have passed since the great post-*Origin* period of phylogeny construction. The morphological and embryological clues are simply not sufficient for the task.[439]

Some will question whether phylogeny construction has failed in light of the horse phylogeny or other phylogenies. Raup* responds that the number of arguably correct phylogenies is shrinking:

> The record of evolution is still surprisingly jerky and, *ironically, we have even fewer examples of evolutionary transition than we had in Darwin's time*. By this I mean that some of the classic cases of [D]arwinian change in the fossil record, such as the evolution of the *horse* in North America, have had to be *discarded or modified* as a result of more detailed information—what appeared to be a nice simple progression when relatively few data were available now appears to be much more complex and much less gradualistic.[440]

Denton* agrees that the "handful of cases" are weak, and in fact merely "may be exceptions":

> Considering that the total number of known fossil species is nearly one hundred thousand, the fact that the only relatively convincing morphological sequences are a *handful of cases like the horse*, which do not involve a great deal of change, and which in many cases like the elephant may not even represent phylogenetic sequences at all, serves to emphasize the *remarkable lack of any direct evidence* for major evolutionary transformations in the fossil record.
>
> . . ..
>
> It is possible to view such series in a very different light and read the fossil evidence directly as it stands; and infer that what is exceptional about such sequences is not their preservation but rather the fact that they occurred. *They may be exceptions which prove a very different rule*: that in general, *nature cannot be arranged in terms of sequences* and that where sequence does exist it is exceptional or relatively trivial.[441]

The various specific phylogenies are discussed in Section 3.5.

Thus, the phylogeny argument for biological macroevolution is viewed by many evolutionist scientists as impossible (according to cladists and others), totally speculative (compared to everything from "weeds" (Boyden*) to "rubbish" (Sokal*)), "circular" (Thomson* and others), and a "failure" (Saiff* and others). In this important area, the biological theories of macroevolution and Darwinism are not compellingly established.

c. Classification Argument and Difficulties

The classification argument for macroevolution is based on the hierarchical structure in nature; classification is "the theory and practice of naming, describing, and classifying organisms."[442] There are "three prevailing systems of classification, known as phenetic, cladistic, and evolutionary."[443]

The most basic problem with the classification argument is that half of one school (transformed cladists)[444] and much of another school (pheneticists)[445] deny that classification supports or is even relevant to evolution. "In 'transformed cladistics', . . . evolution is deliberately ignored, being considered unproven and possibly unprovable," as one of its critics, Charig*, protests.[446] Patterson* agrees:

> As I understand it, cladistics is *theoretically neutral* so far as evolution is concerned. *It has nothing to say about evolution.* You don't even need to know about evolution, or *believe in it*, to do cladistic analysis.[447]

He suggests that the branching diagrams produced by cladists "can be seen not as evolutionary trees" and as not supporting "common ancestry."[448]

Critics of transformed cladistics lambast its "non-evolutionary" or anti-evolutionary thinking, such as Oldroyd*:

> Indeed, as is well known, *much modern taxonomy has abandoned its Darwinian, historicist or genealogical approach*, and has adopted a positivistic methodology based simply on an examination of observable morphological similarities and differences, and excluding attempted reconstructions of genealogies. This so-called cladistics is *fundamentally a nonevolutionary classification.* As such, it generates something *very like the nineteenth-century typologies* of authors such as Henri Milne-Edwards. Cladistics, which is, of course, an *anathema to neo-Darwinians*, is favoured by those who prefer not to transcend the observable data in their theorizing to "speculate" about genealogical relationships.[449]

Ball* also laments that transformed cladistics operates "in a non-evolutionary domain."[450] Beatty* observes that, "[a]pparently in response to the perceived crisis in evolutionary biology, cladists have taken more or less extreme measures to sever their ties from that discipline,"[451] and are not merely "evolutionarily neutral" but "at odds with evolutionary thinking."[452] Ridley* states that transformed cladists "are asserting that they can do cladism without evolution, and what they can do, they will."[453] Benton* observes that they classify "without any prior assumptions that evolution has taken place."[454]

Proponents of transformed cladistics agree that "cladistics calls into question much of conventional evolutionary history."[455] "Gareth Nelson and Norman Platnick lodge a frontal assault on Darwinism in systematics by claiming it to be falsified," Cracraft* notes,[456] and they indeed do so by arguing that evolutionary phylogenies should be replaced with classifications that "include no ancestral taxa":

> If phylogenies of one sort . . . are to pass away, is the notion of phylogeny doomed also? We judge not, for *there is an alternative notion, here simply termed classification . . .*. Notions of this kind can be looked upon as phylogenies—as historical statements of ancestry and descent. But they are different in character. *They include no ancestral taxa. They deny the postulates of Darwinian systematics*: that ancestral taxa have an objective identity independent of their descendants; that ancestral taxa can be discovered and identified as such; that ancestral taxa are under the constraints of empirical investigation.[457]

The "phenetic schools refrain from taking any evidence from descent into account," Mayr* notes.[458] Simpson* concluded that phenetics brought "retrogression in taxonomic principle . . . a conscious revival of pre-evolutionary, 18th century, principles."[459] Thus, in the phenetics school, "some more radical numerical taxonomists have abandoned the goal of building a taxonomy that reflects evolutionary descent."[460] In the view of these specialists, the groupings in nature do not support Darwinian macroevolution but instead are at best irrelevant if not contrary to it.

A related problem is that essentially the same classification system was historically founded and developed by creationist scientists (Linnaeus and others), and was defended as more consistent with the theory of creation than with the theory of evolution by many scientists at the time of Darwin* (Agassiz, Sedgwick, and others), as Stansfield*,[461] Dobzhansky*,[462] and Patterson*[463] note. Darwin* himself "took these relations to be established by previous biology," and "was clearly of the opinion that they were independent of that theory."[464]

In fact, this pre-Darwinian classification system "has undergone surprisingly little change in the times following it, and such changes as have been made have depended only to a trifling extent on . . . phylogenetic relationships" proposed by macroevolution, Mayr* concedes:

> The fact is that the classification of organisms that existed before the advent of evolutionary theories has undergone *surprisingly little change* in the times following it, and such changes as have been made have depended only to a trifling extent on the elucidation of the actual phy-

logenetic relationship through paleontological evidence. The phylogenetic interpretation has been simply superimposed on the existing classification; *a rejection of the former fails to do any violence to the latter.* The
subdivisions of the animal and plant *kingdoms established by Linnaeus
are, with few exceptions, retained in the modern classification,* and this
despite the enormous number of new forms discovered since then. The
new forms were either included in the Linnaean groups, or new groups
have been created to accommodate them. There has been no necessity for
a basic change in the classification.[465]

Simpson* acknowledges that, with the appearance of Darwin*,
"classification continued to develop with no immediate evidence of
revolution in principles."[466] Blackwelder* agrees that, since that
time, "[e]volutionary taxonomy never has been really different from
classical taxonomy, in spite of all the fireworks."[467] Thus, classification does not really provide an argument in favor of macroevolution
or Darwinism.

Another weakness, of the evolutionary school of classification, is
that the use of classification to support macroevolution involves
circular reasoning because "[c]lassifications are designed primarily, we are so often told, to 'state,' or 'reflect,' or 'be consistent with,'
evolutionary and genetic relationships," Kitts* points out.[468] Further,
a "classification based on the idea of phylogenetic descent must at
best remain highly speculative, for, save in a few fossil lineages, we
do not and cannot know the actual course of events in the evolution
of a group," as Huxley* noted.[469] Finally, the "two sources of information are often contradictory" that are used by the evolutionary
school of classification, according to Luria*, Gould*, and Singer*.[470]

A final difficulty of the classification argument, the one point on
which all schools of classification generally would agree, is that it
has not yielded much information about evolutionary relationships.
Mayr* summarizes the "uncertainty" and "ignorance":

> It comes as rather a *surprise to most nontaxonomists how uncertain our
> understanding of degrees of relationship* among organisms still is today.
> For instance, it is still unknown for most orders of birds which other
> order is a given order's nearest relative. The same is true for many
> mammalian families and genera, for instance the Lagomorpha, Tubuli-
> dentata, Xenarthra, and *Tupaia.*
>
> . . ..
> . . .Honesty compels us to admit that *our ignorance concerning these
> relationships is still great,* not to say overwhelming.[471]

Part of that uncertainty results from the "artificial" and rather
arbitrary nature of the higher categories of classification themselves, which Stansfield* describes:

[H]igher categories (genera, families, orders, classes, phyla, and even kingdoms), though they do represent greater levels of evolutionary divergence, are still artificial groupings made by humans for convenience in taxonomic work. They are not natural groups the way that species are.[472] Raup* and Stanley* agree that higher categories have "no comparable objective basis" or division points.[473] Richards* suggests a view that "nearly all biologists must share, the species is the only taxonomic category that has at least in more favorable examples a completely objective basis. Higher categories are all more or less a matter of opinion."[474] Hence, there is no objective meaning of or agreement on what classifications mean or what the categories are.

Thus, the classification argument for biological macroevolution and Darwinism actually provides no support, because classification is not scientifically or historically supportive of macroevolution, according to the transformed cladistic school and part of the phenetic school of classification. Specifically, classification "has nothing to say about evolution," according to proponents of transformed cladistics such as Patterson*,[475] which "is fundamentally a non-evolutionary classification," according to critics such as Oldroyd*.[476] The evolutionary school of classification only supports macroevolution through circular reasoning, and is speculative, according to Kitts* and Huxley*.[477] Here, the biological theories of macroevolution and Darwinism do not have a compelling status, according to many of their scientific proponents.

d. Comparative Anatomy and Physiology Argument and Difficulties

The comparative anatomy argument for macroevolution, which focuses on comparing anatomical structure,[478] is based on the similarity of structure of various organisms. Most evolutionists interpret some, but not all, similar structure to show common ancestry. The comparative anatomy evidence that is anomalous, in the sense of indicating the unrelatedness or distinct ancestry of organisms, has been discussed in Section 2.7(b). The comparative anatomy and physiology argument is constructed on a problematic foundation that can be viewed causally and historically.

That basic problem is that similar anatomy or physiology does not necessarily indicate common ancestry and evolutionary descent. First, nearly all evolutionist scientists acknowledge that "there exists no a priori relation between the appearance of two structures and their relatedness," as Schwabe* and Warr* state,[479] along with Cracraft*,[480] Denton*,[481] and Patterson*.[482] Eleven prominent scientists recently published their complaint about homology that "[i]ts rampant use in the loose sense is clogging the literature on protein and nucleic acid sequence comparisons with muddy writing and, in some cases, muddy thinking":

> Not all similarity connotes homology but that can be easily overlooked if similarities are called homologies. Thus in this third case, we can deceive ourselves into thinking we have proved something substantial (evolutionary homology) when, in actuality, we have merely established a simple fact (a similarity, mislabeled as homology). Homology among similar structures is a hypothesis that may be correct or mistaken....[482A]

Boyden* adds that

> such general resemblances in protoplasmic systems as we find in *all* living organisms *do not necessarily mean genetic relationship.* Rather, such *resemblances may be fundamentally convergent,* and represent only the minimum requirements or "conditions of existence" which all living systems must possess.[483]

Yet Thomas Hunt Morgan*, the great zoologist at Columbia, acknowledged the fatal consequences if homology did not necessarily indicate ancestry:

> If, then, it can be established beyond dispute that similarity or even identity of the same character in different species is *not always* to be interpreted to mean that both have arisen from a *common ancestor,* the *whole argument from comparative anatomy seems to tumble in ruins.*[484]

There are two types of similarities that indisputably do not mean common ancestry: convergences and parallelisms, and other similar structures with nonhomologous genes.

Second, the convergences and parallelisms to which Boyden* referred (anatomical or physiological similarities that do not reflect common ancestry) are strong arguments that similar anatomies or physiologies "do not imply any close biological relationship," as Denton* notes:

> Then there is the problem of convergence. *Nature abounds in examples of convergence.* . . .. In all the above cases the similarities, although very striking, *do not imply any close biological relationship.*[485]

Numerous acknowledgments were cited in Section 2.7(b) of "massive convergence"—"the bugbear of the taxonomist"—as Dawkins* describes it.[486] So widespread are convergences and parallelisms that, Ross* concludes, "[m]ore often than not functional comparisons turned up phylogenetic paradoxes instead of parallels."[487]

In fact, third, the assumption that similar anatomy indicates common ancestry is generally wrong, because the genes that produce the similar anatomical structures are generally not sufficiently similar (homologous), as de Beer*, a former embryologist at University College of London and former director of the British Museum of Natural History, points out:

> It is now clear that the pride with which it was assumed that the inheritance of homologous structures from a common ancestor explained homology was misplaced; for such inheritance cannot be ascribed to identity of genes. *The attempt to find 'homologous' genes, except in closely related species, has been given up as hopeless. . . .*
>
> It is useless to speculate on any explanation in the absence of facts. . . .[488]

Thus Zuckerman*, an eminent anatomist, agreed that "relationships which are inferred on the basis of comparative anatomy may not necessarily correspond to true genetic relationships," and "are in the final analysis speculations."[489] For similar reasons, transformed cladists generally reject the alleged relation between similar anatomy and common ancestry, even though they classify organisms by some similar anatomical features (synapomorphies), because such cladists argue that similar features "need have no evolutionary implications."[490]

Furthermore, an equally basic difficulty is that this alleged relation to common ancestry is contradicted by the history of comparative anatomy and physiology. Linnaeus, "the father of systematic biology" and a creationist scientist, established the classification system by grouping organisms that "resemble one another in body structure" (anatomy), but "did not interpret this propinquity as a consequence of common descent," Dobzhansky* observed.[491] The anti-Darwinian scientist Owen* then developed the basis of comparative anatomy, while disagreeing that it supports evolution:

> The central concept of comparative anatomy is *homology*, a term introduced by Sir Richard Owen, the first director of the British Museum (Natural History), London, and a powerful antievolutionist.[492]

Therefore, the comparative anatomy argument "provides no evidence for evolution," in Denton's* words:

> In the last analysis the *facts of comparative anatomy provide no evidence for evolution* in the way conceived by Darwin, and even if we were to construe with the eye of faith some "evidence" in the pattern of diversity for the Darwinian model of evolution this could only be seen, at best, as indirect or circumstantial. . . .
>
> The same deep homologous resemblance which serves to link all the members of one class together into a natural group also serves to distinguish that class unambiguously from all other classes. Similarly, the same hierarchic pattern which may be explained in terms of a theory of

common descent, also, by its very nature, implies the existence of deep divisions in the order of nature. *The same facts of comparative anatomy which proclaim unity also proclaim division*; while resemblance suggests evolution, division, especially where it appears profound, is *counter-evidence against the whole notion of transmutation.*[493]

Similarly, the comparative physiology argument has "not contributed much" to knowledge about macroevolutionary relationships, in Ross's* assessment:

It is an unspoken assumption that the data of comparative physiology must have implications for phylogeny. Is this realistic? . . .

. . . .

Without multiplying the examples, one can safely say that the *data of comparative physiology have not contributed much to our views about phylogenetic relationships*. That is not to say that these data are irrelevant for theories of evolutionary processes. . . .

It seems that *most of the stated aims and general objectives of comparative physiology in all its aspects have been unfulfilled.* "Illusory" may be too strong a word to describe these objectives but, as I hope to show, it is not just that these objectives have been unrealized but *probably that they are unrealizable.*[494]

The basic difficulties with the comparative anatomy argument are that similarity "may not necessarily correspond to true genetic relationships,"[495] and the "attempt to find homologous genes has been given up as hopeless."[496] The widespread anomalies in comparative anatomy may even better support the theory of abrupt appearance, as discussed in Section 2.7(b). In this area, the biological theories of macroevolution and Darwinism are not compelling.

e. *Comparative Embryology Argument and Difficulties*

The comparative embryology argument for macroevolution, which focuses on the embryology or development of tissues and organs in a particular organism,[497] arises from the rough similarity of that development in various organisms. Most evolutionists view that similar development as reflecting common ancestry and descent. This argument too faces serious difficulties that many evolutionists acknowledge.

First, the "biogenetic law" was the center of the embryology argument for early Darwinists, and stated that "the embryological development (ontogeny) of an organism repeats (recapitulates) the evolutionary history (phylogeny) of its species."[498] That biogenetic law has "been demonstrated to be wrong by numerous subsequent scholars," according to Bock*, who was a biology professor at Columbia:

the *biogenetic law was widely accepted* by biologists and served as the basis for the surge of embryological research that continues unabated to this day. Moreover, the biogenetic law has become so deeply rooted in biological thought that *it cannot be weeded out* in spite of its having been *demonstrated to be wrong by numerous subsequent scholars*. Even today both subtle and overt uses of the biogenetic law are frequently encountered in the general biological literature as well as in more specialized evolutionary and systematic studies.[499]

Raup* and Stanley* call the biogenetic law "largely in error";[500] Ehrlich* and Holm* note its "shortcomings" and its place in "biological mythology";[501] Danson* says that it is "intellectually barren";[502] de Beer* refers to the "evidence against the 'biogenetic law' of recapitulation in Haeckel's sense";[503] Bonner* of Princeton calls it "probably nonsense";[504] *Encyclopaedia Britannica* calls it "in error";[505] and even Mayr* of Harvard describes the biogenetic law as "invalid."[506] In fact, Haeckel*, the formulator of the "biogenetic law," supported it with "faked" drawings.[507]

Second, the modern embryological argument shares the same foundational problem as the comparative anatomy argument, with which it is "very closely related":[508] that similar embryological development does not necessarily indicate common ancestry and evolutionary descent.[509] Oldroyd* of University of New South Wales describes one aspect of the problem:

> Anatomically homologous parts in different related organisms appear to have quite different embryonic origins. This is almost *impossible to reconcile with orthodox Darwinian or neo-Darwinian theory*, and it is by no means evident at the time of writing how such problems may be overcome.[510]

Furthermore, "organisms indeed differ fundamentally in developmental strategy," according to Davidson* of California Institute of Technology.[510A] An example is given by Romer* in connection with the embryonic kidney.[511]

Third, the vestigial organ aspect of this embryology argument (that modern organs with no use or reduced usefulness are vestiges of evolutionary stages with former usefulness) is "invalid", as zoologist Scadding* notes:

> An analysis of the difficulties in unambiguously identifying functionless structures and an analysis of the nature of the argument, leads to the conclusion that *'vestigial organs' provide no evidence for evolutionary theory*.
>
> . . ..
>
> I would suggest that the *entire argument* that vestigial organs provide evidence for evolution is *invalid on two grounds*, one practical, the other more theoretical. The practical problem is that of unambiguously identi-

fying vestigial organs, i.e., those that have no function. The analysis of Wiedersheim's list of vestigial organs points out the difficulties. *As our knowledge has increased the list of vestigial structures has decreased.* Wiedersheim could list about one hundred in humans; recent authors usually list four or five. Even the current short list of vestigial structures in humans is questionable. . . .

. . .Similarly, for other 'vestigial organs' there is reasonable ground for supposing that they are functional albeit in a minor way. . . .

The other major objections to citing vestigial organs as evidence of evolution is a more theoretical one based on the nature of the argument. The 'vestigial organ' argument uses as a *premise* the assertion that the organ in question has no function. There is *no way, however, in which this negative assertion can be arrived at scientifically.* . . .

Since it is not possible to unambiguously identify useless structures, and since the structure of the argument used is not scientifically valid, I conclude that 'vestigial organs' provide *no special evidence for the theory of evolution.*[512]

The alleged vestigial organs—such as human "gill slits" (which do not exist),[513] male nipples, Wolffian and Mullerian ducts, tonsils, appendix, coccyx ("tail bone"), thymus, and facial muscles—almost all have been found to have functions and not to be vestigial:

A fourth category of *vestigial organs* would be those that are *vestiges of the reproductive structures of the opposite sex,* e.g. nipples in men, vestiges (in the female) of the Wolffian duct, and (in the male) of the Mullerian ducts. These structures, however, clearly reflect the embryonic development of a sexually dimorphic organism which begins its development in a sexually indifferent condition with structures characteristic of both sexes. They certainly do *not reflect phylogenetic development.* No one supposes males evolved from females or vice versa. On the basis of this analysis, I would suggest that *Wiedersheim was largely in error in compiling his long list of vestigial organs. Most of them do have at least a minor function at some point in life.*[514]

"In man, however, gills do never exist"[514A] and "are not gills at all,"[514B] and "the coccygeal vertebrae—tailbone is a clear misnomer—are in no wise vestigial."[514C]

Thus, the comparative embryology argument for biological macroevolution and Darwinism also offers little support, in the view of many evolutionists. The "biogenetic law" has been "demonstrated to be wrong";[515] "homologous parts in different related organisms appear to have quite different embryonic origins";[516] and the vestigial organ argument is generally "invalid."[517] In the embryology area, the biological theories of macroevolution and Darwinism are not compellingly established.

f. Comparative Biochemistry Argument and Difficulties

The comparative biochemistry argument for macroevolution centers around "homologies at the molecular level" that evolutionists believe reflect "the degree of genetic relationship [in which] evolutionary lineages are optimally expressed."[518] Those molecular comparisons involve the similarity of hemoglobin, cytochrome *c*, insulin, and other molecules in various organisms.[519] The argument from some molecular similarities to macroevolution (common ancestry) and to Darwinian mechanisms involves several difficulties that numerous evolutionists acknowledge.

First, the comparative biochemistry evidence that is anomalous, in the sense of indicating significant differences between allegedly closely related organisms, is so widespread that it may instead better support the discontinuous or distinct ancestry of natural groups of organisms, as discussed in Section 2.7(c). Those widespread anomalies lead Denton*, a molecular biologist, to conclude that comparative biochemistry contradicts macroevolution:

> This new era of comparative biology illustrates just how erroneous is the assumption that advances in biological knowledge are continually confirming the traditional evolutionary story. There is no avoiding the serious nature of the challenge to the whole evolutionary framework implicit in these findings.[520]

For example, a study of cytochrome *c* by Jukes* and Holmquist* reveals "anomalies" showing amphibians and reptiles to be more distant in an evolutionary sense than a bird and a fish, a mammal and a fish, or a mammal and an insect:

> In either case, certain *anomalies* appear in certain vertebrates with respect to the magnitude of these changes and their relationship to time. Such anomalies show up on "phylogenetic trees" as apparently negative rates of evolutionary divergence, or incorrect taxonomic placement of an organism in the wrong family.
>
> . . ..
>
> . . .However, the *difference between turtle and rattlesnake of 21 amino acid residues* per 100 codons is *notably larger than many differences* between representatives of widely separated classes, for example, 17 between chicken and lamprey, or 16 between horse and dogfish, or even 15 between dog and screw worm fly in two different phyla.[521]

Macroevolution and Darwinism, by contrast, involve an evolutionary sequence from invertebrates (including insects) to vertebrate fish, to amphibians, to reptiles, to birds and mammals.

Studies of relaxin by biochemists Schwabe* and Warr* similarly "do not fit the evolutionary clock model" for comparative biochemistry:

Thus the conclusion to be drawn from the *relaxin sequence data* is that they *do not fit the evolutionary clock model*. The alternative models, those based on positive selection, depend on spurts of mutation fixation or a hypothetical gene duplication whenever a molecule does not fit into a monophyletic evolutionary tree. In fact, the neo-Darwinism of molecular evolution is used exclusively to fit molecular data into paleontologically derived evolutionary trees which in themselves are controversial. That is, the hypothesis is *not based on independent scientific reasoning* that would allow predictions to be made and tested.[522]

Studies of DNA by Vawter* and Brown* yield such anomalies that the authors call for throwing out the molecular clock hypothesis entirely:

[The] disparity in relative rates of mitochondrial and nuclear DNA divergence suggests that the controls and constraints under which the mitochondrial and nuclear genomes operate are evolving independently, and provides evidence that is independent of fossil dating for a *robust rejection of a generalized molecular clock hypothesis of DNA evolution.*[523]

Many other anomalies, which also "do not fit the evolutionary clock model," were given earlier.[524]

Second, the "molecular clock" of comparative biochemistry is conceptually flawed, as Denton* describes:

The difficulties associated with attempting to explain how a family of homologous proteins could have evolved at constant rates has created chaos in evolutionary thought. The evolutionary community has divided into two camps—those still adhering to the selectionist position, and those rejecting it in favour of the neutralist. The devastating aspect of this controversy is that neither side can adequately account for the constancy of the rate of molecular evolution, yet each side fatally weakens the other. The selectionists wound the neutralists' position by pointing to the *disparity in the rates of mutation per unit time*, while the neutralists destroy the selectionist position by showing how *ludicrous it is to believe that selection would have caused equal rates of divergence in "junk" proteins or along phylogenetic lines so dissimilar as those of man and carp.* Both sides win valid points, but in the process the credibility of the *molecular clock hypothesis is severely strained* and with it the whole paradigm of evolution itself is endangered.

There is simply *no way of explaining how a uniform rate of evolution could have occurred in any family of homologous proteins* by either chance or selection; and, even if we could advance an explanation for one particular protein family, we would still be left with the *mystifying problem of explaining why other protein families should have evolved at different rates.*[525]

In fact, the common explanation of inconvenient anomalies, as the result of different rates of molecular evolution (used for example by Jukes* in connection with the cytochrome *c* results[526]), is simply an "ad hoc argument" that resets the molecular clock whenever it is convenient to macroevolution, as Schwabe* and Warr* note:

> Consider species A suddenly divided into A1, A2 and A3 by insurmountable obstacles. . . .

> . . .If instead of the expected equal distribution of differences one were to observe that the insulins of A1 and A2 differ by four residues whereas the insulin of A3 differs by 25 residues from both A1 and A2 then one would have discovered *an exception to the neo-Darwinian hypothesis.* There are virtually no degrees of freedom in this scenario so that *contradiction can be smoothed over only by ad hoc arguments* such as faster rates of evolution, lateral gene migration or gross errors committed by paleontologists in determining the time of branching of A1, A2 and A3.[527]

Third, the accuracy of the "molecular clock" is unsatisfactorily poor, because the techniques for measuring molecular distance are all unsatisfactory, according to Farris*:

> It seems that the only general conclusion one can draw is that *nothing about present techniques for analyzing molecular distance data is satisfactory.* The distance Wagner method seems to be the best available method for arriving at genealogies efficiently—certainly it is far more effective than Prager and Wilson imagined—but, at least for minimizing %SD, further improvement seems possible. But using any method that fits branch lengths to a distance matrix *presupposes* that the distances are suitable for this sort of analysis. That supposition seems *unjustified* for any distance measure now in use.

> *None of the known measures of genetic distance seems able to provide a logically defensible method*, and it appears that some altogether different approach will have to be adopted for analyzing electrophoretic data. . . .

> *Sequence data* have sometimes been analyzed by way of distances, although perhaps more often they have been treated by character analysis methods (for example Goodman et al., 1979). While sequence differences do not seem to offer the severe problem of interpretability of branch lengths that plague genetic distances, *neither is there any good reason to rely on distance techniques.* Reducing character data to distances, once again, simply wastes evidence on kinship.

> *Immunological distances, like genetic distances, cannot be truly clock-like,* nor can they be analyzed by branch length fitting, but there is no recourse to underlying character data in this case. . . .[528]

Farris* is more qualified than almost anyone to analyze those techniques, because he developed one of the most used techniques for measuring molecular distance.

Fourth, the comparative biochemistry argument, like the other comparative arguments, in any event is based on the problematic assumption that similarities between organisms reflect common ancestry rather than engineering design or basic conditions for life:

> It could be argued that the universality of much of biochemistry is *merely consistent* with the concept of a common ancestral population but does not in any sense prove it since the *same basic reaction patterns may be required for all life.*[529]

Therefore, the comparative biochemistry argument for macroevolution and Darwinism involves a "molecular clock" that does not work and is simply an "apologetic tautology," according to Denton*:

> The hold of the evolutionary paradigm is so powerful that an idea which is more like a principle of medieval astrology than a serious twentieth-century scientific theory has become a reality for evolutionary biologists.
>
> Here is, perhaps, the most dramatic example of the principle that wherever we find significant empirical discontinuities in nature we invariably face great, if not insurmountable, conceptual problems in envisaging how the gaps could have been bridged in terms of gradual random processes. We saw this in the fossil record, we saw it in the case of the feather, in the case of the avian lung and in the case of the wing of the bat. We saw it again in the case of the origin of life and we see it here in this new area of *comparative biochemistry.*
>
> What has been revealed as a result of the sequential comparisons of homologous proteins is an order as emphatic as that of the periodic table. Yet in the face of this extraordinary discovery the biological community seems content to offer explanations which are no more than *apologetic tautologies.*[530]

Comparative biochemical information is simply "at odds" with neo-Darwinism, in the assessment of Schwabe*:

> One might ask why the neo-[D]arwinian paradigm does not weaken or disappear if it is at odds with critical factual information.[531]

Thus, at least in the area of comparative biochemistry or molecular biology, the theories of macroevolution and Darwinism are not compellingly established, in the view of many evolutionists.

g. Population Genetics Argument and Difficulties

The population genetics argument for macroevolution and Darwinism, which focuses on gene changes within a population,[532] is founded on extrapolation of small changes in gene frequencies to major transformations from a common ancestor to evolutionary descendants. It is "[p]erhaps the most important source of evidence in support of the theory of evolution," according to Stansfield*,[533] and "contains the core mechanisms of neo-Darwinian evolutionary theory," in the words of Ruse*.[534] Yet that extrapolation is questionable, and the argument has failed, in the view of many evolutionist as well as nonevolutionist scientists.

First, population genetic changes (microevolution) *tell nothing about macroevolution* or even the origin of species, as Lewontin* of Harvard (a noted population geneticist) and Grassé* of University of Paris (a leading zoologist) observe:

> It is an irony of *evolutionary genetics* that, although it is a fusion of Mendelism and Darwinism, it has made *no direct contribution to what Darwin obviously saw as the fundamental problem: the origin of species.*[535]

> To assert that population dynamics gives a picture of evolution in action is an *unfounded opinion*, or rather a postulate, that relies on *not a single proved fact showing that transformations* in the two kingdoms have been essentially *linked to changes in the balance of genes in a population.... [A]s for seeking in it proof of the formation of new species, there is no such hope.*[536]

Mayr*, a systematist, said that "the most cogent objection against population genetics raised by Grassé" was that he "could not see any connection between changes in gene frequencies . . . and the evolutionary events . . . of species and higher taxa."[537]

Rosen*, an ichthyologist at the American Museum, concurs that population genetics "cannot, and does not purport to, explain the origin . . . of new codons" (parts of new genes).[538] Spiess* concedes that "we are a long way from describing the origin of species . . . with methods of experimental population genetics."[539] Saunders* and Ho* add that population genetics simply "is not, however, a theory of evolution."[540] Kempthorne*, while wishfully assuming that after nearly a century "population genetics theory is in its infancy," cautions that a "real danger is that the theory is generated primarily by the mathematics we can do, rather than by the biological processes that should be included."[541] Lambert* suggests that, because "evolution is . . . most especially not a population genetics problem," but "a problem of the origin of form," then "population genetics is not a tool to investigate evolution."[542] Similar observations are made indirectly by all the evolutionist scientists who object to extrapolation from microevolution to macroevolution.[543]

Second, population genetics come periously close to *explaining nothing*, as Lewontin* concludes:

> The theory *explains nothing* because it explains everything. It is my contention that a good deal of the structure of evolutionary genetics comes perilously close to being of this sort.
> . . ..

For many years population genetics was an immensely rich and powerful theory with virtually no suitable facts on which to operate. It was like a complex and exquisite machine, designed to process a raw material that no one had succeeded in mining. Occasionally some unusually clever or lucky prospector would come upon a natural outcrop of high-grade ore, and part of the machinery would be started up to prove to its backers that it really would work. But for the most part the machine was left to the engineers, forever tinkering, forever making improvements, in anticipation of the day when it would be called upon to carry out full production.

Quite suddenly the situation has changed. The mother-lode has been tapped and facts in profusion have been poured into the hoppers of this theory machine. And from the other end has issued—*nothing*. It is not that the machinery does not work, for a great clashing of gears is clearly audible, if not deafening, but it somehow cannot transform into a finished product the great volume of raw material that has been provided. *The entire relationship between the theory and the facts needs to be reconsidered.*[544]

Roughgarden*, a leading population geneticist, concurs that "[w]e need to reassess the relevance of population genetics to these kinds of evolutionary issues" of "long-term evolutionary phenomena" that it was assumed would be explained.[545] And Saiff* concludes that leading population geneticists find that their field "contributes very little to evolutionary theory":

The leading workers in this field have confessed, more or less reluctantly, that *population genetics contributes very little to evolutionary theory*. We will cite three such leaders.

. . ..

If the leading authorities on population genetics confess to this dismal lack of achievement and even chuckle about it, *it is altogether fitting and proper for the rank and file to take them at their word*. Therefore it seems to follow that *there is no need to teach population genetics in introductory courses on evolution*, although advanced courses may include it as a matter of history.[546]

Finally, and related to its failure, population genetics embodies *circular reasoning* when it is used to support evolution, as Forey* argues:

The hope of many of the authors of trees is that the synthetic approach (Bock 1974) will combine the analysis of pattern with the theories of the population biologists/geneticists in mutual support. The problem is that both are ultimately derived from the theory of evolution: the fossil record being interpreted in the light of *population biology* theory and expressed as ancestor-descendant relationships (Simpson 1953). One might remark that, far from being mutually supportive, *this is merely "the blind leading the blind."*[547]

Because the "idea of differential reproduction to explain evolutionary change formed the basis for what today is the field of population genetics,"[548] the problems of natural selection in terms of macroevolutionary effect and evidence (Section 3.3(a)) and in terms of tautology and nonexplanation (Section 10.2(a)) apply equally to population genetics.

Thus, the population genetics argument for macroevolution and Darwinism "is not, however, a theory of evolution,"[549] "explains nothing,"[550] and "is merely 'the blind leading the blind' " in a circular path.[551] In this area, macroevolution and Darwinian mechanisms are not compelling, in the view of many leading researchers.

h. Artificial Selection Argument and Difficulties

The artificial selection argument for macroevolution is based on extrapolation from breeding experiments (artificial selection) to natural selection and then to macroevolution. In fact, "more than almost any other single factor, domestic breeding has been used as an argument for evolution," according to Eiseley*, an internationally known anthropologist,[552] as well as Dobzhansky*, Ayala*, Stebbins*, and Valentine*.[553] The second extrapolation, which even many evolutionists question, has been discussed above.[554] The first extrapolation entails serious problems.

First, artificial selection is not relevant to natural selection, and thus is not a persuasive argument for it, according to Wassermann*:

> *Artificial selection* is often considered as a means for testing population genetic theories (cf. Lewontin [1974], p. 250). But there remain, in my opinion, *serious doubts* about the role that artificial selection could or should play. Dobzhansky ([1970], p. 201) argued that
>> Darwin used artificial selection as a model of the natural process; a mathematical theory of selection must almost necessarily be derived from experiments on artificial selection.
> This belief, however (and its *doubtful* conclusion), rests on the implicit hypothesis that artificial selection necessarily simulates some natural selection process. *One could only confirm this hypothesis by studying first the natural selection process* extensively and then examine how well artificial selection simulates it. *But if one could study the natural process in the first place, then one would not need any simulation,* unless the simulation process could be better controlled (and provided the controls do not change the effects of the simulation process much from those of the natural process).[555]

Other aspects of the irrelevance of artificial selection to natural selection are identified by Macbeth*:

> At the same time, however, *Darwin fell into the traps* that Fischer warns

against. First, he was so enchanted with the similarities that *he paid little attention to the obvious dissimilarities* (presence of a guiding intelligence in artificial selection, plus the breeders' concentration on micro changes rather than on the big gaps). Second, he offered the analogy as a *proof*: see pages 14-15 and Chapter 4 of *The Origin*.

Although the analogy had nobly performed its function in stimulating Darwin's imagination, *it furnished no evidence of the correctness of Natural Selection.* It has historical interest, but it was not essential to the understanding or proof of Natural Selection. Alfred Russel Wallace did not need it to reach the same conclusion as Darwin; to the contrary, McKinney (1972, p. 144-145) shows that he rejected the analogy . . .. [556]

Second, artificial selection is not just an irrelevant proof, but it is an irrelevant analogy, for macroevolution and Darwinism, as Russell* states:

> It is important to note that in all these processes there is *no "selection"* in the proper meaning of the word. It is unfortunate that Darwin ever introduced the term "natural selection", for it has given rise to much confusion of thought. He did so, of course, because he arrived at his theory through studying the effects of selection as practiced by man in the breeding of domesticated animals and cultivated plants. Here the use of the word is entirely legitimate. But the *action of man in selective breeding is not analogous to the action of "natural selection"*, but *almost its direct opposite*, as Woltereck (1931) in particular has pointed out. Man has an aim or an end in view; "natural selection" can have none. Man picks out the individuals he wishes to cross, choosing them by the characters he seeks to perpetuate or enhance. He protects them and their issue by all means in his power, guarding them thus from the operation of natural selection, which would speedily eliminate many freaks; he continues his active and purposeful selection from generation to generation until he reaches, if possible, his goal. *Nothing of this kind happens, or can happen, through the blind process of differential elimination and differential survival* which we miscall "natural selection."[557]

Even Dobzhansky* *et al.* join in the argument that artificial selection is too different from natural selection to be relevant.[558] Just as human ability to construct bridges does not establish that bridges evolved without engineering, human ability to breed varieties of cows does not help establish that cows arose through macroevolution.

Third, artificial selection supports not the possibility of macroevolution but the genetic limits on viable microevolution. Those "more or less fixed limitations," and "limits to the development possible," were noted by Burbank*, the most famous breeder of this century.[559] Deevey* concurs that artificial selection faces a "species barrier."[560] Eiseley* acknowledges that variations "cannot be selectively pushed beyond a certain point."[561] Falconer* points out that, for breeding experiments, "only the fact that domesticated plants and animals do not live under natural conditions has allowed these improvements."[562] Those genetic limits on viable change are discussed further in Section 2.6.

Therefore, the artificial selection argument for macroevolution and Darwinism "furnishe[s] no evidence of the correctness of Natural Selection,"[563] and "is not analogous to the action of 'natural selection,' but almost its direct opposite."[564] Here the biological theories of macroevolution and Darwinism are not compellingly established, many evolutionists admit.

Summary. Thus, each of the various alleged evidences for macroevolution and Darwinism is noncompelling, in the view of many evolutionist scientists. That has been shown by scores of sources, and the following are typical. Each should be read in its full context earlier in this section.

(a) The paleontology argument "contributed . . . nothing to evolutionary biology" (Hoffman*[565]), and in fact the "extreme rarity of transitional forms in the fossil record persists as the trade secret of paleontology" (Gould*[566]).

(b) The phylogeny argument has a "chief question with respect to phylogenetic reconstruction" of "its feasibility" (Hull*[567]), has produced only "meaningness waffle" (Charig*[568]), has an "Achilles' heel" of "circularity in the [evolutionary] approach" (Thomson*[569]), and has been "another miserable failure" (Saiff*[570]).

(c) The classification argument "has nothing to say about evolution" according to the transformed cladist school of classification (Patterson*[571]), while part of the phenetics school has "abandoned the goal of building a taxonomy that reflects evolutionary descent" (Luria and Gould*[572]). The classification system devised by pre-Darwinian creationists "has undergone surprisingly little change" (Mayr*[573]), and modern classification has not cured the "ignorance concerning these relationships [that] is still great" (Mayr*[574]).

(d) The "facts of comparative anatomy provide no evidence for evolution" (Denton*[575]). "[T]here exists no a priori relation between the appearance of two structures and their relatedness" (Schwabe* and Warr*[576]), and the greatest proofs are that "[n]ature abounds in examples of convergence" and parallelism that involve similar structures in unrelated organisms (Denton*[577]), and that the "attempt to find 'homologous' genes . . . has been given up as hopeless" (de Beer*[578]).

(e) The embryological argument only offers a biogenetic law that has "been demonstrated to be wrong by numerous subsequent scholars" (Bock*[579]), a conundrum that "[a]natomically homologous parts in different related organisms appear to have quite different origins" (Oldroyd*[580]), and a vestigial organ argument that "provide[s] no evidence for evolutionary theory" (Scadding*[581]).

(f) The comparative biochemistry argument offers a "serious... challenge to the whole evolutionary framework" rather than support (Denton*[582]), by widespread anomalies that require "a robust rejection of a generalized molecular clock hypothesis of DNA evolution" (Vawter* and Brown*[583]), and by "nothing about present techniques for analyzing molecular distance data [being] satisfactory" (Farris*[584]).

(g) The population genetics argument has made "no direct contribution to what Darwin obviously saw as the fundamental problem: the origin of species" (Lewontin*[585]), simply "is not, however, a theory of evolution" (Saunders* and Ho*[586]), has come "perilously close" to "explain[ing] nothing" (Lewontin*[587]), and is so circular that it "is merely 'the blind leading the blind' (Forey*[588]).

(h) Finally, the artificial selection argument "furnished no evidence of the correctness of Natural Selection" (Macbeth*[589]), and "selective breeding is not analogous to the action of 'natural selection' " (Russell*[590]).

Moreover, several of these arguments may well better support the theory of abrupt appearance than the theory of macroevolution, such as the paleontology argument (Sections 2.1-2.2), the population genetics argument (Section 2.6), the classification argument (Section 2.7(a)), and the comparative biochemistry argument (Section 2.7(c)), advocates of the theory of abrupt appearance point out. *Ecce signum.*

3.5 The Postulated Stages of Macroevolution and Darwinism: Single Cells to All Plants and Animals and Missing Links

Macroevolution, which has been defined as "[e]volutionary change above the species level"[591] and as including the "process by which all organisms have arisen by descent from a common ancestor,"[592]

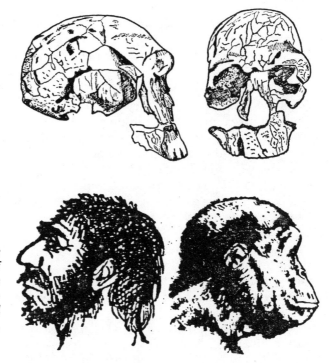

*Figure 3.5
Evolution on the
artist's palette of
Zinjanthropus
(from B. Camp-
bell*, Humankind
Emerging (3d ed.
1982))*

includes several stages. These macroevolutionary stages are summarized by biologist Thompson* of University of Missouri as
follows:

> [A]ll living forms in the world have arisen from a single source that came
> from an inorganic beginning. So, according to the model of evolution, [a]
> the first living cell "evolved" into [b] complex multicellular forms of life;
> these "evolved" into [c] animals with backbones. Fish evolved into [d]
> amphibia, amphibia into [e] reptiles, reptiles into [f] birds and [g] mam-
> mals, early mammals into [h] primates, and primates into [i] man.[593]

Similar descriptions of the stages are given by Dobzhansky*,[594]
Stebbins*,[595] and typical public school biology texts.[596]

The postulated stages of macroevolution are assessed as follows:
(a) from prokaryotes to eukaryotes, (b) to invertebrate animals, (c) to
fish, (d) to amphibians, (e) to reptiles, (f) to birds and (g) to lower
mammals, (h) to primates, and (i) to man; as well as (j) to higher
plants. However, the evidence for the proposed stages is not that
clear, according to Bonner* of Princeton:

> The particular truth is simply that *we have no reliable evidence as to the*

evolutionary sequence . . .. One can find qualified, professional *arguments for any group being the descendant of almost any other.*[597]
A similar conclusion is reached by Kerkut*,[598] Grassé*,[599] Denton*,[600] and a number of other biologists.[601]

a. To Eukaryotes and Problems

Macroevolution from prokaryotes to eukaryotes involves a transformation from generally single-celled organisms "that lack a nucleus" (prokaryotes) to single-celled organisms "that have a distinct nucleus containing chromosomes" (unicellular eukaryotes).[602] There are two major hypotheses of how that transformation might have occurred. The endosymbiont hypothesis proposes that prokaryotic bacteria were eaten by or invaded an amoeba-like cell, and the bacteria evolved into mitochondria while a nuclear membrane evolved in the host cell.[603] The autogenous hypothesis postulates that gradual compartmentalization of genes and enzymes produced cellular organelles.

The problems with this major step from prokaryotes to eukaryotes—an "area of speculation"—have been discussed in detail by Whitfield*:

> All hypotheses in this area of *speculation* are so multifaceted that it is extraordinarily difficult to set predictive tests for them which enable the hypotheses to be refuted . . .. *Symbiosis in Cell Evolution* handles the potentially testing issues of prokaryotic endocytosis, and the genetic organization of mitochondrial DNA.
>
> Prokaryotic endocytosis is the cellular mechanism on which the whole of S.E.T. [Serial Endosymbiotic Theory] presumably rests. If one prokaryote could not engulf another it is difficult to imagine how endosymbioses could be set up. Unfortunately for Margulis and S.E.T., *no modern examples* of prokaryotic endocytosis or endosymbiosis exist. . . .
>
> To turn to the second testing issue, the book examines the nature of yeast mitochondrial DNA. The essential nature of the facts is not in question. There is no doubt that the mitochondrial DNA of eukaryotic yeast cells, like that of eukaryotic nuclei, is composed of split genes. This would appear to be quite the *reverse of the state of affairs that S.E.T. would predict.* . . . For this reviewer, at least, such *special pleading* makes the extreme versions of S.E.T. increasingly *untenable.* . . .[604]

The endosymbiont hypothesis has been criticized widely, for example, by Lloyd*,[605] Gray* and Doolittle*,[606] and Raff* and Mahler*.[607]

Each aspect of the transition from prokaryotes to eukaryotes involves speculation,[608] most of which is "no more than microbial Just So Stories," according to Levin* and Lenski*:

We have made a number of general and specific statements about the nature and direction of coevolution in bacteria and their viruses and plasmids. . . . Most of these statements about how things came to be are *no more than microbial Just So Stories*. As is the case with other evolutionary phenomena, there is *no way to formally demonstrate* that the suggested pathways are indeed the actual ways things came to be.[609]

The differences between prokaryotes and eukaryotes in messenger RNA formation "are so profound as to suggest that sequential prokaryotic to eukaryotic cell evolution seems unlikely," Darnell* states:

> The *differences in the biochemistry of messenger RNA formation in eukaryotes compared to prokaryotes* are so profound as to suggest that sequential prokaryotic to eukaryotic cell evolution seems unlikely. The recently discovered noncontiguous sequences in eukaryotic DNA that encode messenger RNA may reflect an ancient, rather than a new, distribution of information in DNA and that eukaryotes evolved independently of prokaryotes.[610]

"It is not known just what were the ancestors of Protozoa," Hickman* notes.[611] There is "as yet no definite evidence about the way in which the Viruses, Bacteria or Protozoa are interrelated," Kerkut* adds.[612] A postulated transition from prokaryotic algae to eukaryotic algae was questioned because the transition was "so fraught with confusion and contradiction that most modern biologists have ignored it,"[613] and subsequently was abandoned. The confusion is so great generally that some researchers have proposed that eukaryotes evolved into prokaryotes, rather than the reverse.[614]

The fossil evidence is not much more clear. It is clear that prokaryote fossils exist in Precambrian rocks, "but we do not know the time or the circumstances of their origin," Shapiro* notes.[615] Also, "[i]f these critics are right, then we have no evidence for eukaryotes until the very latest Precambrian, just before the great Cambrian 'explosion', " Gould* points out.[616] Claims periodically are made about alleged discoveries of fossilized cells, but should be viewed with "doubt and skepticism," Shapiro* cautions:

> The American Chemical Society met in Washington, D.C., in the summer of 1979, and its news magazine, *Chemical and Engineering News*, reported the exciting tidings. A headline proclaimed: "Evidence of Life Found in Oldest-Known Rocks.". . . The report mentioned that actual fossils, which would provide more convincing evidence of life, had not been found thus far.
>
> This deficiency was remedied by others. An article appeared at about the same time in the prestigious British scientific journal *Nature* . . ..

They had found "cell-like inclusions" at Isua . . .. They coined the name Isuasphaera for their find and commented: "There is little doubt that Isuasphaera is an organism." . . .

A certain *absence of doubt and skepticism* in these reports should serve as a warning flag for us. In cases where scientists are unwilling to play devil's advocate for themselves, others are usually quite willing to oblige. In this case the rude awakening came eighteen months later, in several articles also published in *Nature*. . . .

Isuasphaera suffered no kinder a fate, and was dispatched down the same path as Eozoon. The supposed fossils were examined by an international team which included scientists prominent in the studies of the Australian and South African fossils. They concluded that the Isua structures were *demonstrably inorganic artifacts* and did *not constitute evidence for life.* . . .[617]

Furthermore, there is little or no evidence of metazoan fossils before the Cambrian.[618] After a thorough review of the relevant studies, Pflug* of University of Giessen in Germany finds a "gap" between the Precambrian organisms and the Cambrian metazoa:

A critical comparison of the present fossil record shows that few of these Precambrian lineages can be traced with certainty into the lower Cambrian. A gap separates the Precambrian and Cambrian world of Metazoa. The discontinuity corresponds to a major faunal break in the sense of Schindewolf (1954) and Sokolov & Fedonkin (1984).[619]

b. To Invertebrates and Problems

Macroevolution from early eukaryotes to invertebrate animals[620] is not supported by fossil evidence, as is acknowledged by Dobzhansky*, Ayala*, Stebbins*, and Valentine*:

The first problem does not arise with respect to animals, since the gap between Protista and the animal kingdom, which according to the present treatment is synonymous with the Metazoa, is so great that the *origin of Metazoa is still obscure* (Wells, 1968).

. . ..

. . .Although there is a good fossil record of the major groups that have well-mineralized skeletons, the origins and earliest evolution of the metazoan phyla *cannot be documented from fossil evidence.*[621]

This fossil gap cannot be explained as the result of an inadequate fossil record, because the fossil record is relatively good for invertebrates, Stanley* notes:

Human evolution now seems to be *largely immune to the "poor fossil record" argument* of phyletic gradualism. This argument also largely disappears for *well-fossilized invertebrate animals*, in general, when we consider that these creatures, unlike the vertebrates, have records that for major segments of geologic time are widely distributed in space and are also well studied.[622]

The best fossil evidence for this transition is the Ediacaran fauna. Yet they "may not be metazoans at all," Valentine* and Erwin* state.[623] Simpson* adds that "animals, strictly speaking, as unmistakable metazoans, are not known before the Ediacaran fauna, which occurs so late that it has been suggested that it be referred to the earliest Cambrian rather than to the latest Precambrian. Yet the animals of the Ediacaran fauna are so varied and some of them are so complex that metazoans must have existed, without leaving traces now known, for a very long earlier time."[623A]

This abrupt appearance of invertebrate animals involved not just a few organisms but representatives of nine phyla and a multitude of species, so the "seas were swarming with highly differentiated aquatic plants and animals," Barghoorn* states.[624] Yet the "first and most important steps of animal evolution remain even more obscure than those of plant evolution," according to Weiss*.[625] For example, insects similarly appear abruptly, and the fossil "evidence for step-by-step changes leading to major evolutionary transitions looks extremely thin."[626]

c. To Fish and Problems

Macroevolution from invertebrates to chordate and vertebrate fish is also not supported by fossil evidence, according to Ommanney*, an international expert on fish:

> How this earliest *chordate* stock evolved, what stages of development it went through to eventually give rise to truly fish-like creatures, *we do not know.*[627]

"The geological record has so far provided no evidence as to the origin of fishes . . .," Norman* concurs.[628] Scientists are "mainly ignorant" of this alleged transformation despite "numerous" fossils, as noted by paleontologist Romer* of Harvard:

> In sediments of late Silurian and early Devonian age, numerous fishlike vertebrates of varied types are present, and it is obvious that a long evolutionary history had taken place before that time. But of that history we are *mainly ignorant.*[629]

"All three subdivisions of the bony fishes first appear in the fossil record at approximately the same time," with "no trace of earlier, intermediate forms," according to Todd*.[630] Each group of fish has its origins "firmly based in nothing," in the words of paleontologist White*, former president of the Linnean Society and an authority on lungfish:

Whatever ideas authorities may have on the subject, the lungfishes, like every other major group of fishes that I know, have their origins firmly *based in nothing.*[631]

Instead, vertebrate fish seem to have appeared suddenly in the Upper Cambrian,[632] as part of the abrupt appearance of complex life in the "Cambrian explosion."[633]

Thus, the "origin of the vertebrates [is] an unsolved problem," Stahl* concedes:

> *What remains to be understood* is the early evolution of the entire ostra-coderm assemblage and the *origin in even more ancient times of the vertebrate line from its nonvertebrate ancestral source.* Difficulties of such magnitude exist, however, in the study of these matters that investigators have had to confine themselves to defining the problems and to building theories on the *small amounts of evidence* they do have. Although nonscientists sometimes accept current theories as the answers given by science to these questions of universal interest, students of evolution understand them as starting points for research.[634]

"As our present information stands, however, the gap remains *unbridged* and the best place to start the evolution of the vertebrates is in the *imagination,*" Smith* says.[635]

d. To Amphibians and Problems

Macroevolution from fish to amphibians again involves "phantoms" and "will-o'-the-wisps" rather than plausible fossil evidence, according to paleontologist Patterson*:

> To me one of the most astonishing consequences of the furor over cladistics is the realization that the *current account of tetrapod evolution,* shown in a thousand diagrams and everywhere acknowledged as the centerpiece of historical biology, is a *will-o'-the-wisp.* For nowhere can one find a clear statement of how and why the Recent groups are interrelated, and the textbook stories are *replete with phantoms*—extinct, uncharacterizable groups giving rise one to another.[636]

Ichthyostega does not constitute a transitional fossil—with it and other fossils "the deficiencies are obvious."[637]

"The transition between the Paleozoic amphibians and the 'modernized' forms is almost completely a blank" as well, as Romer* observes.[638] That "lack of fossil specimens intermediate" allows only "speculations," in Stahl's* words:

> The *lack of fossil specimens intermediate* between anurans or urodeles and the older amphibians has forced paleontologists and students of the living animals to base their *speculations about the evolution of the group* upon evidence from the anatomy and embryology of modern species.

This approach has presented *difficulties that have so far proved insur-mountable.* The structure of the existing amphibians is so specialized that the more generalized condition from which it derived is almost completely obscured. . . .[639]

e. To Reptiles and Problems

Macroevolution from amphibians to reptiles faces similar prob-lems, Stirton* points out:

There is *no direct proof from the fossil record,* but we can readily hypo-thesize the conditions under which it came about.[640]

Such hypotheses are not necessarily plausible, however, because of the problem of the origin of the "land egg" that is the major distinc-tion between amphibians and reptiles:

Every textbook of evolution asserts that reptiles evolved from amphi-bia but none explains how the *major distinguishing adaptation of the reptiles,* the *amniotic egg,* came about gradually as a result of a succes-sive accumulation of small changes. The amniotic egg of the reptile is vastly more complex and utterly different to that of an amphibian. There are hardly two eggs in the whole animal kingdom which *differ* more fundamentally . . ..

The diagram above illustrates some of the main distinguishing fea-tures of the amniotic egg: the tough impervious shell, the two mem-branes, the amnion which encloses a small sac in which the embryo floats, and the allantois in which the waste products formed during the development of the embryo accumulate, and the yolk sac containing the food reserve in the form of the protein albumen. *None of these features are found in the egg of any amphibian.*

The evolution of the amniotic egg is *baffling.* It was this decisive innovation which permitted for the first time genuinely terrestrial verte-brate life, freeing it from the necessity of embryological development in an aquatic environment. Altogether at least eight quite different innova-tions were combined to make the amniotic revolution . . ..[641]

The same difficulty is described by Stahl* and termed the question that "is central to the broad question of reptilian origins."[642]

A further problem is the origin of the heart of the reptiles:

Trying to work out, for example, how the heart and aortic arches of an amphibian could have been gradually converted to the reptilian and mammalian condition raises absolutely horrendous problems.[643]

Seymouria is the most significant alleged intermediate between amphibians and reptiles. However, its first disqualification is from its apparently amphibian reproductive system, as Denton* observes:

In terms of purely skeletal characteristics *Seymouria* would appear to

be a convincing intermediate, but there is a *serious drawback*. The major
difference between amphibians and reptiles lies in their reproductive
systems. Amphibians lay their eggs in water and their larvae undergo a
complex metamorphosis (like a tadpole) before reaching the adult stage.
Reptiles develop inside a hard shell-encased egg and are perfect replicas
of the adult on first emerging. . . . [S]keletal characteristics alone are
insufficient for designating a particular organism or species as intermediate. Recently a fossil of an immature form closely related to *Seymouria*
has been found bearing laval gills (like a tadpole) which *suggests that
this group of amphibians were wholly amphibian in their reproductive
system*. There is a further difficulty with *Seymouria* and that is that *it
appears rather too late* in the fossil record to be an ancestor of the
reptiles.[645]

That second disqualification is that it is considered to be vastly
more recent than the first reptiles, in Kerkut's* words:

Seymouria is sometimes thought of as a link between the Amphibia and
reptiles. Unfortunately *Seymouria* is found in the Permian whilst the
first reptiles arose in the Pennsylvanian, some 20 or so million years
earlier.[645]

The origin of specific groups of reptiles presents similar problems.
The origin of turtles is abrupt with a "lack of early fossils," *Encyclopaedia Britannica* states:

Unfortunately, the origin of this highly successful order is obscured by
the lack of early fossils, although turtles leave more and better fossil
remains than do other vertebrates. By the middle of the Triassic Period
(about 200,000,000 years ago) turtles were numerous and in possession of
basic turtle characteristics. . . . Intermediates between turtles and cotylo-
saurs, the primitive reptiles from which turtles probably sprang, are
entirely lacking. . . .[646]

"The origin of the snakes is still an unsolved problem," according to
Stahl*, and their postulated derivation from lizards is not realistic
because of "peculiarities in the eyes of snakes."[647]

f. To Birds and Problems

Macroevolution from reptiles to birds is not supported by fossil
evidence, as Swinton* (an international expert) states:

The origin of birds is largely a matter of deduction. There is *no fossil
evidence* of the stages through which the remarkable change from reptile
to bird was achieved.[648]

Yet that transformation required an incredible number of changes,
and the various stages should have left fossil remains:

To grasp how much such cases entail, consider the major components of reptile-to-bird; the development of feathers, which are very complicated objects; reform of the respiratory system; reform of the skeletal system, with the bones becoming porous, hollow, and in many cases fused; reform of the digestive system to allow increased fuel consumption while economising on weight; reform of the nervous system, especially the brain and the eyeball; construction of bills and beaks; mastery of nest-building; and, finally, acquisition of flight and all the homing capacities. Any one of these components would be hard to visualize, but when all have to go forward together while keeping the organisms in operation at all times, the *difficulties become overwhelming*. . . .[649]

The two major hypotheses of how flight began are described by Ostrom* of Yale, an expert on birds:

Previous *speculations* on this question have produced two quite different scenarios. Stated very simply these are that birds began to fly "from the trees down"—or "from the ground up." The first is the widely favored and very logical *"arboreal theory"*. . .. The second is the often ridiculed and seemingly less probable *"cursorial theory* . . .."[650]

Ostrom* first criticizes the arboreal hypothesis, then discusses the primary difficulty of the cursorial hypothesis (which he advocates):

The critical point is that in order to fly, the animal first had to be able to climb. However, considering the design of modern birds, together with that of the oldest-known bird, *Archaeopteryx*, that skill may not have been part of the repertoire of primitive birds, or even of bird ancestors. . . ..

. . .One of the key criticisms that has been leveled at this hypothesis is that, once the animal is airborne, the main thrust source (ie traction of the hind feet against the ground) would be lost and velocity would diminish.[651]

Although Pro-avis and *Archaeopteryx* have been frequently discussed as possible transitional forms, neither qualifies according to a number of evolutionist scientists.

Pro-avis is "purely hypothetical", in the words of Ostrom*:

No fossil evidence exists of any pro-avis. It is a *purely hypothetical* pre-bird, but one that *must have existed*—whether or not it resembled the creature shown here.[652]

"The Proavian forms imagined by Heilman . . . are purely hypothetical constructs and may never have existed," Russell* adds.[653] Not only is the Pro-avis hypothesis "highly speculative," but "its wing/weight ratio would be insufficient even for gliding, let alone powered flight," Denton* adds.[654]

Archaeopteryx fossils "do not count" according to Gould* and Eldredge*:

At the higher level of evolutionary transition between basic morphological designs, gradualism has always been in trouble, though it remains the "official" position of most Western evolutionists. *Smooth interme-diates* between Bauplane are *almost impossible* to construct, even in thought experiments; there is certainly no evidence for them in the fossil record (*curious mosaics like Archaeopteryx do not count*).[655]

"This Jurassic bird still stands in splendid isolation" from the rep-tiles and birds according to Romer*,[656] and "seems to be on a separate line from modern birds" as viewed by Chatterjee*.[656A] It does not provide a satisfactory transitional form in the assessment of Denton*:

No doubt it can be argued that *Archaeopteryx* hints of a reptilian ances-try but surely hints do not provide a sufficient basis upon which to secure the concept of the continuity of nature. Moreover, there is no question that this archaic bird is not led up by a series of transitional forms from an ordinary terrestrial reptile through a number of gliding types with increasingly developed feathers until the avian condition is reached....[657]

Archaeopteryx was merely an unusual extinct bird, in the estima-tion of Russell*:

Nothing is known with certainty as to how *birds arose from reptiles* or from what reptilian stock. The famous fossil forms *Archaeopteryx* and *Archaeornis* of the upper Jurassic are *already birds*, with well developed wing and tail feathers, and the power of flight. They are, it is true, more reptilian in character than modern birds . . .. *No intermediate forms* between these two primitive birds and their reptilian ancestors have so far been discovered, and *reconstructions*, such as that proposed by Heil-mann (1926) of the "Proavis", are necessarily *theoretical.*[658]

T.H. Huxley*, "Darwin's bulldog," similarly "refused to view *Archaeopteryx* as a transitional form, interpreting it instead as 'all bird.' "[659] Schindewolf*[661] and Denton* have agreed.[661]

Moreover, *Archaeopteryx* could fly or at least glide, as Feduccia* and Olson* conclude:

It has been suggested that *Archaeopteryx* was strictly terrestrial and could not fly and that its wing feathers were therefore used, perhaps, as insect traps. We now present evidence that the primary feathers on the manus of *Archaeopteryx*, like those of modern flying birds, show an asymmetry that can be associated with an *aerodynamic function.* *Archaeopteryx* was therefore at least able to glide.[662]

The features of *Archaeopteryx* that are alleged to be reptile-like can be found in various modern birds or other extinct birds.[663] Hoyle and his colleagues even argue that *Archaeopteryx* was neither reptile or bird—but instead a forgery[664]—although Charig* and others have disagreed sharply.[665]

Finally, a fairly modern bird has been found in the same time period (Late Jurassic), which effectively would rule *Archaeopteryx* out as a transitional form between reptiles and birds:

> Although *Archaeopteryx* is generally considered the earliest bird on record, a recent find suggests that the creature, which lived some 130 million years ago, may not have been the only bird alive then. A new fossil found by James Jensen of Brigham Young University dates back to the same period—the Late Jurassic—and appears to be the femur (thighbone) of a bird. *If this proves to be the case, then a reexamination of the postulated role of Archaeopteryx as the evolutionary link between reptiles and birds may be in order.*
>
> . . ..
>
> Jensen thinks that he may have found such confirmatory evidence in the form of another, more complete fossil femur excavated just a few feet away from the one in question. According to the Brigham Young investigator, this second femur is very similar to that of modern birds. Ostrom has not yet examined this latest find, however. Until he does, the situation will remain very much up in the air.[666]

Ostrom* did examine the discovery, and agreed: "It is obvious now that we must now look for the ancestors of flying birds in a period of time much earlier than that in which *Archaeopteryx* lived."[667] He concluded that it "is highly improbable that *Archaeopteryx* is actually on the main line" to modern birds.[668] Cracraft* concurs:

> [T]he age of origin of some modern groups of birds is very old, in the Early Cretaceous if not before. This places them very nearly as old as Archaeopteryx and raises the possibility that Archaeopteryx is not the temporal benchmark of avian evolution we so often assume.[669]

The recent discovery of *"Protoavis"* fossils has the same effect on *Archaeopteryx.*[670]

The fossil evidence for a reptile-bird transition is weak enough that "virtually every major group of reptiles has been purported to be closely related, if not ancestral, to birds."[671]

g. To Mammals and Problems

(1) From Reptiles to Lower Mammals. The relationship of reptiles to mammals "is not at all clear," Scheele* states.[672] The "mammal-like reptiles" (synapsids) are proposed as "the one example known where the evolution of one class of vertebrates from another class is well documented by the fossil record,"[673] but these extinct organisms appear suddenly and disappear suddenly without further intermediate forms,[674] in the words of Kemp*:

> *Each species* of mammal-like reptile that has been found *appears suddenly* in the fossil record and is *not preceded by the species that is directly*

ancestral to it. It disappears some time later, equally abruptly, *without leaving a directly descended species*, although we usually find that it has been replaced by some new, related species.[675]

(Kemp's* school of thought that each such species is a transitional group was discussed in Section 3.4(a)(3).)

The inaccuracy of assuming that an animal group roughly intermediate in skeleton is also intermediate in soft parts and in history is stressed by Denton*:

> Given the tremendous diversity of life and ubiquity of the phenomenon of convergence, it is bound to be the case that *certain fossil organisms which appear to be very close on skeletal grounds were in fact in terms of their overall biology only distantly related*, like the placental and marsupial dogs. Further, there is always the possibility that groups, such as the *mammal-like reptiles* which have left no living representative, might have possessed features in their soft biology completely different from any known reptile or mammal which would eliminate them completely as potential mammalian ancestors, just as the discovery of the living coelacanth revealed features in its soft anatomy which were unexpected and cast doubt on the ancestral status of its rhipidistian relatives.[676]

These mammal-like reptiles instead may be simply extinct reptiles. That is the conclusion from study of their reptilian brains:

> Similar considerations cloud the status of the other classic intermediate groups such as the mammal-like reptiles, a group of extinct reptiles in which the morphology of the skull and jaw was very close to the mammalian condition. The *possibility* that the mammal-like reptiles were *completely reptilian* in terms of their anatomy and physiology cannot be excluded. The only evidence we have regarding their soft biology is their cranial endocasts and these suggest that, as far as their central nervous systems were concerned, they were entirely reptilian. Jerison, who has probably had more experience studying the cranial endocasts of fossil species than any other authority in this field, comments on the mammal-like reptile brains:
>
> > . . . these animals *had brains of typical lower vertebrates* . . . . Since their endocasts were all very near the volume of these expected brain sizes, and since the endocasts present maximum limits on their brain sizes, the mammal-like reptiles *could not have had brains that approached a mammalian size.* . . . The mammal-like reptiles, in short, were *reptilian and not mammalian with respect to the evolution of their brains.* . . .
>
> There are few suggestions of mammalian features in the brains of the mammal-like reptile. . . . The forebrain, to the extent that its position is identifiable, was of reptilian size and shape. This was not the case in the earliest known fossil mammals. . . .
>
> The earliest mammal for which there is reasonable evidence, *Tricon-*

odon of the Upper Jurassic period, was apparently already at or near the level of living "primitive" mammals such as the insectivores or the Virginia opossum. It was certainly larger brained than its reptilian ancestors of comparable body size.

Moreover, many quite separate groups of mammal-like reptiles exhibited skeletal mammalian characteristics, yet only one group can have been the hypothetical ancestor of the mammals. Again, as with the rhipidistian fishes, the *similarities must have been in most cases merely convergence.*[677]

Although they are described as mammal-like reptiles primarily because of their jaw articulation, that is an "inadequate" basis for treating them as intermediate forms, according to Gow*:

> *The presence of a squamosal-dentary articulation forming part or all of the joint between the skull and lower jaw is not used as the most practical diagnostic criterion for the class Mammalia.*

This distinction in the jaw articulation was found to be *inadequate*, however. *At least some cynodonts*, such as ictidosaurs and Probainognathus, *have a dentary-squamosal contact, which makes them mammals by strict application of this criterion.* Yet their complex lower jaws and single auditory ossicle in the middle ear are *clearly still reptilian.* Opinion has long been divided as to whether ictidosaurs are reptiles or mammals.[678]

The most-discussed possible "intermediates," *Morganucodon* and *Kuehneotherium*, both were reptiles in terms of their jaw bones, Kermack* and Mussett* suggest:

> Like *Morganucodon, Kuehneotherium* must have had a full complement of the reptilian bones in its lower jaw, and shows a facet for the coronoid bone. . . .[679]

The same is true of the mammal-reptile difference in the middle ear. "Those general statements about the evolution of the mammalian middle ear that appear are in the nature of proclamations. No methods are described which allow the reader to arrive with Fleisher at his 'ancestral' middle ear, nor is the basis for the transformation series illustrated for the middle ear bones explained."[680]

(2) From Lower Mammals to Higher Mammals. Macroevolution from lower mammals to higher mammals poses similar problems: the absence of transitional forms "is true of all the thirty-two orders of mammals," as summarized by Simpson*.[681] The " 'missing links' have for the most part remained missing," in the words of Russell*:

> The absence or extreme scarcity of forms transitional between a presumed, or a known, ancestral form and its later derivatives is a well known peculiarity of the geological record. "Missing links" have for the

most part remained missing. Even in the Mammals, whose geological history is comparatively well documented, *serious gaps* in the record occur just at the time when the *primary differentiation of the Orders* is taking place. As Simpson points out, "The earliest and most primitive members of every order already have the basic ordinal characters, and *in no case is an approximately continuous series* from one order to another known. In most cases the break is so sharp and the gap so large that the origin of the order is speculative and much disputed" (1944, p. 106) . . ..
The Bats, we must assume, have evolved, like other mammalian Orders, from the primitive insectivores of Upper Cretaceous and Paleocene times, but of this great transformation, involving an entirely new mode of life, and a high degree of structural specialisation, we have so far no record. So also with the Whales, as we have already seen. Though in this case primitive forms are known, these are not ancestral to the modern whales, which are not linked to the primitive mammalian stock by any known intermediate forms.[682]

One of the common phylogenies, along with the horse series that is discussed next, is the elephant series from rodent-sized animals (hyraces) to modern elephants. Sikes* criticizes that triumph of "artistic" imagination:

It requires extreme elasticity of the *imagination* to see anything more than a very superficial resemblance between the available parts of the skeleton of the earliest hyraces and those of the *Proboscidea*. . . . In the light of recent comparative studies on the anatomy, physiology, ecology and ethology of the living members of these orders, it is apparent that in the past disproportionate weight was sometimes given to skeletal affinities, while other important characteristics were overlooked.
. . ..
. . .Perhaps we should admit that the siting of *Moeritherium* in an intermediate position in the family tree *savours more of the artistic requirements of the drawing board than of an honest admission of ignorance* as to its proper position.[683]

Denton* comments that this and "[m]any of the other well-known series often depicted in textbooks are not nearly as convincing as the horse when subjected to detailed analysis."[685] The fact is that transformations of that sort involve massive and complex changes. Darwin*, faced with such complex changes, was reduced to wild propositions such as that bears could evolve into whale-like animals:

In North America the black bear was seen by Hearne swimming for hours with widely open mouth, thus catching, like a whale, insects in the water. Even in so extreme a case as this, if the supply of insects were constant, and if better adapted competitors did not already exist in the country, I can see no difficulty in a race of bears being rendered, by natural selection, more and more aquatic in their structure and habits, with larger and larger mouths, till a creature was produced as monstrous as a whale.[685]

(3) Horses and Imagination. The horse series, which is portrayed in many public school texts, has "had to be discarded or modified" according to Raup*:

> The record of evolution is still surprisingly jerky and, ironically, we have even fewer examples of evolutionary transition than we had in Darwin's time. By this I mean that some of the classic cases of [D]arwinian change in the fossil record, such as the *evolution of the horse* in North America, have *had to be discarded or modified* as a result of more detailed information—what appeared to be a nice simple progression when relatively few data were available now appears to be much more complex and much less gradualistic.[687]

That horse series is described as "very deceptive" by Saiff* and Macbeth*:

> At the beginning of this memorandum we mentioned the belief common among nonscientists that the evolutionists had discovered innumerable phylogenies. If we are correct in saying that the search has failed miserably, the reader will ask where this common belief comes from. The answer is that to a large extent it comes from a *very deceptive picture* that has been presented over and over again in the literature. This is the famous chart that shows, in seven neatly graded steps, the supposed descent of the horses from tiny *Eohippus* to the modern *Equus*. This chart is so persuasive that most readers will be shocked to learn that it is *an illusion*.
>
> These seven stages *do not represent ancestors and descendants.* They are fossils that were taken from different times and places, and were then strung together, perhaps innocently, to show how evolution might have (or should have) handled the matter. The experts, good Darwinians though they may be, do not contend that things actually occurred in this simple straightforward way. They regret that the chart was ever made and they *have tried to expunge it* from the record, but it persists despite their efforts and appears in one textbook after another (including Dunbar's of 1949 and Grant's of 1977).[687]

That horse series is "unfortunate" in the view of Hardin*,[688] "largely apocryphal" in the assessment of Denton*,[689] and "standard iconography" but "wrong" as analyzed by Gould*:

> The evolution of the horse—both in textbook charts and museum exhibits—has a *standard iconography.* Marsh began this traditional display in his illustration for Huxley. In doing so, he also initiated an *error* that captures pictorially the most common of all misconceptions about the shape and pattern of evolutionary change.
>
> . . ..
>
> 3. Each genus is itself a bush of several related species, *not a rung on a*

ladder of progress. These species often lived and interacted in the same area at the same time (as different species of zebra do in Africa today). One set of strata in Wyoming, for example, has yielded three species of *Mesohippus* and two of *Miohippus*, all contemporaries.

4. The species of these bushes tend to *arise with geological suddenness* and then *to persist with little change* for long periods. Evolutionary change occurs at the branch points themselves, and trends are not continuous marches up ladders, but concatenations of increments achieved at nodes of branching on evolutionary bushes.

. . .Bushiness now pervades the entire phylogeny of horses.

The model of the ladder is much more than merely *wrong*. It never could provide the promised illustration of evolution progressive and triumphant for it could only be applied to unsuccessful lineages.[690]

The problems of the horse series are numerous. The small *Eohippus* may not have been a horse, as Kerkut* suggests:

We now know that the evolution of the horse did *not always take a simple path*. In the first place it is *not clear that Hyracotherium was the ancestral horse*. Thus Simpson (1945) states, "Matthew has shown and insisted that *Hyracotherium* (including *Eohippus*) is so primitive that it is *not much more definitely equid than tapirid*, rhinocerotid, etc., but it is customary to place it at the root of the equid group."[691]

The series depends on an unsupported assumption of genealogical relation between the fossils, and the sequence depends on arbitrary matching of European and American fossils.

The size has not increased gradually (as in the "iconography"), Hardin* notes:

[T]here was a time when the existing fossils of the horses seemed to indicate a straight-line evolution from small to large, from dog-like to horse-like, from animals with simple grinding teeth to animals with the complicated cusps of the modern horse. It looked straightline—like the links of a chain. But not for long. As more fossils were uncovered, the *chain splayed out into the usual phylogenetic net*, and it was all too apparent that evolution *had not been in a straight line at all*, but that (to consider size only) horses had now grown taller, now shorter, with the passage of time. *Unfortunately*, before the picture was completely clear, an *exhibit* of horses as an example of orthogenesis had been set up at the American Museum of Natural History, photographed, and much reproduced in elementary textbooks (where it is still being reprinted today).[692]

The side toes were not gradually reduced (the picture is "flatly fictitious"), Simpson* of Harvard stressed:

The most famous of all equid trends, "gradual reduction of the side toes" *is flatly fictitious*. There was no such trend in any line of Equidae. . . . Eocene horses all had digitigrade padded, doglike feet with four functional toes in front and three behind. In a rapid transition (not actually

represented by fossils), early Oligocene horses lost one functional front
toe and concentrated weight a little more on the middle hoof as a step-off
point. . . . . This type persisted without essential change in all browsing
horses.[693]

The range in size in the horse series is no greater than for modern
horses, and the number of forms worsen the missing link problems
for other animals, Denton* suggests:

> *The difference between Eohippus and the modern horse is relatively
> trivial,* yet the two forms are separated by sixty million years and at least
> ten genera and a great number of species. The horse series therefore
> tends to emphasize just how vast must have been the number of genera
> and species if all the diverse forms of life on Earth had really evolved in
> the gradual way that Darwinian evolution implies. If the horse series is
> anything to go by their numbers must have been indeed the "infinitude"
> that Darwin imagined. If ten genera separate *Eohippus* from the modern
> horse then think of the uncountable myriads there must have been
> linking such diverse forms as land mammals and whales or molluscs and
> arthropods. Yet all these myriads of life forms have vanished myste-
> riously, without leaving so much as a trace of their existence in the fossil
> record.[694]

Thus, Storer* concludes that the "real origin of horses is unknown,"[695] and some other biologists reach equally cynical
conclusions.[696]

h. To Primates and Problems

Macroevolution from lower mammals to primates is postulated to
have come through insectivores, but is "not documented by fossils,"
according to Kelso*:

> While the fossil record of insectivore evolution is reasonably good in
> some lines, the transition from *insectivore to primate* is *not documented*
> by fossils. The basis of knowledge about the transition is by *inference*
> from living forms.[697]

That lack of fossil evidence is true of both new world monkeys and
old world monkeys:

> The details of the evolutionary background of the *New World monkeys,*
> the Platyrrhinae, would doubtless be informative and interesting, but
> unfortunately *we know very little* about them.
>
>   . . ..
> . . .Clearly, the fossil documentation of the emergence of the *Old World
> monkeys* could provide key insights into the general evolutionary picture
> of the primates, but, in fact, this *record simply does not exist.*[698]

Tree shrews also do not provide the link. Campbell* writes, "I
have attempted to indicate the large number of recent studies whose

results indicate that a close relationship between tupaiids and primates is unlikely."[699]

"In spite of recent findings, the time and place of origin of order Primates remains shrouded in mystery," Simons* concludes.[700] "When and where the first Primates made their appearance is also conjectural. . . . It is clear then that the earliest Primates are not yet known," Hill* adds.[701]

i. To Man and Problems

Macroevolution from primates to man is described as follows in a typical textbook used in public schools: "Man shares a common ancestor with the apes."[702] Dobzhansky*, Ayala*, Stebbins*, and Valentine* are typical of the technical works: "at present, the evolutionary sequence *Australopithecus africanus—Australopithecus* (or *Homo) habilis—Homo erectus—Homo sapiens* seems to be the most plausible one."[703]

Yet this macroevolutionary sequence is not supported by "any fossil traces," according to Zuckerman*:

> But in the final analysis, *the answer to the question of human descent always depends upon preconceptions* about the way this evolution occurred. For example, no scientist could logically dispute the proposition that *man*, without having been involved in any act of divine creation, evolved from some ape-like creature in a very short space of time—speaking in geological terms—*without leaving any fossil traces* of the steps of the transformation.[704]

Gribben* and Cherfas* also concede "the frailty of the conventional history of man and the apes,"[705] others find the evidence less clear than the pictures,[706] and Pilbeam* concludes that human fossil study "reveals more about how humans view themselves than it does about how humans came about":

> My reservations concern not so much this book but the whole subject and methodology of paleoanthropology. . . . [P]erhaps generations of students of human evolution, including myself, have been flailing about in the dark; . . . our data base is too sparse, too slippery, for it to be able to mold our theories. Rather, the theories are more statements about us and ideology than about the past. Paleoanthropology reveals more about how humans view themselves than it does about how humans came about.
> *But that is heresy. . . .*[707]

The problem is not an inadequate fossil record. "Human evolution now seems to be largely immune to the 'poor fossil record' argument of phyletic gradualism," Stanley* writes.[708] The problem is compounded by misleading pictures, which are merely artists' imaginative portrayals:

> These reconstructions *suggest far more knowledge* of human evolution *than we actually possess.* We do *not have a complete skeleton of any fossil older than Neanderthal,* nor do we have any direct evidence about the extent of *hair* in these forms.[709]

Oxnard* remarks on "the completely different portraits that have been drawn for the facial features of a creature such as *Zinjanthropus,*"[710] and Rensberger* describes evolution taking place on the artist's palette:

> *Artists have also been rehabilitating Homo erectus,* a hominid that lived between Australopithecus and Neanderthal, *even without much change in the scientific opinion of this older species' appearance.* Again, Burian is a case in point. His *1952* version shows black, apelike creatures barely distinguishable from chimpanzees. In a *1965* painting his Homo erectus is lighter skinned and, although still hairy, more modern in aspect. Burian's *1975* Homo erectus is hairless and almost indistinguishable from people living today. The newest images of Homo erectus show them as far more modern than all but most recent depictions of their Neanderthal descendants.
>
> Once again, in the view of many paleoanthropologists, the story of *human evolution has been fictionalized* to suit needs other than scientific rigor.[711]

(1) Piltdown Fraud and Nebraska Man. Furthermore, the problem is further magnified by such frauds as Piltdown man (*Eanthropus dawsoni*), which was fraudulently fabricated from a filed down ape jaw and fossil teeth, as Himmelfarb* summarizes:

> Nor can it be maintained, as some Darwinists have done, that the exposure of Piltdown man leaves them no better and no worse off than they were before. It does, in fact, weaken their position in regard to both their theory and their methods. *The zeal with which eminent scientists defended it,* the facility with which even those who did not welcome it managed to accommodate to it, and the way in which the *most respected scientific techniques were soberly and painstakingly applied* to it, with the apparent result of confirming both the genuineness of the fossils and the truth of evolution, are at the very least *suspicious.*[712]

Nebraska man (which its discoverer modestly called *Hesperopithecus haroldcookii*) was a gross misinterpretation built on the slender evidence of a tooth, which turned out to be merely a pig's tooth. Oxnard*, an anatomist and dean of the graduate school at University of Southern California, describes it and other "difficulties":

> But we have merely to remember cases like *Piltdown man,* which turned

out to be a fraudulent composite of a genuine fossil skull cap, and a modern ape jaw, or *Hesperopithecus*, the ape of the West, which eventually was discovered to be a peccary [pig], or even of the *completely different portraits that have been drawn* for the facial features of a creature such as Zinjanthropus (Campbell 1964), to realize that this method also has many inherent difficulties.[713]

A recent hopeful link, touted as a "hominid collarbone," turned out to be a dolphin bone.[714] Anthropologist White* of Berkeley observes:

> The problem with a lot of anthropologists is that they want so much to find a hominid that any scrap of bone becomes a hominid bone.[715]

Zuckerman*, an anatomist and longtime departmental chairman of the British Advisory Council on Science Policy, is equally cynical:

> The [fossil] record is so astonishing that it is legitimate to ask whether much science is yet to be found in this field at all. The study of the Piltdown Man provides a pretty good answer.[716]

(2) Australopithecus and Homo habilis. The missing "fossil traces" are not provided by the fossil remains of Australopithecines (including *Australopithecus*, *Homo habilis*, and *Zinjanthropus*) and *Ramapithecus* (which many view as simply extinct apes), or by Neanderthal man and Cro-Magnon man (which many view as simply ancient men).

Australopithecines were simply apes, according to Zuckerman*,[717] although "facts" have not been able to "stem a tide of opinion based on *ex cathedra* statement" that Australopithecines walked upright:

> For my own part, the anatomical basis for the claim that the Australopithecines walked and ran upright like man is so much more *flimsy* than the evidence which points to the conclusion that their gait was some variant of what one sees in subhuman Primates, that it remains unacceptable.
>
> . . ..
>
> ...Where I went wrong was in supposing that, in the field of anatomy I am talking about, facts such as we have been collecting could stem a *tide of opinion* based on *ex cathedra* statement. We were not the first to make this mistake. Professor Waterston made a similar error, as I pointed out earlier on, with respect to the Piltdown skull, and so too have others, about other fossils. The *unscientific and doctrinaire* character of the whole of this field of study is well epitomised . . ..
>
> . . ..
>
> ...So much glamour still attaches to the theme of the missing link, and to man's relationships with the animal world, that it may always be difficult to exorcise from the comparative study of Primates, living and fossil, the kind of *myths* which the unaided eye is able to conjure out of a well of wishful thinking.[718]

Oxnard* agrees that Australopithecines did not walk upright and are nonhuman:

> [W]hereas the conventional wisdom is that the australopithecine frag-
> ments are generally rather similar to humans and when different deviate
> somewhat towards the condition in the African apes, the new studies
> point to different conclusions. The *new investigations* suggest that the
> fossil fragments are *usually uniquely different from any living form*:
> when they do have similarities with living species, they are as often as
> not *reminiscent of the orangutan.* This does not mean, of course, that the
> fossils are related in any genetic way to the orangutan.[719]

He thus questions whether Australopithecines are intermediate forms between ape-like ancestors and man:

> We may well have to accept that it is rather *unlikely* that any of the
> australopithecines, including *Homo habilis,* can have had *any direct
> phylogenetic link with the genus Homo.*[720]

Oxnard's position has become more and more widespread:

> *Oxnard has concluded that Australopithecus could not have been ances-
> tral to Homo* . . . .
>
> Whatever the difficulties with Oxnard's phylogenetic assessment of
> Australopithecus, his conclusions regarding morphology and behavior
> have been prophetic. His and his collaborators' claims that *Australo-
> pithecus engaged in a form of locomotion quite different from that of
> modern Homo* were ignored or ridiculed by many for years, but they have
> recently gained support . . . .
>
> Indeed, different workers using more traditional methods of compara-
> tive anatomy (Tuttle and Stern and Susman), as well as other techniques
> (Prost), have all to some degree converged upon the view presented by
> Oxnard that *australopithecines were more proficient in the trees and
> more different from modern Homo* in their form of bipedalism than was
> previously believed.[721]

In fact, Australopithecines could not be ancestors of man, because the more modern *Homo erectus* overlapped the same general time and place. As Mary Leakey* states:

> *Homo erectus, Homo habilis* and a robust australopithecine all existed at
> Olduvai during Bed II times.[722]

DeVore* found *Homo erectus* in the same stratum as *Australopithe-
cus robustus* in South Africa.[723] Richard Leakey* located a similar more-human skull (Skull 1470) that was older than Australopithe-
cines, Java man, or Peking man, and concluded, "Either we toss out this skull or we toss out our theories of early man."[724] Shipman* and others discovered another such skull (KNM-WT 1700) that "reduced all our nicely organized constructs to a rubble":

> What the new skull does, in a single stroke, is *overturn all previous
> notions of the course of early hominid evolution.*

. . ..
...And then where is the ancestral hominid species? The best answer
we can give right now is that we no longer have a very clear idea of who
gave rise to whom: we only know who didn't. This uncomfortable state of
affairs can be summarized in three simple statements: (1) *Robustus*
didn't evolve into *boisei*. (2) *Africanus* didn't evolve into *boisei*. (3) *Boisei*
didn't evolve into either *africanus* or *robustus*. In fact, we don't even
know what sort of "ancestral species" we're looking for. . . . Like an
earthquake, *the new skull has reduced our nicely organized constructs to
a rubble* of awkward, sharp-edged new hypotheses. It's a sure sign of
scientific progress.[725]

A recent fossil species, "Lucy" (*Australopithecus afarensis*), has
been proposed as a common ancestor. However, "Lucy's legs were
clearly diminutive and more like those of an ape than a human," in
the view of Jungers*.[726] Thus, Lucy probably swung from trees and
did not walk upright, Cherfas*, Stern*, and Susman* conclude.[727]
Moreover, Lucy co-existed with a more modern species, in the analysis of Tuttle*,[728] and is a younger woman than her proponents claim,
in the view of some researchers:

> A geologist and an anthropologist, working independently, have recently
> challenged the age of the Hadar fossil site in Ethiopia, raising questions
> about the age and significance of the Hadar's most famous hominid,
> Lucy. Lucy's American proprietors, while welcoming the geological clar-
> ification of the shaky Hadar dates, have rejected the anthropological
> work wholesale, charging their critic with methodological clumsiness
> and intellectual dishonesty.[729]

Homo habilis has been assessed as merely a species of *Australopithecus* and thus as an "improperly proposed" name, by Brace*.[730]
"The bones of *Homo habilis* are in many ways so similar to those of
Australopithecus africanus that placing the former species in the
genus *Homo* together with modern man is questionable," according
to Dobzhansky*, Ayala*, Stebbins*, and Valentine*, although they
see the misclassification as less consequential.[731]

(3) Ramapithecus and Homo Erectus. Ramapithecus falls in the
ape category too, according to many researchers. Fossils of "*Ramapithecus* ... seem to have been apes—morphologically, ecologically,
and behaviorally," Eckhardt* concludes.[732] In fact, the "entire
Ramapithecus, walking upright, has been 'reconstructed' from only
jaws and teeth. In 1961, an ancestral human was badly wanted.
[*Ramapithecus*] latched onto the position by his teeth, and has been
hanging on ever since. . . ."[733] Even those teeth are unlike "modern
man," according to Walker* and Andrews*:

> It seems like that R[*amapithecus*] *wickeri* had very small incisors indeed
> and posteriorly diverging and nearly straight cheek-tooth rows, *rather*

than widely separated and curved tooth rows such as are *found in modern man.*[734]

The weak state of the evidence has led "David Pilbeam, long an advocate of the hominid status of *Ramapithecus*, [to] recant his view,"[735] and Zihlman* and Lowenstein* to remain agnostic:

> There are still no skulls, no pelvic or limb bones unequivocally associated with the teeth to show whether Ramapithecus had a brain like a hominid, swung through the trees like an ape, or walked upright like a human.[736]

"*Homo* (or *Pithecanthropus*) *erectus*" was "discovered in Java... by ... Dubois," and later in Peking (hence the names Java man and Peking man).[737] The textbooks and treatises seldom mention that Dubois* himself later abandoned his belief that Java man was human rather than ape:

> *Pithecanthropus* was *not a man*, but a gigantic genus *allied to the Gibbons*, superior to its near relatives on account of its exceedingly large brain volume, and distinguished at the same time by its erect attitude.
>
> It was the surprising volume of the brain—evidenced by the size of the fossil calvaria which is very much too large for an anthropoid ape, and which is small compared with the average, though not smaller than the smallest human brain—that led to the now almost general (although, in my opinion, erroneous) view that the Ape 'Man' of Trinil, Java, was really a primitive Man. Morphologically, however, the calvaria closely resembles that of anthropoid apes, especially the gibbon. . . .[738]

Some other fossils, such as Olduvai Hominid 8, have some features "completely different from man"[739] and "reminiscent" of modern and fossil apes instead,[740] according to Oxnard*.

(4) Neanderthal and Cro-Magnon Men. Neanderthal man and Cro-Magnon man are categorized in the same species as modern humans (*Homo sapiens*). "Neanderthal man walked as erect as any modern man" and "was every bit as intelligent as we are today," according to anthropologist Montagu* of Princeton:

> Owing to want of a little knowledge of elementary anatomy, some of these 'authorities' who have engaged in 'reconstruction' of Neanderthal man have represented him with a bull neck, grotesque features, and walking with a stoop. . . . It has also often been asserted that Neanderthal man must have been of low intelligence because he had a low forehead. *All these slanders are indefensible.*[741]

One specimen of Neanderthal man appears to have been a human with a bone disease such as rickets, as Ivanhoe* diagnoses:

> Nearly a hundred years ago *Virchow diagnosed rickets in the Neandert[h]al* bones, accounting so for their peculiar simian cast. . . . But the growth of knowledge since, anthropological as well as medical, suggests that *Virchow's view may have been essentially correct.*[742]

Straus* and Cave* reach the same conclusion.[743]

(5) Apes and Man. Apes and man differ in category rather than merely in degree. One difference is in language: "almost all the psychologists and linguists who have studied the evidence closely are quite satisfied that there is a major discontinuity between human speech and the sign-making capacity of apes," Leach* points out.[744] Others reach the same conclusion.[745] Another difference is in the mind, which is "a difference in kind, and not one of degree," according to Dobzhansky*, Ayala*, Stebbins*, and Valentine* in their highly-regarded treatise:

> *Without doubt, the human mind sets our species apart* from nonhuman animals. Unfortunately, what we call the mind is notoriously refractory to scientific study. It is something that everyone apprehends by introspection, not by objective examination or measurement by some scientific means. . . .
>
> . . ..
>
> . . . Human self-awareness obviously differs greatly from any rudiments of mind that may be present in nonhuman animals. *The magnitude of the difference makes it a difference in kind, and not one of degree.* Owing primarily to this difference, mankind became an extraordinary and unique product of biological evolution.[746]

A further difference between human beings and apes is in ethics, which the same treatise and Simpson* note:

> Competent biologists disagree whether animals other than man possess capacities for ethics. Some ascribe rudiments of moral sense, for example, to dogs, which occasionally behave as though they have guilt feelings and bad conscience. *Others believe that ethics and values are exclusively in the human domain.* . . . At the same time, *one must agree with Simpson (1964) that "it is nonsensical to speak of ethics in connection with any animal other than man.* . . . There is really no point in discussing ethics, indeed one might say that the concept of ethics is meaningless, unless the following conditions exist: (a) There are alternative modes of action; (b) man is capable of judging the alternatives in ethical terms; and (c) he is free to choose what he judges to be ethically good. . . ."[747]

The fossil record—"no fossil traces"—is corroborated by the other grounds for these "natural groupings," in the view of many biologists.

Some evolutionists have ridiculed the position of nonevolutionist scientists as arguing against the straw man of "man evolving from apes." First, nonevolutionist scientists generally state the evolutionist position correctly as being that "man and apes evolved from a common ancestor." Second, the phrase "man evolved from apes"

is not a straw man, but is precisely what many if not most evolutionists claim, as Simpson* (a leading evolutionist) acknowledges:

> On this subject, by the way, there has been too much pussyfooting.
> Apologists emphasize that man cannot be a descendant of any living
> ape—a statement that is obvious to the verge of imbecility—and go on to
> state or imply that man is not really descended from an ape or monkey at
> all, but from an earlier common ancestor. In fact, *that earlier ancestor
> would certainly be called an ape or monkey* in popular speech by anyone
> who saw it. Since the terms ape and monkey are defined by popular
> usage, *man's ancestors were apes or monkeys* (or successively both). *It is
> pusillanimous if not dishonest for an informed investigator to say
> otherwise.*[748]

Darwin* himself argued that from "Old World monkeys" came
"Man":

> The Simiadae then branched off into two great stems, the New World
> and Old World monkeys; and from the latter at a remote period, Man, the
> wonder and the glory of the universe, proceeded.[749]

Dozens of other evolutionist authors make the same "ape to man"
argument, such as Montagu*,[750] Rhodes*,[751] Stokes*,[752] Eiseley*,[753]
Shapiro*,[754] Washburn*,[755] Muller*,[756] Dart*,[757] and other
Darwinians.[758]

In this field of the origin of man, Lewin* concludes that theory
relies so heavily on interpretation of a few scraps of bone that it
never can be unbiased, and Harper* sees a "clear influence of metaphysical beliefs."[758A] Here, "the mythic element is greatest" among
sciences, and "stories . . . frequently arise unprompted by data,"
according to Hill*, an anthropologist at Harvard:

> Compared to other sciences, the *mythic element is greatest in paleoan-
> thropology.* Hypotheses and stories of human evolution frequently arise
> *unprompted by data* and contain a large measure of general *preconcep-
> tions*, and the data which do exist are often insufficient to falsify or even
> substantiate them. *Many interpretations are possible.* These books all
> provide new alternatives, some refining the subject with new informa-
> tion; all, in varying degrees, *supplant the old myths with new ones.*[759]

That is precisely the point of this book: "Many interpretations are
possible."

j. To Plants and Problems

Macroevolution from early life to plants, and then to higher
plants, is contradicted by the fossil record, which actually "is in

favour of special creation," as assessed by botanist Corner* of Cambridge:

> Much evidence can be adduced in favour of the theory of evolution—from biology, bio-geography and palaeontology, but I still think that, to the unprejudiced, the *fossil record of plants* is in *favour of special creation*. If, however, another explanation could be found for this hierarchy of classification, it would be the knell of the theory of evolution. Can you imagine how an orchid, a duckweed, and a palm have come from the *same ancestry*, and *have we any evidence* for this assumption? The evolutionist must be prepared with an answer, but I think that *most would break down before an inquisition.*[760]

Darwin* himself was perplexed by the apparently "very sudden" development of higher plants:

> Nothing is more extraordinary in the history of the Vegetable Kingdom, as it seems to me, than the *apparently* very sudden or abrupt development of the higher plants.[761]

Those plants are now parentless, according to Denton* and Axelrod*:

> Again, just as in the case of the absence of pre-Cambrian fossils, no forms have ever been found in pre-Cretaceous rocks linking the angiosperms with any other group of plants. According to Daniel Axelrod
>> The ancestral group that gave rise to angiosperms has not yet been identified in the fossil record, and no living angiosperm points to such an ancestral alliance. In addition, the record has shed almost no light on relations between taxa at ordinal and family level.[762]

Early land plants are in the same straits, Axelrod* states in another article:

> As we bring early land plants into sharper focus in terms of their geologic, ecologic, and evolutionary relations, it seems clear that *our phyletic charts need extensive revision*, possibly on the order suggested here (fig. 3). Obviously, no final answers can be given to these *problems* that still surround the origins of the Psilophyte Paleoflora, and they *will be with us for years to come.* . . .[763]

Summary. These ten alleged stages of macroevolution are supported by much ardent belief but little persuasive evidence, as many evolutionists as well as discontinuitists have concluded.[764] One example is Kerkut*:

> There is a theory which states that many living animals can be observed over the course of time to undergo *changes* so that *new species are formed.* This can be called [*microevolution* or] the "Special Theory of Evolution" and can be demonstrated in certain cases by experiments. On the other hand there is the theory that *all the living forms in the world have arisen from a single source* which itself came from an inorganic form. This theory can be called [*macroevolution* or] the "General Theory

of Evolution" and the evidence that supports it is *not sufficiently strong to allow us to consider it as anything more than a working hypothesis. It is not clear whether the changes that bring about speciation are of the same nature as those that brought about the development of new phyla.* The answer will be found by future experimental work and not by dogmatic assertions that the General Theory of Evolution must be correct because there is nothing else that will satisfactorily take its place.[765]
The stages of biological macroevolution simply do not have a compelling status, and reasonable difference of opinion is possible, in the view of many scientists along with Kerkut* (but not necessarily in the view of the following scientists). The following brief quotations should be read in their full context that was given in this section.

(a) Macroevolution from prokaryotes to eukaryotes is an "area of speculation" (Whitfield*[766]) with many "microbial Just So Stories" (Levin* and Lenski*[767]). "It is not known just what were the ancestors of Protozoa" (Hickman*[768]), and there is "as yet no definite evidence from the way in which the Viruses, Bacteria or Protozoa are interrelated" (Kerkut*[769]).

(b) Macroevolution from early eukaryotes to invertebrate animals (early Metazoa) "cannot be documented from fossil evidence," so that "the origin of Metazoa is still obscure" (Dobzhansky*, Ayala*, Stebbins*, and Valentine*[770]). The "first and most important steps of animal evolution remain even more obscure than those of plant evolution" (Weiss*[771]), although nine phyla appeared so that the "seas were swarming with highly differentiated aquatic plants and animals" (Barghoorn*[772]) and so that such invertebrates are "largely immune to the 'poor fossil record' argument" (Stanley*[773]).

(c) Macroevolution from invertebrate to chordate and vertebrate fish is assumed, although "[h]ow this earliest chordate stock evolved, what stages of development it went through to eventually give rise to truly fish-like creatures, we do not know" (Ommanney*[774]), and although the "geological record has so far provided no evidence as to the origin of fishes" (Norman*[775]). There are fossils of "numerous fishlike vertebrates" (Romer*[776]), but "every other major group of fishes" have "their origins firmly based in nothing" (White*[777]).

(d) Macroevolution from fish to amphibians is such that "the gap remains unbridged and the best place to start the evolution of the vertebrates is in the imagination" (Smith*[778]). The "origin of the vertebrates [is] an unsolved problem" (Stahl*[779]), and the replacement for plausible evidence is "phantoms" and "will-o'-the-wisps"

(Patterson*[780]). Macroevolution from earlier amphibians to " 'modernized' forms is almost completely a blank" too (Romer*[781]), and "speculations about the evolution of the group" are what remain (Stahl*[782]).

(e) Macroevolution from amphibians to reptiles has "no direct proof from the fossil record" (Stirton*[783]), and "the major distinguishing adaptation of the reptiles, the amniotic egg," is unexplained and "baffling" (Denton*[784]).

(f) Macroevolution from reptiles to birds also offers "no fossil evidence of the stages through which the remarkable change ... was achieved" (Swinton*[785]), and for imagining such complex changes "the difficulties become overwhelming" (Macbeth*[786]). Although *Archaeopteryx* is often proposed as a transitional form, its fossils "do not count" (Gould* and Eldredge*[787]), "stand[] in splendid isolation" (Romer*[788]), "do not provide a sufficient basis" for the transition (Denton*[789]), and in fact are "already birds" (Russell*[790]), are " 'all bird' " (Huxley*[791]), are younger than a fairly modern bird (Marx*[792]), and are "highly improbable" to be "on the main line" to modern birds (Ostrom*[793]).

(g) Macroevolution from reptiles to mammals confronts the difficulty that "[e]ach species of mammal-like reptile that has been found appears suddenly in the fossil record and is not preceded by the species that is directly ancestral to it" (Kemp*[794]). Such "mammal-like reptiles" (on the basis of skeletons) may be "in fact in terms of their overall biology only distantly related" (Denton*[795]), possibly "were completely reptilian" (Jerison*[796]), and are described as "mammal-like reptiles" primarily on the "inadequate" basis of their jaw structure (Gow*[797]) and middle ear structure (Lombard*[798]). Macroevolution from lower mammals to higher mammals faces an absence of transitional forms that "is true of all the thirty-two orders of mammals" (Simpson*[799]), and " 'missing links' [that] have for the most part remained missing" (Russell*[800]). The horse series that has been made famous by textbook and museum "iconography" (Gould*[801]) has "had to be discarded or modified" (Raup*[802]), is "very deceptive" (Saiff* and Macbeth*[803]) and "unfortunate" (Hardin*[804]), is "largely apocryphal" (Denton*[805]) and "wrong" (Gould*[806]), and for the important changes in side toes and size is "flatly fictitious" (Simpson*[807]) and "relatively trivial" (Denton*[808]).

(h) Macroevolution from other mammals to primates is "not documented by fossils" (Kelso*[809]), and "we know very little" about the evolutionary details of the New World monkeys and the "record simply does not exist" for the Old World monkeys (Kelso*[810]). "When and where the first Primates made their appearance is also conjectural" (Hill*[811]).

(i) Macroevolution from primates to man is not supported by "any fossil traces" (Zuckerman*[812]), so that some biologists acknowledge "the frailty of the conventional history" (Gribben* and Cherfas*[813]), others conclude that human fossil study "reveals more about how humans view themselves than it does about how humans came about"—which "is heresy" (Pilbeam*[814]), and some biologists concede that "the mythic element is greatest" in human evolutionary "stories" that "frequently arise unprompted by data" (Hill*[815]). "Many interpretations are possible," a Harvard anthropologist notes (Hill*[816]). The illustrations "suggest far more knowledge of human evolution than we actually possess" such as skeletal details without complete skeletons and hair without direct evidence (Campbell*[817]), and that yields "the completely different portraits that have been drawn for the facial features of a creature such as *Zinjanthropus*" (Oxnard*[818]), and also enables artists to have "been rehabilitating *Homo erectus*" (Rensberger*[819]). As a leading researcher cautions,

> But we have merely to remember cases like Piltdown Man, which turned out to be a fraudulent composite of a genuine fossil skull cap, and a modern ape jaw, or Hesperopithecus, the ape of the West, which eventually was discovered to be a peccary [pig], or even of the completely different portraits that have been drawn for the facial features of a creature such as Zinjanthropus (Campbell 1964), to realize that this method also has many inherent difficulties. (Oxnard*[820])

Each stage of human evolution has similar difficulties, in the assessment of many researchers.

(j) Finally, macroevolution from early life to plants confronts, "to the unprejudiced, the fossil record . . . in favour of special creation" and evolutionary proposals that mostly "would break down before an inquisition" (Corner*[821]). For early land plants, "our phyletic charts need extensive revision" (Axelrod*[822]), and for flowering plants, "no forms have been found in pre-Cretaceous rocks linking the angiosperms with any other group of plants" (Denton*[823]).

Macroevolution and Darwinism, in light of this extensive authority and weak evidence, are simply noncompellingly established. Their description as unquestionable fact is mere *licentia vatum.*- Thus, alternative scientific views are possible.

Why does macroevolution still command support? The answer given by Koestler* is the general belief that "a bad theory is better than no theory": "they are unable or unwilling to realize that the citadel they are defending lies in ruins."[824]

How critical is macroevolution to science? Paleontologist Patterson* says that it conveys only "anti-knowledge" (which is as destructive of knowledge as anti-matter is of matter):

> I feel that the effect of hypotheses of common ancestry in systematics has not been merely boring, not just a lack of knowledge; I think it has been positively *anti-knowledge*. . . . Well, what about evolution? It certainly has the function of knowledge but does it convey any? Well, we are back to the question I have been putting to people, "Is there one thing you can tell me about evolution?" The absence of answers seems to suggest that it is true, evolution does *not convey any knowledge* . . . .[825]

Transformed cladists generally deny the value of evolutionary theory to classification,[826] and Rosen*, Forey*, Gardiner*, and Patterson* blame macroevolution for a "lack of progress" in paleontology.[827] Structuralists such as Webster* and Goodwin* also frequently conclude that neo-Darwinism has "extremely limited explanatory power with respect to the problem of form to which it was originally addressed," so as "to render debatable the claim that neo-Darwinism is 'the unifying theory in biology.' "[828] Many other examples have been given of scientists who question the value of neo-Darwinism or macroevolution. Mathews* describes another author as thinking macroevolution's "effect has been bad for biology."[829] Boyden* says that Darwinism led "to the most unscientific attitudes in regard to taxonomic work," and spawned a "host of phylogenies . . . like weeds."[830]

*   *   *

Biological evolution includes macroevolution as well as microevolution, and macroevolution does not have a compelling status according to many of its advocates. (Microevolution is not questioned by the theory of abrupt appearance.) Among *approaches* to macroevolution, classical Darwinian evolution has been essentially abandoned, and the modern evolutionary synthesis (neo-Darwinism) and punctuated equilibria are rejected by the non-Darwinians, many transformed cladists, anti-Darwinians, and anti-evolutionists as well as by discontinuitist scientists. In terms of postulated *mechanisms* for macroevolution, the two clear things that can be said are that evolutionist scientists do not agree on any sufficient mechanism and do not have a plausible mechanism, in the view of many. In terms of proposed *evidence* for macroevolution, the various lines of argument are not compelling, and indeed face much contrary evidence. In terms of postulated *stages* of macroevolution, the evidence is not compelling for a single segment of the alleged evolutionary tree, and the scientific evidence gives at least as much support to the systematic abrupt appearance of complex fossil organisms, the systematic gaps between fossil natural groups, the systematic anomalies in anatomical comparisons and biochemical comparisons, and the systematic consistency of classification with natural groups rather than with evolutionary lineages. Biological macroevolution and Darwinism are not compelling in the assessment of many of their friends.

Notes

[1] *The World's Most Famous Court Trial* 187 (3d ed. 1925) (transcript of *Scopes* trial) (italics added).

[2] Dobzhansky*, *Evolution*, in 10 Encyclopedia Americana 734, 748 (1982). *E.g.*, T. Dobzhansky*, F. Ayala*, G. Stebbins* & J. Valentine*, *Evolution* 129 (1977); N. Eldredge* & I. Tattersall*, *The Myths of Human Evolution* 3 (1982).

[3] F. Ayala* & J. Valentine*, *Evolving: The Theory and Processes of Organic Evolution* 1 (1979) (italics added).

[4] S. Luria*, S. Gould* & S. Singer*, *A View of Life* 767 (1981) (italics added).

[5] *E.g.*, R. Oram*, *Biology: Living Systems* 118, 248-67, 277-94, 602-23, 73T-80T, 142T-45T (3d ed. Teacher's Ed. 1979) (high school text) ("evolved from a single, original, common ancestor"). The teacher's edition of that text even says to "[s]tress the common ancestor approach." *Id.* at 607T.

[6] J. Maynard Smith*, *The Theory of Evolution* 152 (1958) ("The theory of evolution holds that existing plants and animals have originated by descent with modification from one or a few simple ancestral forms."); C. Patterson*, *Evolution* 145 (1978) ("The first is the general thesis that evolution has occurred—all animal and plant species are related by common ancestry...."); Thomson*, *Marginalia: The Meanings of Evolution*, 70 Am. Scientist 529, 529 (1982); W. Stansfield*, *The Science of Evolution* 3 (1977) ("Evolution is a scientific theory proposing that higher forms of life have descended from lower forms").

[7] Hatfield*, *Educators Against Darwin*, Science Digest Special, Winter 1979, at 94, 94.

[8] Olson*, *Morphology, Paleontology, and Evolution*, 1 Evolution after Darwin 523, 523 (S. Tax* ed. 1960).

[9] Patterson*, *Cladistics and Classification*, 94 New Scientist 303, 306 (1982); Beatty*, *Classes and Cladistics*, 31 Systematic Zoology 25, 31 (1982); Section 3.2(e).

[10] Webster* & Goodwin*, *The origin of species: a structuralist approach*, 5 J. Social & Biological Structures 15, 15-16 (1982).

[11] Dobzhansky*, *Book Review*, 29 Evolution 376, 376 (1975).

[12] P. Grassé*, *The Evolution of Living Organisms* 202 (trans. 1977).

[13] Dobzhansky*, *Book Review*, 29 Evolution 376, 376 (1975) (italics added).

[14] S. Løvtrup*, *Darwinism: The Refutation of a Myth* (1987).

[15] M. Denton*, *Evolution: A Theory in Crisis* 358 (1985) ("Ultimately the Darwinian theory of evolution is no more or less than the great cosmogenic myth of the twentieth century.").

[16] E. Ambrose*, *The Nature and Origin of the Biological World* 131 (1982).

[17] G. Sermonti* & R. Fondi*, *Dopo Darwin: Critica all' Evoluzionismo* (1980).

[18] G. Kerkut*, *Implications of Evolution* 157 *passim* (1961); Address of Dr. Colin Patterson* at American Museum of Natural History, tr. at 4 (Nov. 5, 1981) ("The second theme is that evolution not only conveys *no knowledge* but seems somehow to convey *antiknowledge* . . ..").

[19] M. Vernet*, *Révolution en Biologie* (1969).

[20] Lemoine*, *Introduction: De L'Évolution?*, in 5 Encyclopedie Française 06-6 (P. Lemoine* ed. 1937) ("The theories of evolution, with which our studious youth have been deceived, constitute actually a dogma that all the world continues to teach: but each, in his specialty, the zoologist or the botanist, ascertains that none of the explanations furnished is adequate....").

[21] F. Hitching*, *The Neck of the Giraffe: Where Darwin Went Wrong* (1982).

[22] G. Taylor*, *The Great Evolution Mystery* 137 (1983) ("the theory of evolution by natural selection seems either inadequate, implausible or definitely wrong").

[23] N. Macbeth*, *Darwin Retried* (1971).

[24] G. Himmelfarb*, *Darwin and the Darwinian Revolution* (1959).

[25] A. Koestler*, *Janus: A Summing Up* 192 (1978).

[26] J. Rifkin*, *Algeny* 123 (1983).

[27] Bethell*, *Darwin's Mistake*, Harper's Magazine, Feb. 1976, at 70, 72.

[28] G. Simpson*, *This View of Life* 30 (1964).

[29] Austin Analytical Consulting*, Opinion Poll for Biology Teachers q.8 (1986) (nationwide standardized survey, 95% confidence interval).

[30] Ho* & Saunders*, *Preface*, to Beyond Neo-Darwinism ix, ix eds. (M. Ho* & P. Saunders* eds. 1984) (italics added).

[31] M. Denton*, *Evolution: A Theory in Crisis* (1985).

[32] T. Dobzhansky*, F. Ayala*, G. Stebbins* & J. Valentine*, *Evolution* 5 (1977). *See also* D. Raup* & S. Stanley*, *Principles of Paleontology* 103 (2d ed. 1978).

[33] *E.g.*, F. Ayala* & J. Valentine*, *Evolving: The Theory and Processes of*

Organic Evolution 110 (1979); T. Dobzhansky*, F. Ayala*, G. Stebbins* & J. Valentine*, *Evolution* 129 (1977); G. Stebbins*, *Darwin to DNA, Molecules to Humanity* 7 (1982); Mayr*, *Evolution*, in Evolution at 2, 3 (E. Mayr* ed. 1978); T. Dobzhansky*, *Evolution, Genetics, and Man* 2 (1955); Committee on Science and Creation*, *Science and Creation: A View from the National Academy of Sciences* 14 (1984); N. Eldredge* & I. Tattersall*, *The Myths of Human Evolution* 3 (1982); Ayala*, *Biological Evolution: Natural Selection or Random Walk*, 62 Am. Scientist 692, 693 (1974).

34 Riddiford* & Penny*, *The scientific status of modern evolutionary theory*, in Evolutionary Theory: Paths into the Future 1, 4 (J. Pollard* ed. 1984).

35 S. Luria*, S. Gould* & S. Singer*, *A View of Life* 773, 774 (1981) (italics added). *See also* Gould*, *The Return of Hopeful Monsters*, Natural History, June-July 1977, at 22, 22 ("Macroevolution (major structural transition"); "microevolution (flies in bottles)").

36 Mayr*, *Prologue*, in The Evolutionary Synthesis 1, 36 (E. Mayr* & W. Provine* eds. 1980) ("macroevolution, which deals with *evolutionary phenomena above the species level*").

37 Stanley*, *Macroevolution and the Fossil Record*, 36 Evolution 460, 471 (1982).

38 G. Simpson*, *The Major Features of Evolution* 338 (1953).

39 Riddiford* & Penny*, *The scientific status of modern evolutionary theory*, in Evolutionary Theory: Paths into the Future 1, 4 (J. Pollard* ed. 1984) (Macroevolution "considers the question of whether evolution has occurred and by what pathways. It was called the theory of descent by Darwin and the fact of evolution by Julian Huxley.").

40 *E.g.*, S. Stanley*, *Macroevolution: Pattern and Process* (1979); Gould*, *Irrelevance, Submission and Partnership: The Changing Role of Paleontology in Darwin's Three Centennials and a Modest Proposal for Macroevolution*, in Evolution from Molecules to Men 347 (D. Bendall* ed. 1983); Ayala*, *Microevolution and Macroevolution*, in *id.* at 387; Gould* & Eldredge*, *Punctuated equilibria: The tempo and mode of evolution reconsidered*, 3 Paleobiology 115, 139 *passim* (1977); G. Stebbins* & F. Ayala*, *Is a New Evolutionary Synthesis Necessary?*, 213 Science 967, 968, 971 (1981); Gould*, *G.G. Simpson, Paleontology, and the Modern Synthesis*, in The Evolutionary Synthesis 153, 170 (E. Mayr* & W. Provine* eds. 1980); D. Raup* & S. Stanley*, *Principles of Paleontology* 303 (2d ed. 1978); Raup*, *The Geological and Paleontological Arguments of Creation*, in Scientists Confront Creationism 147, 162 (L. Godfrey* ed. 1983).

41 E. Mayr*, *The Growth of Biological Thought* 117 (1982) (Harvard U. Press).

42 A. Kluge*, *Chordate Structure and Function* 22 (2d ed. 1977).

43 Dobzhansky*, *Evolution*, 10 Encyclopedia Americana 734, 748 (1982).

44 Simpson*, *The World into Which Darwin Led Us*, 131 Science 966, 970 (1960) (italics added).

45 G. Hardin*, *Nature and Man's Fate* 66 (1959) (" 'From amoeba to man'

became a catchword after Darwin.").

[46]   G. Stebbins*, *Darwin to DNA, Molecules to Humanity* 174 (1982) ("Part Two: The Course of Evolution: from Molecules to Primates").

[47]   Riddiford* & Penny*, *The scientific status of modern evolutionary theory*, in Evolutionary Theory: Paths into the Future 4 (J. Pollard* ed. 1984).

[48]   R. Good*, *Features of Evolution in the Flowering Plants* 383 (1974).

[49]   *E.g.*, Kenyon, *The Creationist View of Biologic Origins*, NEXA Journal, Spring 1984, at 28, 31-34:

> It is of course *possible that new species, genera, and occasionally even families, may have arisen by natural means* since the original creation, provided that the new forms did not contain significantly more genetic information than their progenitors. Examples here might include Darwin's finches (some of which are known to interbreed in the wild leaving fertile offspring) (Bowman 1982), and the thousands of species of orchids.
>   . . ..
> The field studies reported in the evolutionary journals involve *microevolutionary change*, about which there is *no dispute.*   . . .
>   . . ..
> It is worth mentioning again that besides the origin of life, the major disagreement between creationists and evolutionists involves macroevolution, not microevolution. *Both sides are in substantial agreement about the latter.* In fact creationists regard much of what Darwin wrote to be basically correct. Moreover, they acknowledge the validity of most of the research described in the journals of evolutionary biology. Outside the subject of [macro]evolution there *is substantial agreement between the two sides on at least 90% of the subject matter of the biological sciences.*

Id. at 28 (italics added).

[50]   Grassé* emphasized: "To vary and to evolve are two different things; this can never be sufficiently emphasized...." P. Grassé*, *The Evolution of Living Organisms* 6 (trans. 1977).

[51]   R. Good*, *Features of Evolution in the Flowering Plants* 5 (1974).

[52]   O'Grady*, *Evolutionary Theory and Teleology*, 107 J. Theoretical Biology 563, 567 (1984) (most italics added).

[53]   Riddiford* & Penny*, *The scientific status of modern evolutionary theory*, in Evolutionary Theory: Paths into the Future 1, 4-5 (J. Pollard* ed. 1984) (italics in original).

[54]   E. Mayr*, *The Growth of Biological Thought* 117 (1982).

[55]   C. Sagan*, *Cosmos* 27 (1980) (italics in original).

[56]   Lewontin*, *Evolution/Creation Debate: A Time for Truth*, 31 Bioscience 559 (1981); Hughes*, *The Fact and the Theory of Evolution*, 44 Am. Biology Teacher 25, 27 (1982). Other examples are given in Section 10.4(b).

[57]   T. Dobzhansky*, F. Ayala*, G. Stebbins* & J. Valentine*, *Evolution* 5 (1977) (italics added). "Transspecific evolution" in the quotation means

macroevolution. D. Raup* & S. Stanley*, *Principles of Paleontology* 103 (2d ed. 1978).

58 Gould*, *Darwinism Defined: The Difference between Fact and Theory*, Discover, Jan. 1987, at 64, 65.

59 R. Good*, *Features of Evolution in the Flowering Plants* 2 (1974) (italics added).

60 M. Denton*, *Evolution: A Theory in Crisis* 77 (1985) (italics added).

61 Ayala*, *Evolution: Beyond Reasonable Doubt*, 11 Skeptical Inquirer 149, 149 (1986-87) (italics added).

62 Futuyma*, *World Without Design*, Natural History, March 1987, at 34, 34 (italics added).

63 D. Brooks* & E. Wiley*, *Evolution as Entropy* xii (1986) (U. of Chicago Press) (italics added).

64 G. Kerkut*, *Implications of Evolution* 157 (1960) (italics added).

65 N. Eldredge*, *The Monkey Business: A Scientist Looks at Creationism* 28-29 (1982) (italics added).

66 M. Denton*, *Evolution: A Theory in Crisis* 75 (1985) (italics added).

67 Boyden*, *Systematic Zoology: A Critical Appraisal, Pt. I*, 15 Physiological Zoology 109, 117 (1982) (italics added).

68 Note 4.

69 Note 2.

70 Note 53.

71 Note 51.

72 Note 57.

73 Note 67.

74 Note 65.

75 White*, *Presidential Address: A little on Lung-fishes*, 177 Proc. Linnean Society 8 (1966).

76 Stonehouse*, *Introduction*, to M. Pitman, Adam and Evolution 9, 12 (1984) (italics added).

77 N. Eldredge* & I. Tattersall*, *The Myths of Human Evolution* 45-46 (1982) (italics added).

78 Beckner*, *Darwinism*, 2 Encyclopedia of Philosophy 296, 298 (P. Edwards* ed. 1967). Stansfield* points out this error:

> One of the most damaging omissions to a complete theory of evolution was the lack of knowledge at that time of the mechanism of heredity and the origin of variations through genetic mutation. To fill this void, Darwin proposed a "pangenesis theory," according to which all parts of the body generate minute particles called "gemmules," which were carried by the blood . . ..

W. Stansfield*, *The Science of Evolution* 38 (1977). See also Dobzhansky*, *Evolution*, 10 Encyclopedia Americana 734, 738 (1982).

79 Rosen* notes that macroevolutionists have "redefined natural selection":

> That their concern was justified is indicated by the *retreat of selection-*

ists to a seemingly fortified position which rejected Darwin's original concept as a creative force in the origin of new species and *redefined natural selection* in terms of population genetics.

Rosen*, *Book Review*, 27 Systematic Zoology 370, 370 (1978) (italics added). *See also* Dobzhansky*, *Evolution*, 10 Encyclopedia Americana 734, 743 (1982).

[80] Gould*, *Evolution's Erratic Pace*, Natural History, May 1977, at 13, 14 (italics added). He also states:

To Darwin . . . speciation entailed the same expectation as phyletic evolution: a long and insensibly graded chain of intermediate forms. Our present *texts* have not *abandoned* this view, although *modern biology has.*

Eldredge* & Gould*, *Punctuated Equilibria: An Alternative to Phyletic Gradualism*, in Models in Paleobiology 82, 89 (J. Schopf* ed. 1972).

[81] N. Macbeth*, *Darwin Retried* 6, 134 (1971) (italics added).

[82] Mayr*, *Prologue*, in The Evolutionary Synthesis 1, 1 (E. Mayr* & W. Provine* eds. 1980). *See also* Mayr*, *Evolution*, Scientific Am., Sept. 1978, at 47, 52.

[83] D. Raup* & S. Stanley*, *Principles of Paleontology* 327 (2d ed. 1978); S. Luria*, S. Gould* & S. Singer*, *A View of Life* 765 (1981); T. Dobzhansky*, *Genetics and the Origin of Species* 7-8 (2d ed. 1941).

[84] *E.g.*, T. Dobzhansky*, F. Ayala*, G. Stebbins* & J. Valentine*, *Evolution* 166 (1977) ("The evolution was gradual; sudden radical transformations did not occur.").

[85] Mayr*, *Evolution*, Scientific Am., Sept. 1978, at 47, 52. *See also* T. Dobzhansky*, F. Ayala*, G. Stebbins* & J. Valentine*, *Evolution* 504 (1977).

[86] Gould*, *Is a new and general theory of evolution emerging?*, 6 Paleobiology 120-21 (1980). He states in full:

I have been reluctant to admit it . . . but if Mayr's characterization of the *synthetic theory* is accurate, then that theory, as a general proposition, is *effectively dead, despite its persistence as textbook orthodoxy.*

. . ..

The synthesis is now *breaking down* on both sides of this argument. Many evolutionists now doubt exclusive control by [natural] selection upon genetic change within local populations.

Id. at 120, 121 (italics added).

[87] Saunders*, *Book Review*, New Scientist, Feb. 21, 1985, at 44, 44.

[88] Macbeth*, *How To Defuse a Feud*, Kronos, Summer 1982, at 1, 3-4.

[89] Cracraft*, *Book Review of Beyond Neo-Darwinism*, 1 Cladistics 300, 303 (1985) (italics added).

[90] N. Eldredge* & I. Tattersall*, *The Myths of Human Evolution* 2 (1982).

[91] S. Stanley*, *Macroevolution* 11 (1979).

[92] Gould*, *Darwinism and the Expansion of Evolutionary Theory*, 216 Science 380, 382 (1982); Gould*, *The Return of Hopeful Monsters*, Natural History, June-July 1977, at 22, 22.

[93] N. Eldredge* in "Did Darwin Get It Wrong?," tr. at 6 (NOVA No. 816, WGBH, Boston, Mass., Nov. 1, 1981).

[94] *Id.* (italics added). Gould* elaborates on abrupt appearances and systematic gaps:

The *fossil record offered no support* for gradual change: whole fauna had been wiped out during disarmingly short intervals (see my column of October 1974). New species almost always appeared suddenly in the fossil record with no intermediate links to ancestors in older rocks of the same region.

Gould*, *Evolution's Erratic Pace*, Natural History, May 1977, at 12, 12 (italics added).

[95] S. Stanley*, *Macroevolution* 39 (1979). *See also* S. Stanley*, *The New Evolutionary Timetable* 78 (1981).

[96] Sections 3.3 (introduction) & 3.3(a).

[97] D. Raup* & S. Stanley*, *Principles of Paleontology* 326-27 (2d ed. 1978) (italics added).

[98] *E.g.* G. Stebbins*, *Darwin to DNA, Molecules to Humanity* 475 (1982) (italics added); Gould*, *The Ediacaran Experiment*, Natural History, Feb. 1984, at 14, 23; Gould*, *Toward the Vindication of Punctuational Change*, in Catastrophes and Earth History: The New Uniformitarianism 9, 16-17 (W. Berggren* & J. Van Couvering* eds. 1984) (" 'punctuational change,' that is, by relatively rapid flips between fairly stable equilibria").

[99] Gould* & Eldredge*, *Punctuated equilibria: The tempo and mode of evolution reconsidered*, 3 Paleobiology 115, 115 (1977). *See also* S. Luria*, S. Gould* & S. Singer*, *A View of Life* 625 (1981).

[100] *E.g.*, Gould*, *Evolution's Erratic Pace*, Natural History, May 1977, at 12, 12 ("New species almost always *appeared suddenly* in the fossil record with *no intermediate links* to ancestors in older rocks of the same region."); P. Grassé*, *The Evolution of Living Organisms* 84 (trans. 1977) ("present living beings differ [hardly] at all from those of the past"); Sections 2.1 & 2.2.

[101] Note 90.

[102] Dawkins*, *What was all the fuss about?*, 316 Nature 683 (1985) (italics in original).

[103] R. Dawkins*, *The Blind Watchmaker* 226 (1986).

[104] Section 3.3(e).

[105] Schopf*, *A Critical Assessment of Punctuated Equilibria*, 36 Evolution 1144 (1982).

[106] Maynard Smith*, *Current controversies in evolutionary biology*, in Dimensions of Darwinism 273 (M. Grene* ed. 1983).

[107] Hoffman*, *Species Selection*, 18 Evolutionary Biology 1 (1984); Hoffman* & Hecht*, *Species selection as a causal process: A reply*, in Dimensions of Darwinism 275 (M. Grene* ed. 1983).

[108] W. Arthur*, *Theories of Life* 162-64 (1987).

[109] Levinton* & Simon*, *A Critique of the Punctuated Equilibria Model and Implications for the Detection of Speciation in the Fossil Record*, 29 Systematic Zoology 130 (1980).

[110]   Charlesworth*, Lande* & Slatkin*, *A Neo-Darwinian Commentary on Macroevolution*, 36 Evolution 474, 486 (1982).

[111]   Valentine* & Erwin*, *Interpreting Great Development Experiments: The Fossil Record*, in Development as an Evolutionary Process 71, 95-96 (1987).

[112]   Olson*, *Morphology, Paleontology, and Evolution*, 1 Evolution after Darwin 523, 523 (S. Tax* ed. 1960).

[113]   M. Denton*, *Evolution: A Theory in Crisis* 327-28 (1985) (italics added).

[114]   Riddiford* & Penny*, *The scientific status of modern evolutionary theory*, in Evolutionary Theory: Paths into the Future 1-2 (J. Pollard* ed. 1984).

[115]   Bulhof*, *The Netherlands*, in The Comparative Reception of Darwinism 306 (T. Glick* ed. 1974).

[116]   R. Goldschmidt*, *The Material Basis of Evolution* (1940).

[117]   O. Schindewolf*, *Grundfragen der Paleontologie* (1950).

[118]   Spath*, *The Evolution of the Cephalopoda*, 8 Biol. Rev. 418 (1933).

[119]   A. Clark*, *The New Evolution: Zoogenesis* (1930); *see* G. Simpson*, *The Major Features of Evolution* 360 (1953); Mayr*, *Evolution*, Scientific Am., Sept. 1978, at 47, 49.

[120]   V. Grant*, *Organismic Evolution* (1977).

[121]   M. Wolsky* & A. Wolsky*, *The Mechanism of Evolution: A New Look at Old Ideas* (1976).

[122]   Wassermann*, *Testability of the Role of Natural Selection within Theories of Population Genetics and Evolution*, 29 British J. Philosophy of Science 223, 234 (1978).

[123]   Grene*, *Introduction*, to Dimensions of Darwinism 1, 8 (M. Grene* ed. 1983).

[124]   *Workshop on Structuralism in Biology*, 80 Rivista di Biologia (Biology Forum) 80 (1987).

[125]   Webster* & Goodwin*, *The Origin of Species: A structuralist approach*, 5 J. Social & Biological Structures 15, 15-16, 44 (1982) (italics added). *See also* O'Grady*, Evolutionary Theory and Teleology, 107 J. Theoretical Biology 563, 563 (1984).

[126]   Hughes* & Lambert*, *Functionalism, Structuralism, and "Ways of Seeing,"* 111 J. Theoretical Biology 787, 796 (1984).

[127]   D. Brooks* & E. Wiley*, *Evolution as Entropy* ix (1986) (U. of Chicago Press).

[128]   Szent-Gyorgyi*, *The Evolutionary Paradox and Biological Stability*, in Molecular Evolution: Prebiological and Biological 111 (D. Rohlfing* & A. Oparin* eds. 1972) ("I could never accept this answer. Random shuttling of bricks will never build a castle or a Greek temple, however long the available time.").

[129]   S. Løvtrup*, *Darwinism: The Refutation of a Myth* 352 (1987) (italics added).

[130] Ho*, Saunders* & Fox*, *A new paradigm for evolution*, New Scientist, Feb. 27, 1986, at 41. *See also Evolutionary Theory: Paths into the Future* (J. Pollard* ed. 1984).

[131] Schwabe*, *On the validity of molecular evolution*, 11 Trends in Biochemical Sciences 280, 282 (1986).

[132] Hsü*, *Darwin's three mistakes*, 14 Geology 532, 534 (1986).

[133] Eisenstein*, *Ist die Evolutionstheorie wissenschaftlich begründet?*, 3 Philosophia Naturalis 241, 404 (1975).

[134] P. Grassé*, *The Origin of Living Organisms* (trans. 1977).

[135] Lemoine*, *Introduction: De L'Évolution?*, in 5 Encyclopedie Française 06-6 (P. Lemoine* ed. 1937).

[136] Løvtrup*, *Letter*, 24 Systematic Zoology 507, 507 (1975) ("I think you will appreciate why I find Mr. Norman Macbeth is justified in the criticisms he advances in his extremely readable book and in his letter to you. And that by option for Goldschmidt's theory he demonstrates a deeper understanding of the realities of phylogenetic evolution than most members of the 'fraternity'."); N. Macbeth*, *Darwin Retried* 134 (1971) ("In examining the single parts of classical Darwinism, I concluded that they were all sadly decayed."); Macbeth*, *The Hypothesis of Divergent Ancestry*, 5 Historia Natural 321, 326 (1985) ("the plausibility of the HDA [hypothesis of divergent ancestry] declines to a low point").

[137] E. Ambrose*, *The Nature and Origin of the Biological World* 131 (1982).

[138] E. Russell*, *The Diversity of Animals* 69-71 (1962) ("Also the profusion and variety of form and behaviour is such as to render extremely improbable the theory that these forms have arisen through the natural selection of chance variations which happened to be advantageous in the struggle for existence. . . . These facts, so well illustrated in the Decapods, *must lead us to doubt the general validity of the utilitarian theory of evolution.*").

[139] Martin*, *A Non-Geneticist Looks at Evolution*, 41 Am. Scientist 100, 100, 105 (1953) ("Nevertheless there are some like myself who cannot see that *the mutation-selection theory* is wholly convincing as a means of explaining natural evolution and, perhaps erroneously, we believe that our dissent is not so much due to a failure to master the facts as to our grasp of some facts which we think geneticists are apt to overlook. . . . The object of this paper is to show that *this theory may be an illusion.*") (italics added).

[140] P. Grassé*, *The Evolution of Living Organisms* 202 (trans. 1977). He also states:

Present-day ultra-Darwinism, which is so sure of itself, impresses incompletely informed biologists, *misleads them, and inspires fallacious interpretations.* . . .

. . ..

Through use and abuse of hidden postulates, of bold, often ill-founded extrapolations, a *pseudoscience has been created.* It is taking root in the very heart of biology and is *leading astray* many biochemists and biologists, who sincerely believe that the accuracy of fundamental concepts has been demonstrated, which is not the case. *Id.* at 6 (italics added).

[141] Lemoine*, *Introduction: De L'Evolution?*, in 5 Encyclopedie Française 06-6 (P. Lemoine* ed. 1937) (italics added).

[142] R. Good*, *Features of Evolution in the Flowering Plants* (1974) (italics added) (emeritus professor of botany at U. Hull).

[143] Erbrich*, *On the Probability of the Emergence of a Protein with a Particular Function*, 34 Acta Biotheoretica 53, 78 (1985).

[144] *E.g.*, F. Hitching*, *The Neck of the Giraffe: Where Darwin Went Wrong* (1982).

[145] G. Taylor*, *The Great Evolution Mystery* 137-38 (1983) ("the theory of evolution by natural selection seems either inadequate, implausible or definitely wrong").

[146] J. Rifkin*, *Algeny* 135 (1983)("Darwin and his twentieth-century apologists have been in error.").

[147] G. Himmelfarb*, *Darwin and the Darwinian Revolution* (1959).

[148] A. Koestler*, *Janus: A Summing Up* 185 (1978).

[149] Cladistics is a "philosophy of classification that arranges organisms only by their order of branching in an evolutionary tree and not by their morphological similarity." S. Luria*, S. Gould* & S. Singer*, *A View of Life* 763 (1981). *See also* Platnick*, *Philosophy and the Transformation of Cladistics*, 28 Systematic Zoology 537, 538 (1979).

[150] Ball*, *On Groups, Existence and the Ordering of Nature*, 32 Systematic Zoology 446, 446 (1983).

[151] Beatty*, *Classes and Cladists*, 31 Systematic Zoology 25, 31 (1982).

[152] Patterson*, *Cladistics and Classification*, 94 New Scientist 303, 306 (1982).

[153] Oldroyd*, *Charles Darwin's Theory of Evolution: A Review of Present Understanding*, 1 Biology & Philosophy 133, 154 (1986) (italics added).

[154] Grene*, *Introduction*, to Dimensions of Darwinism 1, 8 (M. Grene* ed. 1983).

[155] Patterson*, *Cladistics*, 27 Biologist 234, 239 (1980) ("But as the theory of cladistics had developed, it has been realized that more and more of the evolutionary framework is inessential, and may be dropped. . . . Platnick refers to the new theory as 'transformed cladistics' and the transformation is away from dependence on evolutionary theory. Indeed, Gareth Nelson, who is chiefly responsible for the transformation, put it like this in a letter to me this summer: 'In a way, I think we are merely rediscovering preevolutionary systematics; or if not rediscovering it, fleshing it out.' "); Forey*, *Neontological Analysis Versus Palaeontological Stories*, in Problems of Phylogenetic Reconstruction 119, 119, 124 (K. Joysey* & A. Friday* eds. 1982).

[156] Address of Dr. Colin Patterson* at American Museum of Natural History, tr. at 1, 4 (Nov. 5, 1981) (italics added).

[157] Cracraft*, *Book Review*, 1 Cladistics 300, 300 (1985). He opposes transformed cladistics.

[158] Nelson* & Platnick*, *Systematics and Evolution*, in Beyond Neo-Darwinism 143, 143-46 (M. Ho* & P. Saunders* eds. 1984).

[159] Olson*, *Morphology, Paleontology, and Evolution*, 1 Evolution after Darwin 523, 523 (S. Tax* ed. 1960).

[160] G. Kerkut*, *Implications of Evolution* 150 (1960).

[161] Lipson*, *A Physicist Looks at Evolution*, 31 Physics Bulletin 138, 138 (1980).

[162] M. Denton*, *Evolution: A Theory in Crisis* 16, 353 (1985) (italics added).

[163] G. Sermonti* & R. Fondi*, *Dopo Darwin: Critica all' Evoluzionismo* (1980). *See also* Sermonti* & Sermonti*, *The null hypothesis in vertebrate evolution*, 80 Rivista di Biologia (Biology Forum) 55 (1987).

[164] M. Vernet*, *Révolution en Biologie* (1969); M. Vernet*, *La Grande Illusion de Teilhard de Chardin* (1964); M. Vernet*, *L'Evolution du Monde Vivant* (1950).

[165] Section 15.2(a).

[166] D. Hull*, *Darwin and His Critics* 450-51 (1973) (U. of Chicago Press).

[167] E. Mayr*, *The Growth of Biological Thought* 218 (1982) (Harvard U. Press).

[168] *E.g.*, J. Rifkin*, *Algeny* 135 (1983) ("The fossil record and modern breeding techniques both argue convincingly that *Darwin and his twentieth-century apologists* have been in *error*. Both the fossils and experiments in breeding overwhelmingly attest to the fact that variations within a species promote stasis, not transformation; yet the extrapolation continues, despite all the concrete evidence to the contrary.") (italics added); A. Standen*, *Science Is a Sacred Cow* (1950).

[169] Note 77.

[170] Note 80.

[171] Note 79.

[172] Note 86.

[173] Quoted in note 88.

[174] Note 87.

[175] Note 89.

[176] Note 103. *E.g.*, notes 105-111.

[177] Note 113.

[178] Note 150.

[179] Note 156

[180] Note 162.

[181] Note 160.

[182] T. Dobzhansky*, F. Ayala*, G. Stebbins* & J. Valentine*, *Evolution* 5 (1977).

[183] *Id.* at 129 (italics added).

[184] G. Stebbins*, *Darwin to DNA, Molecules to Humanity* 24-25 (1982); Dobzhansky*, *Evolution*, 10 Encyclopedia Americana 734, 741 (1982); F.

Ayala* & J. Valentine*, *Evolving: The Theory and Processes of Organic Evolution* 110 (1979).

185 Mayr* similarly states:

The first step is the production (through *recombination, mutation*, and *chance* events) of genetic variability; the second is the ordering of that variability by *selection. Most of the variation* produced by the first step is *random* in that it is not caused by, and is unrelated to, the current needs of the organism or the nature of its environment.

Mayr*, *Evolution*, Scientific Am., Sept. 1978, at 47, 52. *See also* Mayr*, *Prologue*, in The Evolutionary Synthesis 1, 1 (E. Mayr* & W. Provine* eds. 1980).

186 *E.g.*, Smith*, *The Limitations of Evolutionary Theory*, in 2 The Encyclopedia of Ignorance 235, 235-42 (R. Duncan* & M. Weston-Smith* eds. 1977); T. Dobzhansky*, F. Ayala*, G. Stebbins* & J. Valentine*, *Evolution* 72, 157 (1977); S. Luria*, S. Gould* & S. Singer*, *A View of Life* 769 (1981); D. Raup* & S. Stanley*, *Principles of Paleontology* 106 (2d ed. 1978); Alexander*. *Evolution, Creation, and Biology Teaching*, in Evolution versus Creationism 90, 95-96 (J. Zetterberg* ed. 1983); Saunders* & Ho*, *Is Neo-Darwinism Falsifiable?—And Does It Matter?*, 4 Nature & System 179, 180 (1982).

187 *E.g.*, D. Raup* & S. Stanley*, *Principles of Paleontology* 103 (2d ed. 1978) ("Phyletic evolution usually results from the operation of *natural selection* on the genetic composition of one or more populations. Variation in the gene pool produces variation in the *phenotype* (form, structure, physiology, and behavior) of organisms making up the population. This variability arises in various ways. The most fundamental way is by point *mutations*, which represent changes in single genes. . . . [M]ost of the total variability within populations arises as the changed genetic material is *recombined* or reshuffled among all the members of the population in the process of reproduction."); S. Luria*, S. Gould* & S. Singer*, *A View of Life* 625 (1981) ("genes mutate, individuals are selected, and species evolve.").

188 *E.g.*, Stanley*, *Macroevolution and the Fossil Record*, 36 Evolution 460, 471 (1982); Gould*, *The promise of paleobiology as a nomothetic, evolutionary discipline*, 6 Paleobiology 96, 106 (1980); S. Luria*, S. Gould* & S. Singer*, *A View of Life* 618-19, 626 (1981). Species selection was described briefly in Section 3.2(c), and is assessed in Section 3.3(f).

189 *E.g.*, T. Dobzhansky*, F. Ayala*, G. Stebbins* & J. Valentine*, *Evolution* 5 (1977) ("Few biologists now doubt that these three processes, acting concurrently, can be responsible for the origin of diverse races and species."); F. Ayala* & J. Valentine*, *Evolving: The Theory and Processes of Organic Evolution* 110 (1979) ("Thus, evolution may be seen as a two-step process . . . mutation and recombination and natural selection."); Stanley*, *Macroevolution and the Fossil Record*, 36 Evolution 460, 471 (1982) ("phyletic evolution" "amounts to little more than fine tuning," while "speciation events are largely responsible for the origin of higher taxa"); Gould*, *The*

promise of paleobiology as a nomothetic, evolutionary discipline, 6 Paleobiology 96, 106 (1980) ("Macroevolutionary changes are a result of the differential success of species," or species selection).

[190] Lewin*, *Evolutionary Theory Under Fire,* 210 Science 883 (1980).

[191] *E.g.,* T. Dobzhansky*, F. Ayala*, G. Stebbins* & J. Valentine*, *Evolution* 6 (1977) (italics added). They of course assume that extrapolation "can succeed only if it is based upon enough information of the right kind."

[192] Mayr*, *Prologue,* in The Evolutionary Synthesis 1, 1 (E. Mayr* & W. Provine* eds. 1980).

[193] Gould* & Eldredge*, *Punctuated equilibria: The tempo and mode of evolution reconsidered,* 3 Paleobiology 115, 143 (1977).

[194] N. Eldredge* & I. Tattersall*, *The Myths of Human Evolution* 44 (1982) (italics added).

[195] Gould*, *The Return of Hopeful Monsters,* Natural History, June-July 1977, at 22, 24 ("macroevolution is not simply microevolution extrapolated"); Gould*, *The promise of paleobiology as a nomothetic, evolutionary discipline,* 6 Paleobiology 96, 106 (1980) ("this process *cannot be smoothly extrapolated* to encompass evolutionary trends, because macroevolution resides on another level of the evolutionary hierarchy").

[196] Stanley*, *A Theory of Evolution Above the Species Level,* 72 Proc. National Academy of Sciences 646, 648 (1975). *See also* Hoffman*, *Paleobiology at the crossroads: a critique of some modern paleobiological research programs,* in Dimensions of Darwinism 241, 242 (M. Grene* ed. 1983).

[197] Lewin*, *Evolutionary Theory Under Fire,* 210 Science 883, 883 (1980) (there was no consensus that microevolution and macroevolution could be decoupled either).

[198] Saunders* & Ho*, *Is Neo-Darwinism Falsifiable?—And Does it Matter?,* 4 Nature & System 179, 191 (1982) (italics added). Gould* similarly states:

> Geneticists can study the gradual increase of favored genes within populations of *fruit flies* in laboratory bottles. Naturalists can record the steady replacement of light *moths* by dark moths as industrial soot blackens the trees of Britain. Orthodox *neo-Darwinians extrapolate* these even and continuous changes to the most profound structural transitions in the history of life: by a long series of insensibly graded intermediate steps, birds are linked to reptiles, fish with jaws to their jawless ancestors. *Macroevolution* (major structural transition) is nothing more than microevolution (flies in bottles) extended. If black moths can displace white ones in a century, then reptiles can become birds in a few million years by the smooth and sequential summation of countless changes. *Change of gene frequencies* in local populations is an adequate model for all evolutionary processes—or so the current orthodoxy states.

Gould*, *The Return of Hopeful Monsters,* Natural History, June-July 1977, at 22, 22 (italics added, footnotes omitted).

[199] Erwin* & Valentine*, *"Hopeful Monsters," transposons, and Metazoan radiation*, 81 Proc. National Academy Sciences 5482, 5482 (1984) (italics added).

[200] E. Russell*, *The Diversity of Animals* 123 (1962).

[201] G. Kerkut*, *Implications of Evolution* 157 (1961) ("It is not clear whether the changes that bring about speciation are of the same nature as those that brought about the development of new phyla.").

[202] G. Simpson*, *The Major Features of Evolution* 338 (1953) ("Goldschmidt uses his terms to emphasize the belief that microevolution, so defined, is something definitely and qualitatively different from macroevolution and not involved in or leading to the latter.").

[203] V. Grant*, *Organismic Evolution* (1977).

[204] Kitts*, *Paleontology and Evolutionary Theory*, 20 Evolution 458 (1974).

[205] Ricklefs*, *Book Review*, 199 Science 58 (1978).

[206] M. Wolsky* & A. Wolsky*, *The Mechanism of Evolution: A New Look at Old Ideas* (1976).

[207] N. Macbeth*, *Darwin Retried* 34, 35 (1971) ("there is no evidence that micro changes cumulate into macro effects").

[208] P. Grassé*, *The Evolution of Living Organisms* 87-88 (trans. 1977) (italics added).

[209] S. Løvtrup*, *Darwinism: The Refutation of a Myth* 351 (1987).

[210] S. Luria*, S. Gould* & S. Singer*, *A View of Life* 775 (1981). *See also* F. Ayala* & J. Valentine*, *Evolving: The Theory and Processes of Organic Evolution* 440 (1979).

[211] T. Dobzhansky*, F. Ayala*, G. Stebbins* & J. Valentine*, *Evolution* 32, 504 (1977).

[212] Mayr*, *Prologue*, in The Evolutionary Synthesis 1, 24 (E. Mayr* & W. Provine* eds. 1980) ("second of the two principal components of Darwin's theory of evolution").

[213] Mayr*, *Accident or Design, The Paradox of Evolution*, in The Evolution of Living Organisms 1, 7-8 (G. Leeper* ed. 1962) (Cambridge U. Press) (italics added).

[214] Maze*, *Neo-Darwinian Evolution—Panacea or Popgun*, 31 Systematic Zoology 92, 93 (1982) (italics added).

[215] Forey*, *Neontological Analysis Versus Palaeontological Stories*, in Problems of Phylogenetic Reconstruction 119, 124 (K. Joysey* & A. Friday* eds. 1982) ("Suffice it to say that there have been recent views (Løvtrup 1977; Macbeth 1973; Rosen 1978) expressing *serious doubts about the theory of natural selection*, or at least the ways in which it may be tested and placed on a scientific plane. I confess *sympathy* with these views.") (italics added).

[216] Gruner*, *On Evolution and Its Relation to Natural Selection*, 16 Dialogue 708, 714 (1977) ("The belief is now prevalent that evolution and natural selection are connected in that the former—alone or together with other factors—explains why the latter occurs. In fact, however, in the situation of today the belief is lacking in support.").

²¹⁷   Rosen*, *Darwin's Demon*, 27 Systematic Zoology 370, 373 (1978) (hoping that " 'natural selection' is stripped from our technical vocabulary and irrelevant argument ceases in consequence") (italics added).

²¹⁸   G. Simpson*, *The Major Features of Evolution* 118-19 (1953) ("it might be argued that the theory is quite *unsubstantiated* and has status only as a *speculation*.") (italics added).

²¹⁹   Hoffman*, *Paleobiology at the crossroads: a critique of some modern paleobiological research programs*, in Dimensions of Darwinism 241, 262 (M. Grene* ed. 1983) ("natural selection is irrelevant to, or negligible in the context of, macroevolutionary change"); N. Macbeth*, *Darwin Retried* 45-46 (1971); F. Hoyle, *The Intelligent Universe: A New View of Creation and Evolution* 40 (1983) ("Unless it is arbitrarily assumed that these characteristics had some great but unknown different use during their development, it must be concluded that Darwinian natural selection played *little or no part in their origin*.") (italics added).

²²⁰   Stanley*, *A Theory of Evolution Above the Species Level*, 72 Proc. National Academy Sciences 646, 648, 650 (1975). *See also* Gould*, *Is a New and General Theory of Evolution Emerging?*, 6 Paleobiology 119, 121 (1980) ("Many evolutionists now doubt exclusive control by [natural] selection upon genetic change within local populations."); Wiley* & Brooks*, *Victims of History—A Nonequilibrium Approach to Evolution*, 31 Systematic Zoology 1 (1982) (rejecting natural selection as a significant factor in speciation).

²²¹   These are listed and quoted in Section 10.4(b).

²²²   These are listed and quoted in Section 10.3(b).

²²³   These are listed and quoted in Section 10.2(a)(2).

²²⁴   Brady*, *Natural Selection and the Criteria by Which a Theory Is Judged*, 28 Systematic Zoology 600, 600 (1979).

²²⁵   Waddington*, *Evolutionary Adaptation*, in 1 Evolution after Darwin 381, 385 (S. Tax* ed. 1960).

²²⁶   Bradie* & Gromko*, *The Status of the Principle of Natural Selection*, 3 Nature & System 3, 7 (1981).

²²⁷   Hughes* & Lambert, *Functionalism, Structuralism, and "Ways of Seeing,"* 111 J. Theoretical Biology 787, 796-97 (1984) (italics added, original italics deleted).

²²⁸   Rosen*, *Darwin's Demon*, 27 Systematic Zoology 370, 372 (1978).

²²⁹   Cracraft*, *The Use of Functional and Adaptive Criteria in Phylogenetic Systematics*, 21 Am. Zoologist 21, 34-35 (1981) (italics added).

²³⁰   Leith*, *Are the Reports of Darwin's Death Exaggerated?*, 166 The Listener 390, 391 (1981) (italics added).

²³¹   Grene*, a noted philosopher, states that "minute specialised adaptations" are not relevant to macroevolution or even the origin of species:

And if one returns to the *Origin* [*of Species*] with these criticisms in mind, one finds, indeed, that for all the brilliance of its *hypotheses piled on hypotheses*, for all the splendid simplicity of the "mechanism" by which it "explains" so many and so varied phenomena, *it simply is not about the origin of species*, let alone of the great orders and classes and phyla, at all. Its argument moves in a different direction altogether, in the direction of *minute specialised adaptations*, which lead, unless to extinction, nowhere. . . . *.How from single-celled (and for that matter from inanimate)* ancestors there came to be castor beans and moths and snails, and how from these there emerged llamas and hedgehogs and lions and apes—and men—that is a question which neo-Darwinian theory simply leaves unasked.

Grene*, *The Faith of Darwinism*, Encounter, Nov. 1959, at 48, 49 (italics added).

[232] Note 13.

[233] P. Grassé, *The Evolution of Living Organisms* 170 (trans. 1977).

[234] Manly*, *Tests of the Theory of Natural Selection: an Overview*, 15 J. Royal Society of New Zealand 411, 411, 425 (1985) (italics added).

[235] R. Good*, *Features of Evolution in the Flowering Plants* 385-86 (1974) (italics added).

[236] S. Luria*, S. Gould* & S. Singer*, *A View of Life* 626 (1981). Kettlewell*, the primary researcher, modestly calls it "the most striking evolutionary change ever witnessed by man." Kettlewell*, *Darwin's Missing Evidence*, Scientific Am., Mar. 1959, at 48, 48.

[237] P. Grassé*, *The Evolution of Living Organisms* 84 (trans. 1977) (latter italics added).

[238] Mathews*, *Introduction*, to C. Darwin*, The Origin of Species xi (1971) (italics added).

[239] Saunders* & Ho*, *Is Neo-Darwinism Falsifiable?—And Does It Matter?*, 4 Nature & System 179, 191 (1982).

[240] Brady*, *Dogma and Doubt*, 17 Biological J. of the British Linnean Soc. 79, 89, 90 (1982) ("There are two parts to this proposal. The first is that selective pressure can approximate the breeder; the second, which I have termed 'central', is that the differential so produced can culminate in new forms. The *industrial melanism* observations have confirmed prediction with regard to the first part, i.e. a specific change in allele frequency, parallel to that produced by a breeder, may be caused by one-sided predator pressure (one-sided in that the melanistic variant is better camouflaged). Can this confirmation be transferred to part two? Not at all, since this is the more radical claim. There seems to be some confusion about this point, but the argument is simple enough. What if such differentials *do not* culminate in *new forms*? After all, *they did not do so in experiments mentioned*.") (italics added).

[241] Lambert*, Millar* & Hughes*, *Teaching the classic case of natural selection*, 79 Rivista di Biologia 117, 117, 118 (1986), quoting Jones*, *More to melanism than meets the eye*, 300 Nature 109, 109 (1981) ("[W]e suggest that there are many serious problems with these field experiments which purpose to provide supporting evidence for this classic example in neo-Darwinian theory . . .. Jones (1981, p. 109) was quite right when he remarked: 'Industrial melanism is the textbook example of natural selection in action. Like most such examples it is usually presented in a way

which is both incomplete and inaccurate.' ").

242 Grene*, *The Faith of Darwinism*, Encounter, Nov. 1959, at 48, 49 ("There are, indeed, all the minute specialised divergences like those of the *Galapagos finches* which so fascinated Darwin; it is their story that is told in the *Origin* and elaborated by the selectionists to-day. But these are *dead ends*, last minutiae of development; it is not from them that the great massive novelties of evolution could have sprung.") (italics added).

242A Harper*, *A critical review of theories concerning the origin of the Darwin finches*, 14 J. Biogeography 391, 401, 402 (1987).

243 Saunders* & Ho*, *Is Neo-Darwinism Falsifiable?—And Does It Matter?*, 4 Nature & System 179, 191 (1982) (italics added).

244 Section 3.4(h).

245 Raup*, *Conflicts between Darwin and Paleontology*, Field Museum of Natural History Bull., Jan. 1979, at 22, 29 (italics added); N. Macbeth*, *Darwin Retried* 118 (1971). This problem also includes the question why some species have *not* become extinct. G. Simpson*, *The Meaning of Evolution* 202 (rev. ed. 1967); N. Macbeth*, *Darwin Retried* 120-21 (1971).

246 F. Hoyle, *The Intelligent Universe: A New View of Creation and Evolution* 41, 48 (1983) (italics added).

247 Section 3.2(d).

248 L. Eiseley*, *The Unexpected Universe* 142 (1969) (italics added).

249 E. Russell*, *The Diversity of Animals* (1962):

Also the profusion and variety of form and behaviour is such as to render *extremely improbable* the theory that these forms have arisen through the natural selection of chance variations which happened to be advantageous in the struggle for existence.

. . ..

The following questions suggest themselves. *Why are there so many variants* on the same typal theme, so many family and generic sub-types, most of *which do not show any marked adaptive specialization*, so far at least as our limited knowledge goes? Why is there such a profusion of strange and fantastic forms, especially in the deep sea? Why do so many genera split up into a *multiplicity of species, whose differences*, so far as we can see, *are not "adaptive"*? To these questions the utilitarian theory gives no satisfactory answer.

These facts, so well illustrated in the Decapods, *must lead us to doubt* the general validity of the utilitarian theory of evolution.

Id. at 69-71 (italics added).

250 Gould*, *Not Necessarily a Wing*, Natural History, Oct. 1985, at 12, 18.

251 Gould*, *Archetype and Adaptation*, Natural History, Oct. 1986, at 16, 26.

252 Gould*, *Darwinism Defined: The Difference Between Fact and Theory*, Discover, Jan. 1987, at 64, 64. *See also* Section 15.2(b).

253 Beckner*, *Darwinism*, 2 Encyclopedia of Philosophy 296, 299 (P. Edwards* ed. 1967).

254 "Mutation" is "a change in the genetic material" (or DNA). S. Luria*, S.

Gould* & S. Singer*, *A View of Life* 775 (1981); F. Ayala* & J. Valentine*, *Evolving: The Theory and Processes of Organic Evolution* 440 (1979). "They can be classified in one of two major categories: *gene (or point) mutations*, which affect only one or a few nucleotides within a gene; and *chromosomal mutations* (or aberrations), which affect the number of chromosomes, or the number or the arrangement of genes in a chromosome." T. Dobzhansky*, F. Ayala*, G. Stebbins* & J. Valentine*, *Evolution* 57 (1977) (italics added). *See also* Stebbins* & Ayala*, *Is a New Evolutionary Synthesis Necessary?*, 213 Science 967, 967 (1981).

[255] T. Dobzhansky*, F. Ayala*, G. Stebbins* & J. Valentine*, *Evolution* 5, 107 (1977). *See also* Mayr*, *Evolution*, Scientific Am., Sept. 1978, at 47, 52.

[256] Mayr*, *Prologue*, in The Evolutionary Synthesis 1, 20 (E. Mayr* & W. Provine* eds. 1980). *See also* Stebbins* & Ayala*, *Is a New Evolutionary Synthesis Necessary?*, 213 Science 967, 967 (1981) ("mutations are the ultimate source of the genetic variation that makes possible the evolutionary process."); F. Ayala* & J. Valentine*, *Evolving: The Theory and Processes of Organic Evolution* 110 (1979) ("*Mutations* are the *ultimate source of all hereditary variability*.").

[257] S. Luria*, S. Gould* & S. Singer*, *A View of Life* 625 (1981) ("*Mutations* are the ultimate source of *new genetic variability*.").

[258] P. Grassé*, *The Evolution of Living Organisms* 87-88 (trans. 1977) (italics added).

[259] E. Russell*, *The Diversity of Animals* 123 (1962) ("It would seem on the face of it that gene mutations provide a very unpromising raw material for large-scale evolution. Viable mutations are of the same order as the trivial differences between intra-specific races, and as such seem quite incapable of giving rise to the major divergences of structuro-functional organisation which characterise large scale habit and habitat specialisation and typal diversification."). *See also* Martin*, *A Non-Geneticist Looks at Evolution*, 41 Am. Scientist 100, 104 (1953) ("too trifling and insignificant to be credited with even the most microscopic survival value").

[260] Gould* & Eldredge*, *Punctuated equilibria: The tempo and mode of evolution reconsidered*, 3 Paleobiology 115, 151 (1977) ("We do not see how point mutations in structural genes can lead, even by gradual accumulation, to new morphological designs."); Stanley*, *Macroevolution and the Fossil Record*, 36 Evolution 460, 471 (1982) ("the apparently trivial role of mutation pressure"); E. Ambrose*, *The Nature and Origin of the Biological World* 122 (1982) ("minor changes due to point mutations have little effect on the overall integrated activities.").

[261] Byles*, *Limiting Conditions for the Operation of the Probable Mutation Effect*, 19 Social Biology 29, 31-32 (1972) (italics added).

[262] Martin*, *A Non-Geneticist Looks at Evolution*, 41 Am. Scientist 100, 100, 103 (1953) ("*[A]ll mutations seem to be in the nature of injuries* that, to some extent, impair the fertility and viability of the affected organisms. I *doubt* if among the many thousands of known mutant types *one can be*

found which is superior to the wild type in its normal environment[;] only very few can be named which are superior to the wild type in a strange environment. . . . *[A]ll, or almost all, known mutations are unmistakably pathological* and the few remaining ones are highly suspect.") (italics added).

263 2 *The Life and Letters of Charles Darwin* 210 (F. Darwin* ed. 1887).

265 Erwin* & Valentine*, *"Hopeful Monsters," transposons, and Metazoan radiation*, 81 Proc. Nat. Acad. Sciences 5482, 5482 (1984) (italics added).

266 E. Steele*, *Somatic Selection and Adaptive Evolution* 4 (2d ed. 1981) (U. Chicago Press).

267 Byles*, *Limiting Conditions for the Operation of the Probable Mutation Effect*, 19 Social Biology 29, 32 (1972).

268 F. Hoyle, *The Intelligent Universe* 35 (1983).

269 E. Ambrose*, *The Nature and Origin of the Biological World* 120-21 (1982). *See also* J. Huxley*, *Evolution in Action* 45 (1953).

270 E. Ambrose*, *The Nature and Origin of the Biological World* 123-24 (1982) ("The difficulties in explaining the origin of increased complexity as a result of bringing a 'cluster' of genes together within the nuclei of a single organism in terms of probabilities, fade into insignificance when we recognize that there must be a close integration of functions between the individual genes of the cluster, which must also be integrated into the development of the entire organism. The improbability increases at an enormous rate as the number of genes increases from one to five. . . . The problem of bringing together the five mutated genes we are considering, within a single nucleus, and for them to 'fit' immediately into this vast complex of interacting units, is indeed difficult. When it is remembered that they must give some selective advantage, or else become scattered once more within the population at large, due to interbreeding, it seems impossible to explain these events in terms of random mutation alone.").

271 E. Steele*, *Somatic Selection and Adaptive Evolution* 4 (2d ed. 1981).

272 Wald* estimates that "something of the order of 10 million years is needed to establish a mutation. That is, each of these single amino acid changes appears relatively frequently in individuals as pathology; but to establish one such change as a regular characteristic in a species seems to take something of the order of 10 million years." Wald*, *The Problems of Vicarious Selection*, in Mathematical Challenges to the Neo-Darwinian Interpretation of Evolution 59, 59 (P. Moorhead* & M. Kaplan* eds. 1967).

273 McDonald*, *The Molecular Basis of Adaptation*, 14 Ann. Rev. Ecology & Systematics 77, 94 (1983).

274 *Id.* at 92-93 (italics in original).

275 Section 2.6.

276 T. Dobzhansky*, F. Ayala*, G. Stebbins* & J. Valentine*, *Evolution* 5 (1977). *See also* Mayr*, *Prologue*, in The Evolutionary Synthesis 1, 1 (E. Mayr* & W. Provine* eds. 1980).

277 T. Dobzhansky*, F. Ayala*, G. Stebbins* & J. Valentine*, *Evolution* 129 (1977); S. Luria*, S. Gould* & S. Singer*, *A View of Life* 780 (1981).

278 J. Savage*, *Evolution* 73 (3d ed. 1977) (italics added).

279 R. Bohinski*, *Modern Concepts in Biochemistry* 456 (1983). Thus, Bohinski* concludes, "At present there is no understanding of the genetic or evolutionary significance of the existence in DNA of the same gene with and without introns. The extent to which this occurs is also unknown." *Id.*

280 Miklos* & John*, *From Genome to Phenotype*, in Rates of Evolution 263, 267 (K. Campbell* & M. Day* eds. 1987)

281 F. Ayala* & J. Valentine*, *Evolving: The Theory and Processes of Organic Evolution* 115 (1979); Smith*, *The Limitations of Evolutionary Theory*, in 2 The Encyclopedia of Ignorance 235, 235-42 (R. Duncan* & M. Weston-Smith* eds. 1977).

282 T. Dobzhansky*, F. Ayala*, G. Stebbins* & J. Valentine*, *Evolution* 72 (1977). *See also* Smith*, *The Limitations of Evolutionary Theory*, in 2 The Encyclopedia of Ignorance 235, 235-42 (R. Duncan* & M. Weston-Smith* eds. 1977).

283 D. Raup* & S. Stanley*, *Principles of Paleontology* 106 (2d ed. 1978). *See also* F. Ayala* & J. Valentine*, *Evolving: The Theory and Processes of Organic Evolution* 438 (1979).

284 T. Dobzhansky*, F. Ayala*, G. Stebbins* & J. Valentine*, *Evolution* 157 (1977). *See also* E. Dodson*, *Evolution: Process and Product* 258-59 (1960) ("Genetic drift is a force working in opposition to selection, for it tends to preserve or destroy genes without distinction, whether favorable, neutral or unfavorable."); S. Luria*, S. Gould* & S. Singer*, *A View of Life* 769 (1981).

285 Stanley*, *Macroevolution and the Fossil Record*, 36 Evolution 460, 471 (1982) (italics added). Stanley* continues with a discussion of "phylogenetic drift" and "directed speciation," as well as "species selection."

286 Gould*, *The promise of paleobiology as a nomothetic, evolutionary discipline*, 6 Paleobiology 96, 106 (1980); Gould*, *The Ediacaran Experiment*, Natural History, Feb. 1984, at 14, 23; S. Luria*, S. Gould* & S. Singer*, *A View of Life* 618-19 (1981).

287 Stanley*, *A Theory of Evolution Above the Species Level*, 72 Proc. National Acad. Sciences 646, 648 (1975). *See also* Stanley*, *Macroevolution and the Fossil Record*, 36 Evolution 460, 471 (1982).

288 Gould*, *The promise of paleobiology as a nomothetic, evolutionary discipline*, 6 Paleobiology 96, 106 (1980). *See also* S. Luria*, S. Gould*, & S. Singer*, *A View of Life* 518-19 (1981) (It is "the most important process and . . . the key to understanding larger patterns in evolution.").

289 Stanley*, *A Theory of Evolution Above the Species Level*, 72 Proc. National Academy of Sciences 646, 646 (1975).

290 Schopf*, *A Critical Assessment of Punctuated Equilibria*, 36 Evolution 1144, 1155 (1982) (listing "four prominent biases that act to lengthen durations of taxa"); Hoffman*, *Punctuated Versus Gradual Mode of Evolution*, 15 Evolutionary Biology 411, 421 (1982) (arguing "that sympatric specia-

tion may occur under a wide variety of conditions" other than punctuated equilibria factors).

291 Schopf*, *A Critical Assessment of Punctuated Equilibria*, 36 Evolution 1144, 1156 (1982).

292 R. Dawkins*, *The Blind Watchmaker* 268-69 (1986) (italics added). *See also* R. Dawkins*, *The Extended Phenotype* 107-08 (1982):

> My provisional guess is that species selection will not be found to be a generally satisfactory explanation of complex adaptation.

> The theory of species selection, growing out of that of punctuated equilibria, is a stimulating idea which may well explain some single dimensions of quantitative change in macroevolution. *I would be very surprised if it could be used to explain the sort of complex multidimensional adaptation that I find interesting, the 'Paley's watch', or 'Organs of extreme Perfection and Complication', kind of adaptation that seems to demand a shaping agent at least as powerful as a deity. . . .*

293 M. Denton*, *Evolution: A Theory in Crisis* 193 (1986) (italics added).

294 R. Dawkins*, *The Extended Phenotype* 294 (1982) ("it cannot account for the evolution of complex adaptation"); R. Dawkins*, *What was all the fuss about?*, 316 Nature 683, 684 (1985).

295 G. Kerkut*, *Implications of Evolution* 157 (1960).

296 Valentine* & Erwin*, *Interpreting Great Developmental Experiments: The Fossil Record*, in Development as an Evolutionary Process 71, 95 (1987).

297 W. Arthur*, *Theories of Life* 164 (1987).

298 Maynard Smith*, *Current controversies in evolutionary biology*, in Dimensions of Darwinism 273, 279 (M. Grene* ed. 1983) (italics added).

299 R. Dawkins*, *The Blind Watchmaker* 266 (1986) (italics added).

300 Grene*, *Introduction*, to Dimensions of Darwinism 1, 10 (M. Grene* ed. 1983) ("But if a species is selected because 'it' runs faster, that is just shorthand for the fact that its members (in Hullian terms, its parts!) run faster. In such a case, it is the individual phenotype, not the whole species, that the process of natural selection affects.").

301 Hoffman*, *Paleobiology at the crossroads: a critique of some modern paleobiological research programs*, in Dimensions of Darwinism 241, 249 (M. Grene* ed. 1983) ("Third, the community paradigm implies that a significant role in evolution is assigned to group selection. To claim that some ecological and/or evolutionary processes exist that act directly at the community level but are inapplicable at the lower levels of biotic organization, is equivalent to the assertion that some community properties induce a natural selection for certain features that may cause a decrease in individual fitness if it is outweighed by a parallel increase in selection value of the community. *Otherwise, all community properties would be perfectly explicable by reference to the component individuals. However, there is no overall structural property of a community that would be able to impose any constraints directly upon the individual* selection because the community structure itself is, by definition, expressed in terms of population sizes.") (italics added).

[302] R. Dawkins*, *The Blind Watchmaker* 268 (1986).

[303] Hoffman*, *Species Selection*, 18 Evolutionary Biology 1, 15 (1984).

[304] Hoffman* & Hecht*, *Species Selection As a Causal Process: A Reply*, 19 Evolutionary Biology 275, 277 (1985) ("Three conditions must be met in order to demonstrate convincingly the actual operation of species selection: . . . a pattern must be established that calls for an explanation that could be phrased in terms of species selection. Second, a biological property of the clades must be identified that can be reasonably conceived of as *causing* the observed difference. . . . Third, we must be able to show that the inferred species selection is *irreducible to individual selection.* This is needed not because a potential reducibility would rule out the possibility that a particular instance actually is, or includes a component of species selection, but because we could otherwise not distinguish empirically between species selection and individual selection.").

[305] *Id.* at 280 (italics added).

[306] *Id.* at 278 ("However there is absolutely *no evidence* for the claim that the volutids with nonplanktotrophic larvae did indeed undergo founder-induced or peripatric *speciation.* There is, consequently, *no irreducibility of the alleged process to individual selection.* In fact, there is *no compelling evidence for the existence of a pattern that might be interpreted as caused by species selection.* There are no data to demonstrate that the rate of speciation actually was higher in the volutid clades with nonplanktotrophic larvae. Hansen's data contain only species lists at various stratigraphic levels. How much of the apparent turnover from one level to another is due to pseudoextinction and immigration rather than true cladogenesis is unknown.").

[307] *Id.* ("It should also be noted that the importance of speciation by founder events, even among the Hawaiian drosophilids, let alone as a common mechanism of speciation, has *not gone unchallenged* (Barton and Charlesworth, 1984). But even if we accept, for the sake of the argument, that the founder-induced speciation does indeed introduce irreducibility to individual selection and that the Hawaiian drosophilids do indeed owe their enormous speciosity to the increased frequency of this process, this is *not a sufficent condition for the occurrence of species selection as a causal process.* For Sober's necessary condition for selection is not met in this case. The alleged commonness of founder-induced speciation among Hawaiian drosophilids as opposed to their continental relatives is due to environmental conditions rather than to any biological property of the Hawaiian clade(s). In other words, we do not deal here with a case of causal selection at all, but *merely with [natural] selection of* Hawaiian drosophilids, unless, of course, one believes that, in contrast to their continental relatives, the Hawaiian drosophilids have indeed some particular biological properties that make them more prone to undergo founder-induced speciation.").

[308] Schopf*, *A Critical Assessment of Punctuated Equilibria*, 36 Evolution 1144, 1156 (1982) (italics added). *See also* Bookstein*, Gingerich* & Kluge*, *Hierarchical Linear Modeling of the Tempo and Mode of Evolution*, 4

Paleobiology 120 (1978); D. Raup* & R. Crick*, *Evolution of Single Characters in the Jurassic Ammonite* Kosmoceras, 7 Paleobiology 200 (1981).

[309] Hoffman* & Hecht*, *Species Selection As a Causal Process: A Reply*, 19 Evolutionary Biology 275, 276 (1985) (most italics added).

[310] Levinton* & Simon*, *A Critique of the Punctuated Equilibria Model and Implications for the Detection of Speciation in the Fossil Record*, 29 Systematic Zoology 130, 138-40 (1980).

[311] Charlesworth*, Lande* & Slatkin*, *A Neo-Darwinian Commentary on Macroevolution*, 36 Evolution 474, 486, 492 (1982) (emphasis added).

[312] Valentine* & Erwin*, *Interpreting Great Development Experiments: The Fossil Record*, in Development as an Evolutionary Process 71, 96 (1987).

[313] Futuyma*, *World Without Design*, Natural History, March 1987, at 34, 34. He does not acknowledge that that is precisely the point of Gould* and Eldredge*: that neo-Darwinians misinterpret Darwin* as being more gradualistic and less punctuationalistic than he really was.

[314] Hoffman*, *Punctuated versus Gradual Mode of Evolution*, 15 Evolutionary Biology 411, 413 (1982).

[315] S. Luria*, S. Gould* & S. Singer*, *A View of Life*, 626, 639 (1981).

[316] *Interview: Ernst Mayr*, Omni, Feb. 1983, at 73, 78.

[317] Bush*, *What Do We Really Know about Speciation?*, in Perspectives on Evolution 119, 119 (R. Milkman* ed. 1982).

[318] S. Stanley*, *Macroevolution: Pattern and Process* 6 (1979) (italics added).

[319] Stanley* recognizes this problem:

> We might conclude that if large populations, like those in A and B, evolve slowly, and if small populations sometimes evolve rapidly, *then populations of intermediate size may*, on the average, *evolve at intermediate rates*. This is *presumably* the case; yet I will offer evidence that *few major transitions occur* (few higher taxa originate) except in quite small populations.

S. Stanley*, *Macroevolution* 28 (1979) (italics added).

[320] Valentine* & Erwin*, *Interpreting Great Developmental Experiments: The Fossil Record*, in Development as an Evolutionary Process 71, 96, 95 (1987) (italics added).

[321] Ridley*, *Evolution and gaps in the fossil record*, 286 Nature 444, 444 (1980).

[322] Levinton* & Simon*, *A Critique of the Punctuated Equilibria Model and Implications for the Detection of Speciation in the Fossil Record*, 24 Systematic Zoology 130, 132-34 (1980).

[323] *Id.* at 135-36.

[324] Stanley*, *Macroevolution and the Fossil Record*, 36 Evolution 460, 471 (1982).

[325] Hoffman* & Hecht*, *Species Selection As a Causal Process: A Reply*, 19 Evolutionary Biology 275, 280 (1985) (italics added).

[326] For example, "like natural selection itself, [species selection] comes close to being a tautology." W. Arthur*, *Theories of Life* 163-64 (1987).

[327] Cracraft*, *Book Review of Beyond Neo-Darwinism*, 1 Cladistics 300, 301 (1985) (italics added).

[328] S. Luria*, S. Gould* & S. Singer*, *A View of Life* 759 (1981). *See also* A. Kluge*, *Chordate Structure and Function* 7 (2d ed. 1977).

[329] Popper*, *Autobiography of Karl Popper*, in 1 The Philosophy of Karl Popper 1, 137 (P. Schilpp* ed. 1974) (italics added).

[330] Brady*, *Natural Selection and the Criteria by Which a Theory Is Judged*, 28 Systematic Zoology 600, 608 (1979) (italics added).

[331] Simpson*, *The Major Features of Evolution* 278 (1953). *See also* G. Stebbins*, *Variation and Evolution in Plants* 118 (1950) ("Unfortunately, however, the determination of the adaptive character of many types of differences between organisms is one of the most difficult problems in biology."); Dobzhansky*, *Book Review*, 29 Evolution 376 (1975) ("not even a biologist of Grassé's experience can judge reliably which 'characters' are neutral, useful, or harmful in a given species"); Leith*, *Are the Reports of Darwin's Death Exaggerated?*, 166 The Listener 390, 392 (1981) (Patterson*: "I think there is a valid criticism that has been made by a number of people that Darwinists . . . sometimes come up with very *fanciful adaptive explanations* of things. . . . [S]ometimes they're completely fanciful and false.") (italics added).

[332] Grene*, *Introduction*, to Dimensions of Darwinism 1, 11 (M. Grene* ed. 1983).

[333] C. Patterson*, *Evolution* 143 (1978).

[334] Charlesworth*, Lande* & Slatkin*, *A Neo-Darwinian Commentary on Macroevolution*, 36 Evolution 474, 486 (1982) (italics added). *See also* McDonald*, *The Molecular Basis of Adaptation: A Critical Review of Relevant Ideas and Observations*, 14 Annual Rev. Ecology & Systematics 77, 85 (1983).

[335] Miklos* & John*, *From genome to phenotype*, in Rates of Evolution 263, 277 (K. Campbell* & M. Day* eds. 1987).

[336] McDonald*, *The Molecular Basis of Adaptation: A Critical Review of Relevant Ideas and Observations*, 14 Ann. Rev. Ecology & Systematics 77, 92-93 (1983) (italics in original for last sentence, italics otherwise added). *See also* McDonald*, *The Molecular Basis of Adaptation*, 14 Ann. Rev. Ecology & Systematics 77, 85 (1983).

[337] E. Ambrose*, *The Nature and Origin of the Biological World* 124 (1982) (italics added).

[338] Ho* & Saunders*, *What Is the Unit of Natural Selection?*, 5 Evolutionary Theory 169, 170 (1981).

[339] S. Luria*, S. Gould* & S. Singer*, *A View of Life* 636 (1981). *See also* Gould*, *The Return of Hopeful Monsters*, Natural History, June-July 1977, at 22, 30.

[340] S. Luria*, S. Gould* & S. Singer*, *A View of Life* 767 (1981).

[341] Gould*, *The Return of Hopeful Monsters*, Natural History, June-July 1977, at 22; Hoffman*, *Punctuated versus Gradual Mode of Evolution*, 15 Evolutionary Biology 411, 411 (1982).

342 Cracraft*, *Book Review of Beyond Neo-Darwinism*, 1 Cladistics 300, 302 (1985) (italics added).

343 P. Grassé*, *Evolution of Living Organisms* 31 (trans. 1977).

344 Stebbins* & Ayala*, *Is a New Evolutionary Synthesis Necessary?*, 213 Science 967, 969 (1981).

345 E. Mayr*, *Populations, Species and Evolution* 253 (1970) (Harvard U. Press) (italics added).

346 Maynard Smith*, *Current controversies in evolutionary biology*, in Dimensions of Darwinism 273, 276 (M. Grene* ed. 1983).

347 Wright*, *Character Change, Speciation, and the Higher Taxa*, 36 Evolution 427, 440 (1982).

348 Lande*, *Microevolution in Relation to Macroevolution*, in Evolution Now 146, 146 (J. Maynard Smith* ed. 1982).

349 M. Denton*, *Evolution: A Theory in Crisis* 230 (1985).

350 D. Brooks* & E. Wiley*, *Evolution as Entropy* xi (1986) (U. Chicago Press).

351 *See* Sections 2.4-2.5 & 4.1-4.2.

352 Note 211.

353 Note 233.

354 Note 327.

355 Note 287.

356 Note 291.

357 Notes 298-301.

358 Note 305.

359 Note 309.

360 W. Stansfield*, *The Science of Evolution* 98 (1977) (italics added). *See also* Committee on Science and Creationism*, *Science and Creationism: A View from the National Academy of Sciences* 15 (1984).

361 R. Good*, *Features of Evolution in the Flowering Plants* 3 (1974).

362 Gould*, *Darwinism Defined: The Difference Between Fact and Theory*, Discover, Jan. 1987, at 64, 65, 68.

363 P. Grassé, *The Evolution of Living Organisms* 6 (trans. 1977) (italics added).

364 G. Kerkut*, *Implications of Evolution* vii (1960) (italics added).

365 R. Good*, *Features of Evolution in the Flowering Plants* 4 (1974).

366 W. Stansfield*, *The Science of Evolution* 67 (1977).

367 Valentine*, *Darwin's Impact on Paleontology*, 32 BioScience 513, 517 (1982). *See also* P. Grassé*, *The Evolution of Living Organisms* 4 (trans. 1977) ("only paleontology can provide . . . the evidence of evolution and reveal its course or mechanism").

368 T. Dobzhansky*, F. Ayala*, G. Stebbins* & J. Valentine*, *Evolution* 314 (1977). *See also* R. Good*, *Features of Evolution in the Flowering Plants* 4 (1974) ("the fossil record is unquestionably the most satisfying of the evidences of evolution").

369 Sections 2.1-2.2.

370 Ridley*, *Who Doubts Evolution?*, 90 New Scientist 830, 831 (1981).

[371]   Hoffman*, *Paleobiology at the crossroads: a critique of some modern paleobiological research programs*, in Dimensions of Darwinism 241 (M. Grene* ed. 1983).

[372]   Patterson*, *Significance of Fossils in Determining Evolutionary Relationships*, 12 Ann. Rev. Ecology & Systematics 195, 218 (1981) (italics added).

[373]   Gould*, *The Five Kingdoms*, Natural History, June-July 1976, at 30, 37 (italics added).

[374]   Gould*, *Evolution's Erratic Pace*, Natural History, May 1977, at 12, 12 (italics added). *See also* Section 2.1.

[375]   *Id.* at 14 (italics added).

[376]   P. Grassé*, *The Evolution of Living Organisms* 31 (trans. 1977) ("from the *almost total absence of fossil evidence* relative to the origin of the phyla, it follows that any explanation of the *mechanism* in the creative evolution of the fundamental structural plans is heavily burdened with hypotheses.... The lack of direct evidence leads to the formulation of *pure conjectures* as to the genesis of the phyla; we do not even have a basis to determine the extent to which these opinions are correct.") (italics added).

[377]   A. Boyden*, *Perspectives in Zoology* 27 (1973) "It is understandable, then, that since the beginnings of our fossil records, there appear to have been *no major types evolved from other major types*, such evolution, if it did occur, having taken place before the fixation of the original major phyletic types.") (italics added).

[378]   George*, *Fossils in Evolutionary Perspective*, 48 Science Progress 1 (1960) ("Granted an evolutionary origin of the main groups of animals, and not an act of special creation, the absence of any record whatsoever of a single member of any of the phyla in the Precambrian rocks remains as inexplicable on orthodox grounds as it was to Darwin.").

[379]   G. Simpson*, *The Major Features of Evolution* 360 (1953) ("that most new species, genera and families, and that nearly all categories above the level of families, appear in the record suddenly and are not led up to by known, gradual, completely continuous transitional sequences"). *See also* A. Boyden*, *Perspectives in Zoology* 35 (1973) ("The evidences relating to the Age of Stabilization do lend themselves to interpretation on the Neo-Darwinian basis, all this evolution being subspeciational and completely graded in origin, and the gaps between species having been secondarily acquired.").

[380]   Patterson* concludes:

> The diagrams in these books follow two main styles, the *spindle-diagram*, first instituted by the pre-Darwinian Agassiz, which serves to *summarize the fossil record rather than express relationships* (appended vaguely, even apologetically, by broken lines and queries), and the *picket-fence style*, which *seems to deny evolution* rather than illustrate it.

Patterson*, *Significance of Fossils in Determining Evolutionary Relationships*, 12 Ann. Rev. Ecology & Systematics 195, 216 (1981) (italics added).

Hoyle and Wickramasinghe similarly state:

These *diagrams include many divergencies which have not been proved by the fossil record*, so if they occurred the transitions must again have been rapid. The diagrams are therefore *highly conjectural*. It has been through the device of presenting such diagrams with the presumed connections drawn in firm solid lines (unlike the broken lines used in Figure 6.2) that the *general scientific world has been bamboozled into believing that evolution has been proved. Nothing could be further from the truth.*

F. Hoyle & N. Wickramasinghe, *Evolution from Space* 87, 89 (1981) (italics added). *See also* Rosen*, Forey*, Gardiner* & Patterson*, *Lungfishes, Tetrapods, Paleontology, and Pleisiomorphy*, 167 Bull. American Museum of Natural History 163, 178 (1981).

[381] Raup*, *Conflicts Between Darwin and Paleontology*, Field Museum of Natural History Bull., Jan. 1979, at 22, 25 ("By this I mean that some of the classic cases of darwinian change in the fossil record, such as the evolution of the horse in North America, have had to be discarded or modified as a result of more detailed information . . .."). *See also* Valentine*, *Darwin's Impact on Paleontology*, 32 BioScience 513, 516 (1982) ("in some ways the record as we know it today provides even less obvious support for evolution via gradual change through natural selection than in Darwin's time.").

[382] Letter from Dr. Colin Patterson* to Luther D. Sunderland (Apr. 10, 1979). He further describes the problem:

Gould and the American Museum people are hard to contradict when they say that there are *no transitional fossils*. As a palaeontologist myself, I am much occupied with the philosophical problems of identifying ancestral forms in the fossil record. You say that I should at least 'show a photo of the fossil from which each type organism was derived.' I will lay it on the line—*there is not one such fossil for which one could make a watertight argument.* The reason is that statements about ancestry and descent are not applicable in the fossil record. Is *Archaeopteryx* the ancestor of all birds? Perhaps yes, perhaps no: there is no way of answering the question. It is easy enough to make up stories of how one form gave rise to another, and to find reasons why the stages should be favoured by natural selection. But such stories are not part of science, for there is no way of putting them to the test.

Id. (italics added).

[383] M. Denton*, *Evolution: A Theory in Crisis* 117 (1985) (italics added).

[384] Raup*, *Conflicts Between Darwin and Paleontology*, Field Museum of Natural History Bull., Jan. 1979, at 22, 22.

[385] T. Dobzhansky*, *Genetics of the Evolutionary Process* 24 (1970). *See also* E. Mayr*, *Principles of Systematic Zoology* 11-12 (1964) (1,072,300 animal species).

[386] Gould*, *The Return of Hopeful Monsters*, Natural History, June-July 1977, at 22, 24 (cannot even "invent a reasonable sequence of intermediate forms" for some alleged transitions). *See also* Frazzetta*, *From Hopeful*

Monsters to Bolyerine Snakes, 104 Am. Naturalist 55 (1970).

[387] Section 3.5.

[388] W. Stansfield*, *The Science of Evolution* 511 (1977). Transitional forms should often exist in the fossil record if macroevolutionary changes take 100 million years or so, and if the establishment of a mutation in a population takes on the average 10 million years. Those statistics come from J. Huxley*, *Evolution in Action* 13 (1967); Wald*, *The Problems of Vicarious Selection*, in Mathematical Challenges to the Neo-Darwinian Interpretation of Evolution 12, 19 (P. Moorhead* & M. Kaplan* eds. 1967).

[389] C. Darwin*, *The Origin of Species* 302 (1st ed. 1859, repr. 1964) (italics added except subheading italicized in original) (of course, he disputed the occurrence of abrupt appearances). Darwin* also wrote of "the sudden appearance of groups of allied species in the lowest known fossiliferous strata." *Id.* at 306 (italicized in original).

[390] *Id.* at 280 (italics added). *See also* Raup*, *Conflicts Between Darwin and Paleontology*, Field Museum of Natural History Bull., Jan. 1979, at 22, 22-23 ("Darwin was completely aware of this. He was embarrassed by the fossil record because it didn't look the way he predicted it would and, as a result, he devoted a long section of his Origin of Species to an attempt to explain and rationalize the differences. There were several problems, but the principal one was that the geologic record did not then and still does not yield a finely graduated chain of slow and progressive evolution. In other words, there are not enough intermediates.").

[391] T. Huxley*, *Three Lectures on Evolution* 619 (1882).

[392] C. Darwin*, *The Origin of Species* 280 (1st ed. 1859, repr. 1964).

[393] *Id.* at 342.

[394] Note 384.

[395] S. Stanley*, *Macroevolution* 1 (1979) (italics added). He notes the cynical notion in paleontology "that wherever in the fossil record one is looking happens to be where phyletic evolution is not recorded." *Id.* at 88.

[396] D. Raup* & S. Stanley*, *Principles of Paleontology* 303 (2d ed. 1978).

[397] E. Russell*, *The Diversity of Animals* 130 (1962). *See also* F. Hoyle, *The Intelligent Universe* 43 (1983) ("Over ten thousand *fossil* species of insects have been identified, over thirty thousand species of spiders, and similar numbers for many sea-living creatures."); F. Hoyle & N. Wickramasinghe, *Evolution from Space* 147 (1981).

[397A] Hsü, *Darwin's three mistakes*, 14 Geology 532, 534 (1986).

[397B] *Id.*

[398] Cracraft*, *Phylogenetic Analysis, Evolutionary Models, and Paleontology*, in Phylogenetic Analysis and Paleontology 7, 14 (J. Cracraft* & N. Eldredge* eds. 1979) (italics added).

[399] Patterson*, *Significance of Fossils in Determining Evolutionary Relationships*, 12 Annual Rev. Ecology & Systematics 195, 207 (1981). *See also id.* at 218-19 ("From a review of evolutionary and non-evolutionary rela-

tionship, I conclude that the two differ in only one respect: Evolutionary relationship includes an additional type, ancestor-descendent relationship. And it is this type that fossils are expected to document. When viewed as relationship between two groups, descent means that one (the ancestral group) is paraphyletic—characterized only by lack of homologies rather than their presence. Most fossil-based theories of relationship concern such groups. . . . Yet extinct paraphyletic groups seem to me to obscure rather than illuminate relationships, for they exist not in nature but in the minds of evolutionists.").

400 Thompson, *The Status of Species*, in Philosophical Problems in Biology at 67, 69 (V. Smith* ed. 1966) ("The so-called *ancestral insect* is simply a *mental construct*. That we can produce from it, by modifying it in various ways, all the forms whose descent we are investigating, is in no way surprising, because it has been built for this purpose. The biological prestidigitator is *simply taking out of the hat the rabbits he put into it*. The method used in working out the descent is, in fact, a perfect example of the argument in a circle.") (discontinuitist scientist).

401 Rosen*, Forey*, Gardiner* & Patterson*, *Lungfishes, Tetrapods, Paleontology, and Pleisiomorphy*, 168 Bull. Am. Museum of Natural History 163, 178 (1981)

402 Brady*, *Form and Cause in Goethe's Morphology*, in Goethe and the Sciences: A Re-Appraisal 257, 265 (F. Amrine* *et al.* eds. 1983).

403 M. Denton*, *Evolution: A Theory in Crisis* 194-95 (1985) (italics added).

404 Hull*, *Thirty-One Years of Systematic Zoology*, 32 Systematic Zoology 315, 333-35 (1983); Patterson*, *Significance of Fossils in Determining Evolutionary Relationships*, 12 Ann. Rev. of Ecology & Systematics 195, 218 (1981) ("*Most fossil-based theories of relationship concern such* [*extinct nonancestral*] *groups*. The superficial attraction of these stories, apparent illumination of the history of life, has bolstered the belief that fossils determine evolutionary relationships. Yet *extinct paraphyletic groups* seem to me to *obscure rather than illuminate relationships*, for they *exist not in nature but in the minds of evolutionists*. Such groups lead to a sterile inversion of problems of relationships, which come to depend not on comparative analysis of what is accessible—the Recent biota—but on *juggling with what is inaccessible—uncharacterizable abstractions from the fossil record*.") (italics added).

405 C. Patterson*, *Evolution* 133 (1978).

406 Oldroyd*, *Charles Darwin's Theory of Evolution: A Review of our Present Understanding*, 1 Biology & Philosophy 133, 154 (1986) ("Unfortunately, however, this is a very weak empirical reed to lean on, given that one cannot use the palaeontological record with certainty to establish genealogical relationships. Moreover, contemporary researches in developmental biology indicate that there are many puzzling phenomena that are hard to reconcile with Darwin's original conception. Anatomically homologous

parts in different related organisms appear to have quite different embryonic origins. This is almost impossible to reconcile with orthodox Darwinian or neo-Darwinian theory, and it is by no means evident at the time of writing how such problems may be overcome").

[407]   R. Good*, *Features of Evolution in the Flowering Plants* 383 (1974) ("This flaw is the fact that the fossil record, though disclosing an orderly succession of biological types in time, does not, and it would seem cannot, reveal whether the members of this succession constitute an unbroken genealogy in which each has been the immediate progeny of that which preceded it.").

[408]   Brady*, *Form and Cause in Goethe's Morphology*, in Goethe and the Sciences: A Re-Appraisal 257, 266 (F. Amrine* *et al.* eds. 1983).

[409]   F. Ayala* & J. Valentine*, *Evolving: The Theory and Processes of Organic Evolution* 258 (1979).

[410]   Section 2.1.

[411]   Patterson*, *Phylogenies and Fossils*, 29 Systematic Zoology 216, 217 (1980).

[412]   M. Denton*, *Evolution: A Theory in Crisis* 177 (1985) (italics added).

[413]   Patterson*, *Significance of Fossils in Determining Evolutionary Relationships*, 12 Ann. Rev. Ecology & Systematics 195, 207 (1981) (footnotes omitted).

[414]   Gould* gives this reminder about transitional forms, and it logically applies equally to ancestral groups. "And, in any case, the issue is not, can preadaptation save gradualism in some cases, but rather, does it permit us to invent a tale of continuity in most or all cases?" Gould*, *The Return of Hopeful Monsters*, Natural History, June-July 1977, at 22, 28.

[415]   Glenister* & Witzke*, *Interpreting Earth History*, in Did the Devil Make Darwin Do It? Modern Perspectives on the Creation-Evolution Controversy 55, 73-74 (D. Wilson* ed. 1983) (italics added).

[415A]   Sermonti* & Sermonti*, *The null hypothesis in vertebrate evolution*, 80 Rivista di Biologia (Biology Forum) 55, 67 (1987) (discontinuitist scientists).

[416]   Note 370.

[417]   D. Raup* & S. Stanley*, *Principles of Paleontology* 131-32 (2d ed. 1978). Some specialists use evolutionary "bushes."

[418]   F. Ayala* & J. Valentine*, *Evolving: The Theory and Processes of Organic Evolution* 441 (1979). *See also* T. Dobzhansky*, F. Ayala*, G. Stebbins* & J. Valentine*, *Evolution* 262 (1977).

[419]   Cracraft*, *Systematics, Comparative Biology, and Creationism*, in Scientists Confront Creationism 163, 177 (L. Godfrey* ed. 1983). *See also* Leith*, *Are the Reports of Darwin's Death Exaggerated?*, 166 The Listener 390, 390 (1981) ("all one can learn about the history of life is learned from systematics"—the "rest of it is storytelling"). "Systematics" is "the scientific study of the kinds, diversity, and similarities of organisms and of the relationships among them" (including phylogenies). W. Stansfield*, *The Science of Evolution* 98 (1977).

[420]   Hull*, *Thirty-One Years of Systematic Zoology*, 32 Systematic Zoology 315, 333-35 (1983) (italics added).

[421]   Nelson*, *Comments on Hennig's "Phylogenetic Systematics" and Its Influence on Ichthyology*, 21 Systematic Zoology 364, 368 (1972) ("Hennigian relationships embody the principles that all common ancestral species are necessarily hypothetical, and that ancestral species, although they may be reconstructed (e.g., Fitch, 1971), will forever remain unknown and unknowable in a directly empirical sense (e.g., in the sense that species are 'known' by way of inference from observation of study material).").

[422]   Patterson*, *Cladistics and Classification*, 94 New Scientist 303, 306 (1982) (italics added). *See also* Ball*, *On Groups, Existence and the Ordering of Nature*, 32 Systematic Zoology 446, 446 (1983).

[423]   Sections 3.2(e) & 3.4(c).

[424]   Bonner*, *Book Review*, 49 Am. Scientist 240, 242 (1961).

[425]   Ghiselin*, *Models in Phylogeny*, in Models in Paleobiology 130, 131 (T. Schopf* ed. 1972) ("Nonetheless it is true that many works on phylogeny do *read like imaginative literature* rather than science. A disproportionate segment of the literature seeks to fill gaps in the data with *speculations* and nothing more.") (italics added).

[426]   A. Boyden*, *Perspectives in Zoology* 117 (1973).

[427]   R. Good*, *Features of Evolution in the Flowering Plants* 8 (1974).

[428]   Charig*, *Systematics in Biology: A Fundamental Comparison of Some Major Schools of Thought*, in Problems of Phylogenetic Reconstruction 411-12 (K. Joysey* & A. Friday* eds. 1982).

[429]   W. Turrill*, *Joseph Dalton Hooker* 213 (1963).

[430]   Sokal* & Sneath*, *Principles of Numerical Taxonomy* (1963). *See also* Rosen* & Schuh*, *Book Review*, 24 Systematic Zoology 504, 505 (1975).

[431]   Patterson*, *Book Review*, 29 Systematic Zoology 216, 216 (1980) (italics added).

[432]   Forey*, *Neontological Analysis Versus Palaeontological Stories*, in Problems of Phylogenetic Reconstruction 119, 143 (K. Joysey* & A. Friday* eds. 1982).

[433]   Kitts*, *Paleontology and Evolutionary Theory*, 28 Evolution 458, 467 (1974).

[434]   Thomson*, *Marginalia: The Meanings of Evolution*, 70 Am. Scientist 529, 529-30 (1982) (italics added).

[435]   Forey*, *Neontological Analysis Versus Palaeontological Stories*, in Problems of Phylogenetic Reconstruction 119, 124 (K. Joysey* & A. Friday* eds. 1982) ("*Evolutionary taxonomy*, on the other hand, *assumes that the pattern is due to evolutionary theory* and so the construction of trees must, of necessity, have regard to evolutionary theory. . . . *The problem* is that *both are ultimately derived from the theory of evolution*: the fossil record being interpreted in the light of population biology theory and expressed as ancestor-descendant relationships (Simpson 1953).") (italics added).

[436]   Cartmill*, *Hypothesis Testing and Phylogenetic Reconstruction*, in Zeitschrift für Zoologische Systematik und Evolutionsforschung 73, 90

(1981) ("a phylogenetic hypothesis" is intertwined with "assuming certain premises—evolutionary laws").

[437] Kitts*, *Paleontology and Evolutionary Theory*, 28 Evolution 458, 467 (1974) ("I have misgivings about the use of phylogenies as instruments of theoretical investigation but they do not stem from the fact that phylogeny construction obviously presupposes whatever theoretical principles they purport to test.").

[438] E. Saiff* & N. Macbeth*, Evolution (unpublished ms. 1982) (final italics added). *See also* Patterson*, *Significance of Fossils in Determining Evolutionary Relationships*, 12 Ann. Rev. Ecology & Systematics 195, 213 (1981); Macbeth*, *A Third Position in the Textbook Controversy*, 38 Am. Biology Teacher 495, 495 (Nov. 1976) ("The whole aim and purpose of Darwinism is to show how modern forms descended from ancient forms, that is, to construct reliable *phylogenies* (genealogies or family trees). In this it has *utterly failed.*") (italics added).

[439] E. Mayr*, *The Growth of Biological Thought* 218 (1982) (italics added).

[440] Raup*, *Conflicts Between Darwin and Paleontology*, Field Museum of Natural History Bull., Jan. 1979, at 22, 25, (italics added).

[441] M. Denton*, *Evolution: A Theory In Crisis* 185 (1985) (italics added).

[442] W. Stansfield, *The Science of Evolution* 98 (1977). *See also* A. Kluge*, *Chordate Structure and Function* 110 (2d ed. 1977).

[443] T. Dobzhansky*, F. Ayala*, G. Stebbins* & J. Valentine*, *Evolution* 262 (1977). *See also*, S. Luria*, S. Gould* & S. Singer*, *A View of Life* 684 (1981).

[444] Cladistic theory is summarized in E. Mayr*, *The Growth of Biological Thought* 226-27 (1982) (Harvard U. Press), and derives from W. Hennig*, *Theorie der Phylogenetischen Systematik* (1950).

[445] Numerical phenetic theory is summarized in E. Mayr*, *The Growth of Biological Thought* 221-23 (1982), and derives from R. Sokal* & P. Sneath*, *Principles of Numerical Taxonomy* (2d ed. 1973).

[446] Charig*, *Cladistics: A Different Point of View*, in Evolution Now 121, 121 (J. Maynard Smith* ed. 1982). *See also* Platnick*, *Philosophy and the Transformation of Cladists*, 28 Systematic Zoology 537, 537 (1979) ("neither the value nor the success of the methods is limited by the value or success of that evolutionary model").

[447] C. Patterson*, *The Goals, Uses, and Assumptions of Cladistic Analysis* (1981), quoted in Beatty*, *Classes and Clades*, 31 Systematic Zoology 25, 31 (1982).

[448] Patterson*, *Cladistics and Classification*, 94 New Scientist 303, 304 (1982) ("But it is possible to look at diagrams like Figure 3, and at the definitions Hennig associated with them, in a more general framework, one which has no evolutionary implications. Branching diagrams can be seen not as evolutionary trees, but as cladograms in which there is no time scale and the nodes imply shared characteristics (synapomorphies) rather than common ancestry.") (italics added).

[449] Oldroyd*, *Charles Darwin's Theory of Evolution: A Review of our Present Understanding*, 1 Biology & Philosophy 133, 154 (1986) (italics added).

[450] Ball*, *On Groups, Existence and the Ordering of Nature*, 32 Systematic Zoology 446, 446 (1983).

[451] Beatty*, *Classes and Cladists*, 31 Systematic Zoology 25, 29 (1982).

[452] *Id.* at 31 ("But pattern cladistics is not, after all, evolutionarily neutral. It is *at odds* with evolutionary thinking.").

[453] Ridley*, *Can classification do without evolution?*, New Scientist, Dec. 1, 1983, at 647, 651.

[454] Benton*, *Is a dog more like a lizard or a chicken?*, New Scientist, Aug. 16, 1984, at 18, 18.

[455] Patterson*, *Cladistics and Classification*, 94 New Scientist 303, 306 (1982).

[456] Cracraft*, *Book Review*, 1 Cladistics 300, 302 (1985) (he disagrees with their argument).

[457] Nelson* & Platnick*, *Systematics and Evolution*, in Beyond Neo-Darwinism 143, 153-54 (M. Ho* & P. Saunders* eds. 1984) (italics added).

[458] E. Mayr*, *The Growth of Biological Thought* 226 (1982).

[459] *Id.* at 224.

[460] S. Luria*, S. Gould* & S. Singer*, *A View of Life* 676 (1981).

[461] W. Stansfield*, *The Science of Evolution* 99 (1977).

[462] Dobzhansky*, *Evolution*, in 10 Encyclopedia Americana 734, 734 (1982).

[463] C. Patterson*, *Evolution* 121-22 (1978).

[464] Brady*, *On the Independence of Systematics*, 1 Cladistics 113, 113 (1985). Thus, Brady* concludes that the "aspect of systematics concerned with the *identification* of the empirical patterns evidently constitutes a study prior to and independent of theories of *process.*" *Id.* (first italics in original).

[465] E. Mayr*, *Systematics and the Origin of Species* 276 (1942) (italics added).

[466] Simpson*, *The Principles of Classification and the Classification of Mammals*, 85 Bull. Am. Museum of Natural History 4 (1945).

[467] Blackwelder*, *Twenty-Five Years of Taxonomy*, 26 Systematic Zoology 107, 134 (1977). *See also* N. Macbeth*, *Darwin Retried* 20 (1971) ("the charts of relationship were pretty much the same no matter what theory the classifier believed in").

[468] Kitts*, *Karl Popper, Verifiability, and Systematic Zoology*, 26 Systematic Zoology 185, 190 (1977). *See also* S. Gould*, *Hen's Teeth and Horse's Toes* 355 (1983).

[469] J. Huxley*, *Evolution: The Modern Synthesis* 394-95 (1942).

[470] S. Luria*, S. Gould* & S. Singer*, *A View of Life* 763-64 (1981).

[471] E. Mayr*, *The Growth of Biological Thought* 217-18 (1982) (italics added).

472   W. Stansfield*, *The Science of Evolution* 510-11 (1977) (italics added).

473   D. Raup* & S. Stanley*, *Principles of Paleontology* 135, 136, 138 (2d ed. 1978) ("The family, on the other hand, has *no comparable objective basis. Higher categories* are used to express evolutionary relationships but *we do not have*, in the present state of our understanding, *specific rules* that can be applied. In other words, there are *no thresholds* in the transition from genus to family comparable to the threshold between the subspecies and the species (at a single moment in time).").

474   Richards*, *Book Review*, 167 Science 1477, 1477 (1970) ("I think *nearly all biologists must share*, the *species is the only taxonomic category* that has at least in more favorable examples a *completely objective existence. Higher categories* are all more or less a *matter of opinion*."). See also N. Macbeth*, *Darwin Retried* 19 (1971).

475   Note 447.

476   Note 449.

477   Notes 468 & 469.

478   "In comparative anatomy we try to discern genetic affinities as expressed in adult structures rather than in embryological structures." W. Stansfield*, *The Science of Evolution* 113 (1977).

479   Schwabe* & Warr*, *A Polyphyletic View of Evolution: The Genetic Potential Hypothesis*, 27 Perspectives in Biology & Medicine 465, 468 n.1 (1984).

480   Cracraft*, *The Use of Functional and Adaptive Criteria in Phylogenetic Systematics*, 21 Am. Zoologist 21, 32 (1981) ("The causal process is outside the realm of analysis for those investigating historically based events.").

481   M. Denton*, *Evolution: A Theory in Crisis* 178 (1985).

482   Patterson*, *Significance of Fossils in Determining Evolutionary Relationships*, 12 Ann. Rev. Ecology & Systematics 195, 217 (1981) ("Such hypotheses are untestable by morphology alone, which cannot discriminate descent from common ancestry, or from non-evolutionary relationship."); N. Macbeth*, *Darwin Retried* 13, 16 (1971).

482A   Reeck*, de Haen*, Teller*, Doolittle*, Fitch*, Dickerson*, Chambon*, McLachlan*, Margoliash*, Jukes* & Zuckerkandl*, *"Homology" in Proteins and Nucleic Acids: A Terminology Muddle and a Way Out of It*, 50 Cell 667, 667 (1987).

483   A. Boyden*, *Perspectives in Zoology* 27 (1973) (italics added).

484   Morgan*, *The Bearing of Mendelism on the Origin of Species*, 16 Scientific Monthly 237, 246 (1923).

485   M. Denton*, *Evolution: A Theory in Crisis* 178 (1985) (first italics added, second italics in original).

486   R. Dawkins*, *The Blind Watchmaker* 269 (1986).

487   Ross*, *Illusion and reality in comparative physiology*, 59 Canadian J. Zoology 2151, 2153 (1981).

488   G. de Beer*, *Homology, An Unsolved Problem* 16 (1971).

489   S. Zuckerman*, *Beyond the Ivory Tower* 64 (1970) ("We now know that

this view is far too simple, since relationships which are inferred on the basis of *comparative anatomy* may *not necessarily correspond to true genetic relationships.* Nevertheless, lack of other information makes it inevitable that the bulk of our views about evolutionary relationships has to be based on the evidence of structure. Consequently, students of comparative anatomy need to exercise great forbearance, as well as great humility, both in the area of fact and in that of interpretation, simply because the inferences they draw about evolution are in the final analysis *speculations*—speculations that can only be checked by recourse to the facts from which they are derived.") (italics added).

490   Patterson*, *Significance of Fossils in Determining Evolutionary Relationships*, 12 Ann. Rev. Ecology & Systematics 195, 208 (1981). *See also* Patterson*, *Cladistics and Classification*, 94 New Scientist 303, 304 (1982) ("the nodes simply imply shared characteristics (synapomorphies) rather than common ancestry.").

491   Dobzhansky*, *Evolution*, in 10 Encyclopedia Americana 734, 734 (1982). *See also* Patterson*, *Cladistics and Classification*, 94 New Scientist 303, 303 (1982) ("Comparative anatomy developed as a means of searching out these ideal plans.").

492   C. Patterson*, *Evolution* 121-22 (1978) (italics added). Further citations on the historical point are given in Section 2.7(a).

493   M. Denton*, *Evolution: A Theory in Crisis* 155 (1985) (italics added).

494   Ross*, *Illusion and reality in comparative physiology*, 59 Canadian J. Zoology 2151, 2153-54 (1981) (italics added).

495   Note 489.

496   Note 488.

497   "The science of *embryology* is concerned with the cause and effect relationships that lead to differentiation of tissues, organs, and organ systems." W. Stansfield*, *The Science of Evolution* 103 (1977). *See also* D. Raup* & S. Stanley*, *Principles of Paleontology* 354 (2d ed. 1978).

498   W. Stansfield*, *The Science of Evolution* 104 (1977) (the biogenetic law was stated by Haeckel* and others as "ontogeny recapitulates phylogeny").

499   Bock*, *Book Review*, 164 Science 684, 684 (1969) (italics added).

500   D. Raup* & S. Stanley*, *Principles of Paleontology* 354 (2d ed. 1978).

501   P. Ehrlich* & R. Holm*, *The Process of Evolution* 66 (1963) ("Its *shortcomings have been almost universally pointed out* by modern authors, but the idea still has a prominent place in biological *mythology.*") (italics added).

502   Danson*, *Evolution*, 49 New Scientist 35 (1971).

503   de Beer*, *Book Review*, 206 Nature 331, 331 (1965). *See also* G. de Beer*, *Embryos and Ancestors* (3d ed. 1958).

504   Bonner*, *Book Review of Implications of Evolution*, 49 Am. Scientist 240, 242 (1961).

505   Robinson*, *Haeckel, Ernst*, 5 Encyclopaedia Britannica: Micropaedia 610 (15th ed. 1976).

506   E. Mayr*, *The Growth of Biological Thought* 215 (1982). However, he

finds the law heuristically useful and "a modified theory of recapitulation" acceptable. *Id.*

[507]   Rager*, *Human embryology and the law of biogenesis*, 79 Rivista di Biologia (Biology Forum) 449 (1986). *See also* C. Singer*, *A History of Biology* 487 (1931) ("His faults are not hard to see. For a generation and more he purveyed to the semi-educated public a system of the crudest philosophy—if a mass of contradictions can be called by that name. He founded something that wore the habiliments of a religion, of which he was at once the high priest and the congregation.").

[508]   W. Stansfield*, *The Science of Evolution* 113 (1977) ("The two disciplines of comparative anatomy and comparative embryology are very closely related and could be treated under a general heading of 'comparative development'. . ..").

[509]   Section 3.4(d).

[510]   Oldroyd*, *Charles Darwin's Theory of Evolution: A Review of Our Present Understanding*, 1 Biology & Philosophy 133, 154 (1986) (italics added).

[510A]   Davidson*, *Understanding Embryonic Development: A Contemporary View*, 27 Am. Zoologist 581, 589 (1987).

[511]   A. Romer* & T. Parsons*, *The Vertebrate Body* 407 (6th ed. 1986) ("We see the development in the *amniote embryo* of three successive kidney structures: pronephros, mesonephros, and metanephros. It is often stated or implied that these three are distinct kidneys that have *succeeded one another phylogenetically* as they do embryologically. However, there is *little reason* to believe this. The differences are readily explainable on functional grounds . . ..") (italics added).

[512]   Scadding*, *Do "Vestigial Organs" Provide Evidence for Evolution?*, 5 Evolutionary Theory 173, 173, 175, 176 (1981) (italics added).

[513]   J. Langman*, *Medical Embryology* 262 (3d ed. 1975) ("Since the *human embryo never has gills*—brachia—the term pharyngial arches and clefts has been adopted for this book.").

[514]   Scadding*, *Do 'Vestigial Organs' Provide Evidence for Evolution?*, 5 Evolutionary Theory 173, 175 (1981) (italics added).

[514A]   Rager*, *Human embryology and the law of biogenesis*, 79 Rivista di Biologia (Biology Forum) 449, 456 (1986).

[514B]   Smith*, *Two Evolutions*, in On Nature 42, 55 (L. Rouner* ed. 1984).

[514C]   *Id.*

[515]   Note 499.

[516]   Note 510.

[517]   Note 512.

[518]   W. Stansfield*, *The Science of Evolution* 125 (1977).

[519]   *Id.* at 125-27.

[520]   M. Denton*, *Evolution: A Theory in Crisis* 291 (1985) (italics added).

[521]   Jukes* & Holmquist*, *Evolutionary Clock: Nonconstancy of Rate in Different Species*, 177 Science 530, 530 (1972) (footnotes omitted). The

authors see overall support of molecular biology for evolution.

522 Schwabe* & Warr*, *A Polyphyletic View of Evolution: The Genetic Potential Hypothesis*, 27 Perspectives in Biology & Medicine 465, 471 (1984) (italics added).

523 Vawter* & Brown*, *Nuclear and Mitochondrial DNA Comparisons Reveal Extreme Rate Variation in the Molecular Clock*, 234 Science 194, 194 (1986) (italics added).

524 Section 2.7(c).

525 M. Denton*, *Evolution: A Theory in Crisis* 305 (1985) (italics added).

526 Jukes* & Holmquist*, *Evolutionary Clock: Nonconstancy of Rate in Different Species*, 177 Science 530, 530 (1972).

527 Schwabe*, *On the validity of molecular evolution*, 11 Trends in Biochemical Sciences 280, 280 (1986) (italics added, footnotes omitted).

528 Farris*, *Distance Data in Phylogenetic Analysis*, in Advances in Cladistics 3, 22 (V. Funk* & D. Brooks* eds. 1981) (italics added).

529 D. Kenyon* & G. Steinman*, *Biochemical Predestination* 4-5 (1969) (the authors interpreted this as allowing multiple origins of the first living forms) (italics added). *See also* Ross*, *Illusion and reality in comparative physiology*, 59 Canadian J. Zoology 2151, 2154 (1981).

530 M. Denton*, *Evolution: A Theory in Crisis* 306 (1985) (italics added).

531 Schwabe*, *On the validity of molecular evolution*, 11 Trends in Biochemical Sciences 280, 282 (1986) (italics added).

532 "Population genetics" is "concerned with a detailed description of the genetic structure of a population and with changes over a shorter time scale." J. Roughgarden*, *Theory of Population Genetics and Evolutionary Ecology* 5 (1979).

533 Stansfield*, *The Science of Evolution* 129 (1977).

534 M. Ruse*, *Darwinism Defended* 112-13 (1982) ("Appropriately, therefore, this survey of the evidential base for population genetics, that body of knowledge which contains the core mechanisms of neo-Darwinian evolutionary theory, can be concluded. . . . We have yet to see the core part of neo-Darwinian theory—population genetics—in action, as it is applied to the rest of biology.").

535 R. Lewontin*, *The Genetic Basis of Evolutionary Change* 159 (1974) (Columbia U. Press) (italics added).

536 P. Grassé*, *The Evolution of Living Organisms* 170 (trans. 1977) (italics added).

537 Mayr*, *Prologue*, in The Evolutionary Synthesis 1, 11 (E. Mayr* & W. Provine* eds. 1980) ("Naturalists repeatedly objected that they could *not see any connection* between changes in gene frequencies, described by the geneticists, and the evolutionary events at the hierarchical levels of species and higher taxa. As recently as 1973 this is perhaps the most cogent objection against population genetics raised by Grassé.") (Mayr* is not describing his personal view).

538 Rosen*, *Book Review*, 27 Systematic Zoology 370, 372 (1978) ("*Popula-*

tion genetics, in other words, *cannot, and does not purport to, explain the origin and epigenetic history of new codons.* Its focus is entirely on the relation of genetic equilibria to ecological discontinuities and fluctuations.").

539   E. Spiess*, *Genes in Populations* (1977) ("Speciation is one of the most critical processes in nature, but we are a *long way from describing the origin of species* in the field or with methods of experimental *population genetics.*") (italics added).

540   Saunders* & Ho*, *Is Neo-Darwinism Falsifiable?—And Does it Matter?*, 4 Nature & System 179, 185 (1982) ("If *population genetics*, including Weismann's doctrine of the independence of the germ plasm, is considered as part of neo-Darwinism, then that part may be falsifiable. It is *not, however, a theory of evolution.*") (italics added).

541   Kempthorne*, *Evaluation of Current Population Genetics Theory*, 23 Am. Zoologist 111, 120 (1983).

542   Lambert*, *Population Genetics and the 'Third View' of Evolution*, 27 Tuatara 121, 125 (1984) (italics added) ("Genes are surely a component in such a system, but *evolution is not a population problem and most especially not a population genetics problem.* It is a *problem of the origin* of form . . . . Where then is population genetics left? . . . It is simply that *population genetics is not a tool to investigate evolution.*").

543   Section 3.3. *E.g.*, Stanley*, *A Theory of Evolution Above the Species Level*, 72 Proc. National Academy Sciences 646, 648, 650 (1975) ("We must turn not to population genetic studies of established species, but to studies of speciation and extinction in order to decipher the higher-level process that governs the general course of evolution.").

544   R. Lewontin*, *The Genetic Basis of Evolutionary Change* 11-12, 189 (1974) (italics added). *See also* R. Lewontin*, *The Genetic Basis of Evolutionary Change* 267 (1974) ("How can such a rich theoretical structure as *population genetics fail so completely to cope with the body of fact?* Are we simply missing some critical revolutionary insight . . .? Or is the problem more pervading, more deeply built into the essence of our science? I believe it is the latter.") (italics added).

545   J. Roughgarden*, *Theory of Population Genetics and Evolutionary Ecology* 5 (1979) ("When research into population genetics was begun, it was assumed that these kinds of long-term evolutionary phenomena would be explained as a result. We need to reassess the relevance of population genetics to these kinds of evolutionary issues.").

546   Saiff* & Macbeth*, *Population Genetics and Evolutionary Theory*, 26 Tuatara 71, 71-72 (1983) (italics added); *compare* Hewitt*, *The Role of Population Genetics in Our Understanding of Evolution*, 26 Tuatara 73 (1983) *with* Saiff* & Macbeth*, *Reply to Dr. Hewitt, id.* at 75.

547   Forey*, *Neontological Analysis Versus Palaeontological Stories*, in Problems of Phylogenetic Reconstruction 119, 124 (K. Joysey* & A. Friday* eds. 1982) (italics added).

548   Rosen*, *Darwin's Demon*, 27 Systematic Zoology 370, 371 (1978).

549 Note 540.

550 Note 544.

551 Note 547.

552 L. Eiseley*, *The Immense Journey* 223 (1958).

553 T. Dobzhansky*, F. Ayala*, G. Stebbins* & J. Valentine*, *Evolution* 97 (1977).

554 Section 3.3(introduction).

555 Wassermann*, *Testability of the Role of Natural Selection Within Theories of Population Genetics and Evolution*, 29 British J. of Philosophy of Science 223, 235 (1978) (italics added).

556 Macbeth*, *Danger: analogies ahead*, 79 Rivista di Biologia (Biology Forum) 191, 194 (1986) (italics added).

557 E. Russell*, *The Diversity of Animals* 124 (1962) (italics added).

558 T. Dobzhansky*, F. Ayala*, G. Stebbins* & J. Valentine*, *Evolution* 97 (1977) (*"Artificial selection*, practiced by breeders of agricultural plants and domesticated animals, has *commonly been used as a model of the action of natural selection. However*, in Lerner's words, 'Natural selection has no purpose. . . . For any given generation, natural selection is a consequence of the differences between individuals with respect to their capacity to produce progeny. . . . *Artificial Selection, in contrast, is a purposeful process.* It has a goal that can be visualized' (1958). Natural selection can and does take place in domesticated and laboratory organisms, and in mankind, under all sorts of natural and artificial conditions. *Artificial selection is man-made, however.* Natural selection has no selector, it is a self-generated outcome of interactions between organisms and their environments.") (italics added).

559 L. Burbank*, *Partner of Nature* 97-99 (W. Hall* ed. 1939) (quoted in Section 2.6).

560 Deevey*, *The Reply: Letter from Birnam Wood*, 61 Yale Rev. 631, 636 (1967) ("Some remarkable things have been done by crossbreeding and selection *inside the species barrier*, or within a larger circle of closely related species, such as the wheats. *But wheat is still wheat*, and not, for instance, grapefruit; and we can no more grow wings on pigs than hens can make cylindrical eggs.") (italics added).

561 L. Eiseley*, *The Immense Journey* 223 (1958) ("It would appear that careful domestic breeding, whatever it may do to improve the quality of race horses or cabbages, is not actually in itself the road to the endless biological deviation which is evolution."); *id.* at 227 ("W. L. Johannsen notes that 'the *variations* upon which Darwin and Wallace had placed their emphasis *cannot be selectively pushed beyond a certain point*, that such variability does *not contain the secret of 'indefinite departure.'* ") (italics added).

562 D. Falconer*, *Introduction To Quantitative Genetics* 186 (1960) ("The improvements that have been made by selection in these [domesticated breeds] have clearly been accompanied by a *reduction of fitness* for life under natural conditions, and only the fact that domesticated animals and plants do not live under natural conditions has allowed these improvements

to be made.") (italics added). Falconer* was formerly chairman of the department of genetics at University of Edinburgh.

563   Note 556.
564   Note 557.
565   Note 371.
566   Note 375.
567   Note 420.
568   Note 428.
569   Note 434.
570   Note 438.
571   Note 447.
572   Note 460.
573   Note 465.
574   Note 471.
575   Note 493.
576   Note 479.
577   Note 485.
578   Note 488.
579   Note 499.
580   Note 510.
581   Note 512.
582   Note 520.
583   Note 523.
584   Note 528.
585   Note 535.
586   Note 540.
587   Note 544.
588   Note 547.
589   Note 556.
590   E. Russell*, *The Diversity of Animals* 134 (1962) (italics added).
591   S. Luria*, S. Gould* & S. Singer*, *A View of Life* 773 (1981). *See also* Mayr*, *Prologue*, in The Evolutionary Synthesis 1, 36 (E. Mayr* & W. Provine* eds. 1980); note 35.
592   S. Luria*, S. Gould* & S. Singer*, *A View of Life* 767 (1981). *See also* F. Ayala* & J. Valentine*, *Evolving: The Theory and Processes of Organic Evolution* 1 (1979); Section 3.1 (a).
593   Thompson*, *Biology, Zoology, and Genetics* 1 (1983).
594   Dobzhansky*, *Evolution*, 10 Encyclopedia Americana 734, 748 (1982) ("from primordial life, [i] through unicellular and multicellular organisms, [ii-iii] invertebrates and [iv-viii] vertebrate animals, [ix] to man").
595   G. Stebbins*, *Darwin to DNA, Molecules to Humanity* 174 (1982) ("Part Two: The Course of Evolution: from Molecules to Primates").
596   *E.g.*, Biological Sciences Curriculum Study*, *Biological Science: Molecules to Man* (4th ed. 1982); J. Otto* & A. Towle*, *Modern Biology* 252, 272, 412, 419, 437, 438, 451, 452, 456, 469, 471, 473, 488, 516 (1977).

[597] Bonner*, *Book Review*, 49 Am. Scientist 240 (1961) (italics added).

[598] G. Kerkut*, *Implications of Evolution* (1960).

[599] P. Grassé*, *Evolution of Living Organisms* 31 (trans. 1977) ("From the *almost total absence of fossil evidence relative to the origin of the phyla*, it follows that any explanation of the *mechanism* in the creative evolution of the fundamental structural plans is *heavily burdened with hypothesis. This should appear as an epigraph to every book on evolution.* The lack of direct evidence leads to the formulation of *pure conjecture* as to the genesis of the phyla; we do not even have a basis to determine the extent to which these opinions are correct.") (italics added).

[600] M. Denton*, *Evolution: A Theory in Crisis* (1985).

[601] Section 3.2(f).

[602] F. Ayala* & J. Valentine*, *Evolving: The Theory and Processes of Organic Evolution* 437, 441 (1979). *See also* S. Luria*, S. Gould* & S. Singer*, *A View of Life* 767, 779 (1981).

[603] *E.g.*, Sagan*, *On the Origin of Mitosing Cells*, 14 J. Theoretical Biology 225 (1967).

[604] Whitfield*, *Book Review of Symbiosis in Cell Evolution*, 18 Biological J. Linnean Soc. 77, 78-79 (1982) (italics added).

[605] D. Lloyd, *The Mitochondria of Microorganisms* 476 (1974).

[606] Gray* & Doolittle*, *Has the Endosymbiont Hypothesis Been Proven?*, 46 Microbiological Rev. 1, 30 (1982) ("That is, data from animal and fungal mitochondrial sequences do not eliminate the possibility that eukaryotic nuclear and eubacterial genomes diverged from each other more recently than did mitochondrial and eubacterial genomic lineages—a possibility that seems *at odds* with all other, indirect, evidence for a eubacterial *endosymbiotic origin for mitochondria.*").

[607] Raff* & Mahler*, *The Symbiont That Never Was: An Inquiry into the Evolutionary Origin of the Mitochondrion*, 29 Symposia of Soc. for Experimental Biology 41 (1975).

[608] A. Clark*, *The New Evolution* 235-36 (1930) ("It is almost invariably assumed that animals with bodies composed of a single cell represent the primitive animals from which all others are derived. They are commonly supposed to have preceded all other animal types in their appearance. There is *not the slightest basis* for this assumption beyond the circumstance that in arithmetic—which is not zoology—the number one precedes the other numbers.").

[609] Levin* & Lenski*, *Coevolution in bacteria and their viruses and plasmids*, in Coevolution 99, 126-27 (D. Futuyma* & M. Slatkin* eds. 1983) (italics added).

[610] Darnell*, *Implications of RNA-RNA Splicing in Evolution of Eukaryotic Cells*, 202 Science 1257, 1257 (1978) (italics added).

[611] C. Hickman*, *Integrated Principles of Zoology* 111 (3d ed. 1966).

[612] G. Kerkut*, *Implications of Evolution* 151 (1960).

[613] L. Margulis*, *The Origin of Eukaryotic Cells* 27 (1970):

Morphologically and physiologically, *trends from asexual blue green algae [prokaryotes] to sexual eukaryotic algae cannot be found.* The more they have been sought, the more firmly has the *discontinuity* between the two forms been established. At the same time the *assumption of a classical phytoflagellate* has led to a literature on the classification and possible evolution relationships between the blue green algae and the lower eukaryotes so fraught with confusion and contradiction that most modern biologists have ignored it.

[614] *E.g.*, Reanney*, *On the Origin of Prokaryotes*, 48 J. Theoretical Biology 243 (1974).

[615] R. Shapiro*, *Origins: A Skeptic's Guide to the Creation of Life on Earth* 90-91 (1986).

[616] Gould*, *The Five Kingdoms*, Natural History, June-July 1976, at 30, 32.

[617] R. Shapiro*, *Origins: A Skeptic's Guide to the Creation of Life on Earth* 90-91 (1986).

[618] Cowle*, *Life in Pre-Cambrian and Early Cambrian Times*, in The Fossil Record 17, 29 (W. Harland* *et al.* eds. 1967); *see* Cloud*, Gustafson* & Watson*, *The Works of Living Social Insects as Pseudofossils and the Age of the Oldest Known Metozoa*, 210 Science 1013 (1980); Schopf*, *Are the Oldest "Fossils", Fossils?*, 7 Origins of Life 19, 19, 21 (1976) (spheroids). The boundary between the Cambrian and Precambrian is not clearly defined and not agreed on. Morris*, *The Search for the Precambrian-Cambrian Boundary*, 75 Am. Scientist 156 (1987); Simon*, *In with the Older*, 123 Science News 300, 301 (1983).

[619] Pflug* & Reitz*, *Evolutionary Changes in the Proterozoic*, in 8 Lecture Notes in Earth Sciences 102 (O. Walliser* ed. 1986).

[620] "Invertebrates" are animals without backbones. "Metazoa" are "animals that share a common multicellular ancestry with coelenterates and flatworms." T. Dobzhansky*, F. Ayala*, G. Stebbins* & J. Valentine*, *Evolution* 397 (1977).

[621] *Id.* at 373, 397 (italics added) (still contending that it is possible to produce models of metazoan origin and diversification). Paleobotanist Axelrod* of University of California also noted the lack of fossil ancestors:

One of the major unsolved problems of geology and evolution is the occurrence of diversified, multicellular marine invertebrates in Lower Cambrian rocks on all the continents and their absence in rocks of greater age. . . . However, when we turn to examine the Pre-Cambrian rocks for the forerunners of these Early Cambrian fossils, they are nowhere to be found.

Axelrod*, *Early Cambrian Marine Fauna*, 128 Science 7, 7 (1958). Although much research has occurred since that was written, Precambrian metazoa fossils still are rare if not nonexistent. *See* note 623A.

[622] S. Stanley*, *Macroevolution* 88 (1979) (italics added).

[623] Valentine* & Erwin*, *Interpreting Great Developmental Experiments: The Fossil Record*, in Development as an Evolutionary Process 71, 73 (1987).

623A Simpson*, *Editorial Essay*, 7 Precambrian Research 101, 101 (1978).

624 Barghoorn*, *The Oldest Fossils*, Scientific Am., May 1971, at 30, 41 ("Paleozoic seas were swarming with highly differentiated *aquatic plants and animals*, evolved from primitive forebears that had managed to cross all three Precambrian thresholds. Half a billion years does *not seem to be evolutionary 'room' enough to account for such epic progress.*") (italics added).

625 P. Weiss*, *The Science of Biology* 732 (1963).

626 F. Hoyle*, *The Intelligent Universe* 43 (1983) ("Over ten thousand fossil species of insect have been identified, over thirty thousand species of spiders, and similar numbers for many sea-living creatures. Yet so far the evidence for step-by-step changes leading to major evolutionary transitions looks extremely thin. The supposed transition from wingless to winged insects still has to be found, as has the transition between the two main types of winged insects, the paleoptera (mayflies, dragonflies) and the neoptera (ordinary flies, beetles, ants, bees.)"); F. Hoyle & N. Wickramasinghe, *Evolution from Space* 86, 89 (1981) ("It is particularly remarkable that *no forms with the wings at an intermediate stage* of development have been found. Where fossil insects have wings at all they are *fully functional* to serve the purposes of flight, and *often enough in ancient fossils the wings are essentially identical* to what can be found today. *Nor are there intermediate forms between the two kinds of wings. . . .*") (italics added).

627 F. Ommanney*, *The Fishes* 60 (1964) (italics added).

628 J. Norman*, *A History of Fishes* 296 (rev. ed. 1963).

629 A. Romer*, *Vertebrate Paleontology* 15 (3d ed. 1966) (italics added).

630 Todd*, *Evolution of the Lung and the Origin of Bony Fishes—A Causal Relationship?*, 20 Am. Zoologist 757, 757 (1980) ("All three subdivisions of the bony fishes first *appear in the fossil record at approximately the same time.* They are *already widely divergent* morphologically and they are heavily armored. How did they originate? What allowed them to diverge so widely? How did they all come to have heavy armor? And why is there *no trace of earlier, intermediate forms?*") (italics added).

631 White*, *Presidential Address: A little on Lung-fishes*, 177 Proc. British Linnean Society 1, 8 (1966) (italics added).

632 Repetski*, *A Fish from the Upper Cambrian of North America*, 200 Science 529, 529 (1978).

633 Section 2.1(b).

634 B. Stahl*, *Vertebrate History: Problems in Evolution* 34 (1973) (italics added).

635 H. Smith*, *From Fish to Philosopher* 26 (1953) (italics added).

636 Patterson*, *Book Review*, 29 Systematic Zoology 216, 217 (1980) (italics added).

637 Patterson* discusses *Ichthyostega*:

In the second part of his paper, Gingerich discusses the stratophenetic method in relation to the *origins of the major groups of tetrapods.* Here I thought the deficiencies are obvious. To take one example, Gingerich asserts that discovery of *Ichthyostega* "provided an important confirmatory link" between Devonian rhipidistian fishes and Carboniferous amphibians. In support of this, he cites two reputedly rhipidistian features of *Ichthyostega*, neither of which is characteristic of rhipidistians alone amongst fishes, and he neglects to mention that, among the little that is known of *Ichthyostega*, the skull roof, nares, and humerus have all *failed to meet the expectation of smooth transition* from rhipidistians to amphibians. According to Gingerich, tests of stratophenetic phylogenies are provided by new fossils. But *when a new fossil is found and is inconsistent* with the phylogeny (like *Ichthyostega*), the stratopheneticist's answer is that this test has shown that the fossil record was insufficiently dense and continuous for the method to work. And when a new fossil is *consistent* with the phylogeny, the record *was* sufficiently dense and continuous.

Patterson*, *Book Review*, 29 Systematic Zoology 216, 216 (1980) (italics added).

[638]   Romer*, *Book Review*, 162 Science 250, 250 (1968).

[639]   B. Stahl*, *Vertebrate History: Problems in Evolution* 240-41 (italics added).

[640]   R. Stirton*, *Time, Life and Man* 416 (1957) (italics added).

[641]   M. Denton*, *Evolution: A Theory in Crisis* 218 (1985) (italics added).

[642]   B. Stahl*, *Vertebrate History: Problems in Evolution* 268 (1973).

[643]   M. Denton*, *Evolution: A Theory in Crisis* 219 (1985) (italics added).

[644]   *Id.* at 176-177 (italics added).

[645]   G. Kerkut*, *Implications of Evolution* 136 (1960).

[646]   Pope*, *Reptiles*, 26 Encyclopaedia Britannica: Macropaedia 750 (15th ed. 1976) (italics added).

[647]   B. Stahl*, *Vertebrate History: Problems in Evolution* 318, 319 (1973).

[648]   Swinton*, *Biology and Comparative Physiology of Birds* 1 (A. Marshall* ed. 1960) (italics added). Russell* similarly concluded:

> *Nothing is known with certainty* as to how birds arose from reptiles or from what reptilian stock. . . .
>
> . . . .
>
> As we have said above, there are *no palaeontological data* indicating how the transformation of reptile into bird came about; we do not know whether it happened gradually or by abrupt stages. . . .

E. Russell*, *The Diversity of Animals* 118, 120 (1962).

[649]   Macbeth*, *The Hypothesis of Divergent Ancestry*, 5 Historia Natural 321, 326 (1985) (italics added).

[650]   Ostrom*, *Bird Flight: How Did It Begin?*, 67 Am. Scientist 45, 46 (italics added).

[651]   *Id.* at 47. *See also* M. Denton*, *Evolution: A Theory in Crisis* 204-06 (1985).

[652]   Ostrom*, *Bird Flight: How Did It Begin?*, 67 Am. Scientist 46, 47, 50

(1979) (italics added).

653 E. Russell*, *The Diversity of Animals* 120 (1962).

654 M. Denton*, *Evolution: A Theory in Crisis* 205 (1985).

655 Gould* & Eldredge*, *Punctuated equilibria: the tempo and mode of evolution reconsidered*, 3 Paleobiology 115, 147 (1977) (italics added). Gould* also calls *Archaeopteryx* "our premier example of the principle of preadaptation." Gould*, *The promise of paleobiology as a nomothetic, evolutionary discipline*, 6 Paleobiology 96, 113 (1980).

656 A. Romer*, *Notes and Comments on Vertebrate Paleontology* 144-45 (1968) ("*Archaeopteryx*—This Jurassic bird still stands in splendid isolation; we know no more of its presumed thecodont ancestry nor of its relation to later 'proper' birds than before.").

656A Chatterjee*, *Skull of Protoavis and Early Evolution of Birds*, 7 J. Vertebrate Paleontology (Sept. 16, 1987) (supp. to no. 3).

657 M. Denton*, *Evolution: A Theory in Crisis* 176 (1985).

658 E. Russell*, *The Diversity of Animals* 118 (1962) (italics added).

659 Gould*, *The Archaeopteryx Flap*, Natural History, Sept. 1986, at 16, 18.

660 O. Schindewolf*, *Grundfragen der Palaontologie* (1950).

661 M. Denton*, *Evolution: A Theory in Crisis* 175-76 (1985) ("However, in one respect, flight, the most characteristic feature of birds, *Archaeopteryx* was already truly bird. On its wing there were flight feathers as fully developed as any modern bird, and recent research reported in 1979 suggests that it was as capable of powered flight as a modern bird.").

662 Olson* & Feduccia*, *Flight Capability and the Pectoral Girdle of Archaeopteryx*, 278 Nature 247, 248 (1979) (italics added). The significance of asymmetrical features is that they indicate the capability of flying; nonflying birds such as the ostrich and emu have symmetrical feathers.

663 Teeth are the feature of *Archaeopteryx* that is most often cited to support the conclusion that it was not a true bird. *E.g.*, P. Moody*, *Introduction to Evolution* 196-97 (3d ed. 1970). However, other extinct ancient birds had teeth, and every other category of vertebrates contains some organisms with teeth and some without (amphibians, reptiles, extinct birds, mammals, etc.).

664 F. Hoyle & N. Wickramasinghe, *Archaeopteryx, the Primordial Bird: A Case of Fossil Forgery* (1986); Hoyle, Wickramasinghe & Watkins*, *Archaeopteryx*, 132 British J. Photography 693 (1985).

665 Charig* *et al.*, *Archaeopteryx Is Not a Forgery*, 232 Science 622 (1986).

666 Marx*, *The Oldest Fossil Bird: A Rival for Archaeopteryx?*, 199 Science 284, 284 (1978) (italics added).

667 *Bone Bonanza: Early Bird*, 112 Science News 198 (1977).

668 Lecture by John Ostrom* at Iona College (Nov. 5, 1983).

669 Cracraft*, *Phylogenetic Relationships and Monophyly of Loons, Grebes, and Hesperornithiform Birds* . . ., 31 Systematic Zoology 35, 53 (1982).

670 Beardsley*, *Fossil Bird Shakes Evolutionary Hypothesis*, 322 Nature

677, 677 (1986).

[671] Martin*, Stewart* & Whetstone*, *The Origin of Birds: Structure of the Tarsus and Teeth*, 97 The Auk 86 (Jan. 1980). *See also* Benton*, *No Consensus on Archaeopteryx*, Nature, Sept. 8, 1983, at 99, 100.

[672] W. Scheele*, *The First Mammals* 24 (1955) ("The first successful mammals . . . were small insectivore types whose relationships to these reptiles is not at all clear.").

[673] T. Kemp*, *Mammal-Like Reptiles and the Origin of Mammals* 1 (1982).

[674] Hopson*, *Book Review*, 219 Science 49, 50 (1983).

[675] T. Kemp*, *Darwin Up To Date* 33 (1982) (italics added).

[676] M. Denton*, *Evolution: A Theory in Crisis* 181-82 (1985) (italics added).

[677] *Id.* at 180-81 (italics added), quoting H. Jerison*, *Evolution of the Brain and Intelligence* 153-55, 213 (1973) (italics added, conformed to original).

[678] Gow*, *An Ictidosaur Fossil from North America*, (Feb. 1983) (italics added, footnotes omitted).

[679] Kermack*, Kermack* & Mussett*, *The Welsh Pantothere Kuehneotherium Praecursoris*, 47 J. Linnean Society 418, 418 (1968) (italics in original).

[680] R. Lombard*, *Evolution* 1230 (1979).

[681] G. Simpson*, *Tempo and Mode in Evolution* 105 (1944).

[682] E. Russell*, *The Diversity of Animals* 130 (1962) (italics added).

[683] S. Sikes*, *The Natural History of the African Elephant* 2-4 (1971).

[684] M. Denton*, *Evolution: A Theory in Crisis* 184-85 (1985).

[685] C. Darwin*, *The Origin of Species* 184 (1st. ed. 1859, repr. 1964).

[686] Raup*, *Conflicts Between Darwin and Paleontology*, Field Museum of Natural History Bull., Jan. 1979, at 22, 25 (italics added).

[687] E. Saiff* & N. Macbeth*, Evolution (unpublished ms. 1982) (italics added).

[688] G. Hardin*, *Nature and Man's Fate* 225-26 (1959).

[689] M. Denton*, *Evolution: A Theory in Crisis* 182 (1985).

[690] Gould*, *Life's Little Joke*, Natural History, Apr. 1987, at 16, 18, 24-25 (italics added). He states elsewhere:

Paleontologists have documented *virtually no cases* of slow and steady transformation, foot by foot up the strata of a hillslope—*not for horses*, not for humans.

Gould*, *Evolution: Explosion, Not Ascent*, N.Y. Times, Jan. 22, 1978, at E6 (italics added).

[691] G. Kerkut*, *Implications of Evolution* 149 (1960) (italics added except names).

[692] G. Hardin*, *Nature and Man's Fate* 225-26 (1961) (italics added).

[693] G. Simpson*, *The Major Features of Evolution* 263 (1953) (italics added).

[694] M. Denton*, *Evolution: A Theory in Crisis* 85-86 (1985) (italics added).

[695] T. Storer*, *General Zoology* 216 (3d ed. 1957).

[696] For example, Kerkut* concludes:

It is quite likely that further studies will show that the complexity of horse evolution will prove to be as great as that found in the Proboscidea, Rhinocerotidea or Camelidae.

G. Kerkut*, *Implications of Evolution* 149 (1960) (italics added). *See also* F. Hoyle, *The Intelligent Universe: A New View of Creation and Evolution* 41 (1983) ("The evidence that was advanced to support the theory, for example fossil sequences of *horses* of increasing stature, was of *little relevance* since it concerned animals possessing *basically the same genetic structure.* Besides which, such sequences could have involved external factors—*nutrition* for example."); F. Hitching*, *The Neck of the Giraffe: Where Darwin Went Wrong* 28-31 (1982).

697   A. Kelso*, *Physical Anthropology: An Introduction* 142 (2d ed. 1974) (italics added).

698   *Id.* at 150-51 (italics added).

699   Campbell*, *Taxonomic Status of Tree Shrews*, 153 Science 436, 436 (1966).

700   Simons*, *The Origin and Radiation of the Primate*, 167 Annals N.Y. Academy Sciences 318 (1969).

701   1 W. Hill*, *Primates* 25-26 (1953) (italics added).

702   Biological Sciences Curriculum Study*, *Biological Science: Molecules to Man* 383 (3d ed. 1973 & 1976).

703   T. Dobzhansky*, F. Ayala*, G. Stebbins* & J. Valentine*, *Evolution* 447 (1977) (italics in original).

704   S. Zuckerman*, *Beyond the Ivory Tower* 64 (1970) (italics added).

705   Gribben* & Cherfas*, *Descent of Man—Or Ascent of Apes?*, 91 New Scientist 592, 594 (Sept. 3, 1981).

706   *E.g.*, Gould*, *Evolution: Explosion, Not Ascent*, N.Y. Times, Jan. 22, 1978, at E6 ("Paleontologists have documented virtually no cases of slow and steady transformation, foot by foot up the strata of a hillslope—not for horses, not for humans."); R. Leakey*, *The Making of Mankind* 43 (1981) ("science is often seen as a search for answers that, given sufficient time, must surely be forthcoming, but because of the nature of the evidence—or rather, lack of it—this may not be the case in paleoanthropology. David Pilbeam concludes, 'It's my conviction that there may be many aspects of human evolution that will always elude us. We should be straightforward and honest about that.' ").

707   Pilbeam*, *Book Review of Leakey's Origins*, 66 Am. Scientist 378, 379 (1978) (italics added).

708   S. Stanley*, *Macroevolution* 88 (1979).

709   B. Campbell*, *Humankind Emerging* 34 (3d ed. 1982) (although believing that the drawings give a correct sequence and some idea of ancestors' nature).

710   Oxnard*, *Human Fossils: New Views of Old Bones*, 41 Am. Biology Teacher 264, 264 (1979).

711   Rensberger*, *Facing the Past*, Science 81, Oct. 1981, at 41, 49 (italics added).

[712]   G. Himmelfarb*, *Darwin and the Darwinian Revolution* 310-11 (1959). *See also* Straus*, *The Great Piltdown Hoax*, 119 Science 265, 265 (1954).

[713]   Oxnard*, *Human Fossils: New Views of Old Bones*, 41 Am. Biology Teacher 264, 264 (1979) (italics added).

[714]   Anderson*, *Hominid collarbone exposed as dolphin's rib*, 98 New Scientist 199 (Apr. 28, 1983) ("He puts the incident on a *par with two other embarrassing faux pas* by fossil hunters: *Hesperopithecus*, the fossil pig's tooth that was cited as evidence of very early man in North America, and *Eoanthropus* or 'Piltdown Man,' the jaw of an orangutan and the skull of a modern human that were claimed to be the 'earliest Englishman'.") (italics added).

[715]   *Id. See also* S. Zuckerman*, *Beyond the Ivory Tower* 64 (1970).

[716]   S. Zuckerman*, *Beyond the Ivory Tower* 64 (1970).

[717]   *Id.* at 77, 81, 85, 91 (based on size of brain case and pelvic bones).

[718]   *Id.* at 93-94 (italics added).

[719]   Oxnard*, *Human Fossils: New Views of Old Bones*, 41 Am. Biology Teacher 264 (May 1979) (italics added).

[720]   Oxnard*, *The place of the australopithecines in human evolution: grounds for doubt?*, 258 Nature 389, 395 (1975) (italics added). *See also id.* at 395 ("Although most studies emphasize the similarity of the *australopithecines* to modern man, and suggest, therefore, that these creatures were bipedal tool-makers at least one form of which (*Australopithecus africanus*—'*Homo habilis*', '*Homo africanus*') was almost directly ancestral to man, a series of multivariate statistical studies of various postcranial fragments *suggests other conclusions*.") (italics added).

[721]   Shea*, *Primate Morphometrics*, 224 Science 148, 149 (1984) (italics added). Oxnard* then could not rule out *A. afarensis* as a possible ancestor because he had not yet examined the fossils. *See also* Rak* & Clark*, *Ear Ossicle of Australopithecus Robustus*, Nature, May 3, 1979, at 62, 62 ("We report here the discovery of the first ear ossicle, an incus, of a Plio-Pleistocene hominid. It is *substantially different from that of modern man*, and the *dissimilarity exceeds that between the ear bones of Homo sapiens and of the African apes*.") (italics added).

[722]   Leakey*, *Excavations in Beds I and II, 1960-63*, 3 Olduvai Gorge 272 (M. Leakey* ed. 1971).

[723]   DeVore*, *Introduction*, in The Origin of Man 11 (P. DeVore* ed. 1965).

[724]   Leakey*, *Skull 1470—New Clue to Earliest Man?*, 143 National Geographic 819, 819 (1973).

[725]   Shipman*, *Baffling Limb on the Family Tree*, Discover, Sept. 1986, at 87, 89, 92-93 (italics added).

[726]   Lewin*, *Do Ape-Size Legs Mean Ape-Like Gait?*, 221 Science 537, 537 (1983) ("*Jungers compared the length of Lucy's femur with an African ape standard* (a chimpanzee for example) computed to the same body size. There was *virtually no difference* between the two. . . . Lucy's legs were clearly diminutive and more like those of an ape than a human, concluded Jungers.") (italics added). *See also* Jungers*, *Lucy's limbs: Skeletal allome-*

try and locomotion in Australopithecus afarensis, 297 Nature 676 (1982).

[727] Cherfas*, *Trees Have Made Man Upright*, New Scientist, Jan. 20, 1983, at 172; Stern* & Susman*, *The Locomoter Anatomy of Australopithecus Afarensis*, 60 Am. J. Physical Anthropology 279 (1983).

[728] Tuttle*, *Was Lucy a Climber? Dissenting Views of Ancient Bones*, 122 Science News 116, 116 (1982) ("another more human species of ape-man co-existed with *A. afarensis* about 3.7 million years ago").

[729] Herbert*, *Lucy: The trouble with dating an older woman*, 123 Science News 5, 5 (1983).

[730] Brace*, *Humans in Time and Space*, in Scientists Confront Creationism 258 (L. Godfrey* ed. 1981).

[731] T. Dobzhansky*, F. Ayala*, G. Stebbins* & J. Valentine*, *Evolution* 447 (1977).

[732] Eckhardt*, *Population Genetics and Human Origins*, Scientific Am., Jan. 1972, at 94, 101.

[733] Zihlman* & Lowenstein*, *False Start of the Human Parade*, Natural History, Aug. 1979, at 86, 89.

[734] Walker* & Andrews*, *Reconstruction of the Dental Arcades of Ramapithecus wickeri*, 244 Nature 313, 314 (1973) (final italics added).

[735] Zihlman* & Lowenstein*, *False Start of the Human Parade*, Natural History, Aug. 1979, at 86, 91.

[736] *Id.* at 88.

[737] T. Dobzhansky*, F. Ayala*, G. Stebbins* & J. Valentine*, *Evolution* 447 (1977) (italics in original).

[738] Dubois*, *On the Fossil Human Skulls Recently Discovered in Java and Pithecanthropus Erectus*, 37 Man 1, 4-5 (1937) (italics added).

[739] Oxnard*, *Convention and controversy in human evolution*, 30 Homo: Zeitschrift für die Vergleichende Forschung am Menschen 225, 246 (1979) ("*Although most assessments of the Olduvai [8] foot imply* that it is from a creature *bipedal in the manner of man*, a series of *new studies* involving multivariate morphometric analyses of the talus and rearticulation of the entire suite of foot bones shows that the *original designations are in error.* The new studies indicate a foot not entirely like that of any particular present day ape though sharing features with them, but *completely different from man.* Such a finding implies that perhaps this fossil is *not so closely linked with the human lineage* as presently believed and this is corroborated by the results of a series of other studies, using the multivariate morphometric techniques on other anatomical regions of australopithecines from Olduvai and Southern Africa.") (italics added).

[740] Oxnard* & Lisowski*, *Functional Articulation of Some Hominid Foot Bones: Implications for the Olduvai (Hominid 8) Foot*, 52 Am. J. Physical Anthropology 107, 107 (1980) ("Subsequent studies showed the conclusions on the talus to be *wrong*: The fossil talus, as defined by eight measures, *does not resemble that of man but is reminiscent of those of creatures known (extant—orangutans) or believed (extinct—some fossil apes and monkeys) to be arboreal* in habitus . . ..") (italics added).

[741]   A. Montagu*, *Man: His First Million Years* 58 (2d ed. 1962) (italics added).

[742]   Ivanhoe*, *Was Virchow right about Neandert[h]al?*, 227 Nature 577, 577 (1970) (italics added).

[743]   Straus* & Cave*, *Pathology and the Posture of Neanderthal Man*, 32 Q. Rev. of Biology 348 (1957).

[744]   Leach*, *Men, bishops and apes*, 293 Nature 19, 21 (1981).

[745]   J. Mistler-Lachman* & R. Lachman*, *Language in Man, Monkeys and Machines*, 185 Science 871 (1974); Wade*, *Does Man Alone Have Language?*, 208 Science 1349 (1980).

[746]   T. Dobzhansky*, F. Ayala*, G. Stebbins* & J. Valentine*, *Evolution* 453 (1977) (italics in original).

[747]   *Id.* at 452.

[748]   Simpson*, *The World into Which Darwin Led Us*, 131 Science 966, 969 (1960) (italics added). *See also* G. Simpson*, *This View of Life* 12 (1964).

[749]   C. Darwin*, *The Descent of Man* 213 (1871).

[750]   A. Montagu*, *An Introduction to Physical Anthropology* 102 (1951) ("Some authorities interpret the facts to indicate that man . . . originated either from a tarsioid or generalized catarrhine *monkey*. . . .") (italics added); A. Montagu*, *The Science of Man* 14 (1964) ("it was from the Old World *monkey* stock that the early anthropoids arose, and from these, in turn, that the line which led to man came into being.") (italics added).

[751]   F. Rhodes*, *The Evolution of Life* 252 (1962) ("anthropoid *apes* lived in Europe, Asia, and Africa during Miocene times, and it is amongst these that our remote ancestors will probably be found.") (italics added).

[752]   W. Stokes*, *Essentials of Earth History* 361 (1960) ("Either he diverged from the apes at a relatively late time and is a 'made over ape' or he split off from the primates much earlier at the evolutionary stage represented by the tarsiers or lower monkeys.") (italics added).

[753]   L. Eiseley*, *The Immense Journey* 111 (1957) ("The *ape* whose cultural remains at the beginning of the first glaciation can scarcely be distinguished from chance bits of stone has, by the end of the fourth ice age, become artist and world rover, penetrator of the five continents, and master of all.") (italics added); Eiseley*, *The Time of Man*, Horizon, Mar. 1962, at 4 ("Once he was thought a fallen angel; then we found him to be an ascended *ape*.") (italics added).

[754]   H. Shapiro*, *Man, Culture and Society* 5 (1956) ("his recent emergence from the world of *apes*") (italics added).

[755]   Washburn*, *Tools and Human Evolution*, Scientific Am., Sept. 1960, at 63, 63 ("Man began when populations of *apes*. . . started the bipedal, tool-using way of life that gave rise to the man-apes of the genus *Australopithecus*.") (italics added).

[756]   Muller*, *Man's Place in Living Nature*, Scientific Am., May 1957, at 245, 250 ("It is fashionable in some circles to refer slurringly to the inference that *apes were ancestral to men*, . . . and that it is more proper to say that

men and apes, perhaps even men, apes, and monkeys, diverged long ago from a stem form that was more primitive than any of these. This is *mere wishful thinking* on the part of those who resent too vivid a visualization of their lowly origin and their present-day poor relations.") (italics added).

757 R. Dart*, *Adventures with the Missing Link* 215 (1959) ("As Elliot Smith put it: 'The acquisition of speech was, in fact, an essential part of the process of transforming an *ape into a human being.*") (italics added).

758 *E.g.*, E. Hooten*, *Apes, Men, and Morons* 105 (1938) ("He made himself from an *ape* and created human culture.") (italics added); W. Howells*, *Mankind So Far* 3 (1945) ("In body and brain he is simply a made-over *ape*, with no fundamental distinctions at all.") (italics added); Straus*, *The Riddle of Man's Ancestry*, 24 Rev. Biology 200, 203 (1949) ("perhaps the majority of anthropologists and comparative anatomists . . . believe that man has evolved from a true anthropoid *ape* at a relatively late geological date") (italics added); *id.* at 202 (T.H. Huxley's* "concept of man's relationship to the other primates today remains the *orthodox one*, differing only in details imposed by the advance of knowledge. . . . In its present orthodox form, this theory assumes that *man evolved from an animal that would be classified* as an anthropoid *ape.*") (italics added).

758A R. Lewin*, *Bones of Contention: Controversies in the Search for Human Origins* (1987); Harper*, *A critical review of theories concerning the origin of the Darwin finches*, 14 J. Biogeography 391, 402 (1987).

759 Hill*, *Book Review*, 72 Am. Scientist 188, 189 (1984) (italics added).

760 Corner*, *Evolution*, in Contemporary Botanical Thought at 95, 97 (A. MacLeod* & L. Cobley* eds. 1961) (italics added). The "progressive increase in the frequency and taxonomic diversity of trilete spores" may not be "a function of organic evolution" but rather "largely a function of biofacies." Gray* & Boucout*, *Early Silurian Spore Tetrads from New York: Earliest New World Evidence for Vascular Plants?*, 173 Science 918, 920, 921 (1971).

761 3 *The Life and Letters of Charles Darwin* 248 (F. Darwin* ed. 1887) (italics in original).

762 M. Denton*, *Evolution: A Theory in Crisis* 163 (1985), quoting Axelrod*, *The Evolution of Flowering Plants*, in The Evolution of Life 227, 230 (S. Tax* & C. Callendar* eds. 1960).

763 Axelrod*, *Evolution of the Psilophyte Paleoflora*, 13 Evolution 264, 274 (1959).

764 Sections 3.2(d)-(f).

765 G. Kerkut*, *Implications of Evolution* 157 (1960) (italics added).

766 Note 604.

767 Note 609.

768 Note 611.

769 Note 612.

770 Note 621.

771 Note 625.

772 Note 624.

[773] Note 622.
[774] Note 627.
[775] Note 628.
[776] Note 629.
[777] Note 631.
[778] Note 635.
[779] Note 634.
[780] Note 636.
[781] Note 638.
[782] Note 639.
[783] Note 640.
[784] Note 641.
[785] Note 648.
[786] Note 649.
[787] Note 655.
[788] Note 656.
[789] Note 657.
[790] Note 658.
[791] Note 659.
[792] Note 666.
[793] Note 668.
[794] Note 675.
[795] Note 676.
[796] Note 677.
[797] Note 678.
[798] Note 680.
[799] Note 681.
[800] Note 682.
[801] Note 690.
[802] Note 686.
[803] Note 687.
[804] Note 688.
[805] Note 689.
[806] Note 690.
[807] Note 693.
[808] Note 694.
[809] Note 697.
[810] Note 698.
[811] Note 701.
[812] Note 704.
[813] Note 705.
[814] Note 707.
[815] Note 759.
[816] *Id.*

[817]   Note 709.

[818]   Note 710.

[819]   Note 711.

[820]   Note 713.

[821]   Note 760.

[822]   Note 763.

[823]   Note 762.

[824]   A. Koestler*, *Janus: A Summing Up* 192 (1978).

[825]   Address of Dr. Colin Patterson* at American Museum of Natural History, tr. at 3 (Nov. 5, 1981) (italics added).

[826]   *E.g.*, Patterson*, *Significance of Fossils in Determining Evolutionary Relationships*, 12 Ann. Rev. of Ecology & Systematics 195, 211 (1981) ("I cannot avoid the conclusion that before the development of the cladistic method *paleontology was a hindrance* rather than a help, stifling progress towards the goal of determining evolutionary relationships, and promulgating *unjustifiable inferences* about the pattern of evolution in the group.") (italics added).

[827]   Rosen*, Forey* Gardiner* & Patterson*, *Lungfishes, Tetrapods, Paleontology, and Pleisiomorphy*, 167 Bull. Am. Museum of Natural History 163, 178 (1981).

[828]   *E.g.*, Webster* & Goodwin*, *The origin of species: a structuralist approach*, 5 J. Social & Biological Structures 15, 44 (1982).

[829]   Mathews*, *Introduction*, to C. Darwin*, The Origin of Species i-xii (1971).

[830]   A. Boyden*, *Perspectives in Zoology* 117 (1973). *See also* Address of Dr. Colin Patterson* at American Museum of Natural History, tr. at 6 (Nov. 5, 1981) ("I want to use it to make another point about *evolution* being an antitheory that conveys antiknowledge. *It is harmful to systematics.*") (italics added).

PART III

Whether the Theories of Abrupt Appearance and Evolution Are Scientific?

The Origin of the First Life

The theory of evolution normally includes not just biological evolution of all the various plants and animals (macroevolution), but biochemical evolution of the first life.[1] The theory of abrupt appearance also addresses the origin of life.

The biochemical theory of abrupt appearance, like biochemical evolution, consists of scientific evidence along several affirmative lines. Ironically, it is biochemical abrupt appearance rather than biochemical evolution that involves various natural laws, such as the natural laws of biogenesis (life from life), information science, and thermodynamics, as well as the statistical reflection of natural laws in probability theory and the empirical data of isomer preferences. Biochemical abrupt appearance is not without scientific difficulties, but neither are most scientific explanations including biochemical evolution.

The biochemical theory of evolution is conceded by many evolutionists to be rife with "speculation."[2] Yockey* finds it to be "based on faith" and akin to theories of "little green men."[3] Kerkut* con-

293

cludes that there is "little evidence," but merely "suggestive schemes and nothing more," for the "matter of faith" called biochemical evolution.[4] Another author writes that "[s]peculation is bound to be rife, and it has also frequently been wild" and has "shared much with imaginative literature and little with theoretical inference of the kind which can be confronted with observational evidence."[5] Others have simply concluded that biochemical evolution is statistically impossible, such as Eden*, Ambrose*, Hadd*, Golay*, Salisbury*, etc.[6]

In many ways biochemical abrupt appearance and biochemical evolution are comparable. The point is not that either is correct and the other false, but that each is tentative at best in light of the evidence. Denton's* assessment is as follows:

> The failure to give a plausible evolutionary explanation for the origin of life casts a number of shadows over the whole field of evolutionary speculation. It represents *yet another case of a discontinuity* where a lack of empirical evidence of intermediates coincides with great difficulty in providing a plausible hypothetical sequence of transitional forms. It therefore tends to reinforce the possibility that *the discontinuities of nature may be much more fundamental* than merely the artificial result of random sampling that evolution implies.[7]

Notes

[1]   T. Dobzhansky*, F. Ayala*, G. Stebbins* & J. Valentine*, *Evolution* 9 (1977).

[2]   F. Crick*, *Life Itself* 153 (1981).

[3]   Yockey*, *A Calculation of the Probability of Spontaneous Biogenesis by Information Theory*, 67 J. Theoretical Biology 377, 377 (1977).

[4]   G. Kerkut*, *Implications of Evolution* 150 (1960).

[5]   Anon.*, *What Future for Biogenesis?*, 216 Nature 635, 635 (1967).

[6]   Sections 2.4, 2.5, 4.1 & 4.2.

[7]   M. Denton*, *Evolution: A Theory in Crisis* 271 (1985).

CHAPTER 4

Theories of Abrupt Appearance and Empirical Evidence: Biochemical Abrupt Appearance of the First Life

> *But if (and oh! what a big if!) we could conceive in some warm little pond, with all sorts of ammonia and phosphoric salts, light, heat, electricity etc., present, that a protein compound was chemically formed ready to undergo still more complex changes . . ..*
>
> —Charles Darwin*[1]

The biochemical theory of abrupt appearance describes the origin of the first life as through abrupt appearance in complex form, as indicated by empirical evidence and scientific interpretations. That empirical evidence and those scientific interpretations follow at least five affirmative lines:

---

*Scientists cited in this chapter, unless otherwise indicated, are not proponents of, and their quoted statements are not intended as endorsements of, either the theory of abrupt appearance or the theory of creation. However, their quoted statements are acknowledging data that some nonevolutionist scientists interpret as supporting the theory of abrupt appearance better than the theory of evolution.

4.1	Information content argument: Natural laws of information science
4.2	Probability argument: Natural laws reflected in statistics
4.3	Isomers argument: Empirical evidence of left-handed amino acids and right-handed sugars
4.4	Biogenesis argument: Natural law of life from life
4.5	Thermodynamics argument: Natural law of increasing disorder.

This chapter merely summarizes these lines of analysis, and does not attempt to discuss them comprehensively.

The information content argument is based on the vast information content of the least complex living organism, of its genetic coding system, and of its other molecules, which is better explained by biochemical abrupt appearance than by evolution (Section 4.1). The probability argument is founded on the higher probability of abrupt appearance, and the near-zero probability of evolution, of the least complex living organism, including its enzymes, other proteins, and DNA (Section 4.2). The isomers argument is based on the virtually universal presence of L-amino acids in proteins and D-sugars in nucleic acids (Section 4.3). The biogenesis argument centers on the chemical tendency away from life rather than toward life (Section 4.4). The thermodynamics argument is based on the order of the first life being more plausibly explained by abrupt appearance than by evolution (Section 4.5). The scientific evidence that forms the basis of biochemical abrupt appearance has been articulated by some leading discontinuitist scientists such as biophysicist Dean H. Kenyon, a professor of biology at San Francisco State University with a Ph.D. degree in biophysics from Stanford.[2] However, in this chapter that evidence is described solely on the basis of evolutionist technical literature.

These arguments are affirmative rather than negative in the sense that, if true, they render the biochemical theory of abrupt appearance more plausible rather than merely making the biochemical theory of evolution less plausible. Thus, they do not rely on an assumption that abrupt appearance and evolution are the only general alternatives, with the partial exception that the probability argument is stronger if there are only two alternatives.

Darwin* recognized that theories of biochemical evolution involved a very "big if," as quoted at the beginning of this chapter. Cairns-Smith* acknowledges that the evidence, a century and a quarter later, is still unclear enough that it suggests "some other, yet unthought-of explanation":

> What might be the signs of some other, yet unthought-of explanation? One sign might be where, in spite of tests of many predictions in different areas of the doctrine, success is restricted to only one of a few areas. As we have seen, this is the case for chemical evolution.[3]

Figure 4.1
The least complex single-celled organism (like **Paramecium** *here) has information content "comparable to about a hundred million pages of the Encyclopaedia Britannica"* *(Sagan*)*

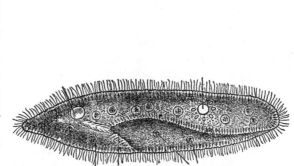

4.1 The Information Content Argument: Natural Laws of Information Science

Information content is a measure of the difference between a random arrangement and a meaningful arrangement. The information content argument is based on the vast information content (a) of the least complex single-celled organism, and (b) of the genetic coding system of all organisms.

That information content is so great that it affirmatively supports the biochemical theory of abrupt appearance and undercuts the biochemical theory of evolution, as Haskins* reluctantly concedes in connection with the genetic coding system:

> Did the code and the means of translating it appear simultaneously in evolution? It seems almost incredible that any such coincidences could have occurred, given the extraordinary complexities of both sides and the requirement that they be coordinated accurately for survival. By a pre-Darwinian (or a skeptic of evolution after Darwin) this puzzle surely would have been interpreted as the *most powerful sort of evidence for special creation.*[4]

For example, proponents of a search for extraterrestrial intelligence acknowledge that radio signals with information content would be best interpreted as evidence of intelligent abrupt appearance—just as organisms with improbable information content are best explained as evidence of abrupt appearance. Ponnamperuma* argues that a "nonrandom pattern" (i.e., information content) would demonstrate extraterrestrial production,[5] and Sagan* notes that a message with high information content would be "an unambiguously artificial interstellar message."[6]

a. Of Organisms

The least complex single-celled organism has a vast information content "comparable to about a hundred million pages of the *Encyclopaedia Britannica*," according to Sagan* of Cornell:

> A living cell is a marvel of detailed and complex architecture. Seen through a microscope there is an appearance of almost frenetic activity. On a deeper level it is known that molecules are being synthesized at an enormous rate. Almost any enzyme catalyzes the synthesis of more than 100 other molecules per second. In ten minutes, a sizable fraction of the total mass of a metabolizing bacterial cell has been synthesized. The *information content of a simple cell* has been estimated as around *10^{12} bits*, comparable to about *a hundred million pages of the Encyclopaedia Britannica*.[7]

Such a bacterial cell is "very close to satisfying the minimum criteria for a fully autonomous cell system capable of independent replication," Denton* points out, because the smallest known bacterial cells have an average diameter less than three times the diameter of "the minimum hypothetical cell" according to Morowitz's* calculations.[8]

That difference between nonlife and the least complex life is so great that the transformation is "at least as great" as the postulated transformation from the least complex life to man, Simpson* of Harvard points out:

> Above the level of the virus, the simplest fully living unit is almost *incredibly complex*. It has become commonplace to speak of evolution from amoeba to man, as if the amoeba were the simple beginning of the process. On the contrary, if, as must almost necessarily be true, life arose as a simple molecular system, the progression from this state to that of the amoeba is *at least as great as from amoeba to man*.[9]

"The origin of even the simplest cell poses a problem hardly less difficult. The most elementary type of cell constitutes a 'mechanism' unimaginably more complex than any machine yet thought up, let alone constructed, by man," Thorpe* concurs.[10]

Yockey*, an information scientist with a Ph.D. degree from Berkeley, has calculated the information content of the least complex life, and has concluded that only a single nonliving protein could have evolved in a billion years:

> Taking into account only the effect of the racemic mixture the longest genome which could be expected with 95% confidence in 10^9 years corresponds to *only 49 amino acid residues*. This is much too short to code a living system so evolution to higher forms could not get started. Geological evidence for the "warm little pond" is missing. . . .
>
> . . ..
> . . .Clearly *10^9 years is far too short* a time and *the universe is far too small* for the goddess to select even one molecule of cytochrome *c* from the primitive milieu. Therefore a belief that proteins basic for life as we know it appeared spontaneously in the primitive milieu on earth is *based on faith.*[11]

b. Of the Genetic Code

The genetic coding system in the least complex cell is very complex, and includes DNA and RNA (which are nucleic acids made up of chains of hundreds of nucleotides per chain), ribosomes (which translate messenger RNA into the amino acid sequences of proteins), at least 70 enzymes and other proteins (which are necessary in transcribing and translating the DNA), ATP (which is the main energy-carrying molecule), and a supply of nucleotides.[12] That genetic coding system even includes a checking mechanism, so that "cells are . . . checking and double-checking [proteins] at particular stages during synthesis."[13]

The fifty or more essential components of the genetic coding system are themselves produced by the genetic coding system—a "vicious circle"—as Popper*, the famous philosopher of science, observes:

> What makes the origin of life and of the genetic code a *disturbing riddle* is this: the genetic code is without any biological function unless it is translated; that is, unless it leads to the synthesis of the proteins whose structure is laid down by the code. But, as Monod points out, the machinery by which the cell [at least the nonprimitive cell which is the only one we know] translates the code "*consists of at least fifty macromolecular components which are themselves coded in DNA.*" Thus the code cannot be translated except by using certain products of its translation. This constitutes a really *baffling circle*: a *vicious circle, it seems, for any attempt to form a model, or theory, of the genesis of the genetic code.*[14]

In other words, the information content is much greater and the improbability is yet higher when the DNA and the fifty molecules must arise together, as Ambrose*[15] and Salisbury*[16] recognize, in order to produce each other in that "baffling circle."[17] Orgel*, a leading researcher, concurs that this is the "most baffling aspect":

> We do not yet understand even the general features of the origin of the genetic code.... The origin of the genetic code is the most baffling aspect of the problem of the origins of life, and a major conceptual or experimental breakthrough may be needed before we can make any substantial progress.[18]

Turning to chromosomes (which are made up of many genes), "the information encoded in a single human chromosome is equivalent to several thousand volumes of small print," Leslie* points out.[19] The information content of this genetic coding system is so great that Schutzenberger* of University of Paris and other scientists concluded at a conference on the mathematical probability problem facing evolution:

> Thus, to conclude, we believe that there is a *considerable gap in the neo-Darwinian theory of evolution*, and we believe this gap to be of such a nature that it *cannot be bridged* within the current conception of biology.[20]

The information content of the genetic coding system does not result from laws of chemistry and mechanical processes, as Polanyi*, former chairman of physical chemistry at University of Manchester, points out:

> As the arrangement of a printed page is extraneous to the chemistry of the printed page, so is the *base sequence in a DNA molecule extraneous to the chemical forces at work in the DNA molecule.* It is this physical indeterminacy of the sequence that produces the improbability of occurrence of any particular sequence and thereby enables it to have a meaning—a meaning that has a mathematically determinate *information content* . . ..[21]

Summary. Every "simple cell" has "information content . . . comparable to about a hundred million pages of the *Encyclopaedia Britannica*," Sagan* estimates, because it is "a marvel of detailed and complex architecture" (Sagan*[22]). The "progression from [molecules] to that of the amoeba is at least as great as from amoeba to man" (Simpson*[23]). So vast is the information content of the least complex life that only a short nonliving protein could have evolved in a billion years (Yockey*[24]). The genetic coding system in each cell adds a "baffling circle," because "the machinery by which the cell . . . translates the code 'consists of at least fifty macromolecular components which are themselves coded in DNA'" (Popper*[25]). Even an evolutionist, Haskins*, reluctantly acknowledges that to "a pre-Darwinian (or a skeptic of evolution after Darwin) this puzzle surely would have been interpreted as the most powerful sort of evidence for special creation" (Haskins*[26]). Despite significant differences from the theory of creation, the theory of abrupt appearance is also supported by the vast information content of life.

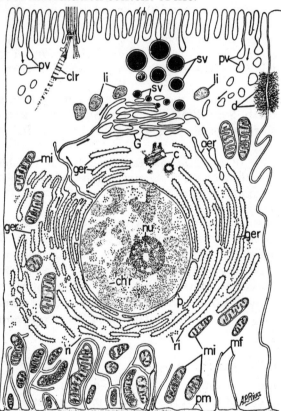

Figure 4.2
The probability of even single celled life to evolve "was virtually zero" (Monod, a Nobel Prize recipient)*

4.2 The Probability Argument: Natural Laws Reflected in Statistics

The probability argument is based on the higher mathematical probability of abrupt appearance, and the near-zero probability of evolution, (a) of the least complex life, and (b) of its enzymes, other proteins, and DNA. Unlike the other arguments for the biochemical theory of abrupt appearance, the probability argument is only compelling if biochemical abrupt appearance and biochemical evolution are the only alternatives, which is discussed in Chapter 11. However, that argument has some force regardless of the number of alternatives. Many noncreationists have agreed that the extreme improbability of evolution corresponds to a probability of creation, such as the brilliant logician John Stuart Mill*:

> Leaving this remarkable speculation [natural selection] to whatever fate the progress of discovery may have in store for it, I think it must be allowed that, in the present state of our knowledge, the adaptations in Nature afford *a large balance of probability in favour of creation* by intelligence. It is equally certain that this is no more than a probability . . . .[27]

Even if biochemical evolution and biochemical abrupt appearance are not the sole alternatives, biochemical abrupt appearance may be the more probable of the alternatives, as Mill* implies and Hoyle states:

> Rather than accept that fantastically small probability of life having arisen through the blind forces of nature, it seemed *better to suppose that the origin of life was a deliberate intellectual act.* By "better" I mean *less likely to be wrong.*[28]

It is, of course, erroneous to state categorically that the incredibly improbable cannot happen, or that the more probable must happen. However, it is more erroneous to state that the incredibly improbable must have happened. Also, it is equally erroneous to state, as many evolutionists do, that the existence of life proves its probability by evolutionary causes, just as the existence of computers does not prove that they originated by evolution without human intelligence.

a. Of Organisms

The least complex single-celled organism has DNA chains that are so complex that the probability of the arrangement is the unimaginably small figure of 1 chance in $10^{2,000,000}$ (which represents 1 followed by 2 million zeros), according to Ambrose*, a cell biologist formerly of University of London:

> When we come to examine the simplest known organism capable of independent existence, the situation becomes even more fantastic. In the DNA chain of the chromosome of the bacterium *E. coli*, a favourite organism used by molecular biologists, the [DNA] helix consists of 3-4 million base pairs. These are all arranged in a sequence that is 'meaningful' in the sense that it gives rise to enzyme molecules which fit the

various metabolites and products used by the cell. This unique sequence represents a choice of *one out of $10^{2,000,000}$ alternative ways* of arranging the bases! We are compelled to conclude that the origin of the first life was a unique event, which *cannot be discussed in terms of probability*.[29]

Looked at another way, in 5 billion years evolution would at best produce a single pair of genes of *E. coli* (corresponding to a tiny part of the full DNA chain), and would produce that only if the entire earth were covered with an inch-thick layer of *E. coli* for that period, according to Eden* of M.I.T.[30]

The probability of a single-celled organism evolving is calculated to be 1 chance in 10^{450} by Golay* for the simplest imaginable organism, and at a "very small" level by Noda*.[32] Similar conclusions are reached by Keosian*:

> [T]he simplest heterotrophic cell is an intricate structural and metabolic unit of harmoniously coordinated parts and chemical pathways. Its spontaneous assembly out of the environment, granting the unlikely simultaneous presence of all the parts, is not a believable possibility.[33]

Photosynthetic capability for a single-celled organism compounds the improbability, so that in a billion years "a FeS-protein may appear sometimes, whereas photopigments and quinones are never expected"; the evolution of photosynthesis "is an unsolved problem" and "no solution can be expected," Scherer* concludes.[34]

These numbers are so tiny that the number of protein molecules that could have existed on earth in 10 billion years is still an "infinitesimal" fraction, Eden* calculates.[35] The "probability was virtually zero" for life to evolve, according to Monod*, a Nobel Prize recipient and biochemist at University of Paris:

> Life appeared on earth: what, before the event, were the chances that this would occur? The present structure of the biosphere certainly does not exclude the possibility that . . . its a priori *probability was virtually zero*.[36]

b. Of Proteins and DNA

The enzymes, other proteins, and DNA in even the least complex organism confront comparable probabilities of abrupt appearance, according to discontinuitist scientists, and comparable improbabilities of evolution, in the view of many evolutionists.

For *enzymes*, the probability of the 2,000 human enzymes is calculated at 1 chance in 10^{20} for each, or 1 chance in $10^{40,000}$ for the full assemblage, by Hoyle and Wickramasinghe (chairman of department of applied mathematics at University College of Cardiff); and that is "even if the whole universe were to consist of organic soup."[37] Hoyle's figure of $10^{-40,000}$ has been criticized as misleading because it assumes present complex enzymes instead of "some immensely simpler system capable of crude evolution," and it assumes production of all 2,000 enzymes "at one specified place and at one specified moment of time."[38] However, the necessity of a large number of enzymes is unquestioned, and the improbability of each individual enzyme is close to Hoyle's figure of 10^{-20} according to Erbrich* and the other calculations described next. That improbability of each individual enzyme is itself inconceivably small:

> At all events, anyone with even a nodding acquaintance with the Rubik cube will concede the near-impossibility of a solution being obtained by a blind person moving the cube faces at random. Now imagine 10^{50} blind persons each with a scrambled Rubik cube, and try to conceive of the chance of them all simultaneously arriving at the solved form. You then have the *chance of arriving by random shuffling of just one of the many biopolymers on which life depends*. The notion that not only the biopolymers but the operating programme of a living cell could be arrived at by chance in a primordial organic soup here on the Earth is evidently *nonsense of a high order....*[39]

"So the simultaneous formation of two or more molecules of any given enzyme purely by chance is fantastically improbable," Thorpe* concludes.[39A]

For *other proteins*, the probability of evolution of a simple protein is set at a mere 1 chance in 10^{130} by Lovell*:

> To form a polypeptide chain of a protein containing one hundred amino acids represents a choice of one out of 10^{130} possibilities. Here again, there is no evidence suggesting that one sequence is more stable than another, energetically. The total number of hydrogen atoms in the universe is only 10^{78}. Lovell points out that the probability of forming one of these polypeptide chains by chance is *unimaginably small*; within the boundary of conditions of time and space we are considering it is effectively zero.[40]

That chance for "the smallest known proteins seems beyond all probability," according to Blum*:

> But the question arises as to how these amino acids could have become joined together into polypeptide chains. It is commonly assumed today that life arose in the oceans, J.B.S. Haldane's 'dilute hot soup' providing a supposedly appropriate medium.
>
> But even if this soup contained a goodly concentration of amino acids, the chances of their forming spontaneously into long chains would seem remote.... [T]he *probability of forming a polypeptide of only ten amino acid units would be something like 10^{-20}*. The spontaneous formation of a polypeptide of the size of the *smallest known proteins seems beyond all probability*. This calculation alone presents serious objection to the idea

that all living systems are descended from a single protein molecule, which was formed as a "chance" act—a view that has been frequently entertained.[41]

Ten amino acid units do not go far toward the 150 units of a "moderate-sized protein," as Ayala* and Valentine* describe proteins.[42]

The "time needed to form, on an average, one such molecule in a material volume equal to that of our terrestrial globe is about 10^{243} billion years" (and the earth is believed to be less than 10^{10} years old), according to du Nouy*, a French biophysicist formerly with the Pasteur Institute.[43] A similar time was calculated by Guye*, on the basis of his conclusion that the chance of formation of a protein-like substance is 1 chance in 10^{160}.[44] The chance of synthesizing "one simple protein" is impossibly small, as calculated by Stokes*:

The problem of synthesizing one simple protein of about 300 amino acids has been cited. . . . A chain of *1000 nucleotides* made of the four basic units might exist in *any of 41,000 ways*, but *only one will form the protein being sought*. The chance that the correct sequence would be achieved by simple random combination is said to be *so small* that it would not occur during billions of years on billions of planets, each covered by a blanket of a concentrated watery solution of the necessary amino acids.[45]

Hoyle and Wickramasinghe concur.[46] Similarly, the probability of evolution of a cytochrome *c* molecule is only 1 chance in 10^{94}, in the view of Yockey*:

The number of sequences of *cytochrome c* is now 7.25 x 10^{60}, the number of sequences for 101 sites is 3.4 x 10^{154}. Therefore the probability of selecting a member of the *cytochrome c* family with the same optical isomers in a given set of 101 rolls of the icosahedral dice is 2.15 x 10^{-94}.[47]

Finally, for *DNA*, the probability of evolution of a DNA chain to produce a medium protein is hardly 1 chance in 10^{600}—and 10^{600} DNA chains would fill many universes—according to Salisbury*.[48]

These probabilities are unimaginably small, Lafont* notes:

The *number of chemical events* which can have occurred on earth or which can occur in the future up to the end of earth's existence is certainly *less than 10^{80}; this is an enormous figure, but it is not infinite.* "The *impossibility threshold* of any chemical phenomenon on earth is a probability of *10^{-100}*."[49]

A similar definition of impossibility is given by Borel*.[50] By way of illustration, the ratio of one atom to all atoms in the known universe of billions of stars is about 1 to 10^{80}. And these are not but a few of the many improbabilities for living systems, as Leslie* indicates:

We can point also to the improbable lefthandedness of almost all the amino acids found in life on earth, when left-handed and right-handed varieties are equally easily made in the laboratory; to the 'improbable' DNA molecule, a million times longer than it is wide; to estimates that the information encoded in a single human chromosome is equivalent to several thousand volumes of small print; to a large mammal's thousand trillion cells of about a thousand different varieties, and to how it took Evolution far longer to invent the cell, so naively called 'simple,' than to make the leap to mammals; and so on.[51]

c. Criticisms of Probability Calculations

These probability calculations have been criticized on a number of grounds, such as that some molecular sequences are more probable than others, "not every possible base sequence in the genes leads to a different amino acid sequence in the proteins," "not . . . every amino acid sequence leads to a functionally different protein," and "amino acids are obviously exchangeable to a certain extent in a manner that does not alter the function of the protein," as listed by Erbrich* of University of Munich.[52] Erbrich* then adjusted for these and other probability-increasing factors, and concluded that "the probability for a de novo or independent emergence of a protein is practically non-existent" still:

The probability for the de novo emergence of a particular protein by chance alone is *extremely small*, even for a very imperfect one. A weak initial adaptiveness may be sufficient, but also necessary to make selection work. Without at least a minimum usefulness there are no alternatives between which to select. Selection does not create; it eliminates or conserves what chance produces, and optimizes what already exists according to the demands of life and environment.

If the *probability for a de novo or independent emergence of a protein is practically non-existent, evolution by convergence of proteins should also be non-existent*, because the latter implies the former (cf. p. 5, 7 f). However, evolution by convergence at the molecular level, and, more generally speaking, the emergence of new molecular structures and functions in the course of evolution seems to be a fact: new structures and functions insofar as they can hardly be traced back to older structures through intermediate stages each of which was functional and even more so than the preceding one.

If evolution by convergence and, by implication, emergence of something new is a fact (and not only an extremely rare one), then we have an evolutionary process which the *Darwinian mechanism* of random mutation and subsequent selection, chance and necessity, *cannot account for* adequately because the role of chance is overtaxed. . . .[53]

He found the "emergence of a particular protein with a particular new function . . . possible" in a five billion year period only by making a number of unrealistic assumptions,[54] and only by "assum-[ing] that there are 12 prefabricated peptides for the construction of different proteins and that our protein with 100 amino acid residues is built up of four such sections with a total of 76 amino acid residues" (which amounts to starting with 76% of the protein already made).[55]

Kaplan* of University of Frankfurt made similar adjustments, and calculated that "the protobionic chances P^2 are 10^{-8} to 10^{-16}" under the most favorable assumptions.[56]

Another criticism of probability calculations is that they omit the role of natural selection. However, Simon* points out that natural selection and other Darwinian processes do not apply until life already exists:

> For example, a number of people have tried to extend the biological notion of natural selection to account for the building up of the first self-replicating system, forgetting that the Darwinian conception already presupposes the existence of a mutable, self-replicating system.[57]

Thus, Kaplan* stresses that "chance plays a deciding role" in biochemical evolution.[58] The inapplicability of natural selection is reaffirmed by a number of other authorities cited in Section 5.3(i).

A further criticism is that numerous molecular combinations might work in producing life and biologically meaningful proteins and DNA. Barrow* and Tipler* disagree about alternative pathways to life, as follows:

> In particular, we shall show that many of the proposed alternative biochemistries have serious drawbacks which would prevent them from serving as a base for an evolutionary pathway to the higher forms of life. . . .
>
> This is not to say that other forms of life are impossible, just that these other forms could not evolve to advanced levels of organization by means of natural selection. . . .[59]

Cairns-Smith* also disagrees that there are alternative pathways for synthesizing proteins:

> *Perhaps there is some other way* of making peptides with more or less specified amino acid sequences; and perhaps this way does not need detailed control. Perhaps it could then have operated before there was life on Earth, before that engineer, natural selection, appeared on the scene. But it is difficult to see how this could have been so. *I think we would know by now* if there was some much easier way.[60]

Summary. The probability of biochemical evolution of a single-celled organism has been calculated variously as 1 chance in

$10^{2,000,000}$ (Ambrose*[61]), 1 in 10^{450} (Golay*[62]), "not a believable possibility" (Keosian*[63]), and "virtually zero" (Monod*[64]). Similar calculations have been made for the biochemical evolution of proteins and DNA. Even when the calculations are modified for introns and exons, multiple pathways and structures, and unrealistic assumptions, "the probability for a de novo or independent emergence of a protein is practically non-existent" (Erbrich*[65]). Thus, as unparalleled a logician as John Stuart Mill found "a large balance of probability in favour of creation," recognizing this as affirmative and persuasive evidence (Mill*[66]). A similar balance of probability favors the theory of abrupt appearance, which differs from the theory of creation.

The probability of biochemical abrupt appearance is very high if it is the only alternative explanation, and is higher than the exceedingly small probability of evolution even if there are other alternatives, in the assessment of many discontinuitist scientists. Those probability considerations are based on the mathematical statistics that reflect biochemical laws, in the sense that such statistical frequencies measure the operation of natural laws of biochemistry, just as statistical frequencies of particular traits reflect the operation of natural laws of genetics.

Figure 4.3
Louis Pasteur, the great
French biologist and
discoverer of isomers in
organisms

4.3 The Isomers Argument: Empirical Evidence of Left-Handed Amino Acids and Right-Handed Sugars

The isomers argument is based on the isomers ("chemical substances with the same atomic composition but different molecular structures"[67]) found in living organisms. The great biologist Pasteur discovered the existence of isomers the year after the publication of *The Origin of Species*,[68] and also discovered the empirical fact that is the basis of the isomers argument, "that the molecules related to life were asymmetric."[69]

a. Optical Isomers

That asymmetry is described by Ponnamperuma*, a leading origin of life researcher and University of Maryland professor:

> The *amino acids found in proteins* of living organisms are *all levorotatory or L-amino acids*, and the *sugars are dextrorotatory or D-sugars*, i.e., the beam of polarized light we discussed earlier is deflected to the left in one instance and to the right in the other. *Outside the living world, everything is racemic*, which means that it consists of equal amounts of the right-handed and left-handed molecules. But, in living organisms, only one form is used. Although there are traces of D-amino acids on the cell walls of certain bacteria, in general the molecular make-up of the living organism is principally asymmetric in nature. Indeed, this specific feature has led many to believe that the presence of optical activity is an infallible criterion of life.[70]

The significant thing is that virtually all proteins are made exclusively of left-handed amino acids (L-amino acids) and virtually all nucleic acids are made exclusively of right-handed sugars (D-sugars) in living organisms,[71] as all authorities agree:

> If a sugar or an amino acid is chemically synthesized in a test-tube, the product will be a mixture of left-handed and right-handed molecules, in roughly equal numbers. But in living organisms of every sort, all the amino acids are L-amino acids, and in nucleic acids all the sugars are D-molecules.[72]

The same point is made by Nobel Prize winner Pauling*,[73] leading biochemical evolutionist Oparin*,[74] Williams* and Smith*,[75] Stansfield*,[76] Meister*,[77] Bresler*,[78] and Dillon*.[79]

Those isomers exist even though the opposites are just as chemically probable: "synthesized in a test tube, the product will be a mixture of left-handed and right-handed molecules, in roughly equal numbers."[80] Moreover, when isomers are left to themselves, they racemize or change back to a mixture of left-handed and right-handed forms. Thus, "after death the L isomers are slowly converted to D isomers (racemized)" and this is so predictable that "racemization dating" is used to determine the age of fossils by "measuring the ratio of D to L forms," Stansfield* notes.[81]

Yet "life cannot and never could exist without molecular dissymmetry" (generally all protein amino acids being of the same handedness and generally all nucleic acid sugars being of the same handedness), according to Terentev* and Klabunovskii* at the First International Symposium on the Origin of Life on Earth.[82] Ponnamperuma* notes that many "believe that the presence of optical [isomer] activity is an infallible criterion of life," and that "the D-configuration of deoxyribose is essential for a viable double helix of DNA."[83] Cairns-Smith* similarly "can no more imagine an effective racemic molecular biology than I can imagine an effective racemic typewriter."[84] And Miller* and Orgel* recently have published their recognition of the problem of "enantiomeric cross-inhibition."[85]

b. Geometrical Isomers

A second category of isomers, involving another form of asymmetry, are geometric isomers. Where double bonds exist between two carbon groups in an organic molecule, additional molecular groups may be on the same side (*cis*) or opposite sides (*trans*) of those double bonds. The interesting point is that the *trans* form is the most stable and requires less energy, and thus would be expected to predominate. Yet the *cis* form predominates rather than the more likely *trans* form, and the *cis* form appears to be exclusive in phospholipids in cell membranes.

The "origins of optical activity present problems to the hypothesis of chemical evolution that are at present insoluble," in the words of Bonner*.[86] "How and why the complete separation of stereoisomers in living tissue was started remains an enigma," Bresler* states.[87] Kenyon* and Steinman* also call isomers an "enigma,"[88] and Cairns-Smith* sees "very great difficulties."[89] Miller* and Orgel* conclude that in the effort to explain the isomer preference among ribosides "there is no basis in organic chemistry for optimism," and "that the problem presented by the optical activity of the nucleosides is even more severe."[89A]

There is no generally accepted theory for the origin of optical asymmetry," Williams* and Smith* concur.[90] The major proposed explanations are the external abiotic explanation and the internal biotic explanation. The abiotic approach has been widely criticized,[91] and both approaches are rejected by Cairns-Smith*:

> As we saw, the "abiotic" way of circumventing this problem (by prevital resolution of enantiomers) seems hopelessly inadequate, and "biotic" mechanisms depend on efficient machinery already in action. . . .[92]

Summary. "The amino acids found in proteins of living organisms are all levorotatory or L-amino acids, and the sugars are dextrorotatory or D-sugars," yet "[o]utside the living world, everything is racemic, which means that it consists of equal amounts of right-handed [D] and left-handed [L] molecules" (Ponnamperuma*[93]). Those isomers in living organisms appear to be essential: "life cannot and never could exist without molecular dissymmetry" (Terentev*[94]). "How and why the complete separation of stereoisomers in living tissue was started remains an enigma" (Bresler*[95]). That "enigma" is better explained by the biochemical theory of abrupt appearance, its proponents suggest, than by the biochemical theory of evolution.

4.4 The Biogenesis Argument: Natural Law of Life from Life

The biogenesis argument involves the biochemical tendency away from life, toward breakdown of chemical bonds outside of living organisms and formation of nonbiological bonds, rather than toward life. The following sections outline (a) the law of biogenesis and (b) that biochemical tendency away from life.

a. Law of Biogenesis

The law of biogenesis is the "principle that a living organism can arise only from another living organism, a principle contrasting with concepts such as that of the spontaneous generation of living from non-living matter. . . ."[96] That law, perhaps "the most fundamental in biology," is the axiom that life only comes from life, as Medawar* defines it:

> In its affirmative form, the law of Biogenesis states that all living organisms are the progeny of living organisms that went before them. The familiar Latin tag is *omne vivum ex vivo*—All that is alive came from something living; in other words, every organism has an unbroken

Figure 4.4
The law of biogenesis is the "principle that a living organism can arise only from another living organism, a principle contrasting with ... spontaneous generation of living from non-living matter" (pictured)

genealogical pedigree extending back to the first living things. In its negative form, the law can be taken to deny the occurrence (or even the possibility) of spontaneous generation. Moreover, the progeny of mice are mice and of men, men—"homogenesis," or like begetting like.

The Law of Biogenesis is arguably the most fundamental in biology, for evolution may be construed as a form of biogenesis that provides for the occasional begetting of a variant form. . . .[97]

Although biological evolution involves mere variant forms, biochemical evolution involves spontaneous generation.

b. Empirical Biochemical Tendency Away from Life

Some aspects of the biochemical tendency away from life are summarized by Abelson*:

First, there are limitations on what can be made by inorganic means; second, all organic matter degrades spontaneously with time; third, some substances are readily destroyed by radiation; fourth, many compounds would have been removed from the ocean by precipitation or adsorption; fifth, there are serious chemical incompatibilities among the constituents of living matter, and some of the components of the soup would react to form nonbiologic substances. In view of these limitations, one is challenged to seek a series of steps toward life that are compatible with the environment.[98]

Wald*, a Nobel Prize recipient and Harvard biologist, acknowledges that "spontaneous dissolution is much more probable, and hence proceeds much more rapidly, than spontaneous synthesis":

Forces of Dissolution

We must still reckon, however, with another destructive force which is disposed of less easily. This can be called *spontaneous dissolution*—the counterpart of spontaneous generation. We have noted that any process catalyzed by an enzyme can occur in time without the enzyme. The trouble is that the processes which synthesize an organic substance are reversible: any chemical reaction which an enzyme may catalyze will go backward as well as forward. We have spoken as though one has only to wait to achieve syntheses of all kinds; it is truer to say that what one achieves by waiting is *equilibria* of all kinds—equilibria in which the synthesis and dissolution of substances come into balance.

In the vast majority of the processes in which we are interested the point of equilibrium lies far over toward the side of dissolution. That is to say, *spontaneous dissolution is much more probable, and hence proceeds much more rapidly, than spontaneous synthesis.* For example, the spontaneous union, step by step, of amino acid units to form a protein has a certain small probability, and hence might occur over a long stretch of time. But the dissolution of the protein or of an intermediate product into its component amino acids is much more probable, and hence will go ever so much more rapidly. The situation we must face is that of patient Penelope waiting for Odysseus, yet much worse: each night she undid the weaving of the preceding day, but here a night could readily undo the work of a year or a century.

How do present-day *organisms* manage to synthesize organic compounds against the forces of dissolution? They do so by a continuous expenditure of energy. . . . A living organism is an intricate machine for performing exactly this function. When, for want of fuel or through some internal failure in its mechanism, an organism stops actively synthesizing itself in opposition to the processes which continuously decompose it, it dies and rapidly disintegrates.

What we ask here is to synthesize organic molecules without such a machine. I believe this to be the most stubborn problem that confronts us—the weakest link at present in our argument. I do not think it by any means disastrous, but it calls for phenomena and forces some of which are as yet only partly understood and some probably still to be discovered.[99]

Indeed, "the reactions that are invoked to synthesize such compounds are seen to be much more effective in decomposing them,"

Hull* and Bernal* note.[100] That is further discussed later in connection with biochemical evolution and origin of life experiments (Sections 5.2(b) and 5.4). Natural selection does not apply to preliving molecules, and so cannot be invoked to overcome the general chemical tendency, as discussed later.[101]

Summary. The law of biogenesis is the concept that life only arises from life, as Pasteur discovered, while the hypothesis of abiogenesis is the proposal that life biochemically evolved from nonlife. Related biochemical considerations are that "spontaneous dissolution is much more probable, and hence proceeds much more rapidly, than spontaneous synthesis" (Wald*[102]). That is evident in the origin of life experiments, where "the reactions that are invoked to synthesize such compounds are seen to be much more effective in decomposing them" (Hull* and Bernal*[103]). The law of biogenesis and the biochemical tendency away from life require abrupt appearance of the first life, and conflict with its evolution.

4.5 The Thermodynamics Argument: Natural Law of Increasing Disorder

The thermodynamics argument is based on the complexity of the first life being more plausibly explained by biochemical abrupt appearance than by biochemical evolution. "The second law of thermodynamics is the postulate that: the entropy of an isolated system can never decrease."[104] Entropy is the thermodynamic characteristic of randomness or disorder within a system.

a. Equilibrium Thermodynamics

That second law of thermodynamics is widely, but not universally, believed to apply to prelife compounds under the theory of classical thermodynamics, as Sommerfeld* of University of Munich states in his textbook on the subject:

> In accordance with the Second Law we can, further, establish that this output can never be negative. Equation (10) together with the inequity $\vartheta\ 0$ can be regarded as the *differential formulation of the Second Law of Thermodynamics.* The statement in integral form, namely that the entropy in an isolated system cannot decrease, can be replaced by its corollary in differential form which asserts that the quantity of entropy generated locally cannot be negative *irrespective of whether the system is isolated or not,* and *irrespective of whether the process under consideration is irreversible or not.*[105]

Hull* says the same in connection with the evolution of life:

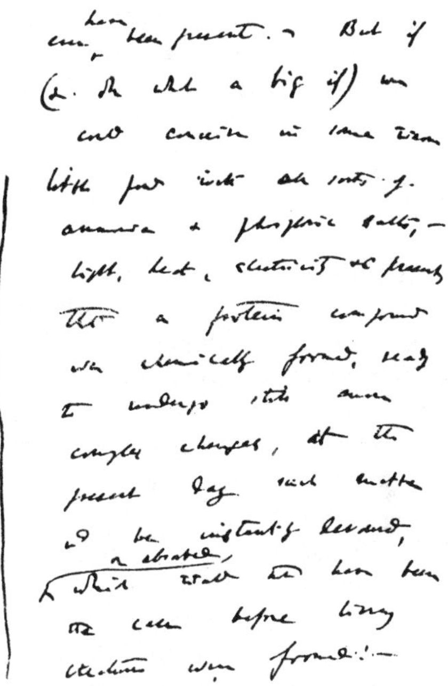

Figure 4.5
The evolution of life in "some warm little pond" was "oh what a big if" to Darwin* (from his original letter)

The *second law of thermodynamics applies* not only to inorganic gases in the atmosphere but also *to organic compounds* in the ocean. Living cells may reverse the process, but in the absence of life, "die Entropie der Welt strebt einem Maximum zu."[106]

Blum* concurs in his book on the subject:

Statements occasionally encountered, to the effect that living organisms do not obey the second law of thermodynamics, are usually based upon the idea that these systems are able to bring about a reduction of the entropy within themselves or their immediate surroundings. Such arguments are beside the point unless the whole thermodynamic balance sheet is taken into account, as their authors seem never to do.[107]

Ross* of Harvard chastises those who argue that the second law does not apply to open systems:

Please be advised that there are no known violations of the second law of thermodynamics. Ordinarily the second law is stated for isolated systems, but *the second law applies equally well to open systems.* However, there is somehow associated with the field of far-from-equilibrium phenomenon the notion that the second law of thermodynamics fails for such systems. It is important to make sure that this error does not perpetuate itself.[108]

Morowitz* of Yale similarly states that "organization in biology is basically rooted in entropic factors."[109]

The effect of the second law of thermodynamics under classical theory is to make biochemical evolution "highly improbable," according to Nobel Prize laureate Prigogine* and others:

> The probability that at ordinary temperatures a macroscopic number of molecules is assembled to give rise to the highly ordered structures and to the coordinated functions characterizing living organisms is *vanishingly small*. The idea of spontaneous genesis of life in its present form is therefore *highly improbable* even on the scale of the billions of years during which prebiotic evolution occurred.[110]

"If equilibrium processes alone were at work, the largest possible fluctuation in the history of the universe is likely to have been no longer than a small peptide," Morowitz* adds, and the probability of spontaneous formation of one bacterium in five billion years is 1 chance in $10^{10^{11}}$.[111] Thus, Prigogine* and Nicolis*, Morowitz*, and others turn from the bleak thermodynamic pasture of classical theory to the greener grass of nonequilibrium theory.

b. Nonequilibrium Thermodynamics

The revision of the second law under nonequilibrium thermodynamic theory, as it applies to open systems such as those in which life would have arisen, is alleged to solve the problem of present specified complexity requiring greater rather than less past complexity.[112] However, that problem of thermodynamic entropy "will not go away nor will the biological evidence to the contrary," according to Yockey*:

> An uninvited guest (Schroedinger, 1955; du Nouy, 1947; Prigogine & Nicolis, 1971; Gatlin, 1972; Prigogine, Nicolis & Babloyantz, 1972; Vol'-kenstein, 1973) at any discussion of the origin of life and of evolution from the materialistic reductionist point of view, is the role of *thermodynamic entropy* and the "heat death" of the universe which it predicts. The universe should in every way go from states which are less probable to those which are more probable. Therefore hot bodies cool; energy is conserved but becomes less available to do work. According to this uninvited guest, the spontaneous generation of life is *highly improbable* (Prigogine, Nicolis & Babloyantz, 1972). The uninvited guest will not go away nor will the biological evidence to the contrary notwithstanding.[113]

The nonequilibrium nature of Prigogine's* system can occur through energy flow, and that energy flow can occur in an open system. However, raw energy flow does not produce organizing work or information content without a converting mechanism, just as burning gasoline does not produce organizing work or information without a complex engine. The existence of the converting mechanism or engine cannot be assumed, because it is the critical but artificial element, discontinuitist scientists stress.

The counterargument is sometimes made that the formation of crystals overcomes the thermodynamic law of entropy, and shows that the biochemical evolution of the first life could also do so. Prigogine* rejects that argument:

> The point is that in a nonisolated system there exists a possibility for formation of ordered, low-entropy structures at sufficiently low temperatures. This ordering principle is responsible for the appearance of ordered structures such as crystals as well as for the phenomena of phase transitions.

> Unfortunately this principle cannot explain the formation of biological structures.[114]

The "fundamental differences" between crystallization and biogenesis are stressed by Stavropoulos*:

> He makes it appear as though crystals and highly ordered organic molecules belong to the same class, when in fact *they do not*. When a crystal is broken up, the smaller crystals are physically and chemically identical to the original. This is never observed with (organic) molecules; when the original molecule is split up lesser molecules appear, and part of the original information is lost. To ignore such *fundamental differences* in an effort to arrive at some general overview or law is to create a false overview, a pseudolaw.[115]

Mora*[116] and Lipson*[117] agree.

Summary. Many researchers state that among thermodynamic laws "the second law applies equally well to open systems," and that the concept is in "error" that "the second law of thermodynamics fails for [nonequilibrium or open] systems" (Ross*[118]). Prigogine* applies classical thermodynamics to the origin of life and concludes that "spontaneous genesis of life in its present form is therefore highly improbable even on the scale of the billions of years during which prebiotic evolution occurred" (Prigogine*, Nicolis*, and Babloyantz*[119]). Although he suggests that nonequilibrium thermodynamics solves the problem, it still must make water run uphill, steep and high. Even under nonequilibrium theory, "the spontaneous generation of life is highly improbable" (Yockey*[120]). Biochemical abrupt appearance is as consistent as biochemical evolution is inconsistent with the downward process toward disorder of nonequilibrium thermodynamics, discontinuitist scientists point out.

* * *

The biochemical theory of abrupt appearance is scientific , not religious, and includes at least five scientific lines of argument, in the estimation of its scientific proponents. The information content, probability, isomers, biogenesis, and thermodynamics arguments affirmatively support biochemical abrupt appearance, and do not merely identify weaknesses of biochemical evolution, according to those proponents. The empirical data on which biochemical abrupt appearance is based is generally accepted by all scientists, although the interpretations of those facts are challenged by most evolutionists. Biochemical abrupt appearance deserves to be heard, particularly in view of the many "myths" of biochemical evolution that evolutionists acknowledge in the next chapter, regardless of which explanation ultimately is shown to be correct.

Notes

[1]   2 *The Life and Letters of Charles Darwin* 202 (F. Darwin* ed. 1887).

[2]   Kenyon has published the empirical data that form the basis of the (1-2) information content and probability arguments, (3) isomer argument, (4) biogenesis argument, and (5) thermodynamics argument:

[1-2] At the heart of the molecular activity of all living cells is the genetic coding and protein-synthesis machinery which stores and translates biologic *information*. This information is contained in the specific linear sequences of the subunits of DNA, RNA and proteins. At least 20 different proteins are required for the replication of DNA. At least another 50 proteins are needed to transcribe and translate the information stored in the DNA molecules into the amino acid sequences of proteins (J. Fox 1978; Sheeler and Bianchi 1980).

. . ..

[3] Another intractable problem concerns the spontaneous origin of the optical isomer preferences found universally in living matter (e.g., L- rather than D- amino acids in proteins, D- rather than L- sugars in nucleic acids).

. . ..

[4] Creationists maintain that laboratory studies have shown that simple organic matter does not move in the direction of the living state; it does *move in other directions*, the most prominent of which is the formation of non-biological macromolecular material. . . .

[5] Another especially helpful feature is the detailed discussion of the implications of *thermodynamics* (Chaps. 7, 8, and 9) for the origin-of-life problem. This important topic is either omitted entirely or is treated superficially in most other books on the chemical origins of life.
Kenyon, *Foreword*, to C. Thaxton, W. Bradley & R. Olsen, *The Mystery of Life's Origin* v-vi (1984) (italics added); Kenyon, *The Creationist View of Biologic Origins*, NEXA Journal, Spring 1984, at 28, 30-31 (italics added).

[3] A. Cairns-Smith*, *Genetic Takeover and the Mineral Origins of Life* 64 (1986) (he is not suggesting that the new explanation will be the theory of abrupt appearance, only the need for a new explanation).

[4] Haskins*, *Advances and Challenges in Science in 1970*, 59 Am. Scientist 298, 305 (1971) (italics added). *See also* F. Hoyle, *The Intelligent Universe: A New View of Creation and Evolution* 243 (1983) ("When this problem is considered in detail—in the way we have done in this book—it is apparent that the origin of life is overwhelmingly a matter of arrangement, of ordering quite common atoms into very special structures and sequences. Whereas we learn in physics that non-living processes tend to destroy order, intelligent control is particularly effective at producing order out of chaos.")

[5] C. Ponnamperuma*, *The Origins of Life* 195 (1972).

[6] C. Sagan*, *Cosmos* 314 (1980).

[7] Sagan*, *Life*, 10 Encyclopaedia Britannica: Macropaedia 893, 894 (15th ed. 1974) (italics added). Sagan* concludes that natural selection is fully adequate to have produced that information content during geological time, and that origin of life experiments and other data such as enormous organic matter he believes to be produced on Titan show that steady state abundances of prebiotic organic matter would be expected on the primitive earth.

[8] M. Denton*, *Evolution: A Theory in Crisis* 264 (1985).

[9] G. Simpson*, *The Meaning of Evolution* 15-16 (1949) (italics added).

[10] Thorpe*, *Reductionism in Biology*, in Studies in the Philosophy of Biology 117 (F. Ayala* & T. Dobzhansky* eds. 1974).

[11] Yockey*, *A Calculation of the Probability of Spontaneous Biogenesis by Information Theory*, 67 J. Theoretical Biology 377, 377 (1977) (italics added). *Cf.* Section 4.2 (probability argument).

[12] *E.g.*, T. Dobzhansky*, F. Ayala*, G. Stebbins* & J. Valentine*, *Evolution* 21-28 (1977); S. Luria*, S. Gould* & S. Singer*, *A View of Life* 71-75 (1981).

[13] *Cell's Energy Use High for Protein Synthesis*, Chemical & Engineering News, Aug. 20, 1979, at 6 ("Most of that energy, perhaps many times more than previously supposed, is used for proofreading processes that ensure the accuracy of such synthesis, according to Michael A. Savageau and Rolf R. Freter of the University of Michigan, Ann Arbor. Living cells are fastidious about their proteins, checking and double-checking them at particular stages during synthesis."). *See also* Guéron*, *Enhanced Selectivity of Enzymes by Kinetic Proofing*, 66 Am. Scientist 202 (1978).

[14] Popper*, *Scientific Reduction and the Essential Incompleteness of All Science*, in Studies in the Philosophy of Biology 259, 270 (1974) (italics added), quoting J. Monod*, *Chance and Necessity* 143 (1971).

[15] E. Ambrose*, *The Nature and Origin of the Biological World* 135 (1982) ("But the enzymes only work because the protein chains are coded in a special sequence by DNA. DNA can only replicate with the help of protein enzymes. We really are in a chicken and egg situation!").

[16] Salisbury*, *Doubts About the Modern Synthetic Theory of Evolution*, 33 Am. Biology Teacher 335, 338 (1971) ("It's as though everything must happen at once: the *entire system must come into being as one unit, or it is worthless.*").

[17] The origin of the genetic coding system cannot be discussed without the origin of the mechanism of protein synthesis being discussed. Crick*, *The Origin of the Genetic Code*, 38 J. Molecular Biology 367 (1968); Woese*, *The Biology Significance of the Genetic Code*, in 1 Progress in Molecular and Subcellular Biology 1 (F. Hahn* et al. eds. 1969).

[18] Orgel*, *Darwinism at the Very Beginning of Life*, 94 New Scientist 149, 151 (1982).

[19] Leslie*, *Cosmology, Probability, and the Need To Explain Life*, in Scientific Explanation and Understanding 53, 64-65 (N. Rescher* ed. 1983).

[20] Schutzenberger*, *Algorithms and the Neo-Darwinian Theory of Evolution*, in Mathematical Challenges to the Neo-Darwinian Interpretation of Evolution 73, 75 (P. Moorhead* & M. Kaplan* eds. 1967) (italics added).

[21] Polanyi*, *Life's Irreducible Structure*, 160 Science 1308, 1309-10 (1968) (italics added).

[22] Note 7.

[23] Note 9.

[24] Note 11.

[25] Note 14.

[26] Note 4.

[27] J. Mill*, *Three Essays on Religion* 174 (2d ed. 1874, repr. 1969) (italics added).

[28] Hoyle, *The Universe: Past and Present Reflections*, Engineering & Science, Nov. 1981, at 8, 12 (italics added).

[29] E. Ambrose*, *The Nature and Origin of the Biological World* 135 (1982) (italics added).

[30] Eden*, *Inadequacies of Neo-Darwinian Evolution as a Scientific Theory*, in Mathematical Challenges to the Neo-Darwinian Interpretation of Evolution 5, 9 (P. Moorhead* & M. Kaplan* eds. 1982).

[31] Golay*, *Reflections of a Communications Engineer*, 33 Analytical Chemistry 23 (June 1961).

[32] Noda*, *Probability of Life, Rareness of Realization in Evolution*, 95 J. Theoretical Biology 145, 150 (1981) ("However, unless there is a definite mechanism of seeding, the probability seems very small for the process of chemical evolution to succeed in forming a system of life within a relatively short time of a life of a sun . . ..").

[33] Keosian*, *Life's Beginnings—Origin or Evolution?*, in Cosmochemical Evolution and the Origins of Life 291 (J. Oró* et al. eds. 1974).

[34] Scherer*, *Basic Functional States in the Evolution of Light-driven Cyclic Electron Transport*, 104 J. Theoretical Biology 289, 296, 298 (1983).

[35] Eden*, *Inadequacies of Neo-Darwinian Evolution as a Scientific Theory*, in Mathematical Challenges to the Neo-Darwinian Interpretation of Evolution 5, 7 (P. Moorhead* & M. Kaplan* eds. 1967).

[36] J. Monod*, *Chance and Necessity* 136 (1972) (italics added).

[37] F. Hoyle & N. Wickramasinghe, *Evolution from Space* 24 (1981) (panspermia advocates).

[38] Huxley*, *How far will Darwin take us?*, in Evolution from Molecules to Men 3, 13-14 (D. Bendall* ed. 1983). *See also* R. Dawkins*, *The Blind Watchmaker* 234 (1986).

[39] Hoyle, *The Big Bang in Astronomy,* 92 New Scientist 521, 527 (1981) (italics added).

[39A] Thorpe*, *Reductionism in Biology*, in Studies in the Philosophy of Biology 117 (F. Ayala* & T. Dobzhansky* eds. 1974).

[40] E. Ambrose*, *The Nature and Origin of the Biological World* 135 (1982) (italics added).

[41] H. Blum*, *Time's Arrow and Evolution* 158 (3d ed. 1968).

[42] F. Ayala* & J. Valentine*, *Evolving: The Theory and Processes of Organic Evolution* 340 (1979).

[43] L. du Nouy*, *Human Destiny* 34 (trans. 1947) ("time needed to form, on an average, one such molecule in a material volume equal to that of our terrestrial globe is about 10^{243} billion years.")

[44] C. Guye*, *L'Evolution Physico-Chimique* (2d ed. 1942).

[45] W. Stokes*, *Essentials of Earth History* 186 (4th ed. 1982) (italics added).

[46] F. Hoyle & N. Wickramasinghe, *Evolution from Space* 148 (1981) ("If only ten amino acids of particular kinds are necessary at particular locations in a polypeptide chain for its proper functioning, the required arrangement (starting from an initially different arrangement) cannot be found by mutations, except as an outrageous fluke. *Darwinian evolution is most unlikely to get even one polypeptide right*, let alone the thousands on which living cells depend for their survival. This situation is well-known to geneticists and yet nobody seems prepared to blow the whistle decisively on the theory.") (italics added).

[47] Yockey*, *A Calculation of the Probability of Spontaneous Biogenesis by Information Theory*, 67 J. Theoretical Biology 377, 387 (1977).

[48] Salisbury*, *Doubts About the Modern Synthetic Theory of Evolution*, 33 Am. Biology Teacher 335, 336 (1971) ("A medium protein might include about 300 amino acids. The DNA gene controlling this would have about 1,000 nucleotides in its chain. Since there are four kinds of nucleotides in a DNA chain, one consisting of 1,000 links could exist in $4^{1,000}$ different forms. Using a little algebra (logarithms), we can see that $4^{1,000} = 10^{600}$. Ten multiplied by itself 600 times gives the figure 1 followed by 600 zeros! . . . [I]magine how may universes it would take to accommodate 10^{600} DNA chains!").

[49] Lafont*, *Book Review*, Permanences, Nov. 1972, at 7, 8 (italics added), quoting G. Salet*, *Chance and Certainty: Evolution in the Light of Modern Biology* (1972).

[50] E. Borel*, *Probabilities and Life* 28 (1962); E. Borel*, *Elements of the Theory of Probability* 57 (1965).

[51] Leslie*, *Cosmology, Probability, and the Need To Explain Life*, in

Scientific Explanation and Understanding 53, 64-65 (N. Rescher* ed. 1983)

[52] Erbrich*, *On the Probability of the Emergence of a Protein with a Particular Function,* 34 Acta Biotheoretica 53, 56, 65, 66 (1985). *See also* I. Asimov*, *Only a Trillion* 103-10 (1957); Huxley*, *How far will Darwin take us?,* in Evolution from Molecules to Men 3, 13-14 (D. Bendall* ed. 1983).

[53] Erbrich*, *On the Probability of the Emergence of a Protein with a Particular Function,* 34 Acta Biotheoretica 53, 77-78 (1985).

[54] *Id.* at 67-68.

[55] *Id.* at 68-69.

[56] Kaplan*, *The Problem of Chance in Formation of Protobionts by Random Aggregation of Macromolecules,* 1 Chemical Evolution and the Origin of Life 319, 325-26 (R. Buvet* & C. Ponnamperuma* eds. 1971).

[57] M. Simon*, *The Matter of Life* 166 (1971).

[58] Kaplan*, *The Problem of Chance in Formation of Protobionts by Random Aggregation of Macromolecules,* 1 Chemical Evolution and the Origin of Life 319, 323 (R. Buvet* & C. Ponnamperuma* eds. 1971).

[59] J. Barrow* & F. Tipler*, *The Anthropic Cosmological Principle* 511 (1986). *See also* W. Stokes*, *Essentials of Earth History* 186 (4th ed. 1982) (for proteins); F. Hoyle, *The Intelligent Universe* 18 (1983) (italics added).

[60] A. Cairns-Smith*, *Genetic Takeover and the Mineral Origins of Life* 55 (1986).

[61] Note 29.

[62] Note 31.

[63] Note 33.

[64] Note 36.

[65] Note 53.

[66] Note 27.

[67] S. Luria*, S. Gould* & S. Singer*, *A View of Life* 772 (1981).

[68] Williams* & Smith*, *A Critical Evaluation of the Application of Amino Acid Racemization to Geochronology and Geothermometry,* 8 Origins of Life 91, 91 (1977).

[69] C. Ponnamperuma*, *The Origins of Life* 105 (1972).

[70] *Id.* at 105-06 (italics added).

[71] The amino acid glycine is neither left- nor right-handed; and D-amino acids appear in some bacteria, earthworms, insects, and antibiotics.

[72] C. Patterson*, *Evolution* 157 (1978).

[73] L. Pauling*, *General Chemistry* 774 (1970).

[74] A. Oparin*, *Life: Its Nature, Origin and Development* 59, 60 (1961).

[75] Williams* & Smith*, *A Critical Evaluation of the Application of Amino Acid Racemization to Geochronology and Geothermometry,* 8 Origins of Life 91, 91 (1977) ("Virtually all proteins contain *exclusively the L-enantiomers of the amino acids* while *natural sugars are of the D-configuration.*").

[76] W. Stansfield*, *The Science of Evolution* 84 (1977) ("All living organisms possess only the L-amino acid isomers in their proteins (excepting glycine).").

[77] 1 A. Meister*, *Biochemistry of the Amino Acids* 113-17 (2d ed. 1965).

[78] S. Bresler*, *Introduction to Molecular Biology* 6-7 (1971) ("By contrast, the proportion of *L-amino acids in proteins is* 100%.").

[79] L. Dillon*, *The Genetic Mechanism and the Origin of Life* 66-67 (1978).

[80] C. Patterson*, *Evolution* 157 (1978) ("synthesized in a test-tube, the product will be a mixture of left-handed and right-handed molecules, in roughly equal numbers"). *See also* S. Bresler*, *Introduction to Molecular Biology* 6 (1971) ("both stereoisomers are thermodynamically and kinetically identical").

[81] W. Stansfield*, *The Science of Evolution* 84 (1977).

[82] Williams* & Smith*, *A Critical Evaluation of the Application of Amino Acid Racemization to Geochronology and Geothermometry*, 8 Origins of Life 91, 91 (1977). *See* note 71 (a few D-amino acids).

[83] C. Ponnamperuma*, *The Origins of Life* 106, 108 (1972).

[84] A. Cairns-Smith*, *Genetic Takeover and the Mineral Origins of Life* 40 (1986).

[85] Joyce*, Schwartz*, Miller* & Orgel*, *The case for an ancestral genetic system involving simple analogues of the nucleotides*, 84 Proc. National Acad. Sciences 4398, 4398 (1987).

[86] Bonner*, *Origins of Molecular Chirality*, in Exobiology 170, 223 (C. Ponnamperuma* ed. 1972).

[87] S. Bresler*, *Introduction to Molecular Biology* 6 (1971).

[88] D. Kenyon* & G. Steinman*, *Biochemical Predestination* (1969).

[89] A. Cairns-Smith*, *Genetic Takeover and the Mineral Origins of Life* 44 (1986).

[89A] Joyce*, Schwartz*, Miller* & Orgel*, *The case for an ancestral genetic system involving simple analogues of the nucleotides*, 84 Proc. National Acad. Sciences 4398, 4398 (1987).

[90] Williams* & Smith*, *A Critical Evaluation of the Application of Amino Acid Racemization to Geochronology and Geothermometry*, 8 Origins of Life 91, 91 (1977).

[91] Selective binding to bentonite and selective adsorption have been rejected. Youatt* & Brown*, *Origins of Chirality in Nature: A Reassessment of the Postulated Role of Bentonite*, 212 Science 1145, 1145 (1981); Miller* & West*, *Life and a lump of clay*, 116 Science News 200, 200 (1979).

[92] A. Cairns-Smith*, *Genetic Takeover and the Mineral Origins of Life* 45 (1986).

[93] Note 70.

[94] Quoted in note 82.

[95] Note 87.

[96] *Oxford Dictionary of Natural History* 77 (M. Allaby* ed. 1985) (Oxford U. Press).

[97] P. Medawar* & J. Medawar*, *Aristotle to Zoos: A Philosophical Dictionary of Biology* 39 (1983) (Harvard U. Press) (italics in original).

[98] Abelson*, *Chemical Events on the Primitive Earth*, 55 Proc. National Academy Sciences 1365, 1369 (1966).

[99] Wald*, *The Origin of Life*, Scientific Am., Aug. 1954, at 44, 49-50 (italics added).

[100] Hull* & Bernal*, *Thermodynamics and kinetics of spontaneous generation*, 186 Nature 693, 694 (1960).

[101] Section 5.3(i).

[102] Note 99.

[103] Note 100.

[104] W. Reynolds*, *Thermodynamics* 157 (2d ed. 1968). *See also* H. Blum*, *Time's Arrow and Evolution* 190 (3d ed. 1968); *see* Morowitz*, *The Entropy Crisis*, Hospital Practice, July 1974, at 32, 32.

[105] A. Sommerfeld*, *Thermodynamics and Statistical Mechanics* 155 (1956) (italics added).

[106] Hull*, *Thermodynamics and kinetics of spontaneous generation*, 186 Nature 693, 694 (1960).

[107] H. Blum*, *Time's Arrow and Evolution* 15 (3d ed. 1968).

[108] Ross*, *Letter*, Chemical & Engineering News, July 7, 1980, at 4 (italics added).

[109] H. Morowitz*, *The Entropy Crisis*, Hospital Practice, July 1974, at 32, 32, 37 (*"organization in biology is basically rooted in entropic factors"*).

[110] Prigogine*, Nicolis* & Babloyantz*, *Thermodynamics of Evolution*, Physics Today, Nov. 1972, at 23, 23.

[111] H. Morowitz*, *Energy Flow and Biology* 67 (1968).

[112] G. Nicolis* & I. Prigogine*, *Self Organization in Nonequilibrium Systems* (1977); Prigogine*, Nicolis* & Babloyantz*, *Thermodynamics of Evolution*, Physics Today, Nov. 1972, at 23.

[113] Yockey*, *A Calculation of the Probability of Spontaneous Biogenesis by Information Theory*, 67 J. Theoretical Biology 377, 380 (1977) (italics added).

[114] Prigogine*, Nicolis* & Babloyantz*, *Thermodynamics of Evolution*, Physics Today, Nov. 1972, at 23, 23 (italics added).

[115] Stravropoulos*, *Letter*, 65 Am. Scientist 674, 674 (1977) (italics added).

[116] Mora*, *Crystallization and the second law*, 199 Nature 216 (1963) ("In crystallization, the full process is determined by the valency, the molecular structure of the components, whether atoms, molecules or polymers. Crystallization occurs because it leads to the lowest energy state and to the most stable arrangement of atoms or molecules under the given conditions. Crystallization leads to *simple*, very uniform repeating structures, which are *inert*. These structures do *not function*, and are not designed by function.") (italics added).

[117] Lipson*, *A Physicist Looks at Evolution*, 31 Physics Bull. 138, 138 (1980).

[118] Note 108.

[119] Note 110.

[120] Note 113.

CHAPTER 5

Evolution as Theory and Conjecture: Biochemical Evolution of the First Life

> [A]ll of us who study the origin of life find
> that the more we look into it, the more we
> feel it is too complex to have evolved any-
> where. We all believe as an article of faith
> that life evolved from dead matter on this
> planet. It is just that its complexity is so
> great, it is hard for us to imagine that it
> did.
>
> —Nobel Prize laureate
> Harold C. Urey[1]

Biochemical evolution involves the postulated transformation from nonliving matter to the first living organisms. That transformation required the evolution in the primitive earth of amino acids, then proteins, then protocells and the genetic coding system, and finally the first living cell.

---

*Scientists cited in this chapter, unless otherwise indicated, are not proponents of, and their quoted statements are not intended as endorsements of, either the theory of abrupt appearance or the theory of creation. However, their quoted statements are acknowledging data that involve weaknesses of the theory of evolution.

Biochemical evolution (or chemical evolution) is generally regarded as part of evolution, as leading evolutionists Dobzhansky*, Ayala*, Stebbins*, and Valentine* acknowledge:

> [T]he concept of evolution has been applied not only to the living world but to the nonbiological as well. Thus, we speak of the evolution of the entire universe, the solar system and the physical earth, apart from the organisms that inhabit it. As we shall show in Chapter 11 ("Cosmic Evolution and the Origin of Life"), the origin of life is best explained as the outcome of precellular *chemical evolution*, which took place over millions of years.[2]

"Evolution" is the process "by which life arose in the first place and by which all living things, past or present, have since developed," Simpson* concurs.[3] Despite occasional idiosyncratic views that the "question of life's origin on our earth lies outside [evolution's] domain,"[4] virtually all other evolutionist luminaries treat the origin of life as an element of evolution, such as Mayr*, Ponnamperuma*,[5] Fox* and Dose*,[6] Huxley*,[7] Olson*,[8] and many other evolutionists.[9] Thus, the terms "biochemical evolution," "chemical evolution," "prebiotic evolution," and "molecular evolution" are the most widely used and generally accepted terms for the origin of life.[10]

The following description of biochemical evolution from a high school textbook used widely in public schools is typical:

> The primitive earth may have had an *atmosphere* largely of hydrogen, which was later lost to space. A secondary atmosphere may have included ammonia, methane, water, and hydrogen sulfide (see diagram on page 836). Ultraviolet light from the sun, electrical storms, and decay of radioactive elements may have provided the energy to combine these molecules as *sugars and amino acids*. Amino acids could have combined to form *proteins*. . . .
>
> . . . . .
>
> The *first self-organizing, self-reproducing blobs* could have appeared in an environment containing amino acids and protein-like substances, sugars, and possibly *ATP* as well as *DNA and RNA*. Many other molecules, including long chains of carbon and hydrogen in fatlike molecules, probably were also present. We can imagine the early living blobs feeding upon other organic molecules in the seas, until such "food" became scarce. Mutations that produced *new proteins*—enzymes capable of synthesizing needed molecules from simpler available materials—eventually must have occurred. Still other mutations eventually led to *cells*—cells that could take energy from the sun and combine carbon dioxide and water into sugars and amino acids.[11]

Similar content is found in most biology textbooks used in public schools,[12] and parallel summaries are given by evolutionist scientists.[13]

The evidence for biochemical evolution is quite weak, as the above statement by Urey* and the following conclusion of biochemist Kerkut* show:

> There is, however, *little evidence* in favour of biogenesis and as yet we have no indication that it can be performed. There are many schemes by which biogenesis could have occurred but these are *still suggestive schemes and nothing more.* They may indicate experiments that can be performed, but *they tell us nothing about what actually happened* some 1,000 million years ago. It is therefore a *matter of faith* on the part of the biologist that biogenesis did occur and he can choose whatever method of biogenesis happens to suit him personally; the evidence for what did happen is not available.[14]

Crick*, who won the Nobel Prize for discovering the structure of DNA, finds the area rife with "speculation" and rejects the prevailing theories:

> Every time I write a paper on the origin of life, I swear I will never write another one, because there is too much speculation running after too few facts . . . .[15]

Yockey* finds too much assumption to be running after too little probability:

> Research on the origin of life seems to be unique in that the conclusion has already been authoritatively accepted (Simpson, 1964; Eigen, 1971). What remains to be done is to find the scenarios which describe the detailed mechanisms and processes by which this happened.[16]

Dobzhansky*, Ayala*, Stebbins*, and Valentine* concede "[o]ther scenarios may be proposed, but all are similarly speculative at this time."[17] Jastrow*, founder and former director of the Goddard Institute of Space Studies at NASA, asks, "What concrete evidence supports that remarkable theory of the origin of life? There is none."[18] Scherer*, a biochemist at University of Konstanz, concludes that rejection of the prevailing origin of life theory "should be considered carefully," and upon rejection "there will remain no scientifically valid model of the self-organization of the first living cells."[19] Fox*, a leading researcher, concedes that "[i]t may well be true that most scientists agree that a scientific solution to the problem of life's origin is nowhere in sight."[20]

The following sections discuss various aspects of biochemical evolution:

5.1 Early atmosphere:
    Questions about an oxygen-free composition
5.2 "Primordial soup":
    Questions about significant organic compounds
5.3 Evolutionary stages:
    Questions about the critical elements for life
5.4 Laboratory experiments:
    Questions about extrapolation to life.

This chapter only attempts an overview, rather than a comprehensive discussion, of the problems of biochemical evolution that many evolutionist scientists acknowledge.

Questions about the assumption of an atmosphere without free oxygen are discussed in Section 5.1. Difficulties with the assumption of a "primordial soup" of necessary organic compounds are assessed in Section 5.2. Questions about the various evolutionary stages are treated in Section 5.3. Concerns about extrapolating laboratory experiments made under unnatural conditions are identified in Section 5.4. Finally, problems with obtaining the vast information content necessary for life, and overcoming the vast improbability of evolution, were discussed in Sections 4.1 and 4.2. Although these scientific problems with biochemical evolution are discussed in such discontinuitist scientific books as *The Mystery of Life's Origin*,[21] the documentation for the following discussion of these evolutionary problems comes instead from evolutionist books and articles.

5.1 The Early Atmosphere for Biochemical Evolution:
Questions about an Oxygen-Free Composition

Proponents of biochemical evolution generally assume the existence of an oxygen-free atmosphere that contained high levels of methane and ammonia, because biochemists agree that the presence of free oxygen would preclude biochemical evolution:

J. B. S. Haldane, the British biochemist, seems to have been the first to appreciate that a reducing atmosphere, one with no free oxygen, was a *requirement for the evolution of life* from nonliving organic matter.[22]

Fox* and Dose*,[23] Miller*,[24] and Brinkmann*[25] similarly acknowledge that requirement. Miller* and Orgel* stress that "there must

Figure 5.1
The primordial
a t m o s p h e r e :
"[P]o s s i b l e
contrary evidence
is shunted aside.
This condition, of
course, again
describes myth-
ology rather than
science." (Sha-
piro*)

have been a period when the earth's atmosphere was reducing [no free oxygen], because the synthesis of compounds of biological interest takes place only under reducing conditions."[26] That is generally assumed in the volatile outgassing model of the atmosphere, the inhomogeneous accretion model, and other models.

However, the recent arguments against an oxygen-free atmosphere are so strong that the "new orthodoxy" is becoming a belief in an early oxidized atmosphere, according to Henderson-Sellers*, Benlow*, and Meadows*:

> *Biologists* concerned with the origin of life still often quote an early atmosphere consisting of reduced gases, but this seems to *stem as much from ignorance* of recent advances as from active opposition to them. In the latter part of the 1970s, the concept of *early oxidized atmospheres* on the terrestrial planets is becoming the *new orthodoxy*.[27]

The concept of an oxygen-rich or at least oxidized atmosphere[28] is encountering barriers to acceptance, however, because it conflicts with the older prevailing theory—"possible contrary evidence is shunted aside"—in the view of Shapiro*, professor of chemistry at New York University:

> We have reached a situation where a theory has been accepted as fact by some, and possible contrary evidence is shunted aside. This condition, of course, again describes *mythology* rather than science.[29]

The primary argument for an oxygen-free atmosphere, the three major problems with it, and arguments for an oxygen-rich atmosphere, are discussed in the following paragraphs.

a. Geology Argument

The major argument for an oxygen-free atmosphere is the geology argument that certain mineral forms found in the earth indicate the absence of oxygen when the oldest strata were deposited, such as banded iron formations containing magnetite that would be more stable in an oxygen-free atmosphere, and red beds of oxidized sediments that appear in newer strata but allegedly not in older strata.

However, the geological features that should exist to provide evidence of an ancient oxygen-free atmosphere are generally "missing," according to Clemmey* and Badham*:

> Geological evidence often presented in favor of an early anoxic atmosphere is both contentious and ambiguous. The features that should be present in the geologic record had there been such an atmosphere seem to be *missing*. Many of the features advanced in support of an anoxic model can be ascribed to diagenetic alterations, and most diagenetic environments are reducing [no free oxygen].[30]

There is "no evidence for . . . but much against" an oxygen-free and methane-rich atmosphere, Abelson* adds:

> The hypothesis of an early *methane-ammonia atmosphere* is found to be *without solid foundation* and indeed is contraindicated. Geologists favor an alternative view—that genesis of air and oceans is a result of planetary outgassing. . . .
>
> If the methane-ammonia hypothesis were correct, *there should be geochemical evidence* supporting it. What is the evidence for a primitive methane-ammonia atmosphere on earth? The answer is that there is *no evidence for it*, but *much against it*. . . .[31]

First, the geologic evidence does not exist that should result from such an atmosphere:

> If large amounts of methane had ever been present in the earth's atmosphere, *geologic evidence for it should also be available*. Laboratory experiments show that one consequence of irradiating a dense, highly reducing atmosphere is the production of hydrophobic organic molecules which are adsorbed by sedimenting clays. The earliest rocks should contain an unusually large proportion of carbon or organic chemicals. This is not the case.[32]

Second, the atmospheric evidence "contraindicate[s]" an oxygen-free and methane-rich atmosphere:

> The composition of the present atmosphere with respect to the gases neon, argon, krypton, and xenon is crucial. *Neon is present on earth to an*

extent about 10⁻¹⁰ that of cosmic abundance, and similarly argon, krypton, and xenon are relatively absent. It seems likely that if xenon of atomic weight 130 could not accumulate, other volatile light constituents such as hydrogen, nitrogen, methane, and carbon monoxide would also be lost at the same time. The concept that the earth had a dense methane-ammonia atmosphere is *not supported by geochemistry,* and it is *contraindicated by the scarcity of xenon and krypton* in our present atmosphere.[33]

Instead, the absence of red beds in some older strata probably results only from their decomposition, according to Clemmey* and Badham*:

Perhaps the most important conclusion is that diagenesis is the factor most overlooked in interpreting the geologic record. Diagenesis destroys red beds by pigment aging; it results in the replacement of ancient evaporites by silica, carbonate, and feldspar; it causes ferruginization of pre-existing rocks to give us many of the banded iron formations; and recognition of many diagenetic phenomena that involve oxidative reactions, or require such reactions as a prior step, provides evidence for atmospheric oxygen. Whole-rock chemistry may even be changed by equilibration with the diagenetic environment, and the most diagenetic environments are reducing (Curtis, 1978).[34]

The lack of red color in some older sediments also may simply result from the flyschlike composition of many such sediments, Pettijohn* suggests.[35]

Banded iron formations indeed contain magnetite, but it consists of more oxidized ferric minerals as well as less oxidized ferrous minerals, which indicates that at least some oxygen was present in order to oxidize those minerals. Moreover, such banded iron formations occur in newer strata when the atmosphere concededly had oxygen as well as in older strata, and in connection with red beds that show the presence of oxygen in the atmostphere. Neither do other factors require an oxygen-free atmosphere, such as the ferrous-ferric iron ratio,[36] or the dentrital uraninite and pyrite according to Walker*,[37] Davidson*,[38] Zeschke*[39] and Grandstaff*.[40]

Kerr* concludes:

No geological or geochemical evidence collected in the last 30 years favors a strongly reducing primitive atmosphere.... Only the success of the laboratory experiments recommends it.[41]

Many others reach much the same conclusion.[42]

b. Geology Problems

One serious problem with the assumption of an oxygen-free atmosphere is that much geological evidence "favor[s] an early oxidized atmosphere," Clemmey* and Badham* point out:

Recent biological and interplanetary studies seem to favor an early oxidized atmosphere rich in CO_2 and possibly containing free molecular oxygen. The existence of early red beds, sea and groundwater sulphate, oxidized terrestrial and sea-floor weathering crusts, and the distribution of ferric iron in sedimentary rocks are geological observations and inferences compatible with the biological and planetary predictions. It is suggested that from the time of the earliest dated rocks at 3.7 b[illion] y[ears] ago, Earth had an *oxygenic atmosphere.*[43]

"The sedimentary distribution of carbon, sulfur, uranium, and ferric and ferrous iron depend greatly upon ambient oxygen pressure," and the "similar distributions of these elements in sedimentary rocks of all ages are here interpreted to indicate the existence of a Precambrian atmosphere containing much oxygen," in the views of Dimroth* and Kimberley*.[44] The presence of ancient oxidized iron sediments and limestone deposits similarly points to the existence of an oxygen-rich or at least oxidized atmosphere, Davidson*[45] and Walker*[46] note.

c. Photolysis of Water Problem

Another serious problem for the oxygen-free atmosphere assumption is that ultraviolet light would have split (by photolysis) water vapor in the upper atmosphere into oxygen and hydrogen, in quantities greater than surface minerals could adequately absorb. Because of photolysis of water vapor, Brinkmann* has calculated that the atmosphere essentially always has had at least a quarter of its present level of oxygen,[47] and Carver* has recalculated the data and concluded that the ancient atmosphere had about a tenth of its present level of oxygen.[48] Many other researchers have similarly concluded that photolysis would have produced significant levels of atmospheric oxygen in the early atmosphere, such as Davidson*,[49] and Dimroth* and Kimberley*.[50]

d. Photodissociation of Other Gases Problem

Another problem is that ultraviolet light would have caused the breakdown of methane and ammonia, which are necessary to biochemical evolution hypotheses, as Shapiro* points out:

> Geologists now realize that a methane and ammonia atmosphere would have been destroyed within a few thousand years by chemical reactions caused by sunlight.[51]

The reason is that methane and ammonia are "very unstable against atmospheric chemicals and photochemical reactions," as Levine* notes:

However, regardless of the possible sources of methane and ammonia in the early atmosphere, recent theoretical computer calculations performed by James C.G. Walker and William R. Kuhn at the University of Michigan, James F. Kasting of the NASA Ames Research Center, and by our group at NASA Langley, among others, indicate that *both gases are very unstable against atmospheric chemical and photochemical reactions* (photochemical reactions are initiated by the absorption of solar radiation or solar photons). Methane and ammonia are *rapidly destroyed by atmospheric photochemical reactions* initiated by the absorption of solar ultraviolet and *destroyed by chemical reaction with the hydroxyl radical* (OH) formed by the photolysis of atmospheric H_2O vapor by solar ultraviolet radiation. In addition, ammonia, a very water-soluble gas, is *rapidly rained out of the atmosphere.* These theoretical studies indicate that, in the absence of continuous sources, the *lifetimes of methane and ammonia in the early atmosphere must have been very short—hundreds of years,* which is an incredibly short time in terms of chemical evolution. In the present atmosphere, both methane and ammonia are minute trace gases at the parts per million and parts per billion level, respectively. However, both are formed as a result of biogenic activity by microorganisms, a process clearly not operable in the prebiotic early atmosphere.[52]

That breakdown of ammonia would have occurred within 10 years to 30,000 years, according to the calculations of Abelson*,[53] Ferris* and Nicodem*,[54] Kuhn* and Atreya*,[55] and Levine*.[56] Methane would have been polymerized rapidly, say Abelson*,[57] Cloud*,[58] and Lasaga*, Holland*, and Dwyer*.[59]

Formaldehyde also would have been broken down (photodissociated) rapidly, according to Pinto* *et al.*,[60] Ellis* and Wells*,[61] Abelson*,[62] and Hulett*.[63] Hydrogen sulfide would have broken down in a mere 10,000 years, as calculated by Ferris* and Nicodem*,[64] and Miller*, Urey*, and Oro*.[65] Even without photodissociation, the amounts of formaldehyde and hydrogen sulphide have been greatly overestimated in possible amount, Hulett* suggests.[66]

Summary. The oxygen-free early atmosphere that is necessary to biochemical evolution is more a matter of wishful thinking than of scientific fact, and strong scientific evidence directly contradicts the possibility of such an atmosphere, according to a number of evolutionist scientists. There is "no evidence for . . . but much against" a primitive oxygen-free and methane-ammonia-rich atmosphere (Abelson*[67]), and "the concept of early oxidizing atmospheres . . . is becoming the new orthodoxy" (Henderson-Sellers*[68]) with much evidence for an early oxygen-rich atmosphere. Yet "the synthesis of compounds of biological interest takes place only under reducing [no free oxygen] conditions," according to Miller* and Orgel*.[69]

(a) The absence of red beds in some older strata is "contentious and ambiguous" evidence on the question of an oxygen-free early atmosphere (Clemmey* and Badham*[70]), and the presence of banded iron formations is inconclusive. In fact, the geologic evidence does not exist that would be produced by an oxygen-free atmosphere, while the atmospheric evidence "contraindicate[s]" such an atmosphere (Abelson*[71]). Some red beds exist in older strata (Clemmey* and Badham*[72]), while missing red beds are better explained by diagenesis and other factors (*id*.; Pettijohn*[73]).

(b) Several considerations rule out an early oxygen-free atmosphere. First, geological factors "indicate the existence of a Precambrian atmosphere containing much oxygen" (Dimroth* and Kimberley*[74]). Second, ultraviolet light would have split water vapor into oxygen and hydrogen in quantities greater than surface minerals could absorb (Carver*[75]). Third, ultraviolet light also would have caused methane and ammonia to be "rapidly destroyed by atmospheric photochemical reactions ... and destroyed by chemical reaction with the hydroxyl radical (OH) formed by the photolysis of atmospheric [water] vapor ... ," so that "the lifetimes of methane and ammonia in the early atmosphere must have been very short—hundreds of years ..." (Levine*[76]). (The preceding quotations should be evaluated in the full context given earlier).

Figure 5.2
The "myth of the
prebiotic soup"
(Sillen)*

5.2 The Primordial Soup for Biochemical Evolution: Questions about Significant Organic Compounds

Biochemical evolutionists also assume the existence of a "primordial soup" (whether in the form of seas or evaporating pools) that was rich in certain organic compounds, which would be essential for the possible formation of amino acids, proteins, the genetic coding system, protocells, and other evolutionary stages.[77]

There are a number of problems with this assumption of a primordial soup, according to many evolutionist researchers, including (a) conflict with the geological evidence, (b) destruction of any such compounds by cross-reactions, (c) destruction by decomposition, (d) destruction of such compounds by radiation, and (e) prevention of biochemical evolution by dilution. Because of those problems, Shapiro* and Sillen* refer to "the myth of the prebiotic soup":

> *The Myth of the Prebiotic Soup*
> The prebiotic soup has fared little better than the reducing atmosphere. The above section heading is not my own, but was taken from an important article by a Swedish geologist, *Lars Gunnar Sillen*. He starts with the assumption of a methane-rich reducing atmosphere, but *questions the survival of a soup* under these conditions. If left to itself, he reasons, it would gradually move to the position of greatest stability, equilibrium. When this position was attained, we would be back at the starting point, with almost all carbon in the form of methane and concentrations of amino acids at negligible levels. A system may be kept away from equilibrium, of course, by a steady input of energy. All life exists in this situation today. *Enormous amounts of energy would be required, however, to maintain an entire ocean in this condition.* Furthermore, *mixtures of organic chemicals are far less adept than living systems at handling a heavy energy flow.* As we saw in the Miller-Urey experiment, they continue to form chemical bonds until a heavy insoluble material, a tar, is produced, unless they are protected in some type of sanctuary.[78]

Shapiro* elsewhere calculated that it is "unlikely that any build-up of nucleic acid components could take place over a long period of time in an aqueous environment."[79] Abelson* finds that various factors "limit the kinds of compounds that might have accumulated" in a primordial soup:

> At least five major factors *limit the kinds of compounds that might have accumulated* in the primitive ocean.

First, there are limitations on what can be made by inorganic means; second, all organic matter degrades spontaneously with time; third, some substances are readily destroyed by radiation; fourth, many compounds would have been removed from the ocean by precipitation or adsorption; fifth, there are serious chemical incompatibilities among the constituents of living matter, and some of the components of the soup would react to form nonbiologic substances. In view of these limitations, one is challenged to seek a series of steps toward life that are compatible with the environment.[80]

Thus, Hull* says that physical chemists "cannot offer any encouragement":

The physical chemist, guided by the proved principles of chemical thermodynamics and kinetics, *cannot offer any encouragement* to the biochemist, who needs an ocean full of organic compounds to form even lifeless coacervates.[81]

Darwin* himself acknowledged that it was "what a big if!" in "some warm little pond, with all sorts of ammonia and phosphoric salt, light, heat, electricity, etc., present, that a protein compound was chemically formed . . .."[82]

a. Geologic Problem

The first problem with the assumption of a "primordial soup" is that the geological remains it would have left do not appear to exist, according to Brooks* and Shaw*:

If there ever was a primitive soup, then we would expect to find at least somewhere on this planet either massive sediments containing enormous amounts of the various nitrogenous organic compounds, amino acids, purines, pyrimidines, and the like, or alternatively in much metamorphosed sediments we should find vast amounts of nitrogenous cokes (graphite-like nitrogen-containing materials). In fact, *no such materials have been found* anywhere on earth. . . . There is, in other words, *pretty good negative evidence that there never was a primitive organic soup* on this planet that could have lasted but a brief moment.[83]

Similarly, there is no geological evidence of the evaporating pools that most evolutionists postulate, Dose* notes.[84]

b. Cross-Reaction Problem

Another problem with the assumption of a primordial soup is that cross-reactions would occur that would destroy or make unavailable many of the organic compounds in that soup. That would be true of amino acids and sugars, which would have formed biologically unusable tar and "prevented the formation of an 'organic soup,'" as Nissenbaum*, Kenyon*, and Oro* recognize:

Summary. One of the major diagenetic pathways of organic matter in recent sediments involves the condensation of cellular constituents, particularly amino acids and sugars, into insoluble melanoidin-type polymers. These polymers consist mainly of humic and fulvic acids and make up the major part of the organic carbon reservoir in recent sediments. We suggest that a similar set of reactions between abiotically formed amino acids and sugars, and more generally between aldehydes and amines, occurred on a large scale in the prebiotic hydrosphere. The rapid *formation of this insoluble polymeric material* would have removed the bulk of the dissolved organic carbon from the primitive oceans and would thus have *prevented the formation of an "organic soup".*

We suggest that the prebiotic scenario involved chemical and protoenzymic reactions at the sediment-ocean interface in relatively shallow waters and under conditions not much different from those of the recent environment.[85]

Such cross-reactions would have made "unlikely . . . more than traces of free glucose, free ribose, or deoxyribose," Abelson* adds:

> In addition, *carbohydrates such as glucose combine readily with amino acids* to form *nonbiologic products.* This reaction proceeds at room temperature, and even at 0 degrees C there is a noticeable reaction in a week. At pH 8-9, amino acids and free carbohydrates are simply incompatible. . . . Thus it is *unlikely that the primitive ocean ever contained more than traces of free glucose, free ribose, or deoxyribose.*
>
> . . ..
>
> . . .[T]here are serious *chemical incompatibilities* among the constituents of living matter, and some of the components of the soup would *react* to form *nonbiologic substances.*[86]

Even if DNA formed somehow with free sugars unavailable, DNA would react with the water of the primordial soup, Shapiro* notes:

> The covalent structure of DNA is unstable in aqueous solution. *It tends to hydrolyze* to its monomeric components, and they themselves are subject to various hydrolytic reactions. These processes are slow, when compared to most familiar chemical reactions. However, a reaction that is slow by these standards may still have great biological significance, if it occurs within the genetic material of an organism. A single base transformation within a DNA molecule may be sufficient to cause a mutation, or inactivate the DNA. Consider a reaction, for example, with a rate constant of 10^{-10} sec^{-1} at pH 7.4, 37°; it will have a half life of 220 years. Assume that, within a DNA, it affects two of the four bases. It will take place once every three hours per million base pairs of DNA, and thus be a *significant source of damage.*[87]

Proteins would have tended to react with formaldehyde to form cross-linkages between proteins, Walker* observes.[88] "Fatty acids form insoluble salts with magnesium and calcium, and hence would be removed from the soup," Abelson* states.[89] Yet, ignoring these chemical incompatibilities, the origin of life experiments typically deal with only a few of the essential biomolecules, and assume if several chemicals will react properly in isolation that they will react similarly with the other biomolecules in a primordial soup or evaporating pool.

c. Decomposition Problem

A difficulty parallel to the cross-reaction problem is the decomposition problem, which Shapiro* summarizes:

> Some evidence from our present world supports this concept. A certain amount of biological material that is released into the oceans is altered by random chemical events so that it is no longer palatable to living organisms. This material may then serve as a model for all of the organic substances present in the ocean before life began. Chemist Arie Nissenbaum has studied its fate, and noted that *it does not accumulate in the oceans*. Concentrations remain quite low, and the average age of the material is no more than 3,500 years. It is *depleted by a number of geological processes*. Heavier molecules settle out and form deposits. Other substances are absorbed by minerals, which compact into sediments. The sediments deposited throughout the entire record of geological history contain organic components of this type. A prebiotic soup, if ever formed, would presumably suffer the same fate, before it had the chance to meet its alternative destiny, the return to equilibrium.[90]

Those "chemical and physical processes" are described as follows by Nissenbaum*:

> The existence of hot or cold 'nutrient broth' or *'primeval soup' is challenged* on the basis of the recent geochemistry of soluble organic carbon in the oceans. Most of the dissolved organic carbon is recycled quickly by organisms, but the residual, biologically retractive, organic matter is efficiently scavenged from the oceans (residence time of 1000 to 3500 years) by nonbiologically mediated *chemical and physical processes*, such as adsorption on sinking minerals, polymerization and aggregation to humic type polymers or by aggregation to particulate matter through bubbling and sinking of this material to the ocean bottom. Since there is no reason to believe that such nonbiological scavenging was not operative in the prebiotic oceans as well, then the prolonged existence of organic soup is very doubtful. . . .[91]

Another form of decomposition is by hydrolysis of "all the major biopolymers," according to Cairns-Smith*:

> There is a third difficulty in prevital synthesis of biopolymers, and this is the most generally recognized: all the major biopolymers are metastable in aqueous solution in relation to their (deactivated) monomers. Left

to itself in water, a polypeptide will hydrolyse to its constituent amino acids: Miller & Orgel (1974) estimate that the half life of alanylalanine is about 8 x 10^7 years at 0°C and about 6 × 10^5 years at 25°C.

Most experimental work on prevital simulation of polymer synthesis has been concerned with this third problem. There have been two main approaches.[92]

A further type of decomposition is racemization, whereby isomers such as exclusively L-amino acids and D-sugars revert naturally to an equal D and L mixture that is incompatible with life,[93] as Dillon* describes:

Under standard ambient conditions, a given enantiomorph undergoes molecular change toward its mirror-image form at a rate that is approximately constant. Hence, it was proposed that the proportions of L- and D-aspartic acid, for example, could be used to date fossil remains, the "half-life" in the example cited being ca. 15,000 years. In the present context, this process of molecular change signifies that, even though some method may be found to produce a given type of optically active material in quantity, in the seas it must be incorporated into living systems relatively quickly or else its purity of type would soon be lost.[94]

For amino acids that "racemization rate would have been" an "important consideration" under primeval conditions.[95]

d. Radiation Problem

Another problem with the alleged primordial soup is that, if amino acids were formed in the atmosphere, about 97% of amino acids formed would never have reached the primordial soup, because they would have been destroyed by ultraviolet light, as Hull* calculates for glycine:

A glycine molecule formed in such an atmosphere is *immediately vulnerable to radiation* up to 3000A., absorbing in a part of the solar spectrum far more intense than that which produced it. Decarboxylation of activated glycine would presumably occur with a quantum efficiency of the order of unity. Thus, any glycine formed would be rapidly decomposed. . . . Thus, 97 per cent of the glycine would be decomposed before it could reach the surface.[96]

If amino acids formed instead in the ocean, most amino acids and proteins similarly would have been destroyed by ultraviolet light, because currents would have brought them near the surface exposed to ultraviolet light:

But even after the glycine reaches the ocean, the victory is not won. Abelson has discussed the possible stability of simple amino-acids throughout geological time; the important effect, however, is not thermal, but *decomposition by ultra-violet radiation.* The ultra-violet reaching the surface would penetrate to a considerable depth. . . . These short lives for decomposition in the atmosphere or ocean clearly preclude the possibility of accumulating useful concentrations of organic compounds over eons of time.[97]

That "ultraviolet light probably penetrated . . . the upper 19 meters of the ocean" or pool, and "the circulation of the ocean exposed the amino acids from greater depths to ultraviolet light also," Dose* stresses.[98]

One consequence of that decomposition by ultraviolet radiation would have been a very low concentration of amino acids, and a "soup" as heavily diluted as the modern ocean:

> The matter was pursued again by Hulett (1969) in an influential paper in which he considered various energy sources but stressed particularly photochemical effects. (The main point is that short-wavelength photons are needed for the synthesis of molecules such as aldehydes and amino acids, while *the much more abundant longer wavelength photons are effective in decomposing them.*) The importance of ultraviolet radiation in destroying organic molecules was again emphasized by Rein, Nir & Stamadiadou (1971). Dose (1974, 1975) has calculated that primitive oceanic concentrations of amino acids would have been around 10^{-7} M if photochemical effects are taken into account. Thus Dose points out that the *concentration of amino acids in the "soup" would have been about the same as their concentrations in the oceans now*. . . .[99]

e. Dilution Problem

A further problem with the alleged primordial soup is dilution, if that soup were the ocean. Nissenbaum*, Kenyon*, and Oro* have stated:

> It is difficult to see how, under such conditions, the "primordial soup" could have existed at all.
>
> . . ..
>
> . . .[I]t is now generally accepted that the *concentration of the "soup" was probably too small* for efficient synthesis, particularly of biopolymers.[100]

The research relevant to dilution problems is summarized by Cairns-Smith*:

> Next there is the *problem of the concentration* of the monomers in primordial waters. It has been emphasized repeatedly that the idea of an oceanic primordial soup is difficult to sustain on thermodynamic and kinetic grounds. For example *Hull* (1960) says: 'First, thermodynamic calculations predict *vanishingly small concentrations* of even the smallest organic compounds. Second, the reactions invoked to synthesise such compounds are seen to be much more effective in decomposition.' Hull

was discussing particularly the effects of ultraviolet radiation which he calculated would have destroyed 97% of amino acids produced in the atmosphere before they reached the oceans. Glycine, he reckoned, would have formed at best a 10^{-12} M solution. *Sillen* (1965) was similarly pessimistic and talked of the '*myth of the pr[e]biotic soup*', and *Abelson* (1966) pointed to the lack of any geological evidence for a thick oceanic soup in the past.... *Dose* points out that the concentration of amino acids in the 'soup' would have been about the same as their concentrations in the oceans now. A similar conclusion has been reached by *Nissenbaum* (1976) on the basis of other (non-biological) geochemical processes that scavenge organic molecules from the oceans (for example adsorption on sinking minerals).[101]

That dilution factor "imposes especially great difficulties," according to Dillon*:

> 4. The *dilution factor*, even with the oceans growing from relatively small bodies as sometimes visualized (Rubey, 1951, 1955; Dillon, 1974), imposes *especially great difficulties* upon the origins of the biological materials. This is a problem *particularly with such dehydration reactions* as peptide linkages and the bonding of nucleosides. Even avoiding the thermodynamic restrictions by carrying out the processes under anhydrous conditions, as has been done, merely changes the problem. The difficulty then is, first, providing large concentrations of pure aspartic or glutamic acid or other amino acid, and, second, melting that substance at a reasonable temperature, and, finally, adding the other amino acids....[102]

As a result of dilution, the primitive ocean would have had a level of amino acids "hopelessly low as starting material for the spontaneous generation of life," in Hull's* words.[103] That concentration would have been "by far too low for direct formation of polymers and more complicated structures," according to Dose*.[104] Specifically, the amino acid level would have been the very low level of 10^{-12} to 10^{-27} molar according to Hull's* calculations (ignoring destruction by cross-reactions),[105] at most 10^{-8} moles per liter as calculated by Dose* (ignoring destruction by ultraviolet radiation in the atmosphere and cross-reactions),[106] and 10^{-7} molar as assayed by Nissenbaum* (ignoring destruction by ultraviolet light).[107]

Some biochemical evolutionists have proposed that the primordial soup occurred in evaporating pools rather than in the full ocean. However, thus solving the dilution problem can only magnify the ultraviolet radiation problem, because an evaporating pool is maximally exposed to ultraviolet light, as Cairns-Smith* points out:

> Perhaps at the margins of oceans there would have been *evaporating rock pools* that would have served to concentrate materials. It would take

a lot of evaporating, though, from 10^{-7} M to the kinds of concentrations that might be needed. And the *ultraviolet sunlight would have been a nuisance* for any concentration process that uses evaporation. . . .[108]

Such pools also would face a serious evaporation problem, that is, the evaporation of such essential compounds as aldehydes and hydrogen cyanide, according to Horowitz* and Hubbard*[109] and Sanchez*, Ferris*, and Orgel*.[110] Evaporating pools also would encounter the geologic problem, that there is no geological evidence for their existence, as Dose* says,[111] as well as the cross-reaction and decomposition problems.

Another evolutionist proposal is that adsorption of biomolecules on clays and other materials should replace a primordial soup. That postulate still confronts the dilution problem as well as weak binding, according to Cairns-Smith*:

> Lahav & Chang (1976) have recently taken up this idea in an analysis of published data on the adsorption and condensation on clays of amino acids, purine and pyrimidine bases, sugars, nucleosides and nucleotides. *None of these types of molecule binds very strongly to ordinary clays.* At equilibrium, between ocean and clay sediments, they would be *very thinly spread* over the available clay surface. Such estimates are necessarily rough, but even supposing that Dose (1975) was pessimistic by two orders of magnitude in his estimate of oceanic amino acid concentrations, the molecules would have been on average at least 10 nm apart. *Additional factors would still be needed to concentrate the molecules sufficiently,* for example evaporation or freezing.[112]

Adsorption scenarios would not resolve the geologic, cross-reaction, and decomposition problems at all.

Summary. Shapiro* and Sillen* refer to "the myth of the prebiotic soup" as a place for formation, concentration, and combination of organic molecules (Shapiro*[113]), and Hull* says that the "physical chemist . . . cannot offer any encouragement to the biochemist, who needs an ocean full of organic compounds to form even lifeless coacervates" (Hull*[114]). The problems with a primordial soup are rife, and most of those problems are shared by the evaporating pool and mineral adsorption alternatives. The following citations should be read in their full context as discussed earlier.

(a) A geologic problem is that a primordial soup would leave distinctive geological remains, but "no such materials have been found" (Brooks* and Shaw*[115]). No geological evidence exists for evaporating pools either (Dose*[116]).

(b) A cross-reaction problem includes the "reactions between abiotically formed amino acids and sugars, and more generally between aldehydes and amines," which would have brought the "rapid formation of this insoluble polymeric material . . . and would thus have prevented the formation of an 'organic soup' " (Nissenbaum*, Kenyon*, and Oro*[117]). Similarly, "DNA is unstable in aqueous solution" and "tends to hydrolyze" (breaking apart) (Shapiro*[118]), proteins would have formed cross-linkages by reacting with formaldehyde (Walker*[119]), and "[f]atty acids form insoluble salts with magnesium and calcium, and hence would be removed from the soup" (Abelson*[120]).

(c) A decomposition problem involves "chemical and physical processes, such as adsorption on sinking materials, polymerization and aggregation to humic type polymers or . . . to particulate matter," such that organic molecules could not accumulate in the ocean (Nissenbaum*[121]). Other aspects are hydrolysis of "all the major biopolymers" (Cairns-Smith*[122]), whether in a primordial ocean or evaporating pools, and racemization of L-amino acids and D-sugars into biologically unusable mixtures of D and L forms (Dillon*[123]).

(d) A radiation problem from ultraviolet light would make amino acids "formed in such an atmosphere . . . immediately vulnerable" and would cause "97 per cent" to be "decomposed before it could reach the surface," whereas amino acids formed in or reaching the ocean still would face "decomposition by ultraviolet radiation" that would "clearly preclude the possibility of accumulating useful concentrations of organic compounds over eons of time" (Hull*[124]). The "circulation of the ocean" would have "exposed the amino acids from greater depths to ultraviolet light also" (Dose*[125]). Thus, "the concentration of amino acids in the 'soup' would have been about the same as their concentrations in the oceans now" (Dose*[126]).

(e) The final difficulty, a dilution problem, throws question on whether "the 'primordial soup' could have existed at all," and leaves it "generally accepted that the concentration of the 'soup' was probably too small for efficient synthesis, particularly of biopolymers" (Nissenbaum*, Kenyon*, and Oro*[127]). A number of researchers acknowledge "the problem of the concentrations of the monomers in primordial waters" (Cairns-Smith*[128]), and that the "dilution factor . . . imposes especially great difficulties upon the origins of the biological materials" (Dillon*[129]). The primordial soup would leave amino acids "hopelessly low as starting material for the spontaneous generation of life" (Hull*[130]), and "by far too low for direct formation of polymers and more complicated structures" (Dose*[131]).

(f) Evaporating pools might solve the dilution problem, but would magnify the radiation problem (Cairns-Smith*[132]), and would still encounter the geological problem (Dose*[133]), the cross-reaction problem, and the decomposition problem, while adding a new problem of evaporation of such essential compounds as aldehydes and hydrogen cyanide (Horowitz* and Hubbard*[134]). Bernal's adsorption on clays would not solve the dilution problem, because "[a]dditional factors would still be needed to concentrate the molecules sufficiently," and would add a new binding problem, that "[n]one of these types of molecule binds very strongly to ordinary clays" (Cairns-Smith*[135]). The geologic, cross-reaction, and decomposition problems would remain.

That "myth of the prebiotic soup," combined with the "myth" of an oxygen-free early atmosphere (Section 5.1), invites cynicism about how much other mythology is included in biochemical evolution.

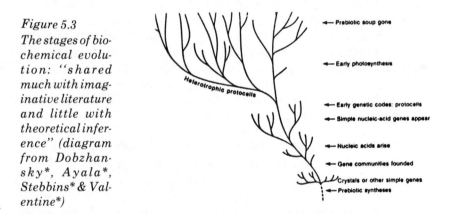

Figure 5.3
The stages of biochemical evolution: "shared much with imaginative literature and little with theoretical inference" (diagram from Dobzhansky*, Ayala*, Stebbins* & Valentine*)

5.3 The Stages of Biochemical Evolution: Questions about the Critical Elements for Life

Biochemical evolution involves the following stages—and each "is the subject of either controversy or complete bewilderment"—as Scott* observes:

[Various forces] made the elements form and then react to produce the chemical building blocks of life: nucleic acids made of sugars and bases, proteins made of amino acids, lipids and carbohydrates. Specific nucleic acids then began to direct the production of specific proteins. Nucleic acids and proteins that acted together to enhance their own multiplication thrived and continued to adapt. They became surrounded by membranes and evolved into complex cells and eventually into us.

But how much of this neat tale is firmly established, and how much remains hopeful speculation? In truth, *the mechanism of almost every major step, from chemical precursors up to the first recognizable cells, is the subject of either controversy or complete bewilderment.*[136]

Thus, "[s]peculation is bound to be rife," and some proposals "have shared much with imaginative literature and little with theoretical inference":

> Those who work on the origin of life must necessarily make bricks without very much straw, which goes a long way to explain why this field of study is so often regarded with deep suspicion. *Speculation* is bound to be rife, and it has also frequently been wild. Some attempts to account for the origin of life on the Earth, however ingenious, have *shared much with imaginative literature and little with theoretical inference* of the kind which can be confronted with observational evidence of some kind or another.[137]

This section discusses the serious problems with each of the postulated stages of biochemical evolution: (a) of amino acids, (b) of proteins in general, (c) of sugars, (d) of enzymatic activity, (e) of lipids, (f) of protocells, (g) of the genetic coding system, and (h) of a living cell. It is very important to note that (i) natural selection is inapplicable to nearly all of these stages.

a. Evolution of Amino Acids

Even the first step, the evolution of a sufficient quantity of amino acids (of which proteins primarily are made) of sufficient purity poses serious problems. As discussed in Section 5.2, cross-reactions and decomposition would have destroyed most amino acids, radiation would have destroyed 97% of the surviving amino acids in the atmosphere and most in the primordial soup or pond, and dilution would have prevented significant formation of proteins.

b. Evolution of Proteins

Assuming nevertheless a sufficient supply of amino acids, many further problems realistically would have prevented the evolution of biologically meaningful proteins from those amino acids. Some of those difficulties lead Cairns-Smith*, senior lecturer in chemistry at University of Glasgow and a prominent origin of life researcher, to see further elements of "unreality to an already unreal line of thought":

It seems to me that the idea of coupling agents putting together poly-peptides on a lifeless Earth adds another dimension of unreality to an already *unreal line of thought*. Remember that primordial simulations generally give *only low yields of amino acids*. Remember that the *products are tars* and that suggestions for *prevital work-up procedures are usually absent*. Remember the *difficulties anyway in building up concentrations* of solutions of amino acids or of the cyanide or phosphate to make a coupling agent. Remember that even from laboratory bottles the agents in question do *not work very well*. Remembering all that, now add the thought that *coupling agents are rather unspecific*.[138]

The "unreal" elements can be categorized as follows.

First, cross-reactions would have occurred between amino acids and sugars, aldehydes, amines, ketones, and carboxylic acids, preventing the amino acids from being available to form proteins, as Nissenbaum* acknowledges.[139] Similarly, cross-reactions would have occurred between any proteins and formaldehyde to form cross-linkages between proteins, as Walker* notes.[140]

Second, the formation of proteins would be generally prevented by the dilution of the primordial soup, so that "it is now generally accepted that the concentration of the 'soup' was probably too small for efficient synthesis, particularly of biopolymers," as Nissenbaum*, Kenyon*, and Oro* point out[141] and as Dose* notes.[142]

Third, any proteins formed would generally be destroyed by the temperatures required to synthesize amino acid intermediates, as Sagan* observes:

> The temperatures required to synthesize the amino acid intermediates rapidly *pyrolyze amino acids, depolymerize polypeptides*, and *degrade microspheres*. I would like to see an order of magnitude calculation in which a probability is assigned to each scene of the scenario, and a total polypeptide abundance over geological time derived. It seems to me that this abundance will be *much less than the large concentration of polypeptides in the primitive seas apparently required* for the origin of life[.] Strecker synthesis of amino acids seems much more likely in primitive times, but the *problem of the large-scale production of polypeptides* remains, I believe, unsolved.[143]

Also, any such proteins and many amino acids formed in a primordial soup generally would be destroyed by hydrolysis through reaction with the water in the soup, and that would occur in a matter of days or months, Dose* concludes.[144]

Fourth, if proteins were not synthesized by thermal processes but by increasing their reactivity, other problems arise that amount to "unreality" without the complex machinery of living cells, as Cairns-Smith* stated above. He adds:

There are several *problems*, though, in attempting to apply this idea to primitive chemistry. Firstly, *energy* must come from somewhere to activate an amino acid. Secondly, even mildly activated species are more or less susceptible to *hydrolysis*. Thirdly, the amino group of an amino acid will usually have to be *protected during activation* if only to prevent premature polymerisation. This means that *separate deprotecting steps* will also be required. In addition side groups of the more reactive amino acids will have to be protected and deprotected.

Instead of using isolable activated intermediates, amide links can be formed by means of coupling or condensing agents such as carbodiimides. . . .

. . .[C]oupling agents are rather unspecific. If a well chosen coupling agent under well chosen laboratory conditions can effectively join the acyl group A to the nucleophile B that is because among the *choices exercised by the experimenter* was the crucial one of only putting A and B into a flask for the coupling agents to couple. Compared with such carefully arranged marriages the affairs of a primordial soup would have been grossly promiscuous.[145]

Fifth, most polypeptides and proteins that could be thus formed would be biologically useless, because they generally would include nonproteinous amino acids (which are four times as numerous as proteinous amino acids). Temussi* *et al.* point out the prevalence in thermal experiments of nonbiological peptide bonds over biologically useful peptide bonds, which lead them to say that "the relevance of thermal condensation in the synthesis of prebiotic polypeptides ought to be critically reexamined":

In fact, these products, although studied from many points of view, have never been properly characterized and *their similarity with naturally occurring peptides has never been demonstrated unambiguously.* . . . On the other hand, it is conceivable that a substantial portion of peptide bonds is *not of the α-peptide type* (as in natural peptides) since thermal condensation can be performed only with mixtures containing large amounts of trifunctional aminoacids to prevent extensive carbonization of the starting amino acids (Fox, 1971). The presence of constitutional differences such as β, γ, or ϵ peptide bonds, is usually *very difficult to detect* by means of either chemical or physical methods. In particular, the spectroscopic methods traditionally employed in the field of synthetic or natural polypeptides (UV, IR, ORD, CD) can only give information on the overall structure of the chains but not on parts of the specific residues (Bradbury *et al.*, 1973). It is possible however to resort to nmr spectroscopy . . ..

. . ..

The general pattern emerging from our investigation is that trifunctional aminoacids, when subjected to thermal condensation tend to form

β, γ, or ϵ peptide units *more easily* than α-peptide units. This finding, if added to the low probability of the proper geological conditions (Miller *et al.* 1959), shows that the relevance of thermal condensation in the synthesis of prebiotic polypeptides ought to be critically reexamined.[146]

Sixth, polypeptides would not be biologically useful to nearly all organisms unless they were made solely of L-amino acids, as Williams* and Smith* point out:

> There is certainly a *unique relationship between optical activity and life.* Virtually all proteins contain exclusively the L-enantiomers of the amino acids while natural sugars are of the D-configuration. Many chemists would agree with the statement made at the First International Symposium on the Origin of Life on Earth by Terentev and Klabunovskii (1957), "we will start from the assumption that *life cannot and never could exist without molecular dissymmetry.*"[147]

However, there would be an equal probability for each constituent amino acid in an early protein to be a D-amino acid, and thus almost all prelife proteins would contain some D-amino acids that would render the proteins biologically meaningless.[148] That produces "a serious problem" and "very great difficulties," as Cairns-Smith* concedes:

> This is a serious problem: for molecular machinery to work at all precisely—and indefinite heritability of characteristics would seem to need precisely working machinery—it looks as if there must be multiple contact interactions between components. But in that case, if the components are chiral, then their chiralities would have to be specified. I cannot be dogmatic, but I can no more imagine an effective racemic molecular biology than I can imagine an effective racemic typewriter (and the same goes for biased D, L molecular biologies or biased D, L typewriters). . . .
> . . . .
> But they are *very great difficulties* all the same. Perhaps we might settle for the comment by Briggs with which Bonner concludes his review of the origin of chirality that "it presents problems to the hypothesis of chemical evolution that are at present insoluble".[149]

"There is no plausible mechanism for the enrichment of one of the optical isomers of a mononucleoside that could lead to an overall enantiomeric excess of even 1%," and "the template-directed polymerization of one enantiomer is likely to be inhibited strongly by the presence of the other," so "there is no basis in organic chemistry for optimism" and a "severe problem," Joyce*, Schwartz*, Miller*, and Orgel* recently conceded.[150] Isomers (chirality) were discussed in Section 4.3.

Sixth, and most important, virtually all protein-like products would be biologically nonmeaningful, because their amino acids and other constituent parts would not be in a biologically meaningful sequence.[151]

Finally, particular proteins have further difficulties of their own. For example, the compounds necessary for energy transfer may not be capable of synthesis in a primordial soup or pond, as Dillon* points out:

> 7. Phosphorylated compounds in general have been relatively poorly explored from the standpoint of their formation *in vitro*. Among the very important members of this category are such compounds as the triphosphorylated nucleosides, including ATP, GTP, and the others vitally essential in cells for the transfer of energy and possibly for the *in vivo* synthesis of nucleic acids.[152]

c. Evolution of Sugars

Sugars would have to evolve before the genetic coding system could evolve, because sugars are an integral part of nucleic acids (DNA and RNA etc., which are elements of the genetic coding system). Although sugars are often postulated to have arisen from condensation of formaldehyde, the evolution of sugars also has serious problems that cause Reid* and Orgel* to conclude that "[w]e do not believe that the formose reaction . . . is a plausible model for the prebiotic accumulation of sugars."[153]

First, much of the formaldehyde in the atmosphere or ocean would have been destroyed, as Abelson* notes.[154]

Second, even though some simple sugars would form, they generally would have been destroyed by cross-reactions with amino acids,[155] or by decomposition from other causes because of their instability, as Cairns-Smith* points out:

> The B-class would again be accessible types but this time only because kinetically favoured. They would be easily made from available starting materials but would *not be particularly stable*. There are plenty of such comparatively *short-lived* molecules in our biochemistry. Sugars are evidently in this category. That sugars appear temporarily in the condensation of formaldehyde may have some relevance to how they were first biosynthesised: but *you do not find sugars in mature products of non-biological semi-chaotic reactions*—they are not in meteorites for example. B-class molecules are simple active metabolites.[156]

Miller* and Orgel* describe related difficulties with sugars:

> First, the only prebiotic synthesis of ribose, the Butlerow reaction, yields a complex mixture of sugars; *ribose never constitutes a major fraction of the products. Furthermore, ribose and the other sugars decompose*

rapidly on a geological timescale, with half-lives that are probably not more than a few hundred years at 0°C and pH8. . . .[157]

Third, the concentration of sugars in a primordial soup would have been far too small, because of their instability.[158] The accumulation more likely would be of caramel-like residues not useful to life than of sugars:

> It is similarly *difficult to imagine anything like polysaccharide being accumulated in primordial waters*. As we saw, the monosaccharides could only have been made easily from formaldehyde, as far as anyone knows, and there is doubt if there could have been sufficient concentrations of that. In any case, as we saw, the product of the formose reaction is a very complex mixture that *easily leads to higher polymers and to caramel*.[159]

Fourth, the genetic coding system today uses only D-sugars, and yet L-sugars would have been equal in quantity.[160] This produces the same problem as the need for L-amino acids and the equal frequency of D-amino acids.

d. Evolution of Enzymes

Enzymes (which are proteins with catalytic ability to accelerate chemical reactions) also are essential to life but also present serious problems that many evolutionists recognize.

First, as many scientists have acknowledged, "[e]nzymes possess exceptional activity and specificity of catalytic action" that "cannot arise accidentally in a simple solution of organic compounds," in Oparin's* words.[161] Even if enzymes with weak catalytic ability would work, their evolution is still implausible.[162] Some have proposed that, before enzymes appeared, minerals acted as weak catalysts, but such minerals would have lacked the necessary specificity according to Cairns-Smith*:

> There is nothing wrong with the idea that the early environment might have provided *catalysts* for early organisms. The environment is still a source of metal ions, such as Zn^{2+}, that are important parts of enzymes. The trouble arises when one tries to imagine the environment as the source of the *specificity* of catalysts, or indeed of any other kind of specificity. . . .[163]

Second, enzymes are not able to replicate themselves, and they would have to be continually produced by biochemical evolution until an early organism could produce them. Dillon* notes the improbability of multiple evolutions of enzymes, their lack of evolutionary value, and the need for their development in living organisms, in connection with catalase:

This major flaw is perhaps most easily demonstrated first in the model of the autocatalytic creation of the enzyme catalase described above. . . . Even if it is granted that the entire process is feasible outside of a cell, there appears to be *no means by which many identical—or even fairly similar—molecules can be produced.* Perhaps one can concede that a single molecule, or a very few, *might* be formed in the postulated manner, but certainly it is *most improbable that any sizable population* of identical molecules could result from random chance processes. That model also fails to include a *mechanism whereby the enzymes can be passed to subsequent generations* of the protobionts—*nor* does it contain even a suggestion as to how the oxidation-reduction processes or their products were of any *value to the early forebears of life.* Thus it becomes evident that, only if the breakdown of hydrogen peroxide has been essential to the metabolism of the protobiont and if the random-chance growth in complexity visualized for the developing catalase had been under the guidance of an evolving genetic mechanism, could that enzyme have increased in abundance and survived to have become incorporated into living creatures. And these observations plainly signify that the catalase *would have had to develop within living organisms, not free in the seas.* Thus the enzymes must actually have resulted from ordinary biological evolutionary processes, not by autocatalysis carried out in the primitive environment.[164]

e. Evolution of Lipids

Lipids (containing fatty acids) "play a very significant role in cells, especially in the formation of membranes, without which cells could not exist."[165] Lipids, too, present difficulties.

First, lipids are extremely difficult to synthesize. Miller* and Orgel*, leading researchers, have concluded that "[n]o satisfactory synthesis of fatty acids is presently available."[166] Biochemical evolution of lipids would have encountered the same difficulties as laboratory synthesis: the need for highly specific enzymes and carrier proteins, the requirement for a specific order of the chemical reactions, and the necessity of a specific order of molecules, which bear further discussion.

Second, lipids occur in isomers and have other features that present "problems . . . so difficult that there almost seems to be a conspiracy not to discuss them," as Cairns-Smith* points out:

And as one goes on to consider the larger molecules, such as lipids and nucleotides, *chemical accessibility dissolves.* These molecules are not at all easy to make. Part of the trouble is how to get up energy gradients: but that is not the only trouble. Because these molecules are bigger, and hence have *richer possibilities for isomerism*, the problems of discrimination—of which chiral discrimination is only one—become so difficult that *there almost seems to be a conspiracy not to discuss them*, but to design experiments as if they had been solved, by *using purified starting materials*.[167]

The isomers to which he refers are *cis* lipids, meaning that certain chemical bonds are on the same side rather than opposite sides of the lipid molecule. Cell membranes are dependent on an exclusively *cis* configuration, and yet the opposite *trans* configuration is more probable under evolutionary processes because it is both more stable and less energy-using, so that an exclusively *cis* lipid molecule would be highly improbable as an evolutionary product.

Third, lipids would rapidly have been destroyed by cross-reactions that formed "insoluble salts with magnesium and calcium" in a primordial soup, and by other forms of decomposition, Abelson* notes.[168]

f. Evolution of Protocells

Protocells are the postulated link between complex proteins (and other substances) and a first living cell; various models of protocell evolution are discussed below.[169]

g. Evolution of the Genetic Coding System

The genetic coding system is essential for replication of a living organism,[170] yet its evolution is also plagued by serious problems that allow "endless speculation," as Dickerson* recognizes:

> The evolution of the genetic machinery is the step for which there are *no laboratory models*; hence we can *speculate endlessly*, unfettered by inconvenient facts.[171]

Sir Francis Crick*, the co-discoverer of the keystone of the genetic coding system and a Nobel Prize recipient, agrees that the evolutionary development of the system is "the major problem in understanding the origin of life":

> The important point to realize is that in spite of the genetic code being almost universal, the mechanism necessary to embody it is far too complex to have arisen in one blow. It must have evolved from something much simpler. Indeed, *the major problem in understanding the origin of life* is trying to *guess what the simpler system might have been*.[172]

Cairns-Smith* describes the "gigantic implausibility" of evolution even of nucleic acids as part of the genetic coding system;[173] Scott* says evolution of the vital gene-protein link is "shrouded in almost complete mystery";[174] Monod* says evolution of the translating machinery is "difficult to imagine" although it must have happened;[175] and Lambert* calls evolution of the enzyme mechanisms "an unsolved problem".[176]

First, evolution of the bases and sugars that are necessary elements of nucleotides, the ladder rungs of DNA, presents at least seven "difficulties" that Cairns-Smith* summarizes:

> Let us consider some of the difficulties. *First*, as we have seen, it is *not even clear* that the primitive Earth would have generated and maintained *organic molecules*. All that we can say is that there might have been prevital organic chemistry going on, at least in special locations. *Second*, high-energy precursors of purines and pyrimidines had to be produced in a sufficiently *concentrated* form (for example at least 0.01 M HCN). *Third*, the *conditions* must now have been right for reactions to give perceptible yields of at least two bases that could pair with each other. *Fourth*, these *bases must then have been separated* from the confusing jumble of similar molecules that would also have been made, and the solutions must have been sufficiently *concentrated*. *Fifth*, in some other location a *formaldehyde concentration* of above 0.01 M must have built up. *Sixth*, this accumulated formaldehyde had to *oligomerise to sugars*. *Seventh*, somehow the sugars must have been separated and resolved, so as to give a moderately good *concentration of*, for example, *D-ribose*. . . .[177]

Second, evolution of nucleosides from bases and sugars raises at least three more difficulties, as the same author continues:

> *Eighth*, bases and sugars must now have come together. *Ninth*, they must have been induced to *react* to make nucleosides. (There are no known ways of bringing about this thermodynamically uphill reaction in aqueous solution: purine nucleosides have been made by dry-phase synthesis, but not even this method has been successful for condensing pyrimidine bases and ribose to give nucleosides (Orgel & Lohrmann, 1974). *Tenth*, whatever the mode of joining base and sugar it had to be *between the correct nitrogen atom* of the base and the correct carbon atom of the sugar. This junction will fix the pentose sugar as either the α-or β-anomer of either the furanose or pyranose forms (see page 29). For nucleic acids it has to be the β-furanose. (In the dry-phase purine nucleoside synthesis referred to above, all four of these isomers were present with never more than 8% of the correct structure.). . .[178]

Third, evolution of nucleotides from nucleosides and phosphate, and their purification, adds still more difficulties:

> *Eleventh*, phosphate must have been, or must now come to have been, present at *reasonable concentrations*. (The concentrations in the oceans would have been very low, so we must think about special situations— evaporating lagoons and such things (Ponnamperuma, 1978). *Twelfth*,

the phosphate must be *activated* in some way—for example as a linear or cyclic polyphosphate—so that (energetically uphill) phosphorylation of the nucleoside is possible. *Thirteenth*, to make standard nucleotides *only the 5'-hydroxyl of the ribose should be phosphorylated.* (In solid-state reations with urea and inorganic phosphates as a phosphorylating agent, this was the dominant species to begin with (Lohrmann & Orgel, 1971). Longer heating gave the nucleoside cyclic 2',3'-phosphate as the major product although various dinucleotide derivatives and nucleoside polyphosphates are also formed (Osterberg, Orgel & Lohrmann, 1973).) *Fourteenth*, if not already activated—for example as the cyclic 2',3'-phosphate—the *nucleotides must now be activated* (for example with polyphosphate: Lohrmann, 1976) and a *reasonably pure solution* of these species created of reasonable concentration. Alternatively, a suitable coupling agent must now have been fed into the system. . . .[179]

Fourth, evolution of nucleotide chains and the necessary conditions involve complex biochemical events:

Fifteenth, the activated nucleotides (or the nucleotides with coupling agent) must now have *polymerised*. Initially this must have happened without a pre-existing polynucleotide template (this has proved very difficult to simulate (Orgel & Lohrmann, 1974)): but more important, it must have come to take place *on pre-existing polynucleotides* if the key function of transmitting information to daughter molecules was to be achieved by abiotic means. This has proved difficult too. Orgel & Lohrmann give *three main classes of problem.* (i) While it has been shown that adenosine derivatives form stable helical structures with poly(U)—they are in fact triple helixes—and while this enhances the condensation of adenylic acid with either adenosine or another adenylic acid—mainly to di(A)—*stable helical structures were not formed* when either poly(A) or poly(G) were used as templates. (ii) It was difficult to find a suitable means of making the *internucleotide bonds.* . . . (iii) Internucleotide bonds formed on a template are *usually a mixture* of 2'-5' and the normal 3'-5' types. Often the 2'-5' bonds predominate although it has been found that Zn^{2+}, as well as acting as an efficient catalyst for the template directed oligomerisation of guanosine 5'-phosphorimidazolide also leads to a preference for the 3'-5' bonds (Lohrmann, Bridson & Orgel, 1980). *Sixteenth*, the *physical and chemical environment* must at all times have been suitable—for example the pH, the temperature, the M^{2+} concentrations. *Seventeenth*, all reactions must have taken place well *out of the ultraviolet sunlight*; that is, not only away from its direct, highly destructive effects on nucleic acid-like molecules, but *away too from the radicals* produced by the sunlight, and from the various longer lived reactive species produced by these radicals. . . .[180]

Moreover, the nucleotide chain must be in very precise order to be biologically meaningful.[181] And it is "unlikely that any build-up of nucleic acid components could take place over a long period of time in an aqueous environment," Shapiro* concludes.[182]

Fifth, evolution of the gene-protein link had to occur, although that is "shrouded in almost complete mystery" according to Scott*:

> None has ever been recreated in the laboratory, and the evidence supporting them all is *very thin*. The emergence of the gene-protein link, an absolutely vital stage on the way up from lifeless atoms to ourselves, is *still shrouded in almost complete mystery*.[183]

Discussion of the origin of the genetic code requires discussion of the origin of the complicated mechanism of protein synthesis, Crick*[184] and Woese*[185] note.

Sixth, evolution of the translation machinery is "difficult to imagine" and is a "riddle," but the "code is meaningless unless translated," as Monod* (a Nobel Prize laureate) stresses:

> The code is meaningless unless translated. The modern cell's *translating machinery consists of at least fifty macromolecular components which are themselves coded in DNA*: the code cannot be translated otherwise than by products of translation. It is the modern expression of *omne vivum ex ovo*. When and how did this circle become closed? It is exceedingly *difficult to imagine*.[186]

"Thus the code cannot be translated except by using certain products of its translation. This constitutes a really baffling circle: a vicious circle, it seems, for any attempt to form a model, or a theory, of the genesis of the genetic code," as Popper* has noted,[187] and as Ambrose* has concurred.[188]

Part of the translation machinery is the "system of enzymatic proof-reading and editing" that minimizes translation errors, which Perutz* describes.[189] Its origin is "a major unsolved problem" in the assessment of Lambert*:

> The derivation of contemporary biological information transfer systems from prebiological systems lacking editing reactions thus constitutes an *unresolved* problem in theoretical biology. The prebiological system appears to face *dissolution and death rather than refinement as a consequence of its nonspecific information transfer*. It is far from clear that the proposals entertained herein (section 5) or even any combination thereof, suffice to account for the chance evolution of life in the light of enzymic editing mechanisms and the implications thereof. Gallant & Prothero (1980) allude to the question of whether primordial translation systems might degenerate toward randomness and conclude ". . . it is beyond question that error feedback must provide such evolutionary possibilities. If it did not, then we would not be here to ponder the question". Presumably these possibilities remain to be discovered as more precise information concerning biological accuracy is forthcoming.

Possibly, an assertion of Woese (1973) regarding the origin of the genetic code, that *"one's basic biological prejudices must be reexamined"* [,] is of relevance. In either event, a consideration of enzymic editing mechanisms as they relate to the origin of biological information transfer reveals *a major unsolved problem* in theoretical biology.[190]

Seventh, no intermediate forms with partial functionability appear to be possible, according to Cairns-Smith*, particularly in view of the inapplicability of natural selection that is discussed later:

> *Eighteenth*, unlike polypeptides, where you can easily imagine functions for imprecisely made products (for capsules, ion-exchange materials, etc.), a *genetic material must work rather well to be any use at all*—otherwise it will quickly let slip any information that it has managed to accumulate. *Nineteenth*, what is required here is not some wild one-off freak of an event: it is not true to say 'it only had to happen once'. *A whole set-up had to be maintained* for perhaps millions of years: a reliable means of production of activated nucleotides at the least.[191]

Furthermore, no "alternative ways of building up nucleotides" appear to exist:

> Now you may say that there are alternative ways of building nucleotides, and perhaps there was some geochemical way on the early Earth. But what we know of the experimental difficulties in nucleotide synthesis speaks *strongly against* any such supposition. However it is to be put together, a nucleotide is too complex and metastable a molecule for there to be any reason to expect an easy synthesis. You might want to argue about the nineteen problems that I chose: and I agree that there is a certain arbitrariness in the sequence of operations chosen. But if in the compounding of improbabilities nineteen is wrong as a number that would be mainly because *it is much too small a number* . If you were to consider in more detail a process such as the purification of an intermediate you would find many subsidiary operations—washings, pH changes and so on. (Remember Merrifield's machine: for one overall reaction, making one peptide bond, there were about 90 distinct operations required.)[192]

Thus, what is left is the "gigantic implausibility of prevital nucleic acids,"[193] and the misinterpreted origin of life experiments actually show "just why prevital nucleic acids are highly implausible," in Cairns-Smith's* words:

> *The implausibility of prevital nucleic acid*
>
> If it is hard to imagine polypeptides or polysaccharides in primordial waters it is *harder still to imagine polynucleotides*. But so powerful has been the effect of *Miller's experiment* on the scientific imagination that to read some of the literature on the origin of life (including many elementary texts) you might think that it had been well demonstrated that nucleotides were probable constituents of a primordial soup and hence

that prevital nucleic acid replication was a plausible speculation based on the results of experiments. There have indeed been many interesting and detailed experiments in this area. But the importance of this work lies, to my mind, not in demonstrating how nucleotides could have formed on the primitive Earth, but in precisely the opposite: *these experiments allow us to see, in much greater detail than would otherwise have been possible, just why prevital nucleic acids are highly implausible.*[194]

h. Evolution of the Living Cell

The most simple living cell is vastly different from the proteins or macromolecules from which it allegedly evolved, as Green* and Goldberger* point out:

> The macromolecule-to-cell transition is a *jump of fantastic dimensions* .... The available facts do *not provide a basis for postulating* that cells arose on this planet.[195]

Thus, "a very large gap separates the most complex model systems from the simplest contemporary living cells," in the words of Kenyon* and Nissenbaum*.[196] Dillon* agrees that "the basic problem with all the models thus far advanced looms so large that an enumeration of their other, more minor failures is made meaningless."[197] The things that contribute to that large gap, which is found in even the least complex cell, are an extremely complicated genetic coding system of DNA, messenger RNA, transfer RNA, chains and cycles of enzymes, other proteins, metabolic pathways, a cell membrane with distinct properties, and other incredibly complex components. Just two of those features are discussed further.

First, the primary requirement of life is self-replication,[198] and the "theory of first replicators" is a "defect of evolutionary theory" according to Kempthorne*:

> I find it curious that in the current public debate on creationism versus evolution, this *defect of evolutionary theory* receives little mention. I surmise that the reason is that *we have almost no ideas.* In saying this, I do not wish at all to lend support to creationist views. No scientific theory is complete.[199]

That defect is not just a minor incompletion but "the great divide":

> Biological evolution, on the other hand, *is* special, as discussed in the opening pages of this book. Above all what makes it special is heredity. This is the great divide: either there is a long-term hereditary mechanism working or there is not. .... It would not have mattered how ingenious or life-like some early system was; *if it lacked the ability to pass on to offspring the secret of its success then it might as well never have existed.*[200]

Replication involves the "paradox" that living things require replication mechanisms, but replication mechanisms arise only within living things, as Dillon* notes:

> *A Paradox in Life's Origins.* The requirement for a means of inheritance in the first living thing makes evident the existence of a paradox, as Woese (1970a, b) has pointed out. This *seemingly self-contradictory* condition is that, while *genetic mechanisms can exist only within living things*, the *organisms themselves could not have come into being without such a device....*[201]

That "most difficult problem" is further described by Kaplan*:

> The *most difficult problem* is certainly the origin of the apparatus of reproduction. Reproduction of present living cells is based on 2 groups of functions of macromolecules: (1) heterocatalytic activities within the cell as well as in the environment; (2) autocatalytic activities causing replication of the information which is used for the generation of those heterocatalytic activities. Since no macromolecules seem to exist which can perform both functions at the same time, both are allotted separately to 2 substances, proteins and nucleic acids, in contemporary organisms. As a consequence, the *synthesis of both polymers must be coupled mutually, proteins being formed due to information from nucleic acids* (translation), and *nucleic acids are replicated by catalysis due to proteins* (replication and transcription)....[202]

Even if a simpler early mechanism were possible, it still would be incredibly complex and still would embody the same paradox, Kaplan* adds:

> The number of components making up the *reproduction apparatus of present life* is large, at least about *80 special proteins and 100 genes* coding for them as well as for tRNA's and rRNA's are necessary. One can assume that protobionts possessed a much simpler apparatus....
>
> In order to estimate the probability of expecting a protobiont among many aggregates, the number of *necessary kinds of functional proteins as well as protogenes*, respectively, is *assumed to be 20 to 40....*[203]

He believes that evolution of such a system is plausible, but concedes that the probability is low.

Second, another "minimal definition of life ... is the capability of synthesizing proteins in at least sufficient quantity to replace those that are catabolized by normal processes,"[204] and that also offers a serious problem for biochemical evolution that Cairns-Smith* describes:

> According to the doctrine of chemical evolution these organisms were heterotrophs, that is to say they depended on organic foods. The diet of primordial soup was so adequate, it is said, that these organisms had no need for metabolic pathways to begin with. Such pathways could evolve

gradually as the foods ran out (by the mechanism proposed by Horowitz in 1945: see figure 1.12).

To have one's food provided sounds like an easy sort of life, but in reality there would be *great difficulties* with such an idea. There are *problems of assimilation.* To be a heterotroph implies an *ability to recognise molecules,* or at the very least to distinguish between classes of them. For the eventual evolution of metabolic pathways, specific recognition devices would be required. Thinking along the lines of current means of biomolecular control, some kind of *structure would seem to be needed that could form specific sockets* corresponding to the molecules in the environment. But until you have the ability to recognise at least some molecular units, how do you reach the point of being able to manufacture such specific devices? Organisms now can presuppose protein-synthesising machinery. And a great variety of transport proteins located in the cell membranes can actively and selectively pull in particular molecules from the environment (Lin, 1970; Wilson, 1978; Rosen, 1978).

The trouble is that a socket (such as that in an enzyme or a transport protein) that can recognise another molecule is much more *difficult to engineer* than the molecule itself. . . .

So that is the problem: how to evolve accurate recognising structures from a molecular technology that probably could not tell glycine from alanine, let alone D from L. . . .[205]

i. Inapplicability of Natural Selection

It is important to note that natural selection, which is an important part of biological evolution, does not apply to biochemical evolution and consequently cannot be relied on to assist biochemical evolution until a functional living organism exists. That has been recognized by the late Professor Dobzhansky*, a leading evolutionist scientist:

Natural selection is differential reproduction, organism perpetuation. In order to have natural selection, you have to have self-reproduction or self-replication and at least two distinct self-replicating units or entities. . .. *Prebiological natural selection is a contradiction in terms.*[206]

That is further explained by Blum*:

The term *natural selection* is sometimes loosely applied to evolution in physical systems, and perhaps a basic difference between chemical evolution and evolution of living organisms should be pointed out. . . . This kind of *chemical evolution,* rigidly governed by energetics and kinetics, we may think of as going on before the advent of life; but this is *very different from mutation and natural selection in living systems.* In the strictly chemical system molecules *lack the property of self reproduction*—the activated molecule does not perpetuate itself by reproducing its kind, but rapidly returns to a normal level if it does not undergo reaction. Reproduction of stable patterns and stable variants of these patterns is *essential for evolution by natural selection*. This was impossible before the advent of systems that could synthesize molecules having the stability and kind of variability associated with proteins and nucleic acids.[207]

Similar points are made by Yockey*,[208] Kaplan*,[209] and Erbrich*.[210] Thus, "a preliminary kind of semi-Darwinian evolution, where microsystems are not able to reproduce but they are already subject to selection," is not possible in the view of Cairns-Smith*.[211]

Summary. Each stage of biochemical evolution, even in the eyes of many advocates, is "the subject of either controversy or complete bewilderment" (Scott*[212]), necessitates that "[s]peculation is bound to be rife" with many proposals sharing "much with imaginative literature and little with theoretical inference,"[213] and "adds another dimension of unreality to an unreal line of thought" (Cairns-Smith*[214]). The following quotations should be read in their full context that was given earlier.

(a) Evolution of amino acids confronts the ultraviolet radiation, cross-reaction, decomposition, and dilution problems that were discussed in Section 5.2.

(b) Evolution of proteins encounters difficulties of cross-reactions that make the starting materials impure (Nissenbaum*[215]); dilution such that "the concentration of the 'soup' was probably too small for efficient synthesis, particularly of biopolymers" (Nissenbaum*, Kenyon*, and Oro*[216]); destruction of proteins by the very temperatures necessary to form them, which "pyrolize amino acids, depolymerize polypeptides, and degrade microspheres" (Sagan*[217]), as well as by hydrolysis (Dose*[218]); formation of biologically useless polymers with "a substantial portion of peptide bonds . . . not of the α-peptide type" (Temussi* *et al*.[219]); and formation of biologically useless proteins not made of "exclusively the L-enantiomers of the amino acids" (Williams*[220]).

(c) Evolution of sugars is generally believed to have begun through the formose reaction, but no less an authority than Orgel* does "not believe that the formose reaction . . . is a plausible model for the prebiotic accumulation of sugars" (Reid* and Orgel* [221]). Difficulties include destruction of much of the formaldehyde in the ancient atmosphere or ocean (Abelson*[222]); destruction of simple sugars by cross-reactions with amino acids or by decomposition from their instability (Cairns-Smith*[223]); a concentration of sugars far too low, and a prevalence of "caramel"-like useless polymers

(Cairns-Smith*[224]); and biologically useless molecules from the equal presence of L-sugars along with D-sugars (Williams*[225]).

(d) Evolution of enzymes must have overcome the problems of necessary "specificity of catalysts" (Cairns-Smith*[226]), and necessary multiple evolutions of each enzyme (Dillon*[227]).

(e) Evolution of lipids involves such a complex chain of biochemical reactions that "[n]o satisfactory synthesis of fatty acids is presently available" (Miller* and Orgel*[228]); such "problems of discrimination," as using the *cis* configuration exclusively over the more probable *trans* configuration, that are "so difficult that there almost seems to be a conspiracy not to discuss them" (Cairns-Smith*[229]); and further difficulties of cross-reactions to form "insoluble salts with magnesium and calcium" (Abelson*[230]).

(f) Evolution of the genetic coding system requires developments so complex that researchers "speculate endlessly, unfettered by inconvenient facts" (Dickerson*[231]); involves "the major problem in understanding the origin of life [of] trying to guess what the simpler system might have been" (Crick*[232]); includes a "gigantic implausibility" of evolution of nucleic acids for nineteen listed reasons (Cairns-Smith*[233]); requires evolution of the gene-protein link that is "shrouded in almost complete mystery" (Scott*[234]); and necessitates an evolution of the translating machinery that is "difficult to imagine" because that "translating machinery consists of at least fifty macromolecular components which are themselves coded in DNA" (Monod*[235]), as well as the emergence of the enzyme editing reactions that is "a major unsolved problem" (Lambert*[236]).

(g) Evolution of life itself "is a jump of fantastic dimensions," and yet "available facts do not provide a basis for postulating that cells arose on this planet" (Green* and Goldberger*[237]), but instead "a very large gap separates the most complex model systems from the simplest contemporary living cells" (Kenyon* and Nissenbaum*[238]). One requirement for life is self-replication, and yet its origin is a "defect of evolutionary theory" because there are "almost no ideas" (Kempthorne*[239]), and its origin poses the "seemingly self-contradictory condition . . . that, while genetic mechanisms can exist only within living things, the organisms themselves could not have come into being without such a device" (Dillon*[240]). Another requirement for life is protein synthesis, and that involves "great difficulties" even if heterotrophs had an adequate supply of organic molecules to consume, such as the need "to recognise molecules, or at the very least to distinguish between classes of them," and "some kind of structure [that] would seem to be needed that could form specific sockets" that are "much more difficult to engineer than the [recognized] molecule itself" (Cairns-Smith*[241]).

(h) Biochemical evolution could not be effectuated by natural selection, because, "to have natural selection, you have to have self-reproduction," so that "[p]rebiological natural selection is a contradiction in terms" (Dobzhansky*[242]). A "preliminary kind of semi-Darwinian evolution, where microsystems are not able to reproduce but they are already subject to selection," is not possible (Cairns-Smith*[243]).

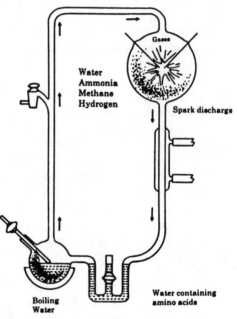

Figure 5.4
The origin of life experiments: "there will remain no scientifically valid model" (Scherer)(Miller* experiment apparatus)*

5.4 The Laboratory Experiments for Biochemical Evolution: Questions about Extrapolation to Life

Carl Sagan* has acknowledged:

> The production of organic molecules necessary for the origin of life is not at all the same as the origin of life.[244]

Too often the implication is given that scientists have "created life in the test tube," when in fact the actual experiments have been limited in scope and often extremely improbable in assumptions.

"The best that one can say about these models is that some of the processes which they postulate might conceivably have happened, but not that they did actually happen in the real history of the earth," as Dobzhansky* notes.[245] In fact, the origin of life experiments show "why prevital nucleic acids are highly implausible" rather than why critical evolutionary elements are plausible, Cairns-Smith* adds:

> But so powerful has been the *effect of Miller's experiment on the scientific imagination* that to read some of the literature on the origin of life (including many elementary texts) *you might think that it had been well demonstrated* that nucleotides were probable constituents of a primordial soup and hence that prevital nucleic acid replication was a plausible speculation based on the results of experiments. There have indeed been many interesting and detailed experiments in this area. But the importance of this work lies, to my mind, not in demonstrating how nucleotides could have formed on the primitive Earth, but in precisely the opposite: *these experiments allow us to see, in much greater detail than would otherwise have been possible,* just *why prevital nucleic acids are highly implausible.*[246]

There may "remain no scientifically valid model of the self-organization of the first living cells on Earth," Scherer* suggests.[247]

In general, the origin of life experiments have quite limited significance because of their implausible conditions, according to a number of researchers. Some improbable conditions are summarized by Shapiro*:

> Many accounts of the origin of life assume that the spontaneous synthesis of a self-replicating nucleic acid could take place readily. Serious chemical obstacles exist, however, which make such an event extremely improbable. . . . However, these procedures use *pure starting materials,* afford *poor yields,* and are run under *conditions which are not compatible with one another.* Any nucleic acid components which were formed on the primitive earth would tend to *hydrolize* by a number of pathways. Their polymerization would be *inhibited by the presence of vast numbers of related substances which would react preferentially* with them.[248]

The pure starting materials, correct sequences, and necessary conditions are wholly unrealistic, Cairns-Smith* notes, and it is "not sensible to suppose that an uninformed geochemistry would fortuitously be expert in such things":

> First of all there is a problem which is seldom discussed. The starting monomers would have been *grossly impure.* On the basis of simulation experiments they would have been present in complex mixtures that contained a great variety of variously reactive molecules.
>
> No sensible organic chemist would hope to get much out of a reaction from starting materials that were *tars containing the reactants as minor*

constituents. Perhaps because they are sensible organic chemists most experimenters, in trying to establish some prevital path to biopolymers, do not start with such complex mixtures. Instead they say something like this: 'monomer A has been shown to be formed under prebiotic conditions and so has reagent B: so we treated A and B (obtained from Maxipure Chemical Corporation) under prebiotic conditions such and such and made the biochemically significant molecule C'. Suggestions as to how A and B might have been purified under prevital conditions are seldom made.

In organic chemistry it is often the *work up rather than the reaction that causes most of the trouble*. Think about the techniques that are used: pH adjustments, solvent extractions, chromatography, evaporations to dryness, recrystallisations, filtrations and so on. Now you can say that such things might have taken place fortuitously under primitive geological conditions. Each individual operation can be imagined—a transfer of a solution, a washing of a precipitate, an evaporation, and so on. *But very many such operations would have had to take place consistently and in the right order*. In a typical work up procedure there are subtle things that can make the difference between success and mess—how long to wait, say, after the pH adjustment before filtering. Practical organic chemistry is not easy. Very much has to be engineered. *It is not sensible to suppose that an uninformed geochemistry would fortuitously be expert in such things*.[249]

The "large quantities of specialized condensing agents, ... which do not occur today either in living organisms or on the earth's surface in comparable form and quantities," also "appear unrealistic" according to Dillon*.[250]

Further, interpretations of these experiments frequently ignore illegitimate forms of investigator involvement, as Brooks* and Shaw* point out:

> These experiments ... claim abiotic synthesis for what has in fact been produced and designed by highly intelligent and very much biotic man.[251]

The following discussion describes experiments (a) synthesizing amino acids, (b) synthesizing alleged proteins, (c) synthesizing components of the genetic coding system, and (d) hypothesizing protocells.

a. Experiments Synthesizing Amino Acids

Stanley Miller* conducted an experiment in which he synthesized some amino acids by circulating a mixture of methane, ammonia, hydrogen, and other gases past an electric spark. That experiment has limited implications for biochemical evolution because of critical but unrealistic conditions such as those just listed, in the view of many evolutionists. In general, "an experiment designed to produce nucleic acids produces little else," Keosian* states,[252] and Miller's* experiment "may have little relevance concerning the origin of life on Earth," Clemmey* and Badham* add.[253] There are "fundamental . . . doubts about the significance of Miller's* experiment," Cairns-Smith* points out.[254]

First, the experiment used a special trap for "selectively removing the product [amino acids]" immediately after their formation, because the very energy sources that generated the amino acids would otherwise destroy them:

> Miller and others . . . have synthesized organic compounds with electrical discharges or ultraviolet light in the laboratory. They have merely used the well-known principle of increasing the yield of a reaction by *selectively removing the product* from the reacting mixture. But the fact that a chemist can carry out an organic synthesis in the laboratory does not prove that the same synthesis will occur in the atmosphere or open sea without the chemist.[255]

Sagan* acknowledges the critical nature of the trap in such experiments:

> The problem we're discussing is a very general one. We use energy sources to make organic molecules. It is found that the *same energy sources can destroy these organic molecules*. The organic chemist has an understandable preference for removing the reaction products from the energy source before they are destroyed. But when we talk of the origin of life I think we should not neglect the fact that degradation occurs as well as synthesis, and that the *course of reaction may be different if the products are not preferentially removed*. In reconstructing the origin of life, we have to *imagine* reasonable scenarios which somehow avoid this difficulty.[256]

The same unrealistic limitation in the Miller* experiment has been stressed by Shapiro*[257] and Harada* and Fox*.[258]

Second, the Miller* experiment only produced two simpler compounds of the "fifty small organic compounds that are called 'building blocks,'" as Shapiro* points out, and even that "was favored by the design of the experiment":

> The experiment performed by *Miller* yielded tar as its most abundant product. Of the smaller molecules that were produced, perhaps thirteen may be considered as preferential products. *There are about fifty small organic compounds that are called "building blocks,"* as they are used to construct the four larger types of molecules important to life. *Only two of these fifty occurred among the preferential Miller-Urey products.* They were glycine and alanine, the two *simplest* amino acids used in proteins,

members of a class that was *favored by the design of the experiment*. These results have been admirably documented by Miller, and are not in question. It is their interpretation that must concern us.

As we have seen, the reaction product bears no resemblance to the actual content of a bacterium, which is an intricate, organized structure built using large molecules. . . .[259]

Third, the experiment works only with "crippling provisos," which have the effect of making biochemical evolution "less plausible":

> It is really too *naive* simply to assert that the prevital simulation experiments confirm the doctrine of chemical evolution. Well, yes they do (in the weak scientific sense)—but *with crippling provisos*. The whole subject of confirmation in science is notoriously tricky, and here we have an example, I think, of a hypothesis that has become *less plausible the more it has been 'confirmed'* (cf. Gardner, 1976).
>
> . . ..
>
> But, as we have seen, the really successful tests of chemical evolution have been restricted to one aspect—chemical accessibility of a number of the smallest molecular units. These molecules can be said to be chemically accessible because they are so often present in complex mixtures formed by uncontrolled reations. *The other aspects are mainly a catalogue of difficulties that have been getting worse:* the early *environment* now looks less clement than was once thought; hopeful possibilities for resolution of *enantiomers* have not worked out; *purification, concentration, activation*, when any kind of solution has been proposed, all call for rather special situations, and they are anyway inefficient. And the significance of those seemingly easy routes to biochemicals from cyanide and formaldehyde becomes less clear when examined in more detail. As we saw, neither cyanide nor formaldehyde would easily have built up to sufficient concentrations. *Yields in these uncontrollable syntheses are very low*, in general, and the products always very complex. *Many of these products—especially sugars—would not have survived long enough* to have accumulated in a 'primordial soup'.[260]

Finally, the experiments frequently use short wavelength ultraviolet light but exclude the long wavelength ultraviolet light that presumably would have been even more abundant,[261] simply because the long wavelength is very effective in destroying any amino acids formed.[262]

Miller* and Orgel* themselves acknowledge, "[m]any interesting scraps of information are available, but no correct pathways have yet been discovered."[263]

b. Experiments Synthesizing Proteins

A major experiment by Sidney Fox* synthesized "proteinoids" (claimed to resemble shorter proteins). However, such experiments have not produced biologically meaningful proteins[264] for at least four reasons.

First, those proteinoids "have scarce resemblance to natural peptidic material" because they generally have nonbiological forms of peptide bonds, as Temussi* *et al.* observe:

> *Summary.* Thermal polycondensation of amino acids as a possible prebiotic path of chemical evolution of life has been critically examined.
>
> The polymeric materials studied by nmr methods have *scarce resemblance to natural peptidic material* because β, γ and ϵ peptide bonds largely predominate over α-peptide bonds.
>
> . . ..
>
> It is apparent that the presence of α-peptide units is the exception rather than the rule.
>
> . . ..
>
> The general pattern emerging from our investigation is that trifunctional aminoacids, when subjected to thermal condensation, tend to form β, γ, or ϵ peptide units more easily than α-peptide units. This finding, if added to the low probability of the proper geological conditions (Miller et al., 1959), shows that *the relevance of thermal condensation in the synthesis of prebiotic polypeptides ought to be critically reexamined.*[265]

In particular, those authors find thermal synthesis to be "of scarce relevance to the prebiotic synthesis of natural amino acids."[266]

Second, those proteinoids appear to be largely random sequences of amino acids very different from biological proteins, as researchers Miller* and Orgel* have noted:

> The degree of nonrandomness in thermal polypeptides so far demonstrated is *minute* compared to nonrandomness of proteins. It is *deceptive*, then, to suggest that thermal polypeptides are similar to proteins in their nonrandomness.[267]

The same contrast is made by Ambrose*[268] and Dillon*.[269]

Third, Fox's* proteinoids and other experimental products include generally equal numbers of L- and D-amino acids, whereas biologically meaningful proteins in all organisms must contain exclusively L-amino acids, as Stansfield* points out:

> All proteins today consist entirely of amino acids that rotate plane-polarized light to the left (L forms). However, none of the prebiotic compounds synthesized in the laboratory under primitive earth conditions have been reported to have optical activity because of racemization (a mixture of D and L forms).[270]

Williams* and Smith*[271] and Folsome*[272] reach similar conclusions.

Fourth, the geological conditions in the Fox* experiments are very unlikely, as Miller* and Urey*[273] and Kenyon* and Nissenbaum*[274] state. Fox's* microspheres are discussed below.

c. Experiments Involving the Genetic Coding System

The genetic coding system of DNA and RNA requires specific sequences of nucleotides (the building units). Probability studies effectively rule out the possibility of workable sequences evolving, as discussed below.[275] The sugars that form part of the nucleotides must be D-sugars, whereas experiments produce equal quantities of L- and D-sugars.[276] As discussed in Section 5.3(g), massive difficulties attend each of the necessary evolutionary steps to produce the genetic coding system: the bases and sugars, the nucleosides, the nucleotide chains, the gene-protein link, the translation machinery, and particularly the replication feature that distinguishes nonlife from life and puts the system to use.

d. Experiments Proposing Protocell Models

The protocell is the form prior to the first living cell that biochemical evolutionists postulate. Difficulties are summarized, and then the two prevailing models (coacervate and proteinoid microsphere) are discussed.

(1) Problems with Protocell Evolution. First, these models are separated by "a very large gap" from the least complex living cell, and have questionable plausibility, according to Kenyon* and Nissenbaum*:

> Although each of the proposed model systems exhibits some rudimentary properties of chemical evolutionary interest, it must be emphasized that a *very large gap* separates the most complex model systems from the simplest contemporary living cells. Moreover, the geochemical *plausibility* of many of these "protocell" models is open to *serious question* (Nissenbaum et al. 1976).[277]

Second, these model protocells are not able to replicate themselves or to produce vital enzymes and other proteins, so that their resemblance to life is only "superficial" and "specious," in Dillon's* estimation:

> Similar difficulties with the coacervates and other particles are also evident (Oparin, 1974). Although the various colloidal droplets are not considered to be alive, the nature of the experiments conducted on them intimates that they are models of how living things came into being. Realistically, though, they can be considered to be *similar to actual*

primitive life only from the most superficial point of view. It is true that they can be induced to carry out enzymatic metabolic processes, but only in a mechanical fashion, for none of the products of the resulting energy is of any value, directly or indirectly, to the colloidal particle. As in the case of catalase, *a genetic mechanism of some sort is required*, both for the acquisition of metabolic processes essential to primitive life and to create the enzymes needed to carry them out. In other words, before photosynthesis, the enzymatic breakdown of a sugar, the synthesis of peptides such as polyphenylalanine (Fox *et al.*, 1974), or any other type of cellular process could have become meaningful in a protobiotic system, *metabolic pathways for the utilization of the products of the particular processes must first have been established on a genetical basis.* Hence, not only sulfobes, but the other models described in this chapter as well, are *specious* in that they bear apparent behavioral similarities to living things but *lack the real requisites of even the simplest protobionts.* This is not to imply that suitable models may not be forthcoming in the future; merely that none has been synthesized to date.[278]

Even if protocells had rudimentary mechanisms for replication and protein production,[279] they would lack the "editing reactions" that are "necessary for the stability of the system and its subsequent evolution rather than breakdown," as Lambert* notes:

> Assertion 2: A Protobiont Could Not Survive Because
> It Lacks Editing Reactions
>
> Given that there would be at least considerable difficulties in maintaining present-day biological information transfer processes in the absence of editing, the question arises as to the feasibility of information transfer in a protobiont which would at least initially lack such reactions. . . .
>
> . . ..
>
> . . .In summary, it is not clear how a protobiont lacking editing reactions and with additional problems of biological inaccuracy resulting from poorly controlled metabolism can attain a "threshold accuracy" necessary for the stability of the system and its subsequent evolution rather than breakdown of all information transfer.[280]

Third, these model protocells are about as uncell-like as soap bubbles, and are very unstable because they lack the internal structure of cells, Day* points out:

> The pseudo-cellular models like clay, soap bubbles, or any other inanimate objects have *neither the mechanism nor the potential of becoming anything beyond what they are.* . . . But the most serious fault of models from particles held together by ionic forces is that they would have been *continually periled with dissolution.* Coacervates are notoriously *unstable* and microspheres exist only in saturated solutions. Their existence in Archean lakes or oceans would have been short-lived.[281]

Conclusions based on outward appearance are "fraught with danger," Ponnamperuma* adds:

> There is an extensive literature dealing with the accumulation of various solutions of organic matter and the resulting cell-like structures. However, the *leap* from morphology to function is *fraught with danger*, especially when we consider entities of several billion years ago.[282]

Fourth, these protocell models involve "unnatural conditions and often complex organic substances required for their formation," so that "doubts inexorably arise concerning the suitability of these colloids for a role as protobiont ancestors," in Dillon's* view.[283] For example, each model requires an impossibly high concentration of its components, which Folsome* calls the "concentration gap":

> Hypothetically, there are ways to circumvent the concentration gap, but all appear to be more *wishful thinking* than plausible facets of reality.[284]

(2) Models of Protocell Evolution. The two prevailing models are the coacervate and the proteinoid microsphere models, although alternatives have been proposed by Woese*, Cairns-Smith* and Bernal*, and others. The prevailing models "no longer can be considered meaningful in the context of the origins of life on earth," Dillon* concludes:

> Thus, although the coacervates, micelles, and proteinoid microspheres have provided much information about the behavior of colloidal droplets and were worthy of exploration during the early period of the search for possible forebears of living things, they *no longer can be considered meaningful* in the context of the origins of life on earth. Neither they nor any other artificial systems are adequate to provide concrete evidence to show clearly how life and the requisite genetic apparatus actually did arise. . . .[285]

First, the coacervate model was proposed by Oparin*, based on the outward resemblance of coacervates (protein macromolecules in the form of tiny droplets) to actual cells. However, coacervates are totally unlike actual cells because they "are quite unstable,"[286] lack structure, lack a metabolic system, and require complex polymers for their formation.[287] Thus, they "lack[] any demonstrable direct connection to . . . evolving organisms," Fox* concludes:

> His later treatments were necessarily conditioned by his knowledge of coacervate droplets. The coacervate droplets *lacked any demonstrable direct connection to either prebiotic matter or to evolving organisms.* Such a connection was not possible in that the coacervate droplets are *produced from biopolymers* that are in turn obtained from organisms that emerged *after* the first organisms arose. . . . Although Oparin visualized natural selection as a prebiotic process to improve stability of the

emerging cell, he did not find any prebiotic selective advantage in various coacervate droplets. . . .[288]

Second, the proteinoid microsphere model has been proposed by Fox* as an extension of his work with proteinoid synthesis. However, the microspheres' membranes "are not 'single biological-like' membranes since they do not contain lipids or carry out any of the functions of biological membranes," according to Miller* and Orgel*.[289] Also, the microspheres lack metabolic processes or replication processes, as Oparin* points out:

> Fox's microspheres, since they are obtained thermally, do *not represent very promising results* from this view (i.e., evolving to include *metabolic processes*). Their structure is *static*. This . . . creates difficulties when it comes to converting them into dynamic systems which could be used for modeling the evolution of metabolism.[290]

They involve merely the "formation of unnatural peptide bonds," Temussi* adds.[291] These proteinoid microspheres also require unlikely geological conditions, according to Miller*, Urey*, and Orgel*.[292]

Third, an atmospheric particle model has been proposed by Woese*, which involves prebiotic evolution in particles suspended in a specially organized atmosphere. That proposal "seems not to be a reasonable alternative," as assessed by Scherer*:

> It is concluded that the physical and chemical framework of the new hypothesis *conflicts with the conditions necessary for the evolution of the progenitors of life* in the atmosphere of the early Earth. Therefore this model seems not to be a reasonable alternative to the Oparin thesis.
>
> . . ..
> . . .The arguments presented . . . show that within the physical and chemical framework of *Woese's* new hypothesis, the evolution of living systems would have been *improbable*; therefore this model does not seem to be a reasonable alternative to the Oparin thesis. . . .[293]

Fourth, "genetic takeover" is a model proposed by Cairns-Smith*, which postulates that life arose from inorganic crystals that could replicate and catalyze reactions, and followed the biochemical economy of the least complex pathways for a particular reaction.[294] That proposal is "highly speculative," according to Dobzhansky*, Ayala*, Stebbins*, and Valentine*:

> Cairns-Smith's scenario is *highly speculative*. We do not know that life followed such a protoadaptive pathway from prebiotic materials to living cells. We have presented this particular speculation because it illustrates one way in which the origin of selection in a genetic system can be accounted for. Other scenarios may be proposed, but *all are similarly speculative* at this time.[295]

In assessing Cairns-Smith's* views, Scott* concludes that "[t]he fact that they are taken seriously indicates how insecure the traditional tale of life's origin really is."[296]

Summary. Although "so powerful has been the effect of Miller's* experiment on the scientific imagination that to read some of the literature on the origin of life (including many elementary texts) you might think that it had been well demonstrated...," actually "these experiments allow us to see ... just why prevital nucleic acids are highly implausible" (Cairns-Smith*[297]), and indeed that biochemical evolution is highly implausible. Their significance is vastly reduced because they "use pure starting materials, afford poor yields, ... are run under conditions which are not compatible with one another," ignore that nucleic acid components "would tend to hydrolyze," and "would be inhibited by ... related substances which would react preferentially with them" (Shapiro*[298]). The following quotations should be evaluated in their full context cited earlier in this section.

(a) The experiments synthesizing amino acids "may have little relevance concerning the origin of life on Earth" (Clemmey* and Badham*[299]), and reflect the principle that "an experiment designed to produce nucleic acids produces little else" (Keosian*[300]). The experiments depend on a trap that "we have to imagine" in a primordial soup, because "the course of reaction may be different if the products are not preferentially removed" (Sagan*[301]); and also depend on other "crippling provisos" that "are mainly a catalogue of difficulties that have been getting worse" (Cairns-Smith*[302]). Even then, the Miller* experiment forms "[o]nly two of these fifty" building blocks of necessary molecules (Shapiro*[303]).

(b) The experiments synthesizing proteins have only "scarce relevance to the prebiotic synthesis of natural amino acids" (Temussi* *et al.*[304]). The experiments actually only synthesize proteinoids that "have scarce resemblance to natural peptidic material" because of nonbiological peptide bonds (Temussi* *et al.*[305]), and that have such randomness of composition that "[i]t is deceptive ... to suggest that thermal polypeptides are similar to proteins" (Miller* and Orgel*[306]). The experimental products also have "a mixture of D and L forms" of amino acids, although purity of the L form is essential to life (Stansfield*[307]).

(c) Experiments involving the genetic coding system do not resolve the massive difficulties of evolving bases and sugars, nucleosides, nucleotides, nucleotide chains, gene-protein linkage, translation machinery, and a replication system, as discussed earlier.

(d) Experiments proposing protocell models still leave "a very large gap" from life (Kenyon* and Nissenbaum*[308]), and "are specious in that they bear apparent behavioral similarities to living things but lack the real requisites of even the simplest protobionts" (Dillon*[309]). The "protocells" are about as lifelike as "soap bubbles" and are "notoriously unstable" (Day*[310]), and they invoke such "unnatural conditions and often complex organic substances required for their formation" that "doubts inexorably arise concerning the suitability of these colloids for a role as protobiont ancestors" (Dillon*[311]). The coacervate and proteinoid microsphere models "no longer can be considered meaningful in the context of the origins of life on earth," and "[n]either they nor any other artificial systems are adequate to provide concrete evidence to show clearly how life and the requisite genetic apparatus actually did arise" (Dillon*[312]).

(e) The vast improbability of biochemical evolution has been calculated by many researchers, at levels such as 1 chance in $10^{2,000,000}$ (Ambrose*[313]), and 1 chance in 10^{94} (Yockey*[314]). Thus, some conclude "that belief in currently accepted scenarios of spontaneous biogenesis is based on faith" (Yockey*[315]).

* * *

The postulations of biochemical evolution must be compared with the probabilities and information content of the least complex life. The most that biochemical evolution could have accomplished in a billion years is formation of a single short protein according to Yockey*,[316] and a single pair of genes under the analysis of of Eden*.[317] The probability of the least complex single-celled organism evolving is only 1 chance in $10^{2,000,000}$ according to Ambrose*,[318] merely 1 chance in 10^{450} according to Golay*,[319] "not a believable possibility" in terms of spontaneous assembly in the view of Keosian*,[320] and of "very small" probability within the "life of a sun" of billions of years in the words of Noda*.[321] The probability of evolving a simple protein is merely 1 chance in 10^{130} according to Lovell*[322]; of a cytochrome c protein is only 1 chance in 10^{94} under the calculations of Yockey*[323]; of a DNA chain for producing a simple protein is merely 1 chance in 10^{600} according to Salisbury*,[324] and Leslie*[325]; and of human enzymes is only 1 chance in $10^{40,000}$

under the figures of Hoyle and Wickramasinghe.[326] Even Sagan*
agrees that it would take the discovery of life in space " 'to transform
the origin of life from a miracle to a statistic.' "[327] Each of these
probabilities is far less than the level of statistical impossibility in
the universe, and is far less than the ratio of one atom to all atoms in
the universe (1 to 10^{80}).[328] A good summary is given by Hoyle:

> [T]he combinatorial arrangement of *not even one among the many thou-
> sands of biopolymers* on which life depends could have been arrived at by
> natural processes here on the Earth. Astronomers will have a little
> difficulty at understanding this because they will be assured by biolo-
> gists that it is not so, the biologists having been assured in their turn by
> others that it is not so. The "others" are a group of persons who believe,
> quite openly, in *mathematical miracles*.[329]

The specific assumptions underlying these low probabilities, and
the counterarguments made against them, are summarized in Section 4.2.

Biochemical evolution as currently proposed, therefore, is "based
on faith," as Yockey* concludes:

> The Darwin-Oparin-Haldane "warm little pond" scenario for biogenesis
> is examined by *using information theory* to calculate the probability that
> an informational *biomolecule* of reasonable biochemical specificity, long
> enough to provide a genome for the "protobiont", could have appeared in
> 10^9 years in the primitive soup. . . . It is concluded that belief in currently
> accepted scenarios of spontaneous biogenesis is *based on faith*, contrary
> to conventional wisdom.[330]

That "faith" is not warranted by the scientific evidence, but instead
results from a general bias against any theory of creation or of
abrupt appearance, as Wald* acknowledges:

> The reasonable view was to believe in spontaneous generation; the only
> alternative, to believe in a single, primary act of supernatural creation.
> There is no third position. For this reason many scientists a century ago
> chose to regard the belief in spontaneous generation as a "philosophical
> necessity." It is a symptom of the philosophical poverty of our time that
> this necessity is no longer appreciated. Most modern biologists, having
> reviewed with satisfaction the downfall of the spontaneous generation
> hypothesis, yet unwilling to accept the alternative belief in special crea-
> tion, are left with nothing.
>
> I think a scientist has no choice but to approach the origin of life
> through a hypothesis of spontaneous generation.[331]

The communicants of that biochemical faith deserve little credibility when they condemn alternative views as "based on faith," particularly when those alternatives really are based on scientific evidence such as that summarized in Chapter 4.

Thus, there is the myth of the primordial atmosphere, that there is "no evidence for... but much against" an oxygen-free and methane-ammonia-rich atmosphere (Abelson*[332]); the "myth of the prebiotic soup" (Shapiro* and Sillen*[333]); the myth of the stages of biochemical evolution, where "[s]peculation is bound to be rife" and proposals "have shared much with imaginative literature and little with theoretical inference of the kind which can be confronted with observational evidence"[334]; and the myth of the experiments generating life, because the implausibilities of the origin of life experiments may be so great that "there will remain no scientifically valid model of the self-organization of the first living cells on Earth" (Scherer*[335]). Thorpe*, a zoology professor at Cambridge, surveys the Olympus of biochemical evolution as follows:

> I think it is fair to say that all the facile speculations and discussions published during the last 10-15 years explaining the mode of origin of life have been shown to be far *too simple-minded* and to bear *very little weight*. The problem in fact seems as far from solution as it ever was....
>
> The origin of even the simplest cell poses a problem hardly less difficult. The most elementary type of cell constitutes a 'mechanism' *unimaginably more complex* than any machine yet thought up, let alone constructed, by man.... There is *no real clue* as to the way in which any of these riddles were solved, so it is open to anyone to espouse any theory which he finds helpful....[336]

Notes

[1]   Christian Science Monitor, Jan. 4, 1962, at 4 (italics added).

[2]   T. Dobzhansky*, F. Ayala*, G. Stebbins* & J. Valentine*, *Evolution* 9 (1977) (italics added).

[3]   Simpson*, *The World into which Darwin Led Us*, 131 Science 966, 969 (1960).

[4]   Gould*, *Justice Scalia's Misunderstanding*, Natural History, Oct. 1987, at 14, 18.

[5]   Mayr* writes:

Cosmic evolution and *biological evolution* have that much in common.
. . ..

[See *"Chemical Evolution and the Origin of Life"* by Richard E. Dickerson*, p. 70].

Mayr*, *Evolution*, Scientific Am., Sept. 1978, at 47, 47, 51 (italics added). *See also* C. Ponnamperuma*, *The Origins of Life* 39 (1972) ("We think of the process of [Darwinian evolution] as having taken place in stages, from inorganic evolution to organic evolution and then to biological evolution").

[6]   S. Fox* & K. Dose*, *Molecular Evolution and the Origin of Life* 67 (1972).

[7]   Huxley* writes as follows:
[I]t is evolution, in the broad sense, that links *inorganic* nature with life, and the stars with earth, and matter with mind, and animals with man. Huxley*, *At Random*, in 3 Evolution after Darwin 41, 42 (S. Tax* ed. 1960) (italics added).

[8]   E. Olson* & J. Robinson*, *Concepts of Evolution* 10 (1975) ("*Evolutionism* is the doctrine that the universe, including *inorganic* and organic matter in all its manifestations, is the product of gradual and progressive development.") (italics added).

[9]   Wilson*, *The Origin of Life*, in Did the Devil Make Darwin Do It? 85, 86 (D. Wilson* ed. 1983) ("*Evolution*, which is the strongest natural explanation, holds that the gross features of the universe—including galaxies, solar systems and planets; the transition from *non-living matter* to living *organisms*; and the diversity of life forms, including human beings—all arose as a consequence of the innate proclivities of matter and energy, as expressed by the laws of nature.") (italics added); G. Stebbins*, *Darwin to DNA, Molecules to Humanity* 174 (1982) ("Since it left no fossil record, this *prebiotic phase of evolution* cannot be determined by the same methods that scientists use to determine evolutionary sequences of organisms.") (italics added).

[10]   *E.g.*, C. Ponnamperuma*, *The Origins of Life* 9 (1972) ("Chemical evolution connotes all that occurred before the emergence of life."); *The Origin of Life and Evolutionary Biochemistry* (K. Dose*, S. Fox*, G. Deborin* & T. Pavlovskaya* eds. 1974); M. Calvin*, *Chemical Evolution* (1969); *Chemical Evolution and the Origin of Life* (R. Buvet* & C. Ponnamperuma* eds. 1971); *Prebiotic and Biochemical Evolution* (A. Kimball* & J. Oro* eds. 1971); T. Jukes*, *Molecules and Evolution* (1966); *Biochemical Evolution and the Origin of Life* (E. Schoffeniels* ed. 1971); Cowie*, *Life in Pre-Cambrian and Early Cambrian Times*, in The Fossil Record 17, 30 (W. Harland* *et al.* eds. 1967); DeFord*, *Humanism and Atheism I*, Humanist, July-Aug. 1971, at 5; G. Stebbins* & W. Fitch*, *Processes of Molecular and Organismic Evolution* (1987) (Chapter 8 on "The Major Events of Evolution: The origin of life . . ."); H. Blum*, *Time's Arrow and Evolution* 157 *passim* (3d ed. 1968); Committee on Science and Creationism*, *Science and Creation: A View from the National Academy of Sciences* 25, 26 (1984); P. Ehrlich*, R. Holm* & D. Parnell*, *The Process of Evolution* 3 (2d ed. 1974); Dickerson*, *Chemical Evolution and the Origin of Life*, in Evolution at 30 (E. Mayr* ed. 1978); Barghoorn*, *The Oldest Fossils*, Scientific Am., May 1971, at 30, 41, 42; 1 *Evolution after Darwin—The Evolution of Life: Its Origin, History and Future* (S. Tax* & C. Callendar* eds. 1960); *Cosmochemical Evolution and the Origins of Life* (J. Oro* & S. Miller* eds. 1974) (Fourth International Conference on the Origin of Life); Dickerson*, *Chemical Evolution and the Origin of Life*, Scientific Am., Sept. 1978, at 70; D.

Rohlfing* & A. Oparin*, *Molecular Evolution: Pre-biological and Biological* (1972); Eigen*, *Self-Replication and Molecular Evolution*, in Evolution from Molecules to Man 105-30 (D. Bendall* ed. 1973) (section entitled "Molecular and Cellular Evolution"); M. Kimura*, *Molecular Evolution, Protein Polymorphism, and Neutral Theory* (1982); B. Kueppers*, *Molecular Theory of Evolution: Outline of a Physico-Chemical Theory of the Origin of Life* (1983); E. Terzaghi* & A. Wilkins*, *Molecular Evolution* (1983).

[11] Biological Sciences Curriculum Study*, *Biological Science: An Inquiry into Life* 837 (1973) (italics added).

[12] *E.g.*, Biological Sciences Curriculum Study*, *Biological Science: Molecules to Man* 110 (3d ed. 1973 & 1976) ("Recent discoveries in science have helped biologists to see how Darwin's ideas about evolution might also apply to single-celled organisms. Just as today's complex organisms are probably modified descendants of earlier, simpler forms, so simple one-celled organisms have probably evolved from even simpler systems."); Biological Sciences Curriculum Study*, *Biological Science: An Inquiry into Life* 100, 196, 703-08, 786, 836-37 (3d ed. 1973 & 1976); Biological Sciences Curriculum Study*, *Biological Science: Molecules to Man* 106, 113, 116-21, 123-24, 134-42, 162-64, 168, 180, 182-83, 205, 213 (3d ed. 1976); Biological Sciences Curriculum Study*, *Biological Science: An Ecological Approach* 277, 315-16, 396 (3d ed. 1973 & 1976); J. Otto*, A. Towle* & A. Madnick*, *Modern Biology* 149-50, 182 (1977); C. Heimler*, *Focus on Life Sciences* 69 (1977); R. Oram*, *Biology: Living Systems* 283-85 (3d ed. Teacher's Ed. 1979).

[13] *E.g.*, T. Dobzhansky*, F. Ayala*, G. Stebbins* & J. Valentine*, *Evolution* 349-64 (1977); S. Luria*, S. Gould* & S. Singer*, *A View of Life* 686-90 (1981); G. Stebbins*, *Darwin to DNA, Molecules to Humanity* 174-84 (1982).

[14] G. Kerkut*, *Implications of Evolution* 150 (1960) (italics added). *See also* Yockey*, *Self Organization Origin of Life Scenarios and Information Theory*, 91 J. Theoretical Biology 13, 13 (1981) ("It is concluded that at present there are no scientifically valid origin of life scenarios.").

[15] F. Crick*, *Life Itself* 153 (1981).

[16] Yockey* notes the bias reflected by the biochemical evolutionist's search. Yockey*, *A Calculation of the Probability of Spontaneous Biogenesis by Information Theory*, 67 J. Theoretical Biology 377, 379 (1977).

[17] T. Dobzhansky*, F. Ayala*, G. Stebbins* & J. Valentine*, *Evolution* 360 (1977).

[18] R. Jastrow*, *Until the Sun Dies* 60 (1977).

[19] Scherer*, *Could Life Have Arisen in the Primitive Atmosphere?*, 22 J. Molecular Evolution 91, 94 (1985).

[20] Fox*, *Creationism and Evolutionary Protobiogenesis*, in Science and Creationism 208 (A. Montagu* ed. 1984).

[21] C. Thaxton, W. Bradley & R. Olsen, *The Mystery of Life's Origin* 1-187 (1984).

[22] Dickerson*, *Chemical Evolution and the Origin of Life*, in Evolution at

30, 30-31 (E. Mayr* ed. 1978) (italics added). He gives the dual reasons as follows:

Without oxygen in the atmosphere there would have been no high-altitude ozone to block most of the ultraviolet radiation from the sun as there is today. The unblocked ultraviolet radiation reaching the surface of the planet could have then provided the energy for the synthesis of a great many organic compounds from molecules such as water, carbon dioxide and ammonia. Without free oxygen in the atmosphere to destroy them again such compounds would have accumulated in the oceans until, in Haldane's words, "the primitive oceans reached the consistency of hot dilute soup."

[23] S. Fox* & K. Dose*, *Molecular Evolution and the Origin of Life* 44 (1972) ("chemical evolution . . . would be largely inhibited by oxygen").

[24] Miller*, *Production of Some Organic Compounds under Possible Primitive Earth Conditions*, 77 J. Am. Chemical Society 2351, 2361 (1955) ("the organic compounds that make up living systems cannot be synthesized in an oxidizing atmosphere").

[25] Brinkmann*, *Dissociation of Water Vapor and Evolution of Oxygen in the Terrestrial Atmosphere*, 74 J. Geophysical Research 5355, 5366 (1969) ("It does not seem that early [biochemical] evolution could have proceeded in such an atmosphere.").

[26] S. Miller* & L. Orgel*, *The Origins of Life on the Earth* 33 (1974).

[27] Henderson-Sellers*, Benlow* & Meadows*, *The Early Atmospheres of the Terrestrial Planets*, 21 Quarterly J. Royal Astronomical Society 74, 81 (1980) (italics added).

[28] *Smaller planets began with oxidized atmospheres*, 94 New Scientist 112 (1980) ("The time has come, it seems, to accept as the new orthodoxy the idea of early oxidized atmospheres on all three terrestrial planets, and the biological primers which still tell of life on Earth starting out from a methane/ammonia atmosphere energised by electric storms and solar ultraviolet need to be rewritten."); *see* J. Keosian*, *The Origin of Life* 27 (2d ed. 1968) ("There is no general agreement on what constitutes 'primitive earth conditions,' and the diversity of reaction mixtures and energy sources listed in Table 4-2 reflects the dissension.").

[29] R. Shapiro*, *Origins: A Skeptic's Guide to the Creation of Life on Earth* 112 (1986) (italics added).

[30] Clemmey* & Badham*, *Oxygen in the Precambrian Atmosphere: An Evaluation of the Geological Evidence*, 10 Geology 141, 141-42 (1982) (italics added).

[31] Abelson*, *Chemical Events on the Primitive Earth*, 55 Proc. National Academy of Sciences 1365, 1365 (1966) (italics added).

[32] *Id. See also* Dimroth* & Kimberley*, *Precambrian Atmospheric Oxygen: Evidence in the Sedimentary Distributions of Carbon, Sulfur, Uranium, and Iron*, 13 Canadian J. Earth Sciences 1161 (1976) (italics added). ("In general, we find no evidence in the sedimentary distribution of carbon,

sulfur, uranium, or iron that an oxygen-free atmosphere has existed at any time during the span of geological history recorded in well-preserved sedimentary rock.").

[33] *Id.* (italics added).

[34] Clemmey* & Badham*, *Oxygen in the Precambrian Atmosphere: An Evaluation of the Geological Evidence*, 10 Geology 141, 141-42 (1982).

[35] F. Pettijohn*, *Sedimentary Rocks* 596 (3d ed. 1976).

[36] Pettijohn* concludes that the high ferrous-ferric iron ratio in some Precambrian rocks may result from metamorphic reductions rather than an oxygen-free atmosphere, and sulphide and sideritic sediments can be deposited in an oxygen-rich atmosphere. *Id.*

[37] Walker* argues that detrital uraninite and pyrite do not require an oxygen-free atmosphere. J. Walker*, *Evolution of the Atmosphere* 262 (1977).

[38] Davidson*, *The Precambrian Atmosphere*, 197 Nature 893 (1963).

[39] Zeschke*, *Transportation of Uraninite in the Indus River*, 63 Transactions Geological Soc. S. Africa 87 (1960).

[40] Grandstaff*, *A Kinetic Study of the Dissolution of Uraninite*, 71 Economic Geology 1493 (1976).

[41] Kerr*, *Origin of Life: New Ingredients Suggested*, 210 Science 42, 42 (1980).

[42] *E.g.*, Cowen*, *Searching for Life's Origins*, Technology Rev., Apr. 1981, at 8, 8; S. Fox* & K. Dose*, *Molecular Evolution and the Origin of Life* 43 (1972).

[43] Clemmey* & Badham*, *Oxygen in the Precambrian Atmosphere: An Evaluation of the Geological Evidence*, 10 Geology 141, 141 (1982) (italics added). The authors give further specifics:

> We have tried to show here that the geologic data do not seem to support the notion of an anoxic atmosphere 3.7 to 1.9 b.y. ago, and we suggest that it provides ample evidence to the contrary: (1) Ferric iron minerals have been an abundant component of sedimentary rocks since 3.8 b.y. ago; (2) red beds are present in the geologic record from the Archean onward; (3) surface and submarine oxidized weathering crusts are found in the Archean onward; and (4) sulphate seems to have been present in the sea and fresh water from the Archean. It seems also that the lower Proterozoic pyritic and uraniferous conglomerates may not be used as evidence for either a reducing or an anoxic atmosphere.

Id. at 145.

[44] Dimroth* & Kimberley*, *Precambrian Atmospheric Oxygen: Evidence in the Sedimentary Distributions of Carbon, Sulfur, Uranium, and Iron*, 13 Canadian J. Earth Sciences 1161, 1161 (1976).

[45] Davidson*, *Geochemical Aspects of Atmospheric Evolution*, 53 Proc. National Academy Sciences 1194, 1203 (1965) (hematite).

[46] J. Walker*, *Pure Applied Geophysics* 116, 230 (1978) (banded iron formations dated at 3.8 billion years).

[47] Brinkmann*, *Dissociation of Water Vapor and Evolution of Oxygen in the Terrestrial Atmosphere*, 74 J. Geophysics Research 5355 (1969). Although Brinkmann's* assumptions were questioned, the recalculation by Carver* shows his conclusion about a significant oxygen level to be correct.

[48] Carver*, *Prebiotic atmospheric oxygen levels*, 292 Nature 136 (1981).

[49] Davidson*, *Geochemical Aspects of Atmospheric Evolution*, 53 Proc. National Academy Sciences 1194 (1965).

[50] Dimroth* & Kimberley*, *Precambrian Atmospheric Oxygen: Evidence in the Sedimentary Distribution of Carbon, Sulfur, Uranium, and Iron*, 13 Canadian J. Earth Sciences 1161 (1976).

[51] R. Shapiro*, *Origins: A Skeptic's Guide to the Creation of Life on Earth* 111-12 (1986).

[52] J. Levine*, *The Early Atmosphere: A New Picture*, Science Activities, Feb.-Mar. 1986, at 7, 10-11 (italics added).

[53] Abelson*, *Chemical Events on the Primitive Earth*, 55 Proc. National Academy Sciences 1365, 1365 (1966).

[54] Ferris* & Nicodem*, *Ammonia photolysis and the role of ammonia in chemical evolution*, 238 Nature 268 (1972); Ferris* & Nicodem*, *Ammonia: Did It Have a Role in Chemical Evolution?*, in The Origin of Life and Evolutionary Biochemistry 107 (K. Dose* et al. eds. 1974).

[55] Kuhn* & Atreya*, *Ammonia Photolysis and the Greenhouse Effect in the Primordial Atmosphere of the Earth*, 37 Icarus 207 (1979).

[56] Levine*, *The Photochemistry of the Paleoatmosphere*, 18 J. Molecular Evolution 161 (1982).

[57] Abelson*, *Chemical Events on the Primitive Earth*, 55 Proc. National Academy Sciences 1365 (1966).

[58] Cloud*, *Atmospheric and Hydrospheric Evolution on the Primitive Earth*, 160 Science 729 (1968).

[59] Lasaga*, Holland* & Dwyer*, *Primordial Oil Slick*, 174 Science 53 (1971).

[60] Pinto*, Gladstone* & Yung*, *Photochemical Production of Formaldehyde in Earth's Primitive Atmosphere*, 210 Science 183 (1980).

[61] C. Ellis* & A. Wells*, *The Chemical Action of Ultraviolet Rays* 417 (1941).

[62] Abelson*, *Chemical Events on the Primitive Earth*, 55 Proc. National Academy Sciences 1365 (1966).

[63] Hulett*, *Limitations on Prebiological Synthesis*, 24 J. of Theoretical Biology 56 (1969); Hulett*, *Energy Sources and the Probability that Life Could Have Originated*, in Proc. of 4th Conference on Origins of Life: Chemistry and Radioastronomy 80 (L. Margulis* ed. 1973).

[64] Ferris* & Nicodem*, *Ammonia photolysis and the role of ammonia in chemical evolution*, 238 Nature 268 (1972); Ferris* & Nicodem*, *Ammonia: Did It Have a Role in Chemical Evolution?*, in The Origin of Life and Evolutionary Biochemistry 107 (K. Dose* et al. eds. 1974).

[65] Miller*, Urey* & Oro*, *Origin of Organic Compounds on the Primitive Earth and in Meteorites*, 9 J. Molecular Evolution 59 (1976).

[66] Hulett*, *Formaldehyde and Ammonia as Precursors to Prebiotic Amino Acids*, 174 Science 1038 (1971); Hulett*, *Limitations on Prebiological Synthesis*, 24 J. Theoretical Biology 56 (1969).

[67] Note 31.

[68] Note 27.

[69] Note 26.

[70] Note 30.

[71] Note 31.

[72] Note 43.

[73] Note 35.

[74] Note 44.

[75] Note 48.

[76] Note 52.

[77] Note 13.

[78] R. Shapiro*, *Origins: A Skeptic's Guide to the Creation of Life on Earth* 112-13 (1986) (italics added).

[79] Shapiro*, *Damage to DNA Caused by Hydrolysis*, in Chromosome Damage and Repair 3, 17 (E. Seeberg* & K. Kleppe* eds. 1981).

[80] Abelson*, *Chemical Events on the Primitive Earth*, 55 Proc. National Academy Sciences 1365, 1369 (1966) (italics added).

[81] Hull*, *Thermodynamics and kinetics of spontaneous generation*, 186 Nature 693, 694 (1960) (italics added).

[82] 2 *The Life and Letters of Charles Darwin* 202 (F. Darwin* ed. 1887).

[83] J. Brooks* & G. Shaw*, *Origins and Development of Living Systems* 360 (1973) (italics added).

[84] Dose*, *Peptides and Amino Acids in the Primordial Hydrosphere*, in The Origin of Life and Evolutionary Biochemistry 69, 75 (K. Dose* *et al.* eds. 1974).

[85] Nissenbaum*, Kenyon* & Oro*, *On the Possible Role of Organic Melanoidin Polymers as Matrices for Prebiotic Activity*, 6 J. Molecular Evolution 253, 253 (1975) (italics added). Oro* believes that the synthesis rate exceeded the destruction rate so that an organic soup could persist for hundreds of millions of years.

[86] Abelson*, *Chemical Events on the Primitive Earth*, 55 Proc. National Academy Sciences 1365, 1369 (1966) (italics added).

[87] Shapiro*, *Damage to DNA Caused by Hydrolysis*, in Chromosome Damage and Repair 3, 3 (E. Seeberg* & S. Kleppe* eds. 1981) (italics added).

[88] J. Walker*, *Formaldehyde* 399 *passim* (3d ed. 1964).

[89] Abelson*, *Chemical Events on the Primitive Earth*, 55 Proc. National Academy Sciences 1365, 1369 (1966) (italics added). *See also* Wrighton*, *Photochemistry*, Chemical & Engineering News, Sept. 3, 1979, at 29.

[90] R. Shapiro*, *Origins: A Skeptic's Guide to the Creation of Life on Earth* 113 (1986) (italics added).

[91] Nissenbaum*, *Scavenging of Soluble Organic Matter from the Prebiotic Oceans*, 7 Origins of Life 413, 413, 415 (1976) (italics added). He believes that the solution may be in "sediment-water interaction."

[92]   A. Cairns-Smith*, *Genetic Takeover and the Mineral Origins of Life* 48 (1986).

[93]   Section 4.3.

[94]   L. Dillon*, *The Genetic Mechanism and the Origin of Life* 62 (1978) (italics added).

[95]   *Id.* at 67.

[96]   Hull*, *Thermodynamics and kinetics of spontaneous generation*, 186 Nature 693, 693 (1960) (italics added).

[97]   *Id.* (italics added).

[98]   Dose*, *Peptides and Amino Acids in the Primordial Hydrosphere*, in The Origin of Life and Evolutionary Biochemistry 69, 73 (K. Dose* *et al.* eds. 1979).

[99]   Quoted in A. Cairns-Smith*, *Genetic Takeover and the Mineral Origins of Life* 46-47 (1986).

[100]   Nissenbaum*, Kenyon* & Oro*, *On the Possible Role of Organic Melanoidin Polymers as Matrices for Prebiotic Activity*, 6 J. Molecular Evolution 253, 253, 259 (1975) (italics added).

[101]   A. Cairns-Smith*, *Genetic Takeover and the Mineral Origins of Life* 46-47 (1986) (italics added).

[102]   L. Dillon*, *The Genetic Mechanism and the Origin of Life* 61-62 (1978) (italics added).

[103]   Hull*, *Thermodynamics and kinetics of spontaneous generation*, 186 Nature 693, 693 (1960).

[104]   Dose*, *Peptides and Amino Acids in the Primordial Hydrosphere*, in The Origin of Life and Evolutionary Biochemistry 69, 73 (K. Dose* *et al.* eds. 1979).

[105]   Hull*, *Thermodynamics and kinetics of spontaneous generation*, 186 Nature 693, 693 (1960).

[106]   Dose*, *Peptides and Amino Acids in the Primordial Hydrosphere*, in The Origin of Life and Evolutionary Biochemistry 69, 73 (K. Dose* *et al.* eds. 1979).

[107]   Nissenbaum*, *Scavenging of Soluble Organic Matter from the Prebiotic Oceans*, 7 Origins of Life 413 (1976).

[108]   A. Cairns-Smith*, *Genetic Takeover and the Mineral Origins of Life* 47 (1986) (italics added).

[109]   Horowitz* & Hubbard*, *The Origin of Life*, 8 Ann. Rev. Genetics 393 (1974).

[110]   Sanchez*, Ferris* & Orgel*, *Conditions for Purine Synthesis: Did Prebiotic Synthesis Occur at Low Temperatures?*, 153 Science 72 (1966).

[111]   Dose*, *Peptides and Amino Acids in the Primordial Hydrosphere*, in The Origin of Life and Evolutionary Biochemistry 69, 75 (K. Dose* *et al.* eds. 1979).

[112]   A. Cairns-Smith*, *Genetic Takeover and the Mineral Origins of Life* 47-48 (1986) (italics added).

[113]   Note 78.

[114]   Note 81.

[115]   Note 83.
[116]   Note 84.
[117]   Note 85.
[118]   Note 87.
[119]   Note 88.
[120]   Note 89.
[121]   Note 91.
[122]   Note 92.
[123]   Note 94.
[124]   Note 96.
[125]   Note 111.
[126]   Note 99.
[127]   Note 100.
[128]   Note 101.
[129]   Note 102.
[130]   Note 103.
[131]   Note 104.
[132]   Note 108.
[133]   Note 111.
[134]   Note 109.
[135]   Note 112.
[136]   Scott, *Update on Genesis*, New Scientist, May 2, 1985, at 30, 30 (italics added).
[137]   Anon.*, *What Future for Biogenesis?*, 216 Nature 635, 635 (1967) (italics added).
[138]   A. Cairns-Smith*, *Genetic Takeover and the Mineral Origins of Life* 51-52 (1986) (italics added).
[139]   Nissenbaum*, *Scavenging of Soluble Organic Matter from the Prebiotic Oceans*, 7 Origins of Life 413 (1976).
[140]   J. Walker*, *Formaldehyde* 404 (3d ed. 1964).
[141]   Nissenbaum*, Kenyon* & Oro*, *On the Possible Role of Organic Melanoidin Polymers as Matrices for Prebiotic Activity*, 6 J. Molecular Evolution 253, 259 (1975).
[142]   Dose*, *Peptides and Amino Acids in the Primordial Hydrosphere*, in The Origin of Life and Evolutionary Biochemistry 69, 74 (K. Dose* *et al.* eds. 1979).
[143]   Sagan*, *Simulated Natural Experiments*, in The Origins of Prebiological Systems and of Their Molecular Matrices 374-75 (S. Fox* ed. 1965) (italics added).
[144]   Dose*, *Peptides and Amino Acids in the Primordial Hydrosphere*, in The Origin of Life and Evolutionary Biochemistry 69, 73-74 (K. Dose* *et al.* eds. 1979). *See also Amino Acids*, in 1 Encyclopedia of Science and Technology 411-24 (1982).
[145]   A. Cairns-Smith*, *Genetic Takeover and the Mineral Origins of Life* 51-53 (1986) (italics added).
[146]   Temussi*, Paolillo*, Ferrara*, Benedetti* & Andini*, *Structural Char-*

acterization of Thermal Prebiotic Polypeptides, 7 J. Molecular Evolution 105, 105, 109 (1976) (italics added).

[147]   Williams* & Smith*, *A Critical Evaluation of the Application of Amino Acid Racemization to Geochronology and Geothermometry,* 8 Origins of Life 91, 91 (1977) (italics added).

[148]   Section 4.3

[149]   A. Cairns-Smith*, *Genetic Takeover and the Mineral Origins of Life* 40-44 (1986) (italics added). He proposes a resolution of the isomer problem.

[150]   Joyce*, Schwartz*, Miller* & Orgel*, *The case for an ancestral genetic system involving simple analogues of the nucleotides,* 84 Proc. National Acad. Sciences 4398, 4398 (1987).

[151]   Section 4.2.

[152]   L. Dillon*, *The Genetic Mechanism and the Origin of Life* 62 (1978) (italics in original).

[153]   Reid* & Orgel*, *Synthesis of sugars in potentially prebiotic conditions,* 216 Nature 455, 455 (1967).

[154]   Abelson*, *Chemical Events on the Primitive Earth,* 55 Proc. National Academy Sciences 1365 (1966); Hulett*, *Limitations on Prebiological Synthesis,* 24 J. Theoretical Biology 56 (1969).

[155]   S. Fox* & K. Dose*, *Molecular Evolution and the Origin of Life* 106 (1972).

[156]   A. Cairns-Smith*, *Genetic Takeover and the Mineral Origins of Life* 66 (1986) (italics added).

[157]   Joyce*, Schwartz*, Miller* & Orgel*, *The case for an ancestral genetic system involving simple analogues of the nucleotides,* 84 Proc. National Acad. Sciences 4398, 4398 (1987) (italics added, footnotes deleted).

[158]   Abelson*, *Chemical Events on the Primitive Earth,* 55 Proc. National Academy Sciences 1365 (1966).

[159]   A. Cairns-Smith*, *Genetic Takeover and the Mineral Origins of Life* 55 (1986) (italics added).

[160]   Williams* & Smith*, *A Critical Evaluation of the Application of Amino Acid Racemization to Geochronology and Geothermometry,* 8 Origins of Life 91, 91 (1977); C. Patterson*, *Evolution* 157 (1978).

[161]   A. Oparin*, *Genesis and Evolutionary Development of Life* 136 (1968).

[162]   M. Dixon* & M. Webb*, *Enzymes* 665 (2d ed. 1964).

[163]   A. Cairns-Smith*, *Genetic Takeover and the Mineral Origins of Life* 73 (1986) (italics added).

[164]   L. Dillon*, *The Genetic Mechanism and the Origin of Life* 63 (1978) (italics added.) He does not apply this to porphyrins.

[165]   *Id.* at 61.

[166]   S. Miller* & L. Orgel*, *The Origins of Life on the Earth* 98 (1974) ("No satisfactory synthesis of fatty acids is at present available. The action of electric discharges on methane and water gives fairly good yields of acetic and propionic acids, but only small yields of the higher fatty acids. Furthermore, the small quantities of higher fatty acids that are found are highly branched."). They do not find satisfactory the Fischer-Tropsch reaction.

[167] A. Cairns-Smith*, *Genetic Takeover and the Mineral Origins of Life* 63 (1986) (italics added).

[168] Abelson*, *Chemical Events on the Primitive Earth*, 55 Proc. of National Academy Sciences 1365 (1966).

[169] Section 5.4(d).

[170] Orgel*, *Darwinism at the Very Beginning of Life*, 94 New Scientist 151 (1982).

[171] Dickerson*, *Chemical Evolution and the Origin of Life*, Scientific Am., Sept. 1978, at 70, 85 (italics added).

[172] F. Crick*, *Life Itself* 71 (1981) (italics added).

[173] A. Cairns-Smith*, *Genetic Takeover and the Mineral Origins of Life* 62 (1986).

[174] Scott*, *Update on Genesis*, New Scientist, May 2, 1985, at 30, 32.

[175] J. Monod*, *Chance and Necessity* 143 (A. Wainhouse* trans. 1971).

[176] Lambert*, *Enzymatic Editing Mechanisms and the Origin of Biological Information Transfer*, 107 J. Theoretical Biology 387, 387 (1984).

[177] A. Cairns-Smith*, *Genetic Takeover and the Mineral Origins of Life* 56 (1986) (italics added except numbers).

[178] *Id.* at 56-57 (italics added except numbers).

[179] *Id.* at 57 (italics added except numbers).

[180] *Id.* at 57-58 (italics added except numbers).

[181] T. Dobzhansky*, F. Ayala*, G. Stebbins* & J. Valentine*, *Evolution* 21-23 (1977).

[182] Shapiro*, *Damage to DNA Caused by Hydrolysis*, in Chromosome Damage and Repair 3, 17 (E. Seeberg* & K. Kleppe* eds. 1981).

[183] Scott*, *Update on Genesis*, New Scientist, May 2, 1985, at 30, 32 (italics added).

[184] Crick*, *The Origin of the Genetic Code*, 38 J. Molecular Biology 367 (1968).

[185] Woese*, *The Biological Significance of the Genetic Code*, in Progress in Molecular and Subcellular Biology 1 (F. Hahn* et al. eds. 1969).

[186] J. Monod*, *Chance and Necessity* 143 (A. Wainhouse* trans. 1971) (italics added except Latin).

[187] Popper*, *Scientific Reproduction and the Essential Incompleteness of All Science*, in Studies in the Philosophy of Biology 259, 270 (1974).

[188] E. Ambrose*, *The Nature and Origin of the Biological World* 135 (1982).

[189] Perutz*, *Physics and the riddle of life*, 326 Nature 555, 558 (1987).

[190] Lambert*, *Enzymatic Editing Mechanisms and the Origin of Biological Information Transfer*, 107 J. Theoretical Biology 387, 400-01 (1984) (italics added).

[191] A. Cairns-Smith*, *Genetic Takeover and the Mineral Origins of Life* 58 (1986) (italics added).

[192] *Id.* at 58-59 (italics added).

[193] *Id.* at 62.

[194] *Id.* at 56 (italics added).

[195] D. Green* & R. Goldberger*, *Molecular Insights into the Living Process* 407 (1967) (italics added).

[196] Kenyon* & Nissenbaum*, *Melanoidin and Aldocyanin Microspheres: Implications for Chemical Evolution and Early Precambrian Micropaleontology*, 7 J. Molecular Evolution 245, 246 (1976).

[197] L. Dillon*, *The Genetic Mechanism and the Origin of Life* 62-63 (1978).

[198] Dobzhansky*, *Synthesis of Nucleosides and Polynucleotides with Metaphosphate Esters*, in The Origins of Prebiological Systems 299, 310 (S. Fox* ed. 1965).

[199] Kempthorne*, *Evaluation of Current Population Genetics Theory*, 23 Am. Biologist 111, 111 (1983) (italics added).

[200] A. Cairns-Smith*, *Genetic Takeover and the Mineral Origins of Life* 69, 70 (1986) (italics added).

[201] L. Dillon*, *The Genetic Mechanism and the Origin of Life* 65 (1978) (some italics added).

[202] Kaplan*, *The Problem of Chance in Formation of Protobionts by Random Aggregation of Macromolecules*, 1 Chemical Evolution and the Origin of Life 319, 319 (R. Buvet* & C. Ponnamperuma* eds. 1971) (italics added).

[203] *Id.* at 323-24 (italics added).

[204] L. Dillon*, *The Genetic Mechanism and the Origin of Life* 408 (1978).

[205] A. Cairns-Smith*, *Genetic Takeover and the Mineral Origins of Life* 59-60 (1986) (italics added).

[206] Dobzhansky*, *Synthesis of Nucleosides and Polynucleotides with Metaphosphate Esters*, in The Origins of Prebiological Systems 299, 310 (S. Fox* ed. 1965) (italics added).

[207] H. Blum*, *Time's Arrow and Evolution* 157 (3d ed. 1968) (italics added).

[208] Yockey*, *Self Organization Origin of Life Scenarios and Information Theory*, 91 J. Theoretical Biology 13, 13 (1981) ("The information content of amino acid sequences cannot increase until a genetic code with an adaptor function has appeared. Nothing which even vaguely resembles a code exists in the physico-chemical world.").

[209] Kaplan*, *The Problem of Chance in Formation of Protobionts by Random Aggregation of Macromolecules*, 1 Chemical Evolution and the Origin of Life 319, 323 (R. Buvet* & C. Ponnamperuma* eds. 1971) ("Only such living individuals (protocells) are able to compete with one another and can evolve by Darwin's mechanism. Isolated components cannot participate in biological evolution because changes are not inherited.").

[210] Erbrich*, *On the Probability of the Emergence of a Protein with a Particular Function*, 34 Acta Biotheoretica 53, 53 (1985) ("the origin of proteins is held to be a random process, at least ultimately, since selection can work with only what the random process delivers as having a minimum adaptive value").

[211] A. Cairns-Smith*, *Genetic Takeover and the Mineral Origins of Life* 60 (1986).

[212] Note 136.

[213] Note 137.

[214] Note 138.

[215] Note 139.

[216] Note 141.

[217] Note 143.

[218] Note 144.

[219] Note 146.

[220] Note 147.

[221] Note 153.

[222] Note 154.

[223] Note 156.

[224] Note 159.

[225] Note 160.

[226] Note 163.

[227] Note 164.

[228] Note 166.

[229] Note 167.

[230] Note 168.

[231] Note 171.

[232] Note 172.

[233] Note 173.

[234] Note 174.

[235] Note 186.

[236] Note 190.

[237] Note 195.

[238] Note 196.

[239] Note 199.

[240] Note 201.

[241] Note 205.

[242] Note 206.

[243] Note 211.

[244] Sagan*, *Life Beyond the Solar System*, in Exobiology 465, 471 (C. Ponnamperuma* ed. 1972).

[245] T. Dobzhansky*, *The Biology of Ultimate Concern* 46, 46 (1967). *See also* Hull*, *Thermodynamics and kinetics of spontaneous generation*, 186 Nature 693, 694 (1960) ("But the fact that a chemist can carry out an organic synthesis in the laboratory does not prove that the same synthesis will occur in the atmosphere or open sea without the chemist.").

[246] A. Cairns-Smith*, *Genetic Takeover and the Mineral Origins of Life* 56 (1986) (italics added).

[247] Scherer*, *Could Life Have Arisen in the Primitive Atmosphere?*, 22 J. Molecular Evolution 91, 94 (1985).

[248] Shapiro*, *The Improbability of Prebiotic Nucleic Acid Synthesis*, 14 Origin of Life 565, 565 (1984) (italics added).

[249] A. Cairns-Smith*, *Genetic Takeover and the Mineral Origins of Life* 45-46 (1986) (italics added).

[250] L. Dillon*, *The Genetic Mechanism and the Origin of Life* 61 (1978).

[251] J. Brooks* & G. Shaw*, *Origin and Development of Living Systems* 212 (1973).

[252] Keosian*, *Life's Beginnings—Origin or Evolution?*, in The Origin of Life and Evolutionary Biochemistry 221 (K. Dose* *et al.* eds. 1974).

[253] Clemmey* & Badham* similarly note:

> However, the achievements of Miller (1955) and others (for example, papers in Buvet and Ponnamperuma, 1978), while being triumphs for experimental biochemistry, may have *little relevance concerning the origin of life* on Earth or the composition of the early atmosphere.

Clemmey* & Badham*, *Oxygen in the Precambrian Atmosphere: An Evaluation of the Geological Evidence*, 10 Geology 141, 141 (1982) (italics added).

[254] A. Cairns-Smith*, *Genetic Takeover and the Mineral Origins of Life* 61 (1986).

[255] Hull*, *Thermodynamics and kinetics of spontaneous generation*, 186 Nature 693, 694 (1960) (italics added).

[256] Sagan*, *Discussion of K. Harada and S. Fox, The Thermal Synthesis of Amino Acids from a Hypothetically Primitive Terrestrial Atmosphere*, in The Origins of Prebiological Systems and of Their Molecular Matrices 195-96 (S. Fox* ed. 1965) (italics added).

[257] R. Shapiro*, *Origins: A Skeptic's Guide to the Creation of Life on Earth* 101 (1986).

[258] Harada* & Fox*, *The Thermal Synthesis of Amino Acids from a Hypothetically Primitive Terrestrial Atmosphere*, in The Origins of Prebiological Systems and of Their Molecular Matrices 187 (S. Fox* ed. 1965).

[259] R. Shapiro*, *Origins: A Skeptic's Guide to the Creation of Life on Earth* 105 (1986).

[260] A. Cairns-Smith*, *Genetic Takeover and the Mineral Origins of Life* 64-65 (1986) (italics added).

[261] Groth* & Weyssenhoff*, *Protochemische Bildung von Aminosäuren aus Mischung einfacher Gase*, 44 Naturwiss. 510 (1959); Dodonova* & Sidarova*, *Photosynthesis of Amino Acids from a Mixture of Simple Gases under the Influence of Ultraviolet Radiation in a Vacuum*, 6 Biophysics 14 (1961). Although some experiments assume phytosynthesization through gases filtering out destructive ultraviolet light, such gases would have themselves been broken down by photolysis in about 10,000 years. Ferris* & Nicodem*, *Ammonia: Did It Have a Role in Chemical Evolution?*, in The Origin of Life and Evolutionary Biochemistry 113 (K. Dose* *et al.* eds. 1974).

[262] Hulett*, *Limitations on Prebiological Synthesis*, 24 J. of Theoretical Biology 56 (1969); J. Pringle*, *New Biology* 54 (1954); Miller*, Urey* & Oro*, *Origin of Organic Compounds on the Primitive Earth and in Meteorites*, 9 J. Molecular Evolution 59 (1976).

[263] S. Miller* & L. Orgel*, *The Origins of Life on the Earth* 148 (1974).

[264] L. Dillon*, *The Genetic Mechanism and the Origin of Life* 44-46 (1978).

[265] Temussi*, Paolillo*, Ferrara*, Benedetti* & Andini*, *Structural Characterization of Thermal Prebiotic Polypeptides*, 7 J. Molecular Evolution

105, 105, 108-09 (1976) (italics added).

266 *Id.* at 105.

267 S. Miller* & L. Orgel*, *The Origins of Life on Earth* 144 (1974) (italics added).

268 E. Ambrose*, *The Nature and Origin of the Biological World* 143 (1982). The addition of energy "cannot increase the probability of a particular sequence being generated." *Id.*

269 L. Dillon*, *The Genetic Mechanism and the Origin of Life* 62 (1978).

270 W. Stansfield*, *The Science of Evolution* 57 (1977).

271 Williams* & Smith*, *A Critical Evaluation of the Application of Amino Acid Racemization to Geochronology and Geothermometry*, 8 Origins of Life 91, 91 (1977) ("However, in all cases where optical activity has been investigated these origin of life syntheses have produced racemic mixtures of amino acids, neither enantiomer being favored.").

272 C. Folsome*, *The Origin of Life* 87 (1979).

273 S. Miller* & H. Urey*, *The Origins of Life on the Earth* 145 (1974).

274 Kenyon* & Nissenbaum*, *Melanoidin and Aldocyanin Microspheres: Implications for Chemical Evolution and Early Precambrian Micropaleontology*, 7 J. Molecular Evolution 245, 246 (1976).

275 Concluding part of Chapter 5.

276 Williams* & Smith*, *A Critical Evaluation of the Application of Amino Acid Racemization to Geochronology and Geothermometry*, 8 Origins of Life 91, 91 (1977); C. Patterson*, *Evolution* 157 (1978).

277 Kenyon* & Nissenbaum*, *Melanoidin and Aldocyanin Microspheres: Implications for Chemical Evolution and Early Precambrian Micropaleontology*, 7 J. Molecular Evolution 245, 246 (1976) (italics added). Hoyle similarly observes:

> However, the next step—the coming together of subunits into larger organized molecules with the capacity to reproduce themselves—has *not occurred in the laboratory* flask. . . . As for the appearance of complex biochemicals in the primordial soup, there is an *enormous gap in the evidence*, one that seems unlikely ever to be bridged.

F. Hoyle, *The Intelligent Universe* 20-21 (1983).

278 L. Dillon*, *The Genetic Mechanism and the Origin of Life* 63-64 (1978) (italics added). He believes that suitable models might be possible.

279 Others recognize the same difficulty. *E.g.*, Fakhari*, van Roode* & Orgel*, *Synthesis of Oligoguanylates on Oligocytidylate Templates*, 17 J. Molecular Evolution 295, 302 (1981).

280 Lambert*, *Enzymic Editing Mechanisms and the Origin of Biological Information Transfer*, 107 J. Theoretical Biology 387, 396, 398 (1984) (heading in upper case in original).

281 W. Day*, *Genesis of the Planet Earth* 320 (1979) (italics added).

282 C. Ponnamperuma*, *The Origins of Life* 102 (1972).

283 L. Dillon*, *The Genetic Mechanism and the Origin of Life* 60 (1978).

284 C. Folsome*, *The Origin of Life* 84-85 (1979) (italics added).

[285] L. Dillon*, *The Genetic Mechanism and the Origin of Life* 64 (1978).

[286] *Id.* at 43.

[287] Fox*, Harada*, Krampitz* & Mueller*, *Chemical Origins of Cells*, Chemical & Engineering News, June 22, 1970, at 80; S. Fox* & K. Dose*, *Molecular Evolution and the Origins of Life* 220 (2d. ed. 1977).

[288] Fox*, *Molecular Selection and Natural Selection*, 61 Q. Rev. Biology 375, 376 (1986) (italics added).

[289] S. Miller* & L. Orgel*, *The Origins of Life on the Earth* 144 (1974); C. Folsome*, *The Origin of Life* 87 (1979).

[290] A. Oparin*, *Genesis and Evolutionary Development of Life* 105 (1969) (italics added).

[291] Temussi*, *Reply*, 8 J. Molecular Evolution 305 (1976).

[292] Miller* & Urey*, *Organic Compound Synthesis on the Primitive Earth*, 130 Science 245 (1959); S. Miller* & L. Orgel*, *The Origins of Life on the Earth* 145 (1974).

[293] Scherer*, *Could Life Have Arisen in the Primitive Atmosphere?*, 22 J. Molecular Evolution 91, 91, 94 (1985).

[294] A. Cairns-Smith*, *Genetic Takeover and the Mineral Origins of Life* 68 (1986).

[295] T. Dobzhansky*, F. Ayala*, G. Stebbins* & J. Valentine*, *Evolution* 360 (1977).

[296] Scott*, *Update on Genesis*, New Scientist, May 2, 1985, at 30.

[297] Note 246.

[298] Note 248.

[299] Note 253.

[300] Note 252.

[301] Note 256.

[302] Note 260.

[303] Note 259.

[304] Note 266.

[305] Note 265.

[306] Note 267.

[307] Note 270.

[308] Note 277.

[309] Note 278.

[310] Note 281.

[311] Note 283.

[312] *Id.* at 64.

[313] Note 318.

[314] Note 323.

[315] *Id.* at 377.

[316] Yockey*, *A Calculation of the Probability of Spontaneous Biogenesis Explain Life*, in Scientific Explanation and Understanding 53, 64-65 (N. Rescher* ed. 1983).

[326] F. Hoyle & N. Wickramasinghe, *Evolution from Space* 24 (1981) (discontinuitist scientists).

[327] C. Sagan* & I. Shklovskii*, *Intelligent Life in the Universe* 358 (1966) (quoting physicist Philip Morrison*).

[328] Lafont*, *Book Review*, Permanences, Nov. 1972, at 7, 8, quoting G. Salet*, *Chance and Certainty: Evolution in the Light of Modern Biology* 8 (1972). *See also* E. Borel*, *Probabilities and Life* 28 (1963); E. Borel*, *Elements of the Theory of Probability* 57 (1965).

[329] Hoyle, *The Big Bang in Astronomy*, 91 New Scientist 521, 526 (1981) (italics added).

[330] Yockey*, *A Calculation of the Probability of Spontaneous Biogenesis by Information Theory*, 67 J. Theoretical Biology 377, 377 (1977) (italics added).

[331] Wald*, *The Origin of Life*, Scientific Am., Aug. 1954, at 46, 46.

[332] Abelson*, *Chemical Events on the Primitive Earth*, 55 Proc. National Acad. Sciences 1365, 1365 (1966).

[333] R. Shapiro*, *Origins: A Skeptic's Guide to the Creation of Life on Earth* 112-13 (1986).

[334] Anon.*, *What Future for Biogenesis?*, 216 Nature 635 (1967).

[335] Scherer*, *Could Life Have Arisen in the Primitive Atmosphere?*, 22 J. Molecular Evolution 91, 94 (1985).

[336] Thorpe*, *Reductionism in Biology*, in Studies in the Philosophy of Biology 116-17 (F. Ayala* & T. Dobzhansky* eds. 1974).

PART IV

Whether the Theories of Abrupt Appearance and Evolution Are Scientific?

The Origin of the Universe

The final phase of the theories of evolution and abrupt appearance addresses the origin of the universe, now that the origin of plants and animals and the origin of the first life have been considered.

The cosmic theory of abrupt appearance, like biological and biochemical abrupt appearance, consists of affirmative lines of scientific evidence. It is not without difficulties, but has the surprising feature of conforming to such natural laws as those of thermodynamics and information science, as well as better explaining such other empirical observations as anthropic considerations, heterogeneity, galaxy formation, and radiohalos.

The cosmic theory of evolution, according to Sagan*, describes the origin of the universe as involving transformation through the "big bang—clusters of galaxies, galaxies, stars, planets, and, eventually, life...."[1] Yet many evolutionists hold that its two primary lines of evidence, red shift and microwave background radiation, are adequately explained by phenomena other than the big bang and do not require that primordial explosion: "some cosmologists, albeit a minority, do sometimes wonder whether the confidence so often claimed in the big bang picture is justified by our observational

393

evidence . . .."[2] Moreover, the various stages of the big bang involve critical breaks from natural laws and significant difficulties in light of scientific evidence: "A number of scientists are unhappy with the big bang theory."[3] The uneasy relation between the scientific data and the big bang theory is summarized by Corliss*:

> After more than twelve years of scouring the scientific and semiscientific literature for anomalies, my major conclusion is that *this is an amazingly fruitful activity. In fact, organized science should have been doing the same searching and compiling for the past 200 years.* It is simply astounding that a Catalog of Scientific Anomalies does not already exist to guide scientific thinking and research. It is at least as important to realize what is *not* known as it is to recognize the well-explained. . . .
>
> *. . .The anomalies residing in the world's literature seem nearly infinite in number.*[4]

Cosmic abrupt appearance has more empirical support than is often recognized, while cosmic evolution remains more in the area of speculation than many pronouncements acknowledge. The issue is not which is correct, but whether neither is compellingly grounded so that alternatives should be considered.

Notes

[1] C. Sagan, *Cosmos* 247 (1980).

[2] Narlikar*, *Was there a big bang?*, New Scientist, July 2, 1981, at 19, 19.

[3] A. Krauskopf* & A. Beiser*, *The Physical Universe* 645 (3d ed. 1973).

[4] W. Corliss*, *Stars, Galaxies, Cosmos: A Catalog of Astronomical Anomalies* v (1987) (italics added).

CHAPTER 6

Theories of Abrupt Appearance and Empirical Evidence: Cosmic Abrupt Appearance of the Universe

> *I think, however, that we must go further than this and admit that the only acceptable explanation is creation. I know that this is anathema to physicists, as indeed it is to me, but we must not reject a theory that we do not like if the experimental evidence supports it.*[1]
> —H. S. Lipson*, F.R.S.,
> British evolutionist physicist

The cosmic theory of abrupt appearance is the theory that the origin of the universe occurred by discontinuous abrupt appearance in complex form, as indicated by empirical evidence and related scientific interpretations, rather than by a continuous evolutionary process from a big bang and inflationary phase to a complex uni-

---

*Scientists cited in this chapter, unless otherwise indicated, are not proponents of, and their quoted statements are not intended as endorsements of, either the theory of abrupt appearance or the theory of creation. However, their quoted statements are acknowledging data that some nonevolutionist scientists interpret as supporting the theory of abrupt appearance better than the theory of evolution.

verse with high information content. That empirical evidence for cosmic abrupt appearance includes at least six affirmative aspects:

6.1 Thermodynamics argument
6.2 Information content argument
6.3 Anthropic principle argument
6.4 Heterogeneity argument
6.5 Galaxy and star formation argument
6.6 Radiohalos argument.

The purpose of this chapter is only to outline, and not to provide all available documentation for, those lines of scientific evidence.

The thermodynamics argument is based on the first and second laws of thermodynamics, requiring a beginning for matter and energy and precluding an eternal existence for that matter and energy (Section 6.1). The information content argument concerns the vast information content of the present universe, with predictable and orderly motion of galactic clusters, galaxies, stars, our solar system, and comets (Section 6.2). The anthropic principle argument focuses on the numerous "coincidental" but highly improbable conditions of the universe, stellar systems, and earth that are necessary for any plausible form of life to exist (Section 6.3). The heterogeneity argument is based on the significantly uneven distribution or lumpiness of the universe, rather than the more even distribution that a big bang explosion and subsequent evolution most probably would produce over time (Section 6.4). The galaxy and star formation argument involves the origination of galactic clusters, galaxies, and stars (Section 6.5). The radiohalos argument is based on the presence of polonium halos in the earth's crust, which could have formed only if the earth appeared abruptly in a cool rather than molten form, when coupled with the absence of evidence of uranium having been present (Section 6.6).

Those affirmative evidences for the cosmic theory of abrupt appearance were not all formulated in this century; a couple were anticipated by the great physicist and astronomer, Sir Isaac Newton, nearly three centuries ago, and a couple more were advocated by the great scientists Faraday, Maxwell, and Kelvin about a century ago, as discussed below.[2]

Moreover, they indeed are affirmative arguments for a scientific theory of abrupt appearance or of creation, as Lipson* (a British physicist who describes himself as an Agnostic) concluded in the quotation above on considering some of this evidence. (As explained in Chapter 1, the theory of abrupt appearance differs critically from the theory of creation.)

*Figure 6.1
The "laws of thermodynamics ... indicated that the Universe had a beginning" (Jastrow*) (picture of southern Milky Way and surroundings)*

6.1 The Thermodynamics Argument: Natural Laws Requiring Abrupt Appearance

The thermodynamics argument is founded in the first and second laws of thermodynamics, which are the law of conservation of energy and the law of increasing entropy.[3] The "second law of thermodynamics . . . says, roughly spreaking, that in any change the Universe becomes a slightly more disorderly place; the entropy goes up, the information content goes down. This natural tendency towards disintegration and chaos is evident all around us: people grow old, cars rust, houses fall down, mountains erode, stars burn out, clocks run down."[4] This section discusses (a) the effect of thermodynamic laws and (b) objections to their use.

a. Effect of the Laws of Thermodynamics

Stansfield*, an evolutionist scientist and professor at California Polytechnic Institute, accurately describes the thermodynamics argument, agrees that it is an affirmative argument for cosmic abrupt appearance, *and agrees that it is in fact correct* in his college textbook on evolution:

Creationists continually refer to the *laws of thermodynamics* in their arguments against a natural origin for living systems. The *First Law* of Thermodynamics, sometimes called the Law of Conservation of Energy, states that energy can be transformed from one kind to another, but it can neither be created nor destroyed. Since matter and energy have been shown to be interconvertible, the First Law can be modified to state that neither matter nor energy can be created or destroyed. The *Second Law* of Thermodynamics states that in converting one form of energy to another, some of it is lost as unusable heat. Entropy is the thermodynamic quality of randomness or disorder within a system. The Second Law therefore implies that as energy is being transformed throughout the universe, entropy is increasing. *These Laws argue strongly for a created universe.*[5]

Einstein himself grudgingly accepted "the necessity for a beginning."[6]

Jastrow*, the founder and director of NASA's Goddard Institute for Space Studies and a professor of astronomy at Columbia, concurs that the laws of thermodynamics require some form of abrupt appearance of the universe (although he is an Agnostic[7]), and that those laws bar an eternal existence of the universe because of the existence of unused hydrogen:

> This beautiful theory allows the Universe to go on forever in a *timeless* cycle of death and rebirth, *but for one disturbing fact.* Fresh hydrogen is the essential ingredient in the plan; it is the main source of the energy by which stars shine, and it is also the source of all the other elements in the Universe. The moment a star is born it begins to consume some of the hydrogen in the Universe, and continues to use up hydrogen until it dies. Once hydrogen has been burned within that star and converted to heavier elements, it can never be restored to its original state. Minute by minute and year by year, as hydrogen is used up in stars, the supply of this element in the Universe grows smaller.
>
> . . ..
>
> Now three lines of evidence—the motions of the galaxies, the laws of thermodynamics, and the life story of the stars—pointed to one conclusion; all indicated that the *Universe had a beginning.* . . .[8]

Many proponents of the big bang theory, besides Jastrow*, acknowledge that the laws of thermodynamics require abrupt appearance of the initial matter and energy of the Universe. Davies*, professor of theoretical physics at University of Newcastle upon Tyne, agrees that "[t]he Universe cannot have existed forever—there must have been a creation."[9] Gamow*, the principal formulator of the modern big bang theory, describes it as "the creation of the universe,"[10] as do many other proponents.[11]

Numerous opponents of the big bang theory concur that the thermodynamic laws support abrupt appearance of the matter and

energy of the universe. Hoyle*, who is called an "eminent cosmologist" by Gould* of Harvard[12] and was formerly an astronomy
professor at Cambridge, before his change from an evolutionist to a
discontinuitist stance, agreed with Jastrow's* analysis that the
abundance of unburned hydrogen requires a "creation" of the universe.[13] Van Wylen*, chairman of the department of mechanical
engineering at University of Michigan, in his textbook on thermodynamics suggested only creation of the universe as the answer to
the question how the universe could "get in the state of low entropy"
when high entropy "is associated with the natural processes that
are known to us"?[14]

b. Objections to the Thermodynamics Argument

One frequent reply to the thermodynamics argument is that the
universe is eternal. However, the universe cannot be eternal, not
only because of the existence of unused hydrogen that Jastrow*
described, but because of the "fairly strong evidence that the universe is open" and yet "probably cannot be cyclical" (oscillating), as
Wald* states:

> The best estimate of the mass density of the universe due to matter in
> galaxies is about 2.5 X 10^{-31} gm/cu cm. This is some *twenty times less
> than the mass density required for a closed universe*. The galactic mass
> density is, of course, only a lower limit to the true mass density of the
> universe. We know that there must be at least that much mass density
> but there might be more that we do not see. However, the most plausible
> forms in which significant amounts of matter might be hidden—for
> example, in a tenuous hydrogen gas between the galaxies—seem to be
> ruled out by a combination of observational and theoretical arguments.
> Thus, the observation of the mass density of the universe provides *fairly
> strong evidence that the universe is open*.[15]

That reason why the universe is open rather than cyclical, that the
density of matter in the universe is much too small to halt its
expansion and to collapse the universe into another big bang explosion, is the "consensus" view stated by Jastrow* after factoring in
the nonluminous matter in the universe:

> Yet, although the estimated density of matter in the Universe is greatly
> increased as a result of this determination, it is still more than *ten times
> too small* to bring the expansion of the Universe to a halt. Thus the facts
> indicate that the Universe will expand forever. We still come across
> pieces of mass here and there in the Universe, and someday we may find
> the missing matter, but the *consensus* at the moment is that *it will not be
> found*.[16]

Pagel* of the Royal Greenwich Observatory agrees that "this model requires an average density of baryons—particles such as protons and neutrons—at least 10 times less than the density of matter needed to close the Universe."[17]

Speculations about that "missing mass" appear to be based more on the assumption that it must exist somewhere, because the universe is assumed to be closed or oscillating, rather than on evidence. For example, neutrinos do not provide a significant part of the missing mass, and may not "have mass" at all,[18] according to research by Kwon* et al.[19] and others.[20] Recent studies of neutrinos from supernovas confirm "that electron neutrinos do not constitute the major component of the matter density of the Universe," as Bahcall* and Glashow* find.[21]

Proposals for an oscillating universe also are less probable, according to Silk*: "the universe probably cannot be cyclical, unless we introduce new physical laws that would significantly modify our theory of gravitation."[22] Abell* concurs:

> Such speculation is sometimes referred to as the oscillating theory of the universe, but it is not really a theory, for we know of no mechanism that can produce another big bang.[23]

The second frequent reply to the thermodynamics argument is that antimatter[24] exists in the same quantity as matter, so that the two originated from a vacuum fluctuation (from nothing).[25] However, the actual quantity of antimatter appears to be far less than the quantity of matter: "the prevailing opinion among astronomers and astrophysicists is that matter dominates over antimatter in the present universe," Wilczek* summarizes.[26] "We are pretty sure from our observations that the universe today contains matter but very little if any antimatter," Weisskopf* adds.[27]

Hypotheses that the quantities of antimatter and matter are equal confront three major problems, which Silk* notes:

> First, if the Alfvén-Klein cosmology is correct, some mechanism must separate regions of matter and antimatter. Since we know that even intergalactic space contains some matter, galaxies could not be completely separated from antigalaxies. Alfvén has proposed a possible way of separating regions of matter and antimatter, but other astrophysicists remain skeptical about his theory. Second, there must be many regions where annihilation of matter and antimatter would occur. One result of annihilation is to produce copious amounts of high energy gamma rays, which should be observable by space experiments. Astronomers have indeed measured a diffuse cosmic background of gamma rays, but the flux is relatively low. The implication is that very little annihilation can be occurring at present.

Perhaps the *most significant* objection to this cosmology stems from the *presence of the cosmic background radiation.*[28]
Those problems are widely acknowledged, for example by Lake*[29] and Wilczek*.[30]

Summary. Thus, the thermodynamics laws "argue strongly for a created universe" (Stansfield*[31]), and "indicated that the Universe had a beginning" (Jastrow*[32]), many evolutionists concede. Many big bang advocates agree that the "Universe cannot have existed forever—there must have been a creation" (Davies*[33]), while their opponents concur that "[t]o avoid the issue of creation it would be necessary for all the material of the Universe to be infinitely old, and this it cannot be" because "there could be no hydrogen left in the Universe" (Hoyle*[34]). The counterargument of an eternally oscillating universe also fails because its mass "is some twenty times less than the mass density required for a closed universe" (Wald*[35]), or at least "ten times too small" (Jastrow*[36]), notwithstanding black holes and speculations about the "missing mass." The counterargument that matter and antimatter exist in equal quantities conflicts with "the prevailing opinion among astronomers and astrophysicists . . . that matter dominates over antimatter" (Wilczek*[37]), and that there is "very little if any antimatter" (Weisskopf*[38]); and has serious problems of its own (Silk*[39]). The matter and energy of the universe appeared abruptly and discontinuously as required by the thermodynamic laws, many scientists conclude.

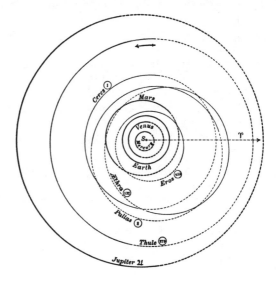

Figure 6.2
"Everywhere in the Universe . . . we encounter . . . much information"
(Davies)*

6.2 The Information Content Argument: Natural Laws of Information Science

This argument is based on the vast information content of the universe, with predictable and nonrandom motion of galactic clusters, their galaxies, their stars, our solar system, and comets.

a. *Empirical Evidence of Great Information Content*

That vast information content in the universe is described by Planck*, the great physicist and Nobel Prize recipient:

> At all events we should say, in summing up, that, according to everything taught by the exact sciences about the immense realm of nature in which our tiny planet plays an insignificant role, *a certain order prevails*—one independent of the human mind. Yet, in so far as we are able to ascertain through our senses, this order can be formulated in terms of purposeful activity. There is evidence of an *intelligent order of the universe* . . . .[40]

The "greatest puzzle of universal information content"[41] also is acknowledged by Davies*:

> *Everywhere* we look in the Universe, from the far flung galaxies to the deepest recesses of the atom, we encounter *order*. . . .
> . . ..
> Central to the idea of a very special, orderly Universe is the concept of *information*. A highly structured system, displaying a great deal of organised activity, needs a lot of information to describe it. Alternatively, we may say that it contains much information. . . .
> . . .We are therefore presented with a curious question. If information and order always has a natural tendency to disappear, where did all the information that made the world such a special place come from originally? The Universe is like a clock slowly running down. How did it get wound up in the first place?[42]

"Every advance in fundamental physics seems to uncover yet another facet of order."[43]

Einstein* viewed the "high degree of order" of the universe as a "miracle" rather than something we are "authorized to expect":

> Well, *a priori one should expect that the world would be rendered lawful only to the extent that we intervene with our ordering intelligence.* It would be a kind of order like the alphabetical order of the words of a language. . . . Even if the axioms of the theory are set by men, the success of such an endeavor presupposes in the objective world *a high degree of order* that we were *a priori* in no way authorized to expect. This is the 'miracle' that is strengthened more and more with the development of our knowledge.[44]

Sir James Jeans, the famous astrophysicist, noted the mathematical nature of that order: "Our efforts to interpret nature in terms of the concepts of pure mathematics have, so far, proved brilliantly successful."[45] Thus, "systems spun out by the brain, for no other purpose than our sheer delight with their beauty, correspond precisely with the intricate design of the natural order which predated man and his brain," Pollard* adds.[46] The "present immense complexity of the universe" is also recognized by Gamow*, along with the problem of explaining its emergence from "primordial chaos":

> We may also assume that in that distant past our universe was considerably less differentiated and complex than it is now and that the state of matter at that time could be accurately described by the classical concept of primordial chaos . . .. The problem of scientific cosmogony can be formulated as an attempt to reconstruct the evolutionary process which led *from simplicity* of the early days of creation *to the present immense complexity* of the universe around us.[47]

That complex order is widely acknowledged, such as by Weisskopf*,[48] and it leads Raymo* to calculate the improbability of the universe existing from chance molecular interaction following a big bang event at 1 chance in 1,000,000,000,000,000.[49]

b. History of the Underlying Argument

The core of this information content argument—the complex order in the universe—was actually formulated as an affirmative argument about its origin by Sir Isaac Newton. For example, he said of the solar system:

> The six primary planets are revolved about the sun in circles concentric with the sun, and with motions directed towards the same parts, and almost in the same plane. Ten moons are revolved about the earth, Jupiter, and Saturn, in circles concentric with them, with the same direction of motion, and nearly in the planes of the orbits of those planets; but it is *not* to be conceived that mere *mechanical causes could give birth to so many regular motions*, since the comets range over all parts of the heavens in very eccentric orbits . . ..[50]

Similarly, Johannes Kepler, the astronomer whose laws describe planetary orbits, pointed out the "clockwork" of the universe.[51] More recently, Bush* noted "the order of the solar system" with its many facets,[52] and others have pointed out the complex information content of other celestial systems.

Summary. "Everywhere we look in the Universe . . . we encounter order. . . . [W]here did all the information that makes the world such a special place come from originally?" (Davies*[53]). The universe contains "a high degree of order," yet "*a priori* one should expect that the world would be rendered lawful only to the extent that we intervene with our ordering intelligence" (Einstein*[54]). The complexity is so great that the improbability of its emergence from a big bang singularity is 1 chance in 1,000,000,000,000,000 (Raymo*[55]). As Newton recognized three centuries ago, "it is not to be conceived that mere mechanical causes could give birth to so many regular motions," but the better interpretation is instead an abrupt appearance of a complex universe (Newton[56]).

Figure 6.3
"If all the grains of sand on all the beaches of the Earth were possible universes.. ., then one grain of sand is the universe we inhabit" (Raymo)*

6.3 The Anthropic Principle Argument: Empirical Evidence of Scientific Teleology

The anthropic argument is related to the anthropic principles of cosmology. The strong and weak anthropic principles are defined in a recent book by Barrow* (astronomy professor at University of Sussex) and Tipler* (physics professor at Tulane University) as follows:

> *Strong Anthropic Principle (SAP)*: The Universe must have those properties which allow life to develop within it at some stage in its history.
>
> . . ..
>
> *Weak Anthropic Principle (WAP)*: The observed values of all physical and cosmological quantities are not equally probable but they take on values restricted by the requirement that there exist sites where carbon-based life can evolve and by the requirement that the Universe be old enough for it to have already done so.[57]

The significance of that "scholarly, philosophically sophisticated and mathematically high-brow" book[58] is described by Press*:

> [T]here really is a place for teleology and related concepts in today's science. . . . [A]rguments, drawn in the main from modern theoretical

cosmology, ... may convince the reader of an astounding claim: *there is a grand design in the Universe* that favours the development of intelligent life. This claim, in certain variations (as we shall see in a moment), is the "anthropic cosmological principle."[59]

The anthropic argument that is presented here is similar to the anthropic principle of Barrow* and Tipler* and other authors, but their giving the problem a name does not solve the problem. Instead, the numerous "special conditions" and "coincidental" critical features of the universe are too improbable to be explained by its cosmic evolution even over a time period many times 10-20 billion years, and are better explained by cosmic abrupt appearance of a complex universe with those critical features, according to many nonevolutionist scientists. Those special conditions and coincidences include (a) the critical expansion rate and inhomogeneity level of the universe, (b) the critical levels of the four fundamental forces, and (c) other critical features of the physical universe. Although he does not agree with the theory of abrupt appearance, Raymo* perceives most of the incredible fortuities:

> No, the coin did not come down on its edge. The situation is more improbable than that. The coin was flipped into the air 10^{15} times, and it came down on its edge but once. If all the grains of sand on all the beaches of the Earth were possible universes—that is, universes consistent with the laws of physics as we know them—and only one of those grains of sand were a universe that allowed for the existence of intelligent life, then that one grain of sand is the universe we inhabit.[60]

a. Critical Expansion Rate and Inhomogeneity Level of the Universe

The expansion of the universe could have arisen from a number of causes, ranging from a big bang explosion to certain steady state scenarios to an abruptly appearing universe. A critical level of the expansion rate, however, would not be a probable result of the big bang theory, and would be better explained by other hypotheses. The expansion rate is indeed "very close to a critical value" that had to be accurate within the incredible range of 1 in a billion billion (10^{-18}), as Davies* states:

> Closer investigation shows that the genesis paradox is actually deeper than this. Careful measurement puts the *rate of expansion very close to a critical value* at which the universe will just escape its own gravity and expand for ever. A little slower, and the cosmos would collapse, a little faster and the cosmic material would have long ago completely dispersed. It is interesting to ask precisely how delicately the rate of expansion has

been '*fine-tuned*' to fall on this narrow dividing line between two catastrophes. If at time I S (by which time the pattern of expansion was
already firmly established) the expansion rate had differed from its
actual value by more than 10^{-18}, it would have been sufficient to throw the
delicate balance out. The explosive vigour of the universe is thus
matched with almost unbelievable accuracy to its gravitating power.
The big bang was not, evidently, any old bang, but an explosion of
exquisitely arranged magnitude. In the traditional version of the big
bang theory we are asked to accept not only that the explosion just
happened, but that it happened in an exceedingly contrived fashion. *The
initial conditions had to be very special indeed.*[61]

That critical rate determines the difference between collapse and
unmanageable dispersal, as Davies* indicated. Lake* calculates
that the expansion rate must "be tuned to an accuracy of one part in
10^{50},"[62] Raymo* finds that it had to be accurate to "one part in
10^{15},"[63] and Leslie* sees disaster from change "by one part in a
million million at an initial stage . . . ."[64]

The inhomogeneity level of the universe at an evolutionary inception also had to have "highly specific initial conditions," which are
related to the previous point, in order to allow galaxies and stars to
form at all, as Gale* points out, if they did not form in one or more
discontinuous abrupt appearances:

MODELS OF COSMIC EVOLUTION indicate that the present universe, characterized both by large-scale isotropy and by smaller scale
inhomogeneities such as galaxies, would not have arisen if the *recessional velocity of the matter formed in the big bang were not equal to the
escape velocity of the matter* (the speed it needs to counteract its gravitational attraction). The first row of drawings shows the actual evolution of
the universe. The big bang had arbitrary, small scale perturbations,
which developed into inhomogeneities that condensed into galaxies. The
second row shows the evolution of a universe in which the *recessional
velocity is greater* than the escape velocity and the big bang is *homogeneous*. The present universe would be completely homogeneous and
thus would have *no galaxies*. The situation would be no better in such a
universe if the big bang had arbitrary, small-scale perturbations, as the
third row indicates. Such perturbations would result in large-scale inhomogeneities that would not condense into galaxies. The fourth row presents the evolution of a universe where the *recessional velocity is less* than
the escape velocity and the big bang has small-scale perturbations. The
perturbations grow into *inhomogeneities* that eventually start to condense. Before galaxies can form, however, the *universe collapses*. It
appears that the observed combination of large-scale isotropy and small-
scale clustering could arise only from highly specific initial conditions.
. . .[65]

Saying the same thing in a different way, Ellis* refers to the "very special initial conditions" whose reason is "obscure" of "why the density of matter is so close to the critical value separating recollapsing universes from ever-expanding universes,"[66] and Trefil* identifies as one of the "four fundamental problems associated with our picture of the Big Bang" "why the mass of the universe is so close to the critical value required to close the universe."[67] That is further discussed in Section 6.4.

b. Critical Levels of the Four Forces

The four physical forces are at critical levels such that "the smallest change" would leave "a Universe in which there could be no life," Jastrow* notes:

> Yes, there is another aspect of modern astronomical discoveries that is, in my view, as remarkable as the evidence for the abrupt birth of the Universe. According to the picture of the evolution of the Universe developed by the astronomer and his fellow scientists, the smallest change in any of the circumstances of the natural world, such as the relative strengths of the forces of nature, or the properties of the elementary particles, would have led to a Universe in which there could be no life and no man.[68]

The critical value of the strong nuclear force is described by Barrow* and Tipler*:

> The existence of deuterium and the non-existence of the di-proton therefore hinge precariously on the precise strength of the nuclear force. If the strong interaction were *a little stronger* the diproton would be a stable bound state with catastrophic consequences—all the hydrogen in the Universe would have been burnt to He^2 during the early stages of the Big Bang and *no hydrogen compounds or long-lived stable stars* would exist today. If the di-proton existed we would not! Also if the nuclear force were *a little weaker* the deuteron would be unbound with other adverse consequences for the nucleosynthesis of biological elements because a key link in the chain of nucleosynthesis would be removed. *Elements heavier than hydrogen would not form. . . .*
>
> . . ..
>
> A 50% decrease in the strength of the nuclear force . . . would adversely affect the stability of all the elements essential to living organisms and biological systems. Similarly, holding the strong force constant, we see that the stability of carbon requires the fine structure constant $å$ to be less than [four times its current level].[69]

Others such as Gale*,[70] Raymo*,[71] and Leslie*[72] concur.

The critical level of the weak nuclear force similarly is such that if it were larger there would be no hydrogen and instead there would be all helium and heavy elements, but if it were smaller there would be all hydrogen and no heavy elements, in either case preventing life.[73]

The critical level of the gravitational force is such that if it were larger then no small stars would form,[74] but if it were smaller then no large stars would form and no heavy elements could be produced, and "the main sequence would consist only of red dwarfs" that "radiate too feebly" for life.[75] The photon-to-baryon ratio is an important "coincidence," because if it were much higher "galaxies and stars would be unable to form through gravitational condensation," Carr* and Rees* note.[76]

The critical level of the electromagnetic force is such that if it were much larger or smaller then no chemical bonds would form. "Increase in electromagnetism's strength by a factor of 1.6 would result in rapid decay of protons into leptons according to recent Unified Theories; if not, then a threefold increase in the electron's charge (which is a manifestation of this strength) would make all but hydrogen impossible, while a comparable decrease would mean that even interstellar heat would destroy all neutral atoms," Leslie* points out.[77]

The mass ratio of the proton to the neutron also is critical:

> For there to exist the couple of hundred stable elements which are the basis of chemistry and biology, the *mass of the neutron* must exceed that of the proton but only by about twice the mass of the electron—and that means *by only one part in a thousand . . ..*[78]

c. Critical Features of the Physical Universe

Many other aspects of the universe are necessary to "allow life to develop within it at some stage in its history," consistent with the strong anthropic principle.

"A planet which can support biological structures must have a temperature" within a narrow range, an atmosphere of certain gases, and a gravitational force within a certain range, Barrow* and Tipler* note.[79] Such a planet also probably must have water, hydrogen and oxygen, and carbon and nitrogen to support any imaginable form of life.[80]

A sun "must radiate enough energy to warm a habitable region of space," and "the red dwarf radiates too feebly."[81] If cosmic evolution is to be possible, a sun also "must live long enough for living organisms to evolve," and a "blue giant burns out too quickly," so that "[w]hat is needed is a star such as the sun, whose position on the main sequence is at the sharp division between the blue giants and the red dwarfs...."[82] The sun also must have a spectral temperature within a narrow range:

> The fact that life can develop on a planet suitably positioned in orbit about a stable, long-lived star relies on the *close proximity of the spectral temperature of starlight to the molecular binding energy* [*1] Rydberg. Were it to greatly exceed this value, living organisms would be either sterilized or destroyed; were it far below it, the delicate photochemical reactions necessary for biology to flourish would proceed too slowly....[83]

The counterargument is often made that there are many worlds, so that what is statistically impossible in this universe also is statistically possible in one of many universes. That concept of quantum mechanics is not based on empirical evidence, of course, but on an assumption that statistical improbability must be thus corrected. Without substantiation, it remains special pleading.

Summary. Therefore, under the strong anthropic principle, the "Universe must have those properties which allow life to develop within it at some stage" (Barrow* and Tipler*[84]). Those properies are not the most likely and expected ones, but are extremely improbable ones, so that "there is a grand design in the Universe that favours the development of intelligent life" (Press*[85]). Instead, those highly improbable properties are better explained by an abruptly appearing universe in initial complex form, according to some non-evolutionist scientists. First, the universe's "rate of expansion [must be] very close to a critical value," and in fact must be "fine-tuned" to one part in a billion billion (Davies*[86]), if not one part in 10^{50} (Lake*[87]). Also, the inhomogeneity level of the early universe, in order to make cosmic evolution anything but impossible, had to have "highly specific initial conditions" such that "the recessional velocity" was "equal to the escape velocity" (Gale*[88]). Second, the four forces had to be at critical levels. If the strong nuclear force changed, it would prevent "hydrogen compounds or long-lived stable stars" in one direction and would prevent "[e]lements heaver than hydrogen" in the other direction (Barrow* and Tipler*[89]). If the weak force changed, it would leave no hydrogen in one direction and all hydrogen in the other, rather than the essential mix of light and heavy elements (Leslie*[90]). Third, physical features of the universe must also be at critical levels to permit any imaginable form of life, such as planets, suns, etc. (Barrow* and Tipler*[91]). Whether or not cosmic evolution can produce a complex universe once so many special initial conditions are present, it can neither produce nor explain so many improbable special conditions, and their abrupt appearance seems much more likely to many scientists.

Figure 6.4
The universe is
characterized by
"inhomogeneity
right up to the
largest observ-
able scales"
(Oldershaw*)

6.4 The Heterogeneity Argument: Empirical Evidence of Abrupt Appearance of the Universe

The heterogeneity argument is founded on the significantly uneven distribution of matter in the universe (the lumpiness of the universe).

a. Empirical Evidence of Inhomogeneity

"Theorists are particularly disturbed, Jeremiah P. Ostriker of Princeton University notes, by the growing evidence of large-scale inhomogeneity in the universe's structure, which conflicts with the uniformity of the cosmic background radiation," a 1987 article points out.[92] In fact, there is "a drastic lack of homogeneity" in the celestial bodies, according to Alfvén*.[93] "[T]here is a growing body of evidence for inhomogeneity right up to the largest observable scales," Oldershaw* adds, and "over the last 300 years we have repeatedly discovered ever-larger inhomogeneities in the distribution of matter: stars, stellar clusters, galaxies, groups of galaxies, clusters of groups, and clusters of clusters."[94] That inhomogeneity probably "characterizes the entire universe," Gregory* and Thompson* add:

> It has become abundantly clear from the red-shift surveys that the present-day distribution of galaxies is highly inhomogeneous out to a

distance of several hundred million light-years. It seems probable that the inhomogeneity extends out to billions of light-years and characterizes the entire universe.[95]

There is a "clumping of matter into galaxies, clusters of galaxies, superclusters of clusters and so on," Guth* and Steinhardt* agree. The universe is simply "strikingly clumpy," Peebles* observes:

> The large-scale distribution of matter is *strikingly clumpy*; we see stars in galaxies, galaxies in groups and clusters, and clusters in superclusters (1).[96]

This "is in fact one of the major unsolved problems of cosmology," Waldrop* notes,[97] and is an "obscure" issue as to "why the Universe is so nearly uniform, and yet not uniform," Ellis* adds.[98]

There is significant inhomogeneity of radiation just as there is of matter. Although the microwave background radiation has long been the textbook example of homogeneity, "even the predicted 'perfect' isotropy of the 3K microwave radiation appears to be in question," Oldershaw* notes:

> Today this category of support for an initial singularity and global homogeneity has been somewhat *weakened* by new evidence.
>
> Troubles began when improved data on the spectrum shape were found to be inconsistent with a simple black body distribution for a single temperature (Woody and Richards, 1979). Today physicists have not only verified *significant deviations* from the predicted spectrum, but more importantly, it has been shown that these deviations are of a type that is completely opposite from those that might have been readily accounted for (Bontz *et al.*, 1981). Cosmologists had pointed out that turbulent energy dissipation, post-recombination reheating and spectra superposition could be invoked if there was an excess of photons at high energies. However, the observed deviations involve excesses at the low-energy end of the spectrum and these features have no ready explanation within the content of 'Big Bang' models. Even more significant was the discovery that the 3K microwave radiation is *not isotropic*.
>
> By 1979 George Smoot and his colleagues at the University of California (Berkeley) had demonstrated a *dipole anisotropy* in the microwave background radiation. . . .[99]

There is also inhomogeneity of the x-ray background radiation (which is further discussed in Section 7.2 (b)):

> Fabian *et al.* (1980) reported that the X-ray background radiation, which is primarily derived from discrete sources, also possessed what appeared to be an intrinsic dipole anisotropy coincident with the microwave background anisotropy. Their data suggested inhomogeneity in the distribution of matter over a scale *equal to or greater than 3000 Mpc.* Finally, the discovery of a quadrupole anisotropy . . . .[100]

The problem is not solved by a counter-distribution of invisible intergalactic gas, according to Vaucouleurs*:

> If so, it seems difficult to believe that, whereas *visible matter is conspicuously clumpy and clustered on all scales*, the invisible intergalactic gas is uniform and homogeneous. This is perhaps conceivable for radiation, but not for matter, whether it be diffused or condensed. Certainly interstellar matter is extremely clumpy and irregularly distributed; so are the high-latitude, high-velocity neutral hydrogen clouds in the galactic corona; why then should intergalactic gas be smoothly spread out throughout the universe?
>
> . . ..
>
> If, therefore, we grant that *clumpiness in the distribution of matter in the universe* is a basic property of fundamental importance for cosmology and not merely a local nuisance that can be ignored in the grand smoothed-out view, we must pay much more attention than we have thus far to the possible consequences of this situation.[101]

Nor is the problem solved by black holes and other nonluminous matter, as discussed in Section 6.1(b).

The extent of heterogeneity is underscored by the recent discovery of a "300-million-light-year gap in the distribution of galaxies" that Waldrop* describes,[102] and vast voids that Silk*[103] and others[104] note. It is also underscored by the contrary homogeneity of the microwave background radiation, which Gale* noted above and Silk*[105] and Leslie*[106] point out.

b. Conflict with the Big Bang Theory

The current heterogeneity of the universe conflicts with the standard big bang explanation, Seiden* acknowledges:

> The standard *Big Bang model does not give rise to lumpiness.* That model assumes the universe started out as a globally smooth, homogeneous expanding gas. If you apply the *laws of physics* to this model, you get a *universe that is uniform*, a cosmic vastness of evenly distributed atoms with no organization of any kind.[107]

The only way that such a smooth and homogeneous universe could be avoided, and that galaxies and stars could be possible, is "a peculiar state of extraordinary but not quite perfect uniformity" during the postulated first fraction of a second after a big bang event, as Guth* and Steinhardt* point out:

> Even with the assumption of large-scale uniformity, the standard big-bang model requires yet another *assumption* to explain the nonuniformity observed on smaller scales. To account for the *clumping of matter into galaxies, superclusters of clusters and so on*, a spectrum of

primordial inhomogeneities must be *assumed* as part of the initial conditions. The fact that the spectrum of inhomogeneities has *no explanation* is a drawback in itself, but the problem becomes even more pronounced when the model is extended back to 10^{-45} second after the big bang. The incipient clumps of matter develop rapidly with time as a result of their gravitational self-attraction, and so a model that begins at a very early time must begin with small inhomogeneities. To begin at 10^{-45} second *the matter must start in a peculiar state of extraordinary but not quite perfect uniformity*. A normal gas in thermal equilibrium would be far too inhomogeneous, owing to the random motion of particles. This peculiarity of the initial state of matter required by the standard model is called the *smoothness problem*.[108]

Note that they call the critical condition an "assumption" that "has no explanation." Gale* concurs that "[t]he only universe in which matter could form both galaxies and exhibit large-scale isotropy is a universe whose recessional velocity is equal to the escape velocity,"[109] and Ellis* calls that the "very special initial condition"[110] that was discussed in Section 6.3.

The "smoothness problem"[111] is generally acknowledged, for example by Lake*,[112] Narlikar* and Padmanabhan*,[113] and Grøn*.[114] Although inflationary universe advocates claim to have provided a solution, that theory comes with its own difficulties.[115]

Summary. The heterogeneity of the universe involves "inhomogeneity right up to the largest observable scales," with the discovery of "ever-larger inhomogeneities in the distribution of matter: stars, stellar clusters, galaxies, groups of galaxies, clusters of groups, and clusters of clusters" (Oldershaw*[116]). That heterogeneity could result only from the abrupt appearance in that complex form or from an explosion with the exceedingly improbable special condition that "the recessional velocity is exactly equal to the escape velocity" (Gale*[117]). That clustering involves a "distribution of galaxies [that] is highly inhomogeneous" probably for the "entire universe" (Gregory* and Thompson*[118]), and between the galaxies vast and uneven voids (Waldrop*[119]). By contrast, "[t]he standard Big Bang model does not give rise to lumpiness" but to "a universe that is uniform, ... with no organization of any kind" (Patrusky*[120]), except by adding the "assumption" with "no explanation" of a big bang starting "in a peculiar state of extraordinary but not quite perfect uniformity"— the "smoothness problem" (Guth* and Steinhardt*[121]). The more natural interpretation of heterogeneity is abrupt appearance of the universe in that form, many nonevolutionist scientists suggest.

Figure 6.5
"One of the chief problems in cosmology is to explain why in an expanding universe matter becomes aggregated into galaxies" (Encyclopaedia Britannica) (picture of the Great Nebula in Andromeda)

6.5 The Galaxy and Star Formation Argument: Empirical Evidence of Abrupt Appearance of Celestial Bodies

The galaxy and star formation argument arises from the origination of clusters of galaxies, of galaxies of stars, and of stars themselves.

a. Galaxy Formation by Discontinuous Abrupt Appearance

The origin of galaxies poses a major problem, as *Encyclopaedia Britannica* notes:

Origin of galaxies. *One of the chief problems in cosmology* is to explain why in an expanding universe matter becomes aggregated into galaxies.
. . .

. . ..

A spherical region that is part of an expanding gas cloud will become unstable when the expansion velocity at its surface is greater than the velocity of sound. When the region becomes unstable, its density increases as compared to the mean density. But the rate of this increase is extremely slow *An expanding universe in fact is not dramatically unstable*; and this has led to an *impasse in the study of galaxy formation....*[122]

One of the "four fundamental problems associated with our picture of the Big Bang" is "how the galaxies could have formed in the time allotted for this process," as Trefil* points out.[123] "The Big Bang theory has not yet resolved . . . the nature of the galaxies," Silk* concedes.[124]

The problem is twofold. First, galaxies could only form after a big bang explosion if highly improbable conditions existed (if at all), as the preceding sections described, so that the expansion rate after the explosion had to be exact "by one part in a million million," and the homogeneity (smoothness) had to be at a critical value.[125]

Second, galaxies somehow had to form around inhomogeneities, and it still "is hard to see how galaxies could have formed in a universe which is flying apart so fast," as Leslie* states:

It seems, for instance, that altering the rate of expansion at the *Big Bang* very marginally would have made our universe fall to bits too fast or undergo recollapse too quickly for Life to stand a chance of evolving. Persuading expanding gases to form themselves into galaxies of stars and planets requires an adjustment of gravitational and explosive forces quite as delicate as that between the two halves of a pencil in balance on a razor's edge. . . .

(a) True, *galaxy formation* is not well understood. Yet the now standard (Friedmann-Robertson-Walker) models of our universe are extremely sensitive to small changes in the expansion rate (and hence to the strength of the gravitational force). *Reduction by one part in a million million at an initial stage would seemingly have led to recollapse* in under 100,000 years and before temperatures had fallen below 10,000 degrees. Equivalently tiny increases would have had similarly huge results. Even as matters stand it is *hard to see how galaxies could have formed in a universe which is flying apart so fast*—and an early speed increase by one thousandth would quickly have led to a thousandfold increase. (b) Again, *very slight reductions in the smoothness* with which matter is distributed. . . would apparently have multiplied the primeval heat billions of times with *disastrous* effects.[126]

The reason why it would be extremely difficult for galaxies to form is described by Breuer*:

The dilemma is a simple one: *within* the early phase, which was dominated by radiation, 'bunching' of matter was prevented. . . . *After the* decoupling of radiation and matter, it was not possible for the very small irregularities then present in the distribution of the gas to increase quickly enough to form entire galaxies.[127] "[S]mall perturbations of the gravitational field and of the distribution of matter in [an] expanding universe either decrease with time or increase so slowly that they cannot serve as centres of formation of separate nebulae or stars," Lifshitz* adds.[128] Thus, "books are full of plausible tales..., but the sad truth is that we do not know how the galaxies came into being," John* concludes.[129]

b. Star Formation by Discontinuous Abrupt Appearance

The origin of stars poses a similar problem, because for gas clouds "ordinarily the internal pressure is much stronger than the gravitation,"[130] so that the gas cloud would expand rather than contract to form a star. Before any stars existed, a fluctuation in the gas pressure could not be caused by star formation or supernovas (star explosions); and thereafter, fluctuations generally could not be great enough to overcome the great disparity between high outward gas pressure and low inward gravitational pressure. Similarly, the cool temperature that could cause a gas cloud to collapse would not come about after a hot big bang.[131]

Proponents of the big bang theory must offer extremely complex sequences for star formation—and still generally assume rather than explain the pivotal contraction of a gas cloud around inhomogeneities. For example, Boss* recently outlined the convoluted present thinking:

> MODELS OF STAR FORMATION grow in accuracy and detail as astrophysicists employ increasingly realistic pictures of a star's parent dust cloud. The *earliest model (A)* pictures the cloud as a perfect sphere that does not rotate. The first panel shows the dynamic-collapse phase, in which gas and dust fall rapidly toward the cloud's center. When the center becomes so dense that it is opaque to infrared radiation, the compressional energy produced by the collapse can no longer radiate from the cloud. Instead it adds to the thermal energy, increasing gas pressure and stopping the dynamic collapse: a first core is formed. Eventually the first core becomes hot enough so that diatomic hydrogen molecules break up into single atoms. As it breaks up, the hydrogen absorbs heat and so the core's temperature falls. Pressure inside the core drops rapidly until it is no longer able to withstand the force of gravity, and a second dynamic collapse occurs. Once all the hydrogen is dissociated the second collapse halts and the final core forms. In a *more sophisticated model (B)* a cloud that is symmetric about an axis rotates.

Matter along the axis collapses faster than matter away from the axis (which feels an apparent "centrifugal force"), and so the cloud assumes a lozenge shape, which eventually turns into a ring. If the rotating cloud is even slightly irregular, the ring may break up into two or more fragments. . . .[132]

That complex and, one suspects, unworkable mechanism resembles the incredibly complex epicycles of Ptolemaic astronomy—and invites Copernican replacement with the theory of abrupt appearance.

c. Solar System Formation by Discontinuous Abrupt Appearance

The origin of the solar system presents similar problems, as Jeffreys* acknowledges:

To sum it up, I think that all suggested accounts of the origin of the Solar System are subject to serious objections. The conclusion in the present state of the subject would be that *the system cannot exist*.[133]

The solar nebula hypothesis seems to be ruled out by the "variations in the isotopic composition of meteorites," the sun, and the planets, Kerr*[134] and Cameron*[135] suggest. Instead,

First, we see that material torn from the Sun would not be at all suitable for the formation of the planets as we know them. Its composition would be hopelessly wrong. And our second point in this contrast is that it is the Sun that is normal and the Earth that is the freak. The interstellar gas and most of the stars are composed of material like the Sun, not like the Earth. . . .[136]

Summary. The formation of galaxies, galactic clusters, stars, and solar systems simply does not result from an explosion such as the big bang, nonevolutionist scientists such as Hoyle suggest:

This persistent weakness has haunted the big bang theory ever since the 1930s. It can probably be understood most easily by thinking to begin with of what happens when a bomb explodes. After detonation, fragments are thrown into the air, moving with essentially uniform motion. As is well-known in physics, *uniform motion is inert*, capable in itself of doing nothing. It is only when the fragments of a bomb strike a target—a building for example—that anything happens. . . . But in a single big bang there are no targets at all, because the whole universe takes part in the explosion. There is nothing for the expanding material to hit against, and after sufficient expansion, the whole affair *should go dead*. However, we actually have a Universe of continuing activity instead of one that is uniform and inert. Instead of matter all the time becoming colder and more spread out, we often see it clustering together to produce the brilliant light of swirling galaxies and exploding stars. Why should this be so against expectations which appear soundly based in all other aspects of physical experience?[137]

[E]ven though outward speeds are maintained in a free explosion, *internal motions are not.* Internal motions die away adiabatically, and the *expanding system becomes inert*, which is exactly why the big bang cosmologies lead to a universe that is dead and done with almost from its beginning.[138]

Even if the expanding debris from an explosion were not inert, "there is no reasonable astronomical scenario in which mineral grains can condense."[139]

Formation of galaxies required not just incredibly accurate critical levels of expansion rate and smoothness, but a process whereby "galaxies could have formed in a universe which is flying apart so fast" (Leslie*[140]) despite that, "[a]fter the decoupling of radiation and matter, it was not possible for the very small irregularities then present in the distribution of the gas to increase quickly enough to form entire galaxies" (Breuer*[141]). Formation of stars confronts similar obstacles, because for gas clouds "ordinarily the internal pressure is much stronger than the gravitation" (Cameron*[142]). Thus, "[o]ne of the chief problems in cosmology is to explain why in an expanding universe matter becomes aggregated into galaxies" (Harrison*[143]), and "[t]he conclusion in the present state of the subject would be that the[solar] system cannot exist" (Jeffreys*[144]).

Figure 6.6
The polonium halos without uranium traces "would imply almost instantaneous cooling and crystallization" of granites (Kazmann)(diagram of polonium and uranium halos)*

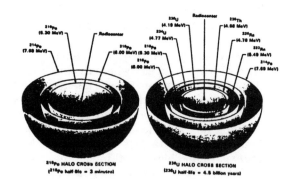

6.6 The Radiohalos Argument: Empirical Evidence of Abrupt Appearance of the Earth

The radiohalos argument is based on the presence of certain polonium halos in the earth's crust, which effectively require a nearly instantaneous appearance of a cool earth in complex form, in view of the following analysis if its assumptions are correct.

A "radiohalo" or radioactive halo is a discolored region in a mineral that contains a radioactive element. The discolored region consists of concentric spheres around the radioactive element produced usually by alpha particles emitted as the radioactive element decays, as Joly* and Mügge* discovered in 1907.[145] Polonium is a radioactive element, and it therefore decays (Po-218 decays into Po-214, then into Po-210, then into Pb-206 (lead)). A "polonium halo" is a discolored region of tiny spheres formed around the polonium as it decays, generally in mica or fluorite in granite. Three forms (isotopes) of polonium (Po-218, Po-214 and Po-210) decay very rapidly, so that their halflives (a halflife is the time required for half of a radioactive material to decay) are extremely short (3.05 minutes, 16/100,000 second, and 138.4 days respectively).[146]

a. Abrupt Appearance of a Cool Earth

The significance of those polonium halos is described by Kazmann* of LSU:

> The polonium halos, especially those produced by[218]Po, are the center of a mystery. The half life of the isotope is only 3 minutes. Yet the halos have been found in granitic rocks . . . in all parts of the world, including Scandinavia, India, Canada, and the United States. The difficulty arises from the observation that there is no identifiable precursor to the polonium: *it appears to be primordial polonium.* If so, how did the surrounding rocks crystallize rapidly enough so that there were crystals available ready to be imprinted with radiohalos by alpha particles from [218]Po? This would *imply almost instantaneous cooling and crystallization* of these granitic minerals, and we know of no mechanism that will remove heat so rapidly: the rocks are supposed to have cooled over millennia, if not tens of millennia.[147]

The "world's foremost expert on the observation and measurement of radiohalos"[148] is Gentry, a creationist physicist, who has researched polonium halos for 20 years and published more than a dozen scholarly articles on his research in standard scientific publications.[149] He summarizes the way in which polonium halos provide affirmative evidence for an abrupt appearance of a complex earth:

> My challenge to this view hinges on the simple fact that I claim the various types of polonium halos that exist in these Precambrian granites initiated from primordial rather than secondary Po radioactivity, and that these primordial Po halos constitute *prima facie evidence of a virtually instantaneous creation* of these rocks.[150]

> Likewise, unless the creation of the radioactivity and rocks were simultaneous there would be no picture—no [polonium] halos. Further, by virtue of the very short half-life, the radioactivity and the formation of the rocks *must be almost instantaneous.*[151]

Gentry has published in several other articles that requirement for instantaneous crystallization,[152] and reports the results of highly sophisticated experimental techniques such as fission track and neutron flux techniques, electron microscope x-ray fluorescence, fossil alpha recoil analysis, and ion microprobe mass spectrometry.

To spell this out further, the polonium halos come from polonium that was present in the earth's crust when the earth originated, for two independent reasons. These are first that the polonium halos are in granite that is believed to be part of the earth's original rocks,[153] and second that no uranium or thorium is present in the polonium halo centers (polonium ordinarily comes from uranium and/or thorium decay).[154] The polonium halos could only form in cool rock and not in molten rock.[155] Because polonium decays so rapidly, two halos (Po-218 and Po-214) had to form in a few minutes and the third halo (Po-210) in a few years. Thus the earth's crust either had to come into existence in cool form or had to cool in a few minutes.

Further, Professor Gentry has outlined specific ways in which his conclusions are falsifiable (and they have not been falsified):

> For over 3½ years I have challenged geologists and others who believe in the evolutionary development of the granites to confirm that hypothesis, first, by synthesizing a hand-sized piece of granite, and second, by synthesizing a single Po-218 halo in that same piece of granite. The first requirement would be accepted as *falsifying* my view that the granites are primordial or created rocks, and the second would *falsify* my view that the Po halos in granites represent primordial radioactivity. With such a grand opportunity to confirm evolution and falsify my view of creation, I have searched for a reason for the deafening silence which my challenge has met.[156]

Additional research should be conducted on the halos and their host rocks.

b. Objections to the Radiohalos Argument

The challenge to Gentry's research, albeit not based on any contrary experimental evidence, is that the daughter polonium must have migrated out of rocks containing parent uranium or thorium and into the host rocks at a time after the earth's crust had cooled, so that the polonium halos would not require instantaneous appearance of a cool earth, according to Meier*,[157] Fremlin*,[158] Moazed*,[159] Dutch*,[160] and Hashemi-Nezhad*.[161] That challenge has been rebutted in several ways.

First, the absence of uranium (or thorium) movement out of, or polonium movement into, halo-containing rocks has been shown by a number of experiments. One experiment used alpha-recoil analysis, which Gentry describes:

> Yet Gentry (6), by using fission-track and α-recoil techniques, found *no evidence for a secondary origin of those Po halos in biotite*, which occurred apart from conduits (cf Figure 1*p, r, s*). Consistent with the ring structure, *fission-track analysis of the Po halo inclusions showed very little, if any, U.* Further, the α-recoil technique (Huang & Walker 33), which permits the observation of a single α-recoil pit in biotite, was employed to measure the distribution of decayed α-radioactivity in regions both adjacent to and far removed from Po halo inclusions. No differences in α-recoil density were noted in the two areas. *If U daughter α-activity had fed the Po inclusions, a significantly higher α-recoil density would have been in evidence.*[162]

Other experiments reaffirming the same point were fission track and neutron flux techniques,[163] and electron microscope x-ray fluorescence spectra analysis.[164] If any question is raised about the sheet-like nature of mica, it is important to note that polonium halos without uranium traces are also found in cordierite.[165]

Second, the absence of a uranium-decay or thorium-decay source for the polonium producing the halos is shown by lead (Pb) isotope ratios. Uranium-235 decays to lead-207, thorium-232 decays to lead-207, and polonium decays to lead-206, so that the decaying parent can be inferred from the decay product. High ratios of lead-206 (from polonium) over lead-207 (from uranium) thus indicate that the lead did not come from the uranium decay chain, as Gentry points out:

> In other Po inclusions the $^{206}Pb/^{207}Pb$ ratio has been determined as ca 10, 12, 18, 22, 25, 40, 62, and 80. The theoretical maximum possible radiogenic $^{206}Pb/^{207}Pb$ ratio, based on an instantaneous production of Pb from normal isotopic U decay, is 21.8. Therefore, $^{206}Pb/^{207}Pb$ *ratios greater than 21.8* not only reflect the existence of a unique type of Pb, but in a different way confirm the existence of *Pb derived from Po decay independent of the normal U decay chain* . . ..[166]

The same result has been reported in other publications.[167]

Finally, it is important to note that not all halos are in the uranium decay sequence; there are also halos of bismuth-212.[168]

Summary. The radiohalos argument has been described by an evolutionist as a "mystery": if it is "primordial polonium," "how did the surrounding rocks crystallize rapidly enough so that there were crystals available ready to be imprinted with radiohalos by α-particles from ^{218}Po? This would imply almost instantaneous cooling and crystallization. . ." (Kazmann*[169]). The original experimentation on the subject has been performed by a creationist physicist working with many evolutionist colleagues, and has been reported in more than a dozen scholarly articles sometimes jointly written with evolutionist coauthors (Gentry[170]). A method of falsification has been offered (Gentry[171]). The objection that the polonium was a decay product of uranium, rather than an original element in the rocks containing the halos, has been countered by numerous experiments using sophisticated techniques such as fission-track and neutron flux methods, electron microscope x-ray fluorescence, fossil alpha recoil analysis, and iron microprobe mass spectrometry, which showed that the polonium did not migrate into and the uranium (or thorium) did not migrate out of the rocks (Gentry[172]), and that the lead isotopes present resulted from polonium rather than uranium decay (Gentry[173]). Although the theory of abrupt appearance is not dependent on this particular affirmative evidence, it is strongly supported by the apparent solidity of the experimental results.

*   *   *

The theory of cosmic abrupt appearance, like biological abrupt appearance and biochemical abrupt appearance, is scientific. It consists of at least six lines of affirmative evidence, and not of mere weaknesses of cosmic evolution, in the areas of thermodynamics, information content, anthropic conditions, heterogeneity, galaxy and star formation, and radiohalos. Many evolutionists acknowledge that the thermodynamics argument requires discontinuous abrupt appearance of the universe in complex form, and admit the facts that are the basis of the other arguments while contesting the discontinuitist interpretations of those facts. Cosmic abrupt appearance deserves a hearing, whether or not it is ultimately proved to be correct, particularly in view of the speculative nature of cosmic evolution that the next chapter surveys.

Notes

[1] Lipson*, *A Physicist Looks at Evolution*, 31 Physics Bulletin 138, 138 (1980) (italics added).

[2] *E.g.*, I. Newton, *Mathematical Principles* 543-44 (2d ed. 1686, A. Motte* trans., F. Cajori* ed. 1946).

[3] For definitions of the laws of thermodynamics, *see* A. Hobson*, *Concepts in Statistical Mechanics* 143 (1971); *Harvard Project Physics* 61, 87 (G. Holton*, F. Rutherford* & F. Watson* eds. 1975).

[4] Davies*, *Chance or choice: is the Universe an accident?*, 80 New Scientist 506, 506 (1978).

[5] W. Stansfield*, *The Science of Evolution* 57 (1977) (italics added).

[6] Douglas*, *Forty Minutes with Einstein*, 50 J. Royal Astronomical Society of Canada 100 (1956).

[7] R. Jastrow*, *God and the Astronomers* 1 (1978).

[8] *Id.* at 109, 111 (italics added, capitalization deleted) (accepting big bang theory as method of origin).

[9] P. Davies*, *The Runaway Universe* 27 (1980) ("The Universe cannot have existed forever—there must have been a creation.") (accepting big bang theory as method of origin).

[10] G. Gamow*, *The Creation of the Universe* (1955).

[11] Section 13.1(b).

[12] Gould*, *The Archaeopteryx Flap*, Natural History, Sept. 1986, at 16, 18.

[13] F. Hoyle*, *The Nature of the Universe* 125 (1950) ("To avoid the issue of *creation* it would be necessary for all the material of the Universe to be infinitely old, and this it *cannot be* for a very practical reason. For if this were so, there could be no hydrogen left in the Universe. As I think I demonstrated when I talked about the insides of the stars, hydrogen is being steadily converted into helium throughout the Universe and this conversion is a one-way process—that is to say, hydrogen cannot be produced in any appreciable quantity through the breakdown of the other elements. How comes it then that the *Universe consists almost entirely of hydrogen? If matter were infinitely old this would be quite impossible.*") (emphasis added) (rejecting big bang theory).

[14] G. Van Wylen* & R. Sonntag*, *Fundamentals of Classical Thermodynamics* 248 (2nd ed. 1971).

[15] R. Wald*, *Space, Time, and Gravity: The Theory of the Big Bang* 61 (1977) (italics added).

[16] R. Jastrow*, *God and the Astronomers* 121-22 (1978) (italics added).

[17] Pagel*, *Observing the Big Bang*, 326 Nature 744, 744 (1987).

[18] *The neutrino lacks weight*, 92 New Scientist 371, 371 (1981) ("It looks as if *neutrinos do not, after all, have mass*. Recent claims to the contrary led to speculation that the existence of massive neutrinos might explain the nature of the 'missing mass', in the Universe and resolve the solar neutrino problem (*New Scientist*, vol. 86, p. 308). But the *latest evidence* from a study

in Grenoble suggests that such optimism was unfounded. . . . If neutrinos have mass, then the theorists expect them to be involved in neutrino oscillations, with the electron neutrinos in the beam spontaneously converting to other neutrinos which would not produce this reaction. But . . . the Grenoble study revealed an energy spectrum of positrons produced . . . consistent with no neutrino oscillations in the beam.") (italics added).

[19] Kwon* et al., *Search for Neutrino Oscillations at a Fission Reactor*, 24 Physical Rev. D 1097, 1097 (1981).

[20] Waldrop*, *Neutrinos: No Oscillations?*, 216 Science 605, 605 (1982) ("Opening another chapter in a continuing controversy, a team of American, German, and Swiss physicists have reported new evidence casting doubt on the idea that neutrinos exhibit a bizarre phenomenon called 'oscillation.' ").

[21] Bahcall* & Glashow*, *Upper limit on the mass of the electron neutrino*, 326 Nature 476, 476 (1987).

[22] J. Silk*, *The Big Bang* 324 (1979).

[23] G. Abell*, *Exploration of the Universe* 648 (4th ed. 1982).

[24] "Antimatter" is defined as follows by an American Institute of Physics publication:

ANTIMATTER—It is believed that all particles have antimatter counterparts, particles with identical mass and spin as the original but with many other properties (such as electric charge) reversed. Although *few such particles exist in nature*, many have been produced artificially in laboratories and small amounts are created in space by cosmic ray collisions. The question of whether material, or even whole galaxies, could be made from antiparticles is being investigated. Presently there is *no evidence for such antigalaxies*.

Glossary of Terms Used in Cosmology 2 (P. Schewe* ed. 1982) (italics added).

[25] The inflationary universe theory is described in Sections 7.1(b) and 13.1(c), and the quantum creation and creation field hypotheses are summarized in Section 13.1(d).

[26] Wilczek*, *The Cosmic Asymmetry between Matter and Antimatter*, Scientific Am., Dec. 1980, at 82, 83.

[27] Weisskopf*, *The Origin of the Universe*, 71 Am. Scientist 473, 479 (1983).

[28] J. Silk*, *The Big Bang* 319-21 (1979) (italics added).

[29] Lake*, *Windows on a New Cosmology*, 224 Science 675, 679 (1984) ("To arrange for the degree of *homogeneity* that must have been present in the early Universe and *yet separate matter and antimatter* on scales of galaxies or clusters of galaxies seems an *impossible* task after nearly two decades of effort (16). Why then is there a pronounced matter-antimatter *asymmetry* in the Universe?") (italics added).

[30] Wilczek*, *The Cosmic Asymmetry between Matter and Antimatter*, Scientific Am., Dec. 1980, at 82, 83 ("What ultimately seems decisive is the

difficulty of imagining how matter and antimatter in the early universe could have become segregated into distinct regions. It seems more likely they would have simply annihilated each other everywhere.").

[31] Note 5.

[32] Note 8.

[33] Note 9.

[34] Note 13.

[35] Note 15.

[36] Note 16.

[37] Note 26.

[38] Note 27.

[39] Note 28.

[40] Address by M. Planck* (May 1937), reprinted in A. Barth, *The Creation* 144 (1968).

[41] Davies* writes:

There is good evidence that the primeval universe was not ordered but highly chaotic: a relic of the primordial chaos survives in a curious radiation from space, believed to be the last fading remnant of the primeval heat, and the characteristics of its spectrum reveal that in the earliest moments of the universe the cosmological material was completely unstructured.

. . ..

The greatest *puzzle is where all the order in the universe came from.* It could not come by random shuffling.

Davies*, *Universe in Reverse—Can Time Run Backwards?*, Second Look 26 (1982) (italics added).

[42] Davies*, *Chance or choice: is the Universe an accident?*, 80 New Scientist 506, 506 (1978) (italics added).

[43] P. Davies*, *Superforce: The Search for a Grand Unified Theory of Nature* 223 (1984). He adds:

The very success of the scientific method depends upon the fact that the physical world operates according to rational principles which can therefore be discerned through rational enquiry. Logically, the universe does not have to be this way. We could conceive of a cosmos where chaos reigns. In place of the orderly and regimented behaviour of matter and energy one would have arbitrary and haphazard activity. Stable structures like atoms or people or stars could not exist. The real world is not this way. *It is ordered and complex.* Is that not itself an astonishing fact at which to marvel?

Id.

[44] A. Einstein*, *Lettres á* Maurice Solovine 114-15 (1956).

[45] J. Jeans*, *The Mysterious Universe* 143 (1930).

[46] W. Pollard*, *Man on a Spaceship* 49 (1967).

[47] G. Gamow*, *The Creation of the Universe* 20 (1955) (italics added).

[48] Weisskopf*, *The Frontiers and Limits of Science*, 65 Am. Scientist

405-11 (1977) ("This evolutionary history of the world, from the 'big bang' to the present universe, is a series of gradual steps *from the simple to the complicated*, from the unordered to the organized, from the formless gas of elementary particles to the morphic atoms and molecules, and further to the still more structured liquids and solids, and finally to the sophisticated living organisms.") (italics added).

[49] C. Raymo*, *The Soul of the Night* 93 (1985).

[50] I. Newton, *Mathematical Principles* 543-44 (2d ed. 1686, A. Motte* trans., F. Cajori* ed. 1946) (italics added). Not all parts of his specific deductions were scientific.

[51] G. Holton*, *Thematic Origins of Scientific Thought* 72 (1973).

[52] F. Bush*, *Astronomy* 420 (1977).

[53] Note 42.

[54] Note 44.

[55] Note 49.

[56] Note 50.

[57] J. Barrow* & F. Tipler*, *The Anthropic Cosmological Principle* 21, 16 (1986) (original in italics).

[58] Press*, *A place for teleology?*, 320 Nature 315, 315 (1986).

[59] *Id.*

[60] C. Raymo*, *The Soul of the Night* 93 (1985).

[61] P. Davies*, *Superforce: The Search for a Grand Unified Theory of Nature* 184 (1984) (italics added).

[62] Lake*, *Windows on a New Cosmology*, 224 Science 675, 678 (1984).

[63] C. Raymo*, *The Soul of the Night* 92 (1985).

[64] Leslie*, *Cosmology, Probability, and the Need To Explain Life*, in Scientific Explanation and Understanding 53, 54 (N. Rescher* ed. 1983).

[65] Gale*, *The Anthropic Principle*, Scientific Am., Dec. 1981, at 154, 164 (italics added).

[66] Ellis*, *Alternatives to the Big Bang*, 22 Ann. Rev. Astronomy & Astrophysics 157, 162 (1984).

[67] J. Trefil*, *The Moment of Creation: Big Bang Physics* 48 (1983).

[68] Jastrow*, *The Astronomer and God*, in The Intellectuals Speak Out About God 15, 21 (R. Varghese* ed. 1984) (italics added) (Jastrow* describes himself as an Agnostic).

[69] J. Barrow* & F. Tipler*, *The Anthropic Cosmological Principle* 322, 327 (1986) (italics added).

[70] Gale*, *The Anthropic Principle*, Scientific Am., Dec. 1981, at 154, 168.

[71] C. Raymo*, *The Soul of the Night* 92 (1985).

[72] Leslie*, *Cosmology, Probability, and the Need To Explain Life*, in Scientific Explanation and Understanding 53, 54 (N. Rescher* ed. 1983).

[73] *Id.*

[74] Gale*, *The Anthropic Principle*, Scientific Am., Dec. 1981, at 154, 168.

[75] *Id.*; C. Raymo*, *The Soul of the Night* 92 (1985).

[76] Carr* & Rees*, *The anthropic principle, and the structure of the physical world*, 278 Nature 605, 605 (1979).

77 Leslie*, *Cosmology, Probability, and the Need To Explain Life*, in Scientific Explanation and Understanding 53, 54 (N. Rescher* ed. 1983).

78 *Id*. (italics added).

79 J. Barrow* & F. Tipler*, *The Anthropic Cosmological Principle* 309, 307 (1986).

80 *Id*. at 524, 541, 545, 548.

81 Gale*, *The Anthropic Principle*, Scientific Am., Dec. 1981, at 154, 168.

82 *Id*.

83 J. Barrow* & F. Tipler*, *The Anthropic Cosmological Principle* 338 (1986).

84 Note 57.

85 Note 59 (not stating his own view but summarizing Barrow* and Tipler*).

86 Note 61.

87 Note 62.

88 Note 65.

89 Note 69.

90 Note 73.

91 Notes 79, 80.

92 Horgan*, *Big-Bang Bashers*, Scientific Am., Sept. 1987, at 22, 24 (although some "unconventional" solutions have been proposed).

93 H. Alfvén*, *Cosmic Plasma* 126 (1981).

94 Oldershaw*, *The Continuing Case for a Hierarchical Cosmology*, 92 Astrophysics & Space Science 347, 349 (1983).

95 Gregory* & Thompson*, *Superclusters and Voids in the Distribution of Galaxies*, Scientific Am., Mar. 1982, at 106, 113.

96 Peebles*, *The Origin of Galaxies and Clusters of Galaxies*, 224 Science 1385, 1385 (1984) (italics added).

97 Waldrop*, *Delving the Hole in Space*, 214 Science 1016, 1016 (1981) ("a striking tangle of clumps and filaments and voids").

98 Ellis*, *Alternatives to the Big Bang*, 22 Ann. Rev. Astronomy & Astrophysics 157, 162 (1984).

99 Oldershaw*, *The Continuing Case for a Hierarchical Cosmology*, 92 Astrophysics & Space Science 347, 352 (1983) (italics added).

100 *Id*. (italics added).

101 Vaucouleurs*, *The Case for a Hierarchical Cosmology*, 167 Science 1203, 1211 (1970) (italics added).

102 Waldrop*, *Delving the Hole in Space*, 214 Science 1016, 1016 (1981).

103 Silk*, *Great Voids in the Universe*, 295 Nature 367 (1982).

104 *Deep Red Shift Survey of Galaxies Suggests Million-Mpc³ Void*, Physics Today, Jan. 1982, at 17.

105 Silk*, *Great Voids in the Universe*, 295 Nature 367, 367 (1982).

106 Leslie*, *Cosmology, Probability, and the Need To Explain Life*, in Scientific Explanation and Understanding 53, 54 (N. Rescher* ed. 1983).

107 B. Patrusky*, *Why Is the Cosmos Lumpy?*, Science 81, June 1981, at 96, 96 (italics added).

[108]   Guth* & Steinhardt*, *The Inflationary Universe*, Scientific Am., May 1984, at 116, 119 (italics added).

[109]   Gale*, *The Anthropic Principle*, Scientific Am., Dec. 1981, at 154, 168.

[110]   Ellis*, *Alternatives to the Big Bang*, 22 Ann. Rev. Astronomy & Astrophysics 157, 162 (1984).

[111]   Guth* & Steinhardt*, *The Inflationary Universe*, Scientific Am., May 1984, at 116, 119.

[112]   Lake*, *Window on a New Cosmology*, 224 Science 675, 678, 680 (1984).

[113]   Narliker* & Padmanabhan*, *Creation-field cosmology: A possible solution to singularity, horizon, and flatness problems*, 32 Physical Rev. D 1928, 1928 (1985).

[114]   Grøn*, *Repulsive gravitation and inflationary universe models*, 54 Am. J. Physics 46, 48 (1986) (he believes the problem may be solved by repulsive gravitation).

[115]   Section 7.1(b).

[116]   Note 94.

[117]   Note 109.

[118]   Note 95.

[119]   Note 102.

[120]   Note 107.

[121]   Note 108.

[122]   Harrison*, *Universe, Origin and Evolution of*, in 18 Encyclopaedia Britannica 1007, 1008 (14th ed. 1974) (italics added).

[123]   J. Trefil*, *The Moment of Creation: Big Bang Physics* 48 (1983).

[124]   J. Silk*, *The Big Bang* 315 (1979).

[125]   Leslie*, *Cosmology, Probability, and the Need To Explain Life*, in Scientific Explanation and Understanding 53, 54 (N. Rescher* ed. 1983).

[126]   *Id.* (italics added).

[127]   R. Breuer*, *Contact with the Stars* 8 (1982).

[128]   Lifshitz*, *On the Gravitational Stability of the Expanding Universe*, 10 J. Physics 116, 116 (1946).

[129]   L. John*, *Cosmology Now* 85, 92 (1976). *See also* Binney*, *Oddballs and Galaxy Formation*, 255 Nature 275 (1975).

[130]   Cameron*, *The Origin and Evolution of the Solar System*, 233 Scientific Am. 35 (1975) (explaining star formation by fluctuations such as from "a supernova explosion, the formation of a massive star or a large rearrangement of the interstellar magnetic field"—"conditions which are quite rare").

[131]   Even if Bok Globules are an exception in possibly contracting, they are not sufficiently numerous to counterbalance the large number of dying stars, much less to have generated a significant portion of the vast present number of stars.

[132]   Boss*, *Collapse and Formation of Stars*, Scientific Am., Jan. 1985, at 40, 40 (italics in original, references to illustration omitted).

[133] H. Jeffreys*, *The Earth: Its Origin, History and Physical Constitution* 359 (5th ed. 1970).

[134] Kerr*, *Isotopic Anomalies in Meteorites: Complications Multiply*, 202 Science 203, 203 (1978).

[135] Cameron*, *The Origin and Evolution of the Solar System*, Scientific Am., Sept. 1975, at 33, 37.

[136] Hoyle*, *The Nature of the Universe: Part IV*, Harper's Magazine, March 1951, at 65.

[137] F. Hoyle, *The Intelligent Universe: A New View of Creation and Evolution* 183-85 (1983) (italics added).

[138] Hoyle, *The Big Bang in Astronomy*, 92 New Scientist 521, 523 (1981) (italics added).

[139] Hoyle & Wickramasinghe, *Where Microbes Boldly Went*, New Scientist 412, 413 (1981).

[140] Note 126.

[141] Note 127.

[142] Note 130.

[143] Note 122.

[144] Note 133.

[145] Gentry, *Radioactive Halos*, 23 Annual Rev. of Nuclear Science 347 (1973); Gentry, *Extinct radioactivity and the discovery of a new pleochroic halo*, 213 Nature 487, 487 (1967).

[146] Kazmann*, *It's About Time: 4.5 Billion Years*, Geotimes, Sept. 1978, at 18, 19; Feather*, *The Unsolved Problem of the Po-haloes in Precambrian Biotite and other Old Minerals*, 11 Commun. to Royal Society of Edinburgh 147, 147 (1978); Gentry, *Radiohalos in a Radiochronological and Cosmological Perspective*, 184 Science 62 (1974); note 149.

[147] Kazmann*, *It's About Time: 4.5 Billion Years*, Geotimes, Sept. 1978, at 18, 19 (he does not necessarily agree with Gentry's interpretations).

[148] National Science Foundation*, NSF Program Review Evaluation of NSF Proposal "Investigations of Polonium Radiohalos" (Sept. 1979).

[149] Gentry, *Abnormally Long Alpha-Particle Tracks in Biotite (Mica)*, 8 Applied Physics Letters 65 (1966); Gentry, *Antimatter content of the Tunguska meteor*, 211 Nature 1071 (1966); Gentry, *Alpha Radioactivity of Unknown Origin and the Discovery of a New Pleochroic Halo*, 1 Earth & Planetary Science Letters 453 (1966); Gentry, *Extinct radioactivity and the discovery of a new pleochroic halo*, 213 Nature 487 (1967); Gentry, *Fossil Alpha-Recoil Analysis of Certain Variant Radioactive Halos*, 160 Science 1228 (1968); Gentry, *Giant Radioactive Halos: Indicators of Unknown Alpha Radioactivity?*, 169 Science 670 (1970); Gentry, *Radioactive Halos in the Lunar Environment*, 1 Proc. Second Lunar Science Conf. 167 (1971); Gentry, *Radiohalos: Some Unique Pb Isotope Ratios and Unknown Alpha Radioactivity*, 173 Science 727 (1971); Gentry, *Ion microprobe confirmation of Pb isotope ratios and search for isomer precursors in Polonium radioha-*

los, 244 Nature 282 (1973); Gentry, *Radioactive Halos*, 23 Annual Rev. Nuclear Science 347 (1973); Gentry, *Radiohalos in a Radiochronological and Cosmological Perspective*, 184 Science 62 (1974); Gentry, *"Spectacle" array of* ^{210}*Po halo radiocentres in biotite*, 252 Nature 564 (1974); Gentry, *Spectacle haloes: Reply*, 258 Nature 269 (1975); Gentry *et al.**, *Radiohalos in Coalified Wood: New Evidence Relating to Time of Uranium Introduction and Coalification*, 194 Science 315 (1976); Gentry *et al.**, *Evidence for Primordial Superheavy Elements*, 37 Physical Rev. Letters 11 (1976); Gentry *et al.**, *Search with Synchrotron Radiation for Superheavy Elements in Giant-Halo Inclusions*, 38 Physical Rev. Letters 205 (1977); Gentry *et al.**, *Evidence Against Superheavy Elements in Giant-Halo Inclusions Reexamined with Synchrotron Radiation*, 40 Physical Rev. Letters 507 (1978); Gentry, *Are Any Unusual Radio Halos Evidence for SHE?*, Proc. International Symposium on Superheavy Elements (Lubbock, Texas, Mar. 9-11, 1978); Gentry *et al.**, *Reinvestigation of the [alpha]-activity of Conway granite*, 273 Nature 217 (1978); Gentry *et al.**, *Implications of unknown radioactivity of giant and dwarf halos in Scandinavian rocks*, 274 Nature 457 (1978); Gentry, *Time: Measured Responses*, 60 E.O.S. 474 (1979); Gentry, *Polonium Halos*, 61 E.O.S. 514 (1980).

150 Gentry, *Letter*, Physics Today, Apr. 1983, at 13, 13 (italics added).

151 Gentry, *Cosmology and the Earth's Invisible Realm*, Medical Opinion & Rev., Oct. 1967, at 65, 78 (italics added).

152 Gentry, *Spectacle haloes: Reply*, 258 Nature 269, 270 (1975) ("Carried to its ultimate conclusion, this means that polonium haloes, of which there are *estimated to be more than 10^{15} in the earth's basement granite rocks*, represent evidence of extinct natural radioactivity, and thus imply only a *brief period between 'nucleosynthesis' and crystallization of the host rocks*.") (italics added); Gentry, *Radiohalos in a Radiochronological and Cosmological Perspective*, 184 Science 62, 63 (1974) ("A further necessary consequence, that such Po halos could have formed only if the host rocks underwent a *rapid crystallization*, renders exceedingly difficult, in my estimation, the prospect of explaining these halos by physical laws as presently understood.") (italics added); Gentry, *Cosmology and Earth's Invisible Realm*, Medical Opinion & Rev., Oct. 1967, at 65, 78 ("This would imply that in some instances *only a few seconds* elapsed before the radioactivity responsible for certain anomalous halos became extinct. Yet if this extinct radioactivity existed for only a few seconds, how did it get buried in the crustal rocks? This is impossible according to some theories of the origin of the earth.") (italics added).

153 Gentry, *Spectacle haloes: Reply*, 258 Nature 269, 270 (1975) ("Earth's basement granitic rocks"); Gentry, *Time: Measured Responses*, 60 E.O.S. [Trans. Am. Geophysical U.] 474, 475 (1979) ("basement rocks"); Gentry, *Cosmology and Earth's Invisible Realm*, Medical Opinion & Rev., Oct. 1967, at 65, 78.

154 Gentry *et al.**, *'Spectacle' array of* ^{210}*Po[lonium] halo radiocentres in*

biotite: A nuclear geophysical enigma, 252 Nature 564, 566 (1974) ("Because the Pb isotope in these inclusions is not explicable as any combination of common, primordial, or from *in situ* Pb derived radiogenically *in situ* from U or Th, we conclude that a different type of Pb, derived from Po [alpha] decay, exists in nature.") (italics added); Gentry, *Spectacle haloes: Reply*, 258 Nature 269, 270 (1975) ("Uranium-daughter diffusion did not produce polonium haloes in rocks"). The absence of any uranium and/or thorium can be determined by scanning electron microscope x-ray fluorescence and ion microprobe mass spectrometry, and is in stark contrast to the clear evidence of uranium and/or thorium in uranium and thorium halos.

[155] See Gentry, *Radiohalos in a Radiochronological and Cosmological Perspective*, 184 Science 62, 63 (1974); Gentry, *Cosmology and the Earth's Invisible Realm*, Medical Opinion & Rev., Oct. 1967, at 65, 78.

[156] Gentry, *Letter*, Physics Today, Apr. 1983, at 13, 13. *See also* Gentry, *Time: Measured Responses*, 60 E.O.S. [Trans. Am. Geophysical U.] 474, 475 (1979) ("I will likewise relinquish any claim for primordial [218]Po halos when coercive evidence (not just plausibility arguments) is provided for a conventional origin. . . . I will consider my thesis to be *doubly falsified* by the synthesis of a biotite which contains just one [218]Po halo (some of my natural specimens contain more than 10[4] Po halos/cm[3]); Gentry, *Polonium Halos*, 61 E.O.S. 514 (1980).

[157] Meier* & Hecker*, *Radioactive Halos as Possible Indicators of Geochemical Processes in Magmatites*, 10 Geochemical J. 185 (1976).

[158] Fremlin*, *Letter*, 258 Nature 269 (1975).

[159] Moazed* et al., *Polonium Radiohalos: An Alternative Interpretation*, 180 Science 1272 (1973).

[160] Dutch*, *Letter*, Physics Today, April 1983, at 11.

[161] Hashemi-Nazhad*, *Polonium Halos in Mica*, 278 Nature 333 (1979).

[162] Gentry, *Radioactive Halos*, 23 Annual Rev. of Nuclear Science 347, 356 (1973) (italics added).

[163] Gentry, *Fossil Alpha-Recoil Analysis of Certain Variant Radioactive Halos*, 160 Science 1228 (1968).

[164] Gentry, *Radiohalos in a Radiochronological and Cosmological Perspective*, 184 Science 62 (1974).

[165] Gentry, *Radioactive Halos*, 23 Annual Rev. Nuclear Science 347, 355 (1973).

[166] *Id.* at 360-61 (italics added).

[167] Gentry, *Radiohalos: Some Unique Pb Isotope Ratios and Unknown Alpha Radioactivity*, 173 Science 727, 727 (1971); Gentry et al.*, *Ion Microprobe Confirmation of Pb Isotope Ratios and Search for Isomer Precursors in Polonium Radiohaloes*, 244 Nature 282 (1973).

[168] Gentry, *Radiohalos: Some Unique Pb Isotope Ratios and Unknown Alpha Radioactivity*, 173 Science 727 (1971); Gentry, *Radioactive Halos*, 23 Annual Rev. Nuclear Science 347, 349, 355 (1973).

[169] Note 147.

[170] Note 149.
[171] Note 156.
[172] Notes 162-65.
[173] Notes 166-67.

CHAPTER 7

Evolution as Theory and Conjecture: Cosmic Evolution of the Universe

> These arguments should indicate to the
> uncommitted that the big-bang picture is
> not as soundly established, either theoret-
> ically or observationally, as it is usually
> claimed to be. This is not to say that the
> picture is wrong and should be aban-
> doned: I simply mean that the cosmologi-
> cal problem is still wide open and alterna-
> tives to the standard big-bang picture
> should be seriously investigated. The rea-
> son that alternatives like these are not so
> well known or not well enough investi-
> gated is partly because of the prevalent
> view that the big-bang picture correctly
> describes the Universe. Personally I think

---

*Scientists cited in this chapter, unless otherwise indicated, are not pro-
ponents of, and their quoted statements are not intended as endorsements
of, either the theory of abrupt appearance or the theory of creation. However, their quoted statements are acknowledging data that involve weaknesses of the theory of evolution.

> *that closing one's options at this stage is*
> *harmful to the development of the subject*
> *as a branch of science. Astrophysicists of*
> *today who hold the view that "the ulti-*
> *mate cosmological problem" has been*
> *more or less solved may well be in for a*
> *few surprises before this century runs out.*
> —Astronomer Jayant Narlikar*[1]

Cosmic evolution is summarized by Carl Sagan* as follows in his best-selling book, *Cosmos*:

> The epic of cosmic evolution had begun, a hierarchy in the condensation of matter from the gas of the big bang—clusters of galaxies, galaxies, stars, planets, and, eventually, life and an intelligence . . . .[2]

"Cosmic evolution" (or "stellar evolution") is generally recognized as part of evolution, by Dobzhansky*, Ayala*, Stebbins* and Valentine*,[3] Mayr*,[4] Blum*,[5] Huxley*,[6] Fox* and Dose*,[7] Ponnamperuma*,[8] and many other scientific writers.[9] "Cosmic evolution" is in fact a generally accepted scientific term,[10] as are stellar evolution[11] and evolution of the universe.[12] For example, Dobzhansky*, a late leading evolutionist, stated:

> Although this article is concerned with biological evolution, it should be recognized that the *concept of evolution is much broader.* . . . There is also *cosmic*, or inorganic, *evolution*, and evolution of human culture. One of the theories advanced by cosmologists sets the beginning of *cosmic evolution* between 5 and 10 billion years ago. The origin of life, which started biological evolution, took place 3 or 4 billion years ago.[13]

The broader scope of evolution similarly has been acknowledged by Huxley*,[14] the National Academy of Sciences*,[15] and dictionary definitions.[16]

The big bang theory is the dominant explanation of cosmic evolution. This chapter discusses its ramifications as follows:

7.1 Description of the big bang and inflationary universe theories`

7.2 Primary evidence for the big bang theory and alternative explanations

7.3 Stages of the big bang and questions.

The purpose of this chapter is not to present definitively, but instead to summarize, the problems with the big bang theory that many evolutionists acknowledge.

*Figure 7.1
Because of doubts
about the big
bang theory,
scientists should
"consider both
modified 'Big
Bang' models and
alternative
models" (Older-
shaw*)*

7.1 The Big Bang and Inflationary Universe Theories: Description of Cosmic Evolution

a. Definition of the Big Bang Theory

A typical high school textbook description of the big bang theory, without presentation of any alternative theories, is as follows:

> The current theory of the origin of the universe is called the *Big Bang*. According to this theory, a fireball exploded 15 to 20 billion years ago. Then matter and energy spread outward in all directions, cooling as it expanded. After about 500,000 years, hydrogen gas formed. The gas collected into clouds which formed *galaxies* during the next half billion years. Now all that remains are galaxies and radiation. Within the galaxies, *stars* form and die and new ones form.
>
> . . . .
>
> Probably the most widely accepted theory for the origin of the *solar system* is the dust cloud theory. According to this idea, a dust cloud began to rotate.... When the mass had swept up most of the material in an eddy, a *planet* was formed.[17]

Most physics and biology texts are similar.[18] The teacher's edition to the text quoted above says to "[r]emind students that the *Big Bang theory* best supports the facts and observations that have been gathered so far by years of research."[19]

Further detail on the "Big Bang" theory of "cosmic evolution" is given by Sagan* in *Cosmos*:

> TEN OR TWENTY BILLION YEARS AGO, something happened—

the *Big Bang*, the event that began our universe. . . . That it happened is reasonably clear. All the matter and energy now in the universe was *concentrated at extremely high density*—a kind of *cosmic egg* . . . . [T]he entire universe, matter and energy and the space they fill, occupied a very small volume. . . .

In that titanic *cosmic explosion*, the universe began an expansion which has never ceased. . . . As space stretched, the matter and energy in the universe *expanded* with it and rapidly cooled. . . . The remnants of that fireball, the *cosmic background radiation*, emanating from all parts of the sky can be detected by radiotelescopes today. . . .

The early universe was filled with radiation and a plenum of *matter, originally hydrogen and helium*, formed from elementary particles in the dense primeval fireball . . . . Then little pockets of gas, small nonuniformities, began to grow. Tendrils of vast gossamer *gas clouds* formed, . . . each a kind of beast eventually to contain a hundred billion shining points. . . . We call them *galaxies*.

About a billion years after the Big Bang, the distribution of matter in the universe had become a little lumpy, perhaps because the Big Bang itself had not been perfectly uniform. . . . Their gravity drew to them substantial quantities of nearby gas, growing clouds of hydrogen and helium that were destined to become *clusters of galaxies*. . . .
. . . ..

Within the nascent galaxies, much smaller clouds were also experiencing gravitational collapse; interior temperatures became very high, thermonuclear reactions were initiated, and the first *stars* turned on. . . . The epic of *cosmic evolution* had begun, a hierarchy in the condensation of matter from the gas of the *Big Bang* . . . .[20]

There are two general formulations of the big bang theory: the single big bang theory and the oscillating universe theory. Sagan* says:

In *one*, the universe is created, somehow, ten or twenty billion years ago and expands forever, the galaxies mutually receding until the last one disappears over our cosmic horizon. . . . In the other, the *oscillating universe*, the Cosmos has no beginning and no end, and we are in the midst of an infinite cycle of cosmic deaths and rebirths . . . .[21]

Sagan* leans toward the eternally oscillating approach, and that approach is ordinarily atheistic in denying the existence and role of a creator.[22] For example, Shapley* gave his antithesis:

In the beginning was the Word, it has been piously recorded, and I might venture that modern astrophysics suggests that the Word was hydrogen gas. In the very beginning, we say, were hydrogen atoms . . . .[23]

The single big bang approach is treated by a large minority of its proponents as theistic and as involving "creation" of matter and energy.

b. Critics of the Big Bang Theory

Many noted scientists, although a minority, reject the big bang theory entirely. "A number of scientists are unhappy with the bang theory," Krauskopf* and Beiser* observe.[24] A recent article describes the dissenters:

> Nevertheless, ever since the theory won general acceptance about 20 years ago a few scientists have persistently attacked some of its fundamental assumptions. One group of critics argues that electromagnetic forces generated by plasma have been more important than gravity in shaping the universe; another asserts that red shifts are not necessarily a relic of the big bang's continuing outward thrust. These groups, although long relegated to "fringe" status by mainstream astrophysicists, have been invigorated of late by new converts and new findings.[25]

Those scientists who reject the big bang theory include physicist Hannes Alfvén*,[26] a Nobel Prize recipient and physicist at the Royal Institute of Technology in Stockholm, astronomer Sir Fred Hoyle,[27] formerly of Cambridge, whom Gould* calls an "eminent cosmologist of years past,"[28] astronomer Jayant Narlikar* of the Tata Institute of Fundamental Research (quoted above),[29] astronomer N. Chandra Wickramasinghe of University of Cardiff,[30] astronomer Geoffrey Burbidge* of University of California at San Diego,[31] physicist Allen D. Allen*,[32] physicist Hermann Bondi*,[33] physicist Robert L. Oldershaw*,[34] and physicist G. de Vaucouleurs*.[35]

Others challenge the persuasiveness of the primary evidence for the big bang theory, as Narlikar* notes:

> Yet, some cosmologists, albeit a minority, do sometimes wonder whether the confidence so often claimed in the big bang picture is justified by our observational knowledge of the Universe. In this article I will air a few of these misgivings.[36]

These doubters include astronomer Arp* of the Max Planck Institute for Physics,[37] mathematician Ellis* of University of Cape Town,[38] astrophysicist Sulentic* of University of Alabama,[39] mathematician Segal* of M.I.T.,[40] physicist Marmet* of University of Laval in Quebec,[41] astrophysicist Wolf* of University of Rochester,[42] and physicist Rees* of Stanford.[43] Even Einstein*, who did not reject the big bang theory, "was not attracted by the idea of Lemaitre's primeval atom," and remarked that "every man has his own cosmology and who can say that his own theory is right!"[44] Their criticisms are summarized in Section 7.2.

The critics argue that "it is inevitable that a new cosmological paradigm must eventually replace the 'Big Bang' paradigm," and until then "it would seem incumbent upon the scientific community

to consider both modified 'Big Bang' models and alternative models
. . . ."[45] One group offers an alternative plasma theory:

> The elder statesman of the plasma dissidents is Hannes Alfvén of the
> Royal Institute of Technology in Stockholm. Alfvén, who won the Nobel
> prize for physics in 1970, believes interstellar space is filled with long
> filaments and other structures of plasma, that is, electrons and positively
> charged ions. The same electromagnetic forces that push plasmas into
> distinctive shapes in the laboratory, Alfvén says, caused this cosmic
> plasma to coalesce into galaxies, stars and planetary systems.
>
> Alfvén believes the universe is expanding, but he speculates that the
> expansion is driven by the energy released when matter and antimatter
> meet and annihilate each other. He also believes the expansion is less
> dramatic than the big-bang theory proposes: a universe dominated by
> electromagnetic forces, he contends, could never have been less than
> one-tenth of its present diameter.[45]
>
> Critics have charged that Alfvén's cosmological ideas are vague and
> unsupported by observations. But Timothy E. Eastman of the Space
> Plasma Physics Branch of the National Aeronautics and Space Admin-
> istration points out that laboratory experiments with ever more powerful
> plasma generators and measurements by space probes have confirmed
> many of Alfvén's predictions concerning plasma within the solar sys-
> tem, at least. "There is a revolution brewing," Eastman remarks, "in
> applying this knowledge to astrophysics."
>
> Workers at the Los Alamos National Laboratory are already doing just
> that. With the help of supercomputers a team led by Anthony L. Peratt
> has created cosmological models based on recent findings about plasmas
> and on Alfvén's theories. . . .[47]

Others have questioned the prevailing interpretation of red shifts as
the "single, frail assumption" of modern astronomy:

> [T]he putative dean of the latter group, Halton C. Arp of the Mount
> Wilson and Las Campanas Observatories, says he does not share
> Alfvén's "plasma approach." Arp is concerned less with proposing
> alternative models of the cosmos than with undermining the Hubble
> relation between red shift and distance, which Arp has called the "single,
> frail assumption on which so much of modern astronomy and cosmology
> is built." Named for the American astronomer Edwin P. Hubble, who
> proposed it, the Hubble relation implies that objects outside our galaxy
> are receding from the earth at speeds proportional to their distance.
>
> Arp says he has observed many objects with red shifts that do not
> conform to the Hubble relation. . . .[48]

Another alternative is the hierarchical universe theory, which
envisages an infinite universe with a hierarchal organization,"[49] as
proposed by Vaucouleurs*.[50] Another group is seeking to modify the
big bang theory, as Narlikar* points out:

Broadly speaking, the attempt to improve upon the big-bang model may be classified into two sets: (a) quantum cosmological models and (b) inflationary models.[51]

Some quantum cosmological models are described in Section 13.1(d), and inflationary models are touched upon in Section 13.1(c).

The big bang theory well may "appear hopelessly premature" to future scientists, and "the few facts . . . are still too little understood and often too poorly established," Vaucouleurs* notes:

Nevertheless, *the few facts and figures* which in the past 40 years have been given prominence as particularly relevant to cosmology are still too little understood and often too poorly established or too recently discovered to form a solid basis for a "final" solution. Also we may well still lack some fundamental knowledge of physical laws on the very large (cosmic) scale or on the very small (particle) scale, or both, to even hope for a realistic solution at the present time. Is it not *possible, indeed probable*, that *our present cosmological ideas on the structure and evolution of the universe as a whole (whatever that may mean) will appear hopelessly premature* and primitive to astronomers of the 21st century? Less than 50 years after the birth of what we are pleased to call "modern cosmology," when so few empirical facts are passably well established, when so many different oversimplified models of the universe are still competing for attention, is it, may we ask, really credible to claim, or even reasonable to hope, that we are presently close to a definite solution of the cosmological problem?

Those who are so optimistic as to answer affirmatively have in effect already made a choice, *primarily for philosophical, aesthetic, or other extraneous reasons*, from among the vast array of possible homogeneous isotropic universes of general relativity.

. . ..

A second reason is that even within the framework of the orthodox "primeval atom" or "big bang" theory we have witnessed in the past 40 years frequent and drastic changes in the fundamental "constants. . . ."[52]

There are "an increasing number of observational facts which are difficult to reconcile" with the big bang theory, Alfvén* adds, which are being suppressed or ignored:

On the other hand, there are an increasing number of observational facts which are difficult to reconcile in the Big-Bang hypothesis. The Big-Bang establishment very seldom mentions these, and when non-believers try to draw attention to them, the powerful establishment refuses to discuss them in a fair way. . . .

The present situation is characterized by rather desperate attempts to reconcile observations with the hypothesis to 'save the phenomena.' One cannot avoid thinking of the state under the Ptolemaean epoch. *An increasing number of ad hoc assumptions* are made, which in a way correspond to the Ptolemaean introduction of more and more epicycles and eccentrics. Without caring very much for logical stringency, the agreement between these *ad hoc* assumptions with the Big-Bang hypothesis is often claimed to support the theory.

In reality, with the possible exception of the microwave background condition, *there is not a single prediction which has been confirmed.*[53] Thus, "there has been remarkably little discussion of whether the basic big bang hypothesis is correct or not," and "the large body of observations which are not in agreement with it are either accounted for by numerous *ad hoc* hypotheses or simply neglected."[54] Oldershaw* agrees that "the standard 'Big Bang' model has come into increasing conflict with improving observational data and may require substantial modification," and that there is "a deliberate refusal on the part of some theorists to accept such results when they appear to be in conflict with some of the present oversimplified . . . theories . . .!"[55]

The inflationary universe theory also is drawing criticism about "serious drawbacks," such as by Narlikar* and Padmanabhan*:

> The inflationary models . . . are also not without *serious drawbacks* of their own. All straightforward inflationary scenarios lead to a *universe far too inhomogeneous* to be acceptable. Even assuming that this problem is somehow sorted out inflation does not solve the *problem of singularity or "creation."* (In the conventional models, the inflationary phase is always preceded by a hot, radiation-dominated epoch which is singular. One can, of course, think of quantum gravitational inflationary models which may avoid the singularity; the objections raised in the previous paragraph are relevant again). Thus inflationary models also *fall short* of the ideal.[56]

Three other difficulties are summarized by Tipler*:

> There are three other problems with inflation which may prove more difficult to handle. First, there is the *problem of the phase transition.* Only if the transition is slow and smooth will there be a sufficient amount of inflation. The "new inflationary universe" was based on a semi-classical calculation of the transition, and it appeared to give the appropriate transition. However, a calculation based on full quantum field theory [by Mazensko, Unruh, & Wald (1985)] suggests that quantum fluctuations would destroy the necessary smoothness. If this is confirmed the inflationary model will have to be abandoned.
>
> The second problem is that *inflation is able to smooth out only rather small irregularities* in a true big bang cosmology (Barrow & Turner 1981). This means that inflation only works in a small subset of the possible cosmological solutions to the Einstein equations. . . .
>
> But this just leads to the third problem. *Infinite de Sitter space* (and hence the steady state theory) is null geodesically incomplete in the worst

possible way: the incomplete null geodesics terminate at a Cauchy horizon through which a unique extension can be made, because the Cauchy horizon is not due to the intrinsic structure of spacetime, as in the examples above, but rather due to a bad choice of the initial data space-like hypersurface (Hawking & Ellis 1973). . . . The usual assumption in general relativity is that the only acceptable Cauchy horizons are due to the intrinsic properties of the spacetime.[57]

Figure 7.2
Under the big bang theory, an "increasing number of ad hoc assumptions . . . correspond to the Ptolemaean introduction of more and more epicycles and eccentrics" (Alfvén*, a Nobel Prize recipient)

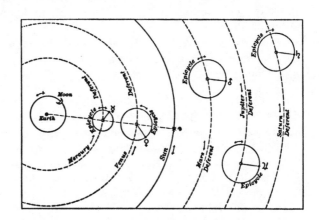

7.2 The Primary Evidence for the Big Bang Theory: Questions from Alternative Explanations

The two critical lines of evidence supporting the big bang theory of cosmic evolution are (a) red shift and (b) microwave background radiation, as Sagan* recognizes:

The discovery of the Big Bang and the recession of the galaxies came from a commonplace of nature called the Doppler effect . . . .

This *red shift*, observed in the spectral lines of distant galaxies and interpreted as a Doppler effect, is the *key to cosmology*. . . .

. . ..

The apparent recession of the galaxies, with the red shift interpreted through the Doppler effect, is not the only evidence for the Big Bang. Independent and *quite persuasive evidence* derives from the *cosmic blackbody background radiation*, . . . at just the intensity expected in our epoch from the now substantially cooled radiation of the Big Bang.[58]

Red shift is the "shift of a spectrum of light toward longer (redder) wavelengths," which can be caused by several factors. Doppler redshifts "are caused by recession of one object in relation to another, and are similar to the Doppler effect of a car rapidly driving away and causing the sound heard by an observer to shift from treble to bass." "A gravitational red shift is the shift to longer wavelengths of light passing through a large gravitational field."[59] Other causes of red shifts are described later in this section.

However, there are significant problems with using each of these primary lines as evidence for the big bang theory, which are recognized by some evolutionists whose conclusions are discussed in this section.[60] Burbidge* concludes that the evidence for a big bang approach is "much less definite than is widely realized," and is not "conclusive":

> The evidence in favour of a *big bang* cosmology is *much less definite than is widely realized*, and it is not impossible that we are living in a steady state universe.
>
> . . ..
>
> This concludes my discussion of direct observational evidence bearing on whether or not the universe is evolving and began in a dense state. I believe that if one attempts to evaluate this evidence objectively *there is still no really conclusive evidence in favour of such a universe.*[61]

Ellis* determines that there are "a variety of possibilities available" besides a big bang event to explain the evidence:

> *There are then a variety of possibilities available*, both within standard general relativity (where a variety of geometrics are considered) and in variations of that theory, for understanding the nature of the origin of the Universe. The SHBB [standard hot big bang theory] is one of this family but is *by no means the only conceivable member; further possibilities are not completely excluded* experimentally or theoretically.[62]

He outlines the areas open to different interpretation:

> The discussion above makes clear the nature of the available *alternatives* if one is to avoid the conclusion that the Universe originates in a SHBB [standard hot big bang]. One *can question*
>
> 1. the *nature of the observed redshifts* (Equations 1-3) by adopting either a different theory of light propagation or a different astrophysical interpretation;
>
> 2. the *conservation laws and/or gravitational field equations* (Equations 5-7);
>
> 3. the *nature of matter* in the Universe, e.g. by assuming some effective contribution to the matter stress tensor that violates the energy conditions (Equation 9).
>
> . . ..
>
> 4. the *assumption of exact spatial homogeneity and isotropy*. Then at least one of the shear, vorticity, and acceleration will be nonzero (so Equation 10 does not follow from Equation 8). Singularities will still occur in the past. . . , but they can be so different from the SHBB in their geometry and physics as to represent quite different initial situations.[63]

The expansion of the universe similarly "does not imply the singularly dense superpositioned state used in the big bang model," and so is not evidence for that theory, Allen* notes:

> Recent computer simulations indicate that a system of gravitating masses breaks up, even when the total energy is negative. As a result, *almost any initial phase-space distribution results in a universe that eventually expands* under the Hubble law. *Hence Hubble expansion implies little regarding an initial cosmic state.* Especially it does not imply the singularly dense superpositioned state used in the big bang model.[64]

In fact, expansion itself poses problems for the big bang, Oldershaw* observes: "One often reads that the observed expansion is highly regular, but one almost never finds references to empirical results that justify this assertion. . . . [E]vidence favoring non-uniform expansion has prevailed during the last decade."[65]

Discontinuitist scientists do *not* question the existence of red shift and microwave background radiation, and generally are equally comfortable with an expanding or other universe, but merely join many evolutionist scientists in questioning the interpretations of those facts as evidence for the big bang theory and for cosmic evolution.

a. Red Shift: The Big Bang Explanation and Alternative Explanations

Many astronomers and astrophysicists, some of whom were listed in Section 7.1(b), have questioned whether the red shifts actually arise from expansion of the universe as big bang proponents believe, and thus whether the acknowledged occurrence of red shift provides any support at all for the big bang theory. Sagan* summarizes the debate:

> The astronomer Halton Arp has found *enigmatic and disturbing cases where a galaxy and a quasar, or a pair of galaxies, that are in apparent physical association have very different red shifts.* Occasionally there seems to be a bridge of gas and dust and stars connecting them. If the red shift is due to the expansion of the universe, very different red shifts imply very different distances. But two galaxies that are physically connected can hardly also be greatly separated from each other—in some cases by a billion light-years. Skeptics say that the association is purely statistical; that, for example, a nearby bright galaxy and a much more distant quasar, each having very different red shifts and very different speeds of recession, are merely accidentally aligned along the line of sight; that they have no real physical association. Such statistical

alignments must happen every now and then. The debate centers on whether the number of coincidences is more than would be expected by chance. Arp points to other cases in which a galaxy with a small red shift is flanked by two quasars of large and almost identical red shift. He believes the quasars are not at cosmological distances but instead are being ejected, left and right, by the "foreground" galaxy; and that *the red shifts are the result of some as-yet-unfathomed mechanism.* Skeptics argue coincidental alignment and the conventional Hubble-Humason interpretation of the red shift. If Arp is right, the exotic mechanisms proposed to explain the energy source of distant quasars—supernova chain reactions, supermassive black holes and the like—would prove unnecessary.[66]

(1) Observational Evidence for Non-Big Bang Red Shifts. Arp* gives a large number of examples supporting his thesis that red shift does not necessarily result from expansion of the universe as required by the big bang theory, and that some discordant red shifts require an entirely different explanation:

It cannot be stressed too strongly, however, that *these discordant redshifts are not discovered in just one or two isolated cases* that have no relation to each other. But *in every case* we can test—large clusters, groups, companions to nearby galaxies, companions to middle-distance galaxies, companions linked by luminous filaments, galaxies interacting gravitationally, chains of galaxies—in every conceivable case, we come out with the same answer: the same discordant redshifts for the same general class of younger, fainter galaxies. . . .[67]

Although the next paragraphs will focus on Arp's research, others have noted the same discordant red shifts and reached similar conclusions, such as Burbidge*,[68] Narlikar*,[69] and Sulentic*.[70]

(a) Nonvelocity Red Shifts and Quasars. Arp*, after extensive study, has found that numerous high-red shift quasars are "associated with nearby low-redshift objects," even though the red shifts should be the same if red shift measures velocity receding away from the earth:

It is important to note that different sets of objects led to the same conclusion, namely, that *high-redshift [quasar] objects were associated with nearby low-redshift objects.* Moreover, tests with independent properties, such as average separation of objects as well as angular alignments, led to the *same conclusion.* The situation then must be faced that if one of these analyses or properties accidentally gave an indication of an association, then the other tests should certainly not have also given a confirmation. The fact that independent tests lead to the same conclusion requires that the separate improbabilities be multiplied, giving an extremely small probability that the association could be spurious. In the final section, further independent tests will be cited that again lead to the same conclusion.

. . ..

Since the quasars have such generally large redshifts, demonstrating that they fall within the bounds of the local supercluster (about 100 Mpc), [that] demonstrates immediately the existence of *discordant redshifts*. . . .[71] Narlikar* agrees that triplets of quasars that "are physically associated," but whose "red shifts . . . are markedly different," and whose alignment by chance rather than physical association is very improbable, leaves "open to doubts" and causes one to "suspect the cosmological intepretation of these red shifts" (that they arise from receding velocity).[72]

(b) Nonvelocity Red Shifts and Galaxies. Arp* and Sulentic* did a massive study of 260 companion galaxies, and found that the red shifts of companion galaxies "systematically" differ significantly, so that the red shifts must reflect "nonvelocity redshift" factors:

Redshift measures at 21 cm wavelength have been made on over *100 galaxies* in more than 40 different groups with the Arecibo radio telescope. These groups generally consist of a large spiral galaxy with one or more companions. This list of galaxies is *supplemented with over 160 galaxies* in more than 40 groups with a dominant galaxy that is brighter than 11.8 mag. . . .

It is shown that the *companion galaxies in these groups have significantly higher redshifts* than the brightest galaxy in the group. This confirms the *result which has emerged from every analysis* made of physical groups of galaxies to date, namely that the *companion galaxies are systematically redshifted* with respect to the dominant galaxy. The most accurate redshifts available in the Local Group (M31) and in the M81 group are analyzed. It is shown that *all 21 of the best-known physical companions* have significantly higher redshifts than the central galaxies. Since neither the values of the redshifts nor the physical association of these companions is in doubt, it is suggested that these companions contain a *component of nonvelocity redshift.*

...*Obviously, no Doppler velocity due to orbital or radial motion could account* for all these companions streaming away from the central galaxy as seen from the arbitrary position of the observer. Therefore, a component of their redshift, a systematic positive component, *must be of nonvelocity origin.*[73]

Earlier, Arp* had tabulated "24 main galaxies and 38 discordant redshift companions,"[74] and had published a catalogue of hundreds of discordant red shifts.[75] His assessment of why his herculean research has been "ignored" is as follows:

This important result has largely been ignored by astronomers because it does not fit in with the current theoretical framework . . ..[76]

Some of the observational examples are as follows:

HOLMBERG'S COMPANIONS
OF MORE DISTANT GALAXIES

The most comprehensive study of the neighborhood of spiral galaxies was made by Holmberg. . . .

But the importance of this result from the standpoint of the subject of discordant redshifts is that *these fainter galaxies were shown with statistical validity to be associated with the central galaxy*. . . . Although the program is far from finished because of lack of telescope observing time, *essentially all the companion redshifts measured so far are much in excess of the redshift of the central galaxy*. . . .[77]

INTERACTING DOUBLES IN THE
NEIGHBORHOOD OF SPIRAL GALAXIES

Working from a *complete list of 32 spiral galaxies* between apparent magnitude 10.0 and 11.2, Arp showed that interacting double galaxies were commonly encountered within about 50 arc min of these spirals. By comparing control fields on the *Sky Atlas* prints he was able to show that these interacting doubles were many times more numerous around the spirals and, hence, that the *majority were physically associated*. Again spectra have not been obtained for all, but enough redshifts have been derived to show that essentially all the peculiar companions are above the $z=5000$ km s^{-1} range, whereas the central galaxies are of the order of $z=1000$ km s^{-1} or less [have more than 5 times the red shift of the central galaxies]. . . .[78]

MULTIPLE INTERACTING COMPANIONS

A more special and rarer case of interacting double galaxies is the case of interacting multiple galaxies. Two examples would be Seyfert's Sextet and Stephan's Quintet. There are only about *six outstanding examples* of such kinds of systems. It has been shown that all of these fall close to large spiral or peculiar galaxies. *In all but one of the cases, the redshift discrepancies* are known to be more than 5000 km s^{-1}. . . .[79]

DISCORDANT REDSHIFTS IN CHAINS OF GALAXIES

The existence of chains of galaxies seems to be a fundamental but puzzling phenomenon. It has been suggested that they arise from ejection processes from central galaxies. . . . [T]heir existence enables us to use them as a criterion of *objects all at the same distance*. There are four chains I would particularly like to mention. . . .

If we were to find only one example of a chain containing a discordant redshift, we might be able to argue that this was the result of some extraordinary coincidence where a background galaxy just happened to project into the right position in a foreground group. But the importance of the above chains is to demonstrate that even though such exactly aligned chains are rare, *they often contain discordant redshift galaxies.* . . .[80]

DISCORDANT REDSHIFT SYSTEMS
CONNECTED BY LUMINOUS FILAMENTS

Another kind of interaction between galaxies which can immediately establish a common distance is one in which the two galaxies are linked together by a luminous filament. One of the *first cases of discordant redshifts* in such a system was discovered by Zwicky. In that one, two galaxies of about $z = 7000$ km s^{-1} were linked together by a filament that led to a third galaxy that had a redshift of only a few hundred km s^{-1}.

More recently, *further examples of connected galaxies with discordant redshifts* have been discovered. . . .[81]

Thus, Arp* concludes that "redshifts cannot be universally applied as distance indicators," and therefore implicitly are not evidence for a big bang cosmology:

In the past 15 [years] considerable evidence has accumulated that *redshifts cannot be universally applied as distance indicators.* The evidence has been of two kinds: (1) *statistical evidence*, which shows that more quasar-galaxy (Arp 1981, 1983; Sulentic 1981) and galaxy-galaxy (Arp 1982a; Sulentic 1983a) discordant redshift associations exist than are expected by chance; and (2) *direct evidence*, which involves apparent luminous connections or signs of gravitational perturbation between objects with different redshift (Arp 1980, 1982b; Sulentic 1983b; Sulentic and Lorre 1983). All the cases above refer to apparent associations of objects with widely discordant redshift values . . . .. Evidence also exists for smaller and more complex redshift anomalies in groups and clusters of galaxies (see, e.g., Tifft 1972, 1980; Sulentic 1984; Arp and Sulentic 1985).[82]

(c) Objections to Non-Velocity Red Shift Observations. As Sagan* indicated, the primary objection to that observational evidence is that a close and a distant object are "accidentally aligned." However, that objection faces serious difficulties. First, the number of discordant red shifts is too large to result from accidental alignments. Arp*, observing 260 galaxy companions in one study,[83] noted that "more quasar-galaxy . . . and galaxy-galaxy . . . discordant redshift associations exist than are expected by chance . . . ."[84] Sulentic* concluded "that, on a statistical basis, these groups are not chance configurations."[85] Second, the number of "near misses" that accidental alignment would produce is far too low:

Against this "accident" argument it can only be countered that the cases of "near misses" which should be found much more frequently are not, in fact, found. It can be argued that the filaments terminate, in general, exactly on the companion. It can be argued that filaments which are so unusual, tending to emerge directly from the centers of galaxies, are very rare and that a very high percentage involved discordant red-shifts. It can be argued that the peculiarity of the high redshift galaxies themselves indicate they are not the usual kind of background galaxies one would expect.[86]

Third, the interaction of many objects can be shown by their "peculiarity of individual lines and spectral features."[87]

(d) Significance of Non-Velocity Red Shift Observations. Burbidge*, the prominent astronomer, assesses the astronomical observations that have been summarized:

> Like most of her colleagues, Rubin, in discussing quasars, manages to ignore any mention of the remarkable results obtained over the last decade or more by *Halton Arp and others* which by now provide *strong evidence that not all red shifts are of cosmological origin.* If this evidence is presented to any gathering of scientists who are not astronomers, as I have done on a number of occasions, it is accepted without any real debate. But among the professionals, *it is largely ignored.* Why? Perhaps because we have no physical theory which will explain the phenomenon, and this is not treated as a challenge but by many as an objection to the evidence. Perhaps because astronomers, knowing that *their subject in this area already rests on rather shaky foundations* as far as hard-proven evidence is concerned, cannot face up to the opening of Pandora's box in extragalactic astronomy.
>
> Rubin states, "most astronomers agree that there are no compelling reasons to doubt that the observed red shifts indicate enormous distances or to believe that 'new physics' is required to understand quasars." However *the evidence is there*, and if we are really searching for the truth, we ignore it at our intellectual peril.[88]

Perhaps the reason why the massive documentation of discordant red shifts is so diligently ignored is the realization that they cast doubt on all stellar red shifts as accurate measures of distance, age, and expansion:

> Because *there is no other parameter besides redshift that is easily observable in a faint, featureless galaxy*, the custom of assigning the distance to such a galaxy according to the size of its redshift has become established. If a galaxy has a faint apparent magnitude for its redshift, we say it is underluminous or a dwarf, and the reverse if it is apparently bright for its measured redshift. I wish to emphasize that *there is no way of ever producing any discordance with the redshift-distance relation for even one single object when operating from the base of current assumptions.* This is true because no matter where a galaxy point falls in the redshift-apparent magnitude diagram its position can be explained in

terms of high or low intrinsic luminosity. For example, the quasars fall generally above the Hubble line in the redshift-apparent magnitude diagram, but they are not concluded to have excess redshift—they are instead said to have excess luminosity.[89]

(2) Theoretical Evidence for Non-Big Bang Red Shifts. As was mentioned earlier, "there has always been a minority of scientists who have argued that Doppler effects may not be the entire story behind the measured redshifts."[90] Most of the alternative interpretations implicitly mean that red shifts are not evidence for a big bang origin of the universe. The theoretical alternatives include (a) Wolf's* red shifts of spectral lines, (b) various tired light approaches, (c) Ellis'* gravitational red shifts, (d) Segal's* and Nicholl's* quadratic alternative to the Hubble constant, and (e) Pecker's*, Roberts'*, and Vigier's* background radiation red shifts.

(a) Non-Velocity Red Shifts of Spectral Lines. The recent theoretical work of Wolf* is summarized as follows:

"Preliminary calculations," Wolf[said], "seem to support a theory I am developing that *there is a noncosmological redshift*," i.e., non-Doppler redshift.

Physicists have generally assumed that once light leaves its source, its spectrum does not change. However, Wolf suggests that *spectra from "unconventional light sources . . . and stellar objects of an unfamiliar kind" may vary* or "evolve" during the journey across the great intergalactic distances. That the spectra of light emitted by common sources like lightbulbs and flames are invariant on propagation, Wolf comments, "is undoubtedly largely responsible for the commonly held, but nevertheless incorrect, belief that spectral invariance is a general property of light."

In an article, . . . Wolf sketched out the mathematical foundation of his theory, which allows for sources that emit noninvariant spectra. . . . [H]e explains how part of the measured redshift values of objects like quasars and so-called superluminary sources might be accounted for by an optical measure, called the "degree of coherence." This measure characterizes the way in which the fluctuations of light emitted from the individual atoms that make up a source of light correlate with each other.[91]

Because "the normalized spectrum of light will, in general, change on propagation in free space," under certain circumstances that "can produce redshifts" that are noncosmological, Wolf* says:

We showed in a recent report . . . that *the normalized spectrum of light will, in general, change on propagation in free space.* We also showed that the normalized spectrum of light emitted by a source of a well-defined class will, however, be the same throughout the far zone if the degree of spectral coherence of the source satisfies a certain scaling law. The usual thermal sources appear to be of this kind. These theoretical predictions were subsequently verified by experiments. Here, we demonstrate that under certain circumstances the modification of the normalized spectrum of the emitted light caused by the correlations between the source fluctuations within the source region *can produce redshifts* of spectral lines in the emitted light. Our results suggest a possible explanation of various puzzling features of the spectra of some stellar objects, particularly quasars.[92]

His conclusions have been published in a number of scholarly articles.[93]

Bocko*, Douglass*, and Knox* have "confirmed experimentally the theoretical prediction that lines in the spectrum of radiation from a partially coherent source may indeed be shifted," with the consequence that "the cosmological interpretation of the quasar redshifts has been questioned."[94] Morris* and Faklis* also have performed successful experiments that "demonstrated that source correlations which violate the scaling law [E. Wolf . . .] produce a normalized spectrum in the far field that is different from the normalized spectrum of light at the source."[95]

(b) Non-Velocity Red Shifts from Tired Light. Ellis* summarizes, while rejecting, two alternative views of red shift that involve the propagation of light:

3.1 *Alternative Theories of Light*

TIRED LIGHT   An alternative theory of light propagation is the "tired light" theory, in which light loses energy progressively while traveling across large distances of extragalactic space. Thus we abandon Equation 2; then the observed redshifts might occur in a static universe, *where no SHBB occurs. . . .*

ALTERNATIVE GEODESICS   Two-metric theories may involve light traveling on geodesics or another metric than that specifying length and time measurements; thus we effectively abandon Equation 2a. . . .[96]

Marmet* proposes that some red shift results from energy loss by light from interaction with gas molecules in space,[97] and Segal* suggests that photons of light lose energy from gravitational interaction.[98] Pecker*, Roberts*, and Vigier* discuss nonvelocity red shifts from "inelastic photon-photon interaction,"[99] and Stewart* earlier proposed "that light quanta may be subject to 'fatigue' during their journey . . .."[100]

Crawford* outlines his tired light explanation as follows:

An alternative explanation—a *gradual energy loss of photons due to their interaction with curved space-time*—is considered here. The basic premise is that because photons have a finite spread they are subject to tidal stresses and that this provides a mechanism for the transfer of momentum from the photon to the mass producing curved space-time.

Any transfer of momentum without an equivalent transfer of energy will destroy the concept of the photon as a single elementary particle. It is therefore postulated that the interaction of the photon with curved space-time *causes it to lose energy* in the form of very low energy secondary photons....[101]

(c) Non-Velocity Red Shifts from Gravity. Ellis* has proposed an approach that expands gravitational red shifts, which are generally viewed as existent but minor, to a major factor:[102]

ESSENTIALLY INHOMOGENEOUS UNIVERSES These are universe models containing no epochs where the space-time is approximately spatially homogeneous; that is, they are never like a FLRW [Friedmann*, etc.] universe model. This assumption, of course, goes against the usual "cosmological principle," which states a priori that the Universe is spatially homogeneous; but that is an unverified and, indeed, possibly unverifiable philosophical statement that could be incorrect.

Perhaps the most radical such proposal is the completely static two-centered universe possibility, where the *redshifts observed for distant galaxies are purely cosmological gravitational redshifts* (cf. Equation 2b). High pressures are needed in these models to cause the acceleration that underlies the gravitational redshift; this is not impossible but is perhaps uncomfortable....[103]

Collins* has offered similar reasoning.[104]

(d) Non-Velocity Red Shifts from a Quadratic Hubble Law. The Hubble law, and Segal's* proposal of a quadratic relation, is described by Hanes*:

Edwin Hubble's original data suggest a linear relationship between velocity (inferred from redshifts) and distance (inferred from apparent luminosities) for galaxies....

...Segal's chronometric cosmology does make a crucial prediction relating to the behaviour of the redshift-apparent magnitude relation for systems of moderate redshift . . .: the observed relation should be quadratic.

...The lesson to be drawn is that the purely astronomical interpretation of such effects is not at all clearcut, even in the simplifying context of a general underlying expansion.[105]

Besides Segal*,[106] the same proposal has been made by Nicoll*[107] and Hawkins*.[108] "Doubts about this constancy have accumulated," Alfvén* states, and "until it has been clearly demonstrated that the Hubble parameter really is a constant, the big bang hypothesis is not supported by the Hubble expansion."[109]

(e) Non-Velocity Red Shifts from Other Causes. A number of other non-velocity causes of red shifts have been offered. For example, Pecker* *et al.* suggest that some red shift is "due to a universal

background of temperature T" that he calculates at a level remarkably close to the microwave background radiation.[110]

The current uncertainty about whether red shifts support a big bang was well stated by Narlikar* and Hoyle* (before he embraced a discontinuitist view):

> If, as seems very possible, the accumulation of data forces us over a watershed (not only in our thinking but in the history of astronomy) *it will clearly become necessary to arrive at a theory of discrepant redshifts.* We wish to emphasize the need for a thoroughly radical assessment of the problem, considering it *unlikely* that a satisfactory theory will be achieved by a *small change* in our concepts. Explicitly, we do *not* think discrepant redshifts will be explained adequately, either as simple *Doppler peculiar motions* or as excess reddening due to gravitation.[111]

Finally, even if red shift does reflect proportional recession, that "expansion tells one virtually nothing about initial cosmic states," and "[e]specially . . . does not imply the singularly dense superpositioned state used in the big bang model,"[112] as Allen* states:

> In this regard, it is the purpose of the present paper to show that there are infinitely *many simple and noncontrived initial cosmic states, all of which lead to a universe that is expanding* under the Hubble law. Hence, for the reason noted above, *Hubble expansion tells one virtually nothing about initial cosmic states.* Especially it does not imply the singular initial state it is thought to imply i.e., a superpositioned universe. *Neither, then, is there any need to postulate a big bang* in order to counteract the overwhelming gravitational field that would accompany such a singularly dense initial state.
>
> In order to put the results of the present paper in perspective, assume for the sake of argument that astronomers had found the galaxies to be moving in a "random" way, just as if they were the molecules of a gas. In this case, most people would recognize that the present cosmic state tells one nothing about an initial cosmic state. In addition, most people would then recognize the present cosmic state as a "natural" state that need not be explained with some singular and intergalactic event, such as the big bang. . . .[113]

b. Microwave Background Radiation:
The Big Bang Explanation and Alternative Explanations

Similar difficulties exist with what Sagan* calls the other "quite persuasive evidence" for the big bang theory: the microwave background radiation. That "microwave background" is "a radiation background or radio 'hiss' at an equivalent blackbody temperature of 2.7 K[elvin]."[114]

(1) Problems with the Big Bang Interpretation of the Microwave

Background. One problem is the weak connection between microwave background radiation and a big bang event. Alfvén*, a Nobel Prize laureate, argues that the "claim that this radiation lends strong support to hot big bang cosmologies is without foundation."[115] He goes on to explain that conclusion:

> However, if we look at the background radiation without any preconceived ideas, how convincing is it? We measure an extremely cold radiation in a 'universe' which is 10^{10} light years or 10^{26}m, and conclude that this must derive from a state which was billions of degrees hot. Indeed, the expansion from, say, a millimeter-sized universe to the present 10^{10} light year size is by a factor 10^{29}. Is there any other field of science where such an extrapolation in one jump is accepted without very strong proof? One seems never to have asked seriously whether at intermediate states there could not have been other mechanisms for isotropisation of the background radiation. . . .[116]

Elsewhere, he spells out the reasons why the extrapolation from background radiation to a big bang explosion is not justified:

> Just as the radiation received from the Sun gives us direct information only about its surface, the microwave background radiation *gives us direct information only about the 'surface of last scattering' when the radiation finally decoupled from matter* and beyond which the metagalaxy remained transparent.
>
> According to our model, this 'surface of last scattering' was the total dust distribution in galaxies or protogalaxies at the epoch Z [equals approximately] 40. Consequently, we cannot obtain direct information about the metagalaxy at earlier epochs (Z > 40), as it was then opaque. This *conflicts* with the detailed canonical model of the hot big bang cosmology. . . .
>
> We stress that the observed *cosmic microwave background radiation does not give us direct information about the state of the metagalaxy further back than the epoch* corresponding to Z [equals approximately] 40, *when galaxies or protogalaxies already existed,* and when its own temperature was only about 110K. To claim that *it is strong evidence in support of the hot big bang cosmology* whose earliest epochs correspond to Z > 10^{12} with corresponding temperatures of matter and radiation [greater than] 10^{10}K, *is completely unjustified.*[117]

The other scientists, who were quoted at the beginning of this section, implicitly agreed in finding the evidence equivocal for the big bang theory. For example, Oldershaw* lists some flaws of the big bang interpretation of the microwave background, as well as some dissenters:

> *The deviations from a simple black-body spectrum, the indications of anisotropy and the fact that the energy density of the microwave background is suspiciously close to that of other noncosmological phenomena*

(Weinberg, 1972; Narlikar, 1981) (such as the energy densities of starlight, cosmic ray particles and galactic magnetic fields) *all serve to strengthen the hypothesis that this radiation also has a non-primordial astrophysical origin.* Rees (1978, 1980), Alfvén (1979), Narlikar (1980), and Carr (1981) have discussed alternative models for generating the microwave background radiation.[118]

Wright* proposed an alternate model, "of the microwave background radiation being produced by stars after the big bang."[119]

Another problem is stressed by Hoyle, as well as by Woody* and Richards*,[120] who concludes that the microwave background should be "between ten and a thousand times more powerful" to result from a big bang event, and thus does not prove but disproves the big bang theory and invites alternative explanations:

> The big bang theory includes a microwave background . . . but this success is tempered by the fact that *it was expected to be between ten and a thousand times more powerful* than is actually the case.[121]

> The latest *data differ by so much* from what theory would suggest as to *kill the big bang cosmologies. But now, because the scientific world is emotionally attracted to the big-bang cosmologies, the data are ignored.*[122]

Related to that, the microwave background shows "deviations from the Planckian [black body] spectrum that are considered statistically significant" as Narlikar* points out:

> According to the calculations the relic radiation from the hot era of a big bang origin of the early Universe *should have the spectrum of blackbody radiation* first calculated by Max Planck in the early days of quantum theory. When, therefore, successive measurements of the microwave background at different wavelengths began to show similarity with the black-body spectrum, the evidence was considered conclusively in favour of the big bang. In 1979, however, measurements by D.P. Woody and P.L. Richards at the University of California, Berkeley, showed deviations from the Planckian spectrum that are considered statistically significant. If future experiments continue to show these deviations, *that should worry the supporters of the big bang.*[123]

At the same time, the x-ray background radiation is quite uneven, but should be isotropic if produced by a big bang explosion.[124] Other evolutionist researchers have similarly concluded that the microwave background radiation does not support the big bang theory.[125]

A third problem is the "horizon problem," that "the observed isotropy of the microwave background radiation has no natural explanation" under the big bang theory, in Grøn's* words:

> The horizon radius was much less than the radius of the universe when the photons of the cosmic background radiation became free. *Then one should not expect that different regions of the universe had the same temperature. This means that the observed isotropy of the cosmic back-*

ground radiation has no natural explanation in the Friedmann models of the universe. It has to be postulated as an ad hoc initial condition. This is the *horizon problem.*[126]

The horizon problem is widely recognized, for example, by Trefil*,[127] Tipler*,[128] and others.[129] It is pushed back, but not solved, by the inflationary universe theory.[130] Because of these problems, Rees*,[131] Allen*,[132] and others reject the argument that the microwave background supports a big bang.

(2) Alternative Explanations of the Microwave Background. Marmet* suggests that photon scattering, as light crosses space and hits gas atoms, would generate bremsstrahlung, which might generate the microwave radiation.[133] Margon* describes bremsstrahlung, and suggests it as the source of the other background radiation, the x-ray radiation:

> Since 1962 it has been known that every part of the sky emits a uniform glow of X rays. After two decades of intensive study the origin of this diffuse X-ray background is still a subject of controversy.
>
> . . ..
>
> One such process for the generation of X rays has been familiar to physicists for decades: it involves the extremely hot, dilute gas called a plasma. In such a gas the electrons and the protons, which are normally bound together to form atoms, are present as an unbound mixture of rapidly moving particles. Since an electron and a proton have opposite electric charge, there is an attractive force between nearby pairs of electrons and protons in the plasma, and near-misses of free electrons attracted to free protons but not colliding with them are common. Since the advent of quantum physics early in the century it has been known that a free electron passing close to a free proton loses some energy, and that the lost energy is carried away by a discrete packet of electromagnetic energy: a photon. The radiation created by the interaction of an electron and a proton is called *bremsstrahlung* (German for "braking radiation").
>
> The exact wavelength (or range of wavelengths) of the photons created by the bremsstrahlung process is sensitively related to the temperature of the plasma. For a plasma with a temperature in the range between 10 and 500 million degrees Kelvin bremsstrahlung is expected to generate X rays with wavelengths predominantly between one angstrom and 10 angstroms. Is there any reason to expect that the universe is more or less uniformly filled with a very hot plasma that generates by the bremsstrahlung process the radiation observed today as the X-ray background? There are a number of reasons to suspect the existence of just such a hot gas.[134]

Some of the same processes that generate x-rays from bremsstrahlung might generate microwaves from it.

Clube* explains the microwave background by a steady state theory "involving recurrent activity in galaxies caused by hypermassive nuclei" and a cold "material vacuum."[135] Carr* points to pregalactic stars,[135A] and others point to a thermal origin[135B] and other explanations.[136]

Summary. "[S]ome cosmologists, albeit a minority, do sometimes wonder whether the confidence so often claimed in the big bang picture is justified by our observational knowledge of the Universe" (Narlikar*[137]), and to future cosmologists, it is "probable that our present cosmological ideas on the structure and evolution of the universe . . . will appear hopelessly premature and primitive" (Vaucouleurs*[138]). In fact, the "evidence in favour of a big bang cosmology is much less definite than is widely realized," and "there is still no really conclusive evidence in favour of such a universe" (Burbidge*[139]). Instead, "[t]here are then a variety of possibilities available," and the big bang theory "is one of this family but is by no means the only conceivable member; further possibilities are not completely excluded experimentally or theoretically" (Ellis*[140]).

(a) The "red shift, observed in the spectral lines of distant galaxies and interpreted as a Doppler effect, is the key to cosmology" and the primary evidence for the big bang theory (Sagan*[141]). However, "high-redshift objects [quasars] were associated with nearby low-redshift objects" (Arp*[142]), and in studies of 260 galaxies, "companion galaxies in these groups have significantly higher redshifts," meaning that "these companions contain a component of non-velocity redshift" to explain the different red shifts of companions (Arp* and Sulentic*[143]). Discordant red shifts of associated galaxies include numerous examples with interacting double galaxies in the neighborhood of spiral galaxies, multiple interacting companions, chains of galaxies, and galaxies connected by luminous filaments (Arp*[144]). Consequently, "redshifts cannot be universally applied as distance indicators" (Sulentic* and Arp*[145]). Although the objection has been raised that these objects are accidentally aligned but non-associated, "more quasar-galaxy . . . and galaxy-galaxy . . . discordant redshift associations exist than are expected by chance" (Arp* and Sulentic*[146]), and " 'near misses' which should be found much more frequently are not, in fact, found" (Arp*[147]). Burbidge* laments that this "strong evidence that not all red shifts are of cosmological origin" "is largely ignored," and suggests that the reason might be that "astronomers knowing that their subject in this area already rests on rather shaky foundations . . . cannot face up to the opening of Pandora's box" (Burbidge*[148]).

Many alternative explanations of red shifts have been offered. Wolf* calculates that "the normalized spectrum of light will, in general, change on propagation in free space," and "can produce redshifts" that are noncosmological (Wolf*[149]); and that theoretical conclusion has been experimentally verified (Bocko* *et al.*[150]). Crawford* gives the alternative explanation for much red shift of "a gradual energy loss of photons due to their interaction with curved space-time" (Crawford*[151]), which others join in (Marmet*[152] and Segal*[153]). Ellis* suggests a "static two-centered universe . . . where the redshifts observed for distant galaxies are purely cosmological gravitational redshifts" (Ellis*[154]). Thus, "it will clearly become necessary to arrive at a theory of discrepant redshifts," and it is unlikely that "discrepant redshifts will be explained adequately . . . as simple Doppler peculiar motions" (recession) (Hoyle* and Narlikar*[155]).

In any event, the universe's "expansion implies little regarding an initial cosmic state," and "[e]specially . . . does not imply the big bang model" (Allen*[156]).

(b) The other "persuasive evidence" for the big bang theory is the "blackbody background radiation" (Sagan*[157]). However, the "claim that it is strong evidence in support of hot big bang cosmology . . . is completely unjustified" (Alfvén*[158]). In fact, the strength of the microwave background should be "between ten and a thousand times more powerful" if it resulted from a big bang event (Hoyle[159]), and its spectrum shows "deviations from the Planckian spectrum that are considered statistically significant" (Narlikar*[160]). Moreover, the "horizon problem" is that "one should not expect that different regions of the universe had the same temperature," and "the observed isotropy of the cosmic background radiation has no natural explanation" under the big bang theory (Grøn*[161]). Instead, various explanations other than a big bang have been offered for the microwave background.

7.3 The Stages of the Big Bang: Questions about the Critical Events

There are a number of other problems with each stage of the big bang theory, which show it to be noncompelling if not, in the views of some scientists, incorrect. The classical four problems are summarized by Trefil*:

Figure 7.3
The big bang theory may
have "been disproved by
present day empirical
evidence" (Bondi*)
(picture of the Pleiades)

There are four fundamental problems associated with our picture of the Big Bang. Three of these are problems of the first kind [fundamental anomalies], and a failure to resolve them would have to be taken as evidence of a major weakness in our understanding. These problems are (1) why there is *so little antimatter in the universe*, (2) how the *galaxies could have formed* in the time allotted for this process, and (3) why the universe is *isotropic* [horizon problem]. In addition, there is one problem of the second kind that is traditionally associated with the three problems of the first kind: why the *mass of the universe is so close to the critical value required to close the universe* [flatness problem].[162] These are recognized by many if not most researchers,[163] and have been touched on in Sections 6.1, 6.5, 6.3, and 6.4 respectively.

Other problems include (a) the source of matter and energy for the oscillating big bang theory, (b) the cause of concentration of the universe into an incredibly compressed state, (c) the cause of the explosion and then the incredibly precise rate of expansion required thereafter (related to the flatness problem), (d) the cause of galaxy and star formation (related to the horizon problem), and (e) the cause or source of complex information and order.[164]

a. Source of Matter and Energy

Under the oscillating big bang theory, the universe with its matter and energy is eternal. However, the existence of unconsumed hydrogen rules out an eternal universe, according to Jastrow*[165] and some other astronomers.[166] On the other hand, the first law of thermodynamics rules out a big bang that brings matter into existence, as Narlikar* and Padmanabhan* point out:

> The *conservation of energy*—one of the most cherished principles of physics—*is violated* in the big-bang model. Since the left-handed side of Einstein's equations has zero-divergence, it follows that the source on the right-hand side must have zero divergence. On the other hand, the energy density in the big bang model is positive definite. Thus it is impossible for matter to come into existence without violating energy conservation. It is customary to water down this difficulty by statements like "the laws of physics break down at a singularity;" however the essential truth remains the same. . . .[167]

Nor can an inflationary universe theory, which posits that matter and energy arose from a false vacuum, explain the origin of the vacuum or of space, as Davies* states:

> In spite of the great success of inflation in explaining the origin of the universe, a *mystery* remains: *How did the universe arrive in the false vacuum state in the first place?* What happened before inflation?
>
> A completely satisfactory scientific account of the creation would *have to explain how space (strictly spacetime) came to exist*, in order that it might then undergo inflation. . . .[168]

This problem of ultimate origins leaves a "number of scientists . . . unhappy with the big bang theory," Krauskopf* and Beiser* note:

> A number of scientists are unhappy with the big bang theory . . . . For one thing, it leaves unanswered the questions that always arise when a precise date is given for the creation of the universe: Where did the matter come from in the first place?[169]

Under either the oscillating or single bang approach to the big bang theory, the origin of the universe of matter and energy is scientifically "unknowable" (at least other than by the laws of thermodynamics), in the words of Shapley*:

> *In the very beginning, we say, were hydrogen atoms;* of course there must have been something antecedent, but *we are not wise enough to know what.* Whence came these atoms of hydrogen, these atoms, 20,000,000,000,000 (and 66 additional zeros) in number—atoms that we now believe have been forged into the material make-up of the universe? What preceded their appearance, if anything? That is perhaps a question for metaphysics. The origin of origins is beyond astronomy. It is perhaps beyond philosophy, in the realm of the to us Unknowable.[170]

"[O]ne has to stop" at "the origins of prime matter," North* concurs.[171] Natural laws do not answer this question; thus only philosophic or religious beliefs can inform a dogmatic insistence on an eternally oscillating universe.

b. Cause of Concentration

A second problem with the big bang theory is the cause of concentration of the universe into an incredibly dense compressed state, the "cosmic egg."[172] That cause was simply "some unknown force," according to Jastrow*:

> But assuming that *some unknown force* brought the Universe into being in a hot and highly compressed state, physicists can predict with confidence what happened thereafter.[173]

Alfvén* notes:

> Proponents of the theory turn extremely vague when asked about what happened before the big bang. Sometimes they suggest that a prior universe existed and may have been very much like the one we have now. It then contracted to form an ylem.[174]

Krauskopf* objects that this is an "unanswered" question,[175] and Tipler* calls it "an outstanding theoretical problem."[176] Larson* says "no physical principles" allow such concentration, which "invalidate[s] the Big Bang theory."[176A]

c. Cause of Explosion and Precise Expansion

Another serious problem with the big bang theory is the cause of the explosion and of the incredibly precise rate of expansion that the theory requires. The problem of "how did this expansion occur" is noted by Narlikar*,[177] and the "extreme improbability that such a coherent, synchronized eruption would occur spontaneously" is acknowledged by Davies*.[178] Simply put, a compacted universe was the ultimate black hole, and black holes may not be exploding today and certainly do not produce galaxies, stars, planets, and other complexity.

Moreover, the problem that the expansion must be incredibly "tuned to an accuracy of one part in 10^{50}" is summarized by Lake*:

> What we find from this is that the initial data (expansion rate and density), specified at a time 10^{-39} second after the Bang, have to be *tuned to an accuracy of one part in 10^{50}*, even though p is so poorly known today. This tuning would have to be done to 1 part in 10^{14} even if we imagined starting the Universe just before the light elements were formed.[179]

Leslie* affirms the need for a precise expansion rate:

> Yet the now standard (Friedmann-Robertson-Walker) models of our universe are extremely sensitive to small changes in the *expansion rate* (and hence to the strength of the gravitational force). Reduction by *one part in a million million* at an initial stage would seemingly have led to recollapse in under 100,000 years and before temperatures had fallen below

10,000 degrees. Equivalently tiny increases would have had similarly huge results. Even as matters stand it is hard to see how galaxies could have formed in a universe which is flying apart so fast—and an early speed increase by one thousandth would quickly have led to a thousand-fold increase. (b) Again, very *slight reductions* in the *smoothness* with which matter is distributed . . . would apparently have multiplied the primeval heat billions of times with disastrous effect.[180]

That problem was discussed in Section 6.3. In essence, explosions are not accurate, and certainly are not accurate to such an incredible tolerance.

A related problem is the incredibly precise relations of the four universal forces required for a successful big bang, as described by Leslie*:

(c) Carbon, probably crucial to all living things, can be synthesized in stars only thanks to the *strong nuclear force's* being *to one part in a hundred* neither stronger nor weaker than it actually is. A 2% increase in this same force would probably stop quarks forming protons, essential constituents of all atoms; if not, then a 10% increase would yield a stable bi-proton so that no hydrogen (essential to water and to long-lived stable stars) would come out of the Big Bang; a decrease of 15% or less would make synthesis of elements other than hydrogen impossible. (d) *Slight changes* in the *weak nuclear force* would again have stopped any hydrogen coming out of the Bang, probably also making it impossible for supernovae to scatter the heavy elements out of which living things are built. (e) Increase in *electromagnetism's strength* by a factor of 1.6 would result in rapid decay of protons into leptons according to recent Unified Theories; if not, then a threefold increase in the electron's charge (which is a manifestation of this strength) would make all but hydrogen impossible, while a comparable decrease would mean that even interstellar heat would destroy all neutral atoms. (f) For there to exist the couple of hundred stable elements which are the basis of chemistry and biology, the *mass of the neutron* must exceed that of the proton but only by about twice the mass of the electron—and that means *by only one part in a thousand*. . . And so on and so on. All which is against the background of the facts, (i), that gravitation, electromagnetism and the weak and strong forces are *believed to have had equal strengths in the universe's early instants*, this symmetry later being broken spontaneously and perhaps largely arbitrarily in phase transitions which also allocated non-zero rest masses to all quarks, leptons, intermediary bosons and superheavy bosons; and (ii), that the four forces *now have strengths differing so greatly* that the strongest is ten thousand billion billion billion billion times more powerful than the weakest.[181]

These requirements are extraordinarily improbable under natural laws, which again give little encouragement to the big bang theory.

d. Cause of Galaxy and Star Formation

A fourth problem with the big bang theory is the formation of galaxies and stars, as discussed in Section 6.5. The big bang view offers "no physical understanding of the situation," and "the strongest argument against a big bang is that . . . the theory is able to explain so little," as Burbidge* states:

> Finally, we come to the *vexed question* of the origin of galaxies. As the big bang bandwagon has gained momentum, an increasing number of investigations have been carried out in which attempts are made to explain the condensation of dense objects from an initial cloud of matter and radiation which is expanding. It has been known for many years that *this is very difficult to understand,* and the investigations have now reached the point where it is generally accepted that the *existence of dense objects cannot be understood unless very large density fluctuations in a highly turbulent medium, or otherwise, are invoked* in the first place. *There is again no physical understanding of the situation; it is a condition which is put in, in a hypothetical state,* to explain a major property of the universe. Thus these "theories" amount to nothing more than the statement that protogalaxies have a cosmological origin, and their origin cannot be understood any better than can the original baryons and leptons in an evolving universe. . . . Probably the *strongest argument against a big bang* is that when we come to the universe in total and the large number of complex condensed objects in it, *the theory is able to explain so little.*[182]

Gott* notes that "the various theoretical models have enough free parameters . . . so that they can be made to fit the observations very well."[183]

Galaxies simply are not formed by an explosion that "merely throws matter apart," as Hoyle notes:

> The big bang theory holds that the universe began with a single explosion. Yet as can be seen below, an *explosion merely throws matter apart, while the big bang has mysteriously produced the opposite effect, with matter clumping together in the form of galaxies.*
>
> . . .However, we actually have a universe of continuing activity instead of one that is uniform and inert. Instead of matter all the time becoming colder and more spread out, we often see it clustering together to produce the brilliant light of swirling galaxies and exploding stars. Why should this be so against expectations which appear soundly based in all other aspects of physical experience?
>
> Although it does not receive much publicity, this *predicted inertness* of the expanding Universe according to the big bang theory is still a *major headache for its supporters.*[184]

Among explanations "nothing works," Finkbeiner*[184 A] and Corliss*[184B] state.

e. Cause of Complex Information and Order

Another serious problem for the big bang theory is the complex information and order in the universe, which was described earlier. Explosions cause disorder and not order or information, as astronomer Hoyle points out:

> even though outward speeds are maintained in a free explosion, internal motions are not. *Internal motions die away adiabatically*, and the expanding system *becomes inert*, which is exactly why the big bang cosmologies lead to a universe that is dead and done with almost from its beginning.[185]

This dying away of internal motions occurs according to the second law of thermodynamics, a natural law. Although fluctuations can occur, the second law of thermodynamics precludes fluctuations vast enough to yield the complex order of the known universe.[186]

Summary. The stages of cosmic evolution, like its primary evidence, embody serious difficulties. There are the "four fundamental problems" of "why there is so little antimatter," "how the galaxies could have formed in the time alloted," the horizon problem of large scale isotropy, and the flatness problem of a critical mass level (Trefil*[187]).

In addition, the problem of the origin of matter and energy involves the dilemma on the one side of the "disturbing fact" that "hydrogen is used up in stars" so that unburned hydrogen precludes an eternally oscillating universe (Jastrow*[188]), and on the other side of the thermodynamic law of "conservation of energy" that "is violated in the big-bang model" or inflationary model that requires energy and "matter to come into existence" (Narlikar* and Padmanabhan*[189]). The inflationary universe model does not solve the "mystery" of "how space (strictly spacetime) came to exist" and "[h]ow did the universe arrive in the false vacuum state in the first place?" (Davies*[190]). The "outstanding theoretical problem" (Tipler*[191]) with the next stage, the compression of the universe, is that it requires "assuming . . . some unknown force" (Jastrow*[192]), about which "[p]roponents of the theory turn extremely vague" (Alfvén*[193]).

The problems with the explosion and expansion stages are "how did this explosion occur" (Narlikar*[194]) and how to escape the "extreme improbability that such a coherent, synchronized eruption would occur spontaneously" (Davies*[195]), and then how the expansion was "tuned to an accuracy of one part in 10^{50}" (Lake*[196]). The "vexed question of the origin of galaxies" is such that the big bang offers "no physical understanding of the situation" but only an assumption of incredibly precise inhomogeneities (Burbidge*[197]); "it is hard to see how galaxies could have formed in a universe which is flying apart so fast" from an explosion (Leslie*[198]). The origin of complex information similarly conflicts with an explosion whose "[i]nternal motions die away adiabatically" and "lead to a universe that is dead . . . almost from its beginning" (Hoyle[199]).

* * *

The big bang theory of cosmic evolution is not compellingly established, has "serious difficulties" both with its primary evidence and with its alleged stages, and lies under a "sickly pall," in Hoyle's assessment:

[A] number of serious difficulties have to be ignored, swept under the rug, difficulties which indeed it may never be possible to resolve from within this particular theory. . . .

I have little hesitation in saying that as a result a *sickly pall* now hangs over the *big bang theory*. As I have mentioned earlier, when a pattern of facts becomes set against a theory, experience shows that it rarely recovers. Jayant Narlikar, an Indian professor of cosmology, is a leading theoretical physicist who also shares this view.[200]

That is why[201] Allen* concludes that "the big bang is not needed."[202] Bondi* suggests that the theory has "been disproved by present day empirical evidence,"[203] and many others reinterpret its proposed evidence.[204] The evidence in the field may always be partial and indirect, because "cosmology has always been—and will by definition always remain—a borderland between science and philosophy—some would say religion," Alvén* adds.[205]

Notes

[1] Narlikar*, *Was There a Big Bang?*, New Scientist, July 2, 1981, at 19, 21 (italics added).

[2] C. Sagan*, *Cosmos* 247 (1980).

[3] They write:

During the century and more since Darwinism came into being, the

concept of *evolution has been applied* not only to the living world but to the non-biological as well. Thus, we speak of the *evolution of the entire universe, the solar system, and the physical earth . . ..*
T. Dobzhansky*, F. Ayala*, G. Stebbins* & J. Valentine*, *Evolution* 9 (1977) (chapter 11 is entitled *"Cosmic Evolution* and the Origin of Life") (italics added). Dobzhansky* similarly writes:

> *Cosmic Evolution.* Discoveries made in various branches of science during the nineteenth and twentieth centuries have converged to establish an evolutionary approach to the understanding of nature. The universe has not always been as it is now. Nature as we observe it today is the outcome of a historical process of development, evolution.

T. Dobzhansky*, *Evolution, Genetics, and Man* 1 (1955) (italics added).

    4 Mayr*, *Evolution*, Scientific Am., Sept. 1978, at 47, 47 ("Cosmic evolution and biological evolution have that much in common.").

    5 H. Blum*, *Time's Arrow and Evolution* 4 (3d ed. 1968) ("Most works dealing with organic evolution focus attention on its strictly biological aspects, disregarding to a great extent those physical factors that have determined the basic pattern along which living systems could subsequently develop. To understand these factors and restrictions, one needs to go back to the origin of life, and beyond into the domains of terrestrial and *cosmic evolution.*") (italics added).

    6 Huxley*, *At Random*, in 3 Evolution after Darwin 41, 42 (S. Tax* ed. 1960) ("it is evolution, in the broad sense, that links inorganic nature with life, and the *stars with earth*, and matter with mind, and animals with man.") (italics added).

    7 S. Fox* & D. Dose*, *Molecular Evolution and the Origin of Life* 67 1972) ("The ideal concept of the several evolutionary sequences on the atomic and molecular level as treated in Chapters 2-5 is summarized by the following flowsheet: Origin of the Universe —> Evolution of stars and elements—>. . . Formation of macromolecules . . ..").

    8 C. Ponnamperuma*, *The Origins of Life* 39 (1972) ("Darwinian evolution. We think of the process as having taken place in stages, from inorganic evolution to organic evolution and then to biological evolution").

    9 E. Olson* & J. Robinson*, *Concepts of Evolution* 10 (1975) ("*Evolutionism* is the doctrine that the *universe*, including inorganic and organic matter in all its manifestations, is the product of gradual and progressive development.") (italics added); Wilson*, *The Origin of Life*, in Did the Devil Make Darwin Do It? 85, 86 (D. Wilson* ed. 1983) ("*Evolution*, which is the strongest natural explanation, holds that the gross features of the *universe*— including galaxies, solar systems and planets; the transition from non-living matter to living organisms; and the diversity of life forms, including human beings—all arose as a consequence of the innate proclivities of matter and energy, as expressed by the laws of nature.") (italics added).

    10 *E.g.*, C. Sagan*, *Cosmos* 247 (1980) ("cosmic evolution"); Gamow*, *Modern Cosmology*, 190 Scientific Am. 55, 60 (1954) ("Cosmos Evolved", "Universe's Evolution"); Dobzhansky*, *A Biologist's World View*, 175

Science 49, 49 (1972) ("cosmic evolution"); H. Blum*, *Time's Arrow and Evolution* 4 (3d ed. 1968) ("cosmic evolution"); T. Dobzhansky*, *Evolution, Genetics, and Man* 1 (1955) ("cosmic evolution"); G. Stebbins* & W. Fitch*, *Processes of Molecular and Organismic Evolution* (1987) (chapter 11: "Cosmic Evolution"); J. Boodin*, *Cosmic Evolution* (1925, repr. 1970); G. Gamow*, *The Creation of the Universe* 4-5 (1959) ("cosmic evolution," "universe resulted from a continuous evolutionary process," "stellar evolution"); Harneck*, *Carl Sagan: Cosmic Evolution v. the Creationist Myth,* Humanist, Jul.-Aug. 1981, at 5; Alfvén* & Mendis*, *Interpretation of Observed Microwave Background Radiation,* 266 Nature 698, 699 (1977) ("evolutionary cosmology").

[11]   *E.g.*, D. Clayton*, *Principles of Stellar Evolution and Nucleosynthesis* (1983); H. Miller*, *Evolution: From Stellar Dust to Technological Society* (1975); H. Goldberg* & M. Scadron*, *Physics of Stellar Evolution and Cosmology* (1984); Brown*, *Stellar Evolution,* Am. Atheist, Mar. 1982, at 21.

[12]   *E.g.*, Committee on Science & Creation*, *Science and Creation: A View from the National Academy of Sciences* 11-12 (1984) ("evolution of the universe"); J. Barrow* & J. Silk*, *The Left Hand of Creation: The Origin and Evolution of the Expanding Universe* (1983); I. Novikov*, *Evolution of the Universe* (1983); J. Silk*, *The Big Bang: The Creation and Evolution of the Universe* (1980); Gamow*, *Modern Cosmology,* Scientific Am., Mar. 1954, at 55, 60 ("cosmos evolved," "Universe's evolution"); DeFord*, *Humanism and Atheism I,* Humanist, July-Aug. 1971, at 5 ("evolution of the universe"); G. Whitrow*, *The Structure and Evolution of the Universe* (1959); K. Krauskopf* & A. Beiser*, *The Physical Universe* 645 (3d ed. 1973) (heading "Evolution of the Universe"); R. Wald*, *Space, Time, and Gravity* 55 (1971) (chapter 5 entitled "The Evolution of Our Universe"); Guth* & Steinhardt*, *The Inflationary Universe,* Scientific Am., May 1984, at 116, 127 ("evolution of the universe").

[13]   T. Dobzhansky*, *Evolution,* in 10 Encyclopedia Americana 734, 734 (1982) (italics added).

[14]   He wrote:

I am quite aware that many people object to the use of the term *evolution* for anything but the transformations of living substance. But I think this is *undesirably narrow.* Some term is undoubtedly needed for the comprehensive process in all its aspects, and no other convenient designation exists at present save that of evolution.

The over-all process of evolution in this comprehensive sense comprises *three main phases.* . . . We may call these three phases the inorganic or, if you like, *cosmological;* the organic or biological; and the human or psycho-social.

J. Huxley*, *Evolution in Action* 10 (1964) (italics added).

[15]   The NAS recently published a booklet that states:

The processes by which new galaxies, stars, and our own planetary system are formed are sometimes referred to as the *"evolution" of the universe, the stars, and the solar system.* The word *evolution* in this context has a very different meaning than it does when applied to the evolution of organisms. In both instances there is an unfolding, but the processes involved are entirely different. The relevant sciences involved are also different—biological sciences in the evolution of organisms and the physical sciences in the *evolution of the universe* and its constituent domains.

Evidence that the *evolution of the universe* has taken place over at least several billion years is overwhelming.
Committee on Science & Creation*, *Science and Creationism: A View from the National Academy of Sciences* 11, 12 (1984) (italics added).

[16]   *Evolution*, 3 Oxford English Dictionary 354 (1971) ("8. The *formation of the heavenly bodies* according to the received theory which supposes it to have taken place by the concentration and consolidation of *cosmic* matter.") (italics added).

[17]   M. Bishop*, B. Sutherland* & P. Lewis*, *Focus on Earth Science* 470 (Teacher's Ed. 1981) (italics added).

[18]   J. Murphy*, *Physics: Principles and Problems* 251 (1982); Biological Sciences Curriculum Study*, *Biological Science: Molecules to Man* 123 (3d ed. 1973 & 1976); Biological Sciences Curriculum Study*, *Biological Science: An Inquiry Into Life* 702-03, 705, 832-35 (3d ed. 1973 & 1976); J. Otto*, A. Towle* & M. Madnick*, *Modern Biology* 253 (1977).

[19]   M. Bishop*, B. Sutherland* & P. Lewis*, *Focus on Earth Science* 117T (Teacher's Ed. 1981) (italics added).

[20]   C. Sagan*, *Cosmos* 246-47 (1980) (italics added).

[21]   *Id.* at 259 (italics added).

[22]   R. Jastrow*, *Until the Sun Dies* 31, 36 (1977).

[23]   Shapley*, *On the Evolution of Atoms, Stars and Galaxies*, in Adventures in Earth History 77, 78-79 (P. Cloud* ed. 1970).

[24]   A. Krauskopf* & A. Beiser*, *The Physical Universe* 645 (3d ed. 1973) ("A number of scientists are unhappy with the big bang theory.").

[25]   Horgan*, *Big-Bang Bashers*, Scientific Am., Sept. 1987, at 22, 22.

[26]   Alfvén* & Mendis*, *Interpretation of observed microwave background radiation*, 266 Nature 698 (1977).

[27]   F. Hoyle, *The Intelligent Universe* 186 (1983) (discontinuitist cosmologist). *See also* Hoyle, *The Big Bang in Astronomy*, 92 New Scientist 521, 526 (1981) ("I continue to be obstinately doubtful about the dead-and-done-for universe of the big-bang cosmologies.").

[28]   Gould*, *The Archaeopteryx Flap*, Natural History, Sept. 1986, at 16, 18.
[29]   Note 1.
[30]   F. Hoyle & N. Wickramasinghe, *Evolution from Space* (1981).
[31]   Burbidge*, *Was there really a Big Bang?*, 233 Nature 36 (1971).
[32]   Allen*, *The Big Bang Is Not Needed*, 6 Foundations of Physics 59-63 (1976).
[33]   Bondi*, *Letter*, 87 New Scientist 611 (1980) ("As an erstwhile cosmologist, I speak with feeling of the fact that theories of the origin of the Universe have been disproved by present day empirical evidence, as have

various theories of the origin of the Solar System").

[34] Oldershaw*, *The Continuing Case for a Hierarchical Cosmology*, 92 Astrophysics & Space Science 347 (1983).

[35] Vaucouleurs*, *The Case for a Hierarchical Cosmology*, 167 Science 1203 (1979).

[36] Narlikar*, *Was there a big bang?*, New Scientist, July 2, 1981, at 19, 19.

[37] *E.g.*, Arp*, *Analysis of Groups of Galaxies with Accurate Redshifts*, 294 Astrophysical J. 88 (1985); Arp*, *Evidence for Discordant Redshifts*, in The Redshift Controversy 15 (G. Field* ed. 1973).

[38] Ellis*, *Alternatives to the Big Bang*, 22 Ann. Rev. Astronomy & Astrophysics 157 (1984).

[39] Sulentic*, *On the Density of Galaxy Quartets and the Statistical Likelihood of Discordant Redshift Groups*, 270 Astrophysical J. 417 (1983).

[40] I. Segal*, *Mathematical Cosmology and Extragalactic Astronomy* (1976).

[41] P. Marmet*, *A New Non-Doppler Redshift* (1981).

[42] Wolf*, *Non-cosmological redshifts of spectral lines*, 326 Nature 363 (1987).

[43] Rees*, *Origin of pregalactic microwave background*, 275 Nature 35 (1978).

[44] Douglas*, *Forty Minutes with Dr. Einstein*, 50 J. Royal Astronomical Soc. of Canada 99, 100 (1956).

[45] Oldershaw*, *The Continuing Case for a Hierarchical Cosmology*, 92 Astrophysics & Space Science 347, 355 (1983).

[46] Horgan*, *Big-Bang Bashers*, Scientific Am., Sept. 1987, at 22, 22.

[47] *Id.*

[48] *Id.*

[49] Alfvén*, *Cosmology: Myth or Science?*, 5 J. Astrophysics & Astronomy 79, 92 (1984).

[50] Vaucouleurs*, *The Case for a Hierarchical Cosmology*, 167 Science 1203, 1203 (1970).

[51] Narlikar* & Padmanabhan*, *Creation-field cosmology: A possible solution to singularity, horizon, and flatness problems*, 32 Physical Rev. D 1928, 1928 (1985).

[52] Vaucouleurs*, *The Case for a Hierarchical Cosmology*, 167 Science 1203, 1203 (1970) (italics added).

[53] Alfvén*, *Cosmology: Myth or Science?*, 5 J. Astrophysics & Astronomy 79, 90 (1984) (italics added).

[54] H. Alfvén*, *Cosmic Plasma* 125 (1981).

[55] Oldershaw*, *The Continuing Case for a Hierarchical Cosmology*, 92 Astrophysics & Space Science 347, 357 (1983).

[56] Narlikar* & Padmanabhan*, *Creation-field cosmology: A possible solution to singularity, horizon, and flatness problems*, 32 Physical Rev. D 1928, 1929 (1985).

[57] Tipler*, *How to Construct a Falsifiable Theory in Which the Universe Came Into Being Several Thousand Years Ago*, 2 Philosophy of Science

Association 873, 880-81 (1984).

58 C. Sagan*, *Cosmos* 252-53, 256 (1980) (italics added).

59 *Glossary of Terms Used in Cosmology* 17-18 (P. Schewe* ed. 1982) (American Institute of Physics) (also interpreting red shift to support the big bang theory).

60 Moreover, "all the evidence needed for a scientific study of the cause of the great explosion was melted down and destroyed" in "the searing heat of that first moment." R. Jastrow*, *God and the Astronomers* 12 (1978).

61 Burbidge*, *Was there really a Big Bang?*, 233 Nature 36, 36, 39 (1971) (italics added).

62 Ellis*, *Alternatives to the Big Bang*, 22 Ann. Rev. Astronomy & Astrophysics 157, 164 (1984) (italics added).

63 *Id.* at 164 (italics added).

64 Allen*, *The Big Bang Is Not Needed*, 6 Foundations of Physics 59, 59 (1976) (italics deleted).

65 Oldershaw*, *The Continuing Case for a Hierarchical Cosmology*, 92 Astrophysics & Space Science 347, 351 (1983).

66 C. Sagan*, *Cosmos* 255-56 (1980) (italics added).

67 Arp*, *Evidence for Discordant Redshifts*, in The Redshift Controversy 15, 54-55 (G. Field* ed. 1973) (italics added).

68 Burbidge*, *Redshifts and distances*, 286 Nature 307 (1980).

69 Narlikar*, *Was there a big bang?*, New Scientist, July 2, 1981, at 19, 20.

70 Sulentic*, *On the Density of Galaxy Quartets and the Statistical Likelihood of Discordant Redshift Groups*, 270 Astrophysical J. 417 (1983).

71 Arp*, *Evidence for Discordant Redshifts*, in The Redshift Controversy 15, 26-27, 31 (G. Field* ed. 1973) (italics added).

72 Narlikar*, *Was there a big bang?*, New Scientist, July 2, 1981, at 19, 20.

73 Arp* & Sulentic*, *Analysis of Groups of Galaxies with Accurate Redshifts*, 291 Astrophysical J. 88, 88 (1985) (italics added).

74 Arp*, *Further Examples of Companion Galaxies with Discordant Redshifts and Their Spectral Peculiarities*, 263 Astrophysical J. 54, 54 (1982).

75 H. Arp* & B. Madore*, *Catalogue of Southern Peculiar Galaxies and Associations* (1977).

76 Arp*, *Further Examples of Companion Galaxies with Discordant Redshifts and Their Spectral Peculiarities*, 263 Astrophysical J. 54, 54 (1982).

77 Arp*, *Evidence for Discordant Redshifts*, in The Redshift Controversy 15, 35-36 (G. Field* et al.eds. 1973) (italics added). *See also* Arp*, *Evidence for Interaction in Two Discordant Redshift Pairs of Galaxies*, 297 Astrophysical J. 572, 572 (1985) (discordant interacting pairs of galaxies); Arp*, *Further Examples of Companion Galaxies with Discordant Redshifts and Their Spectral Peculiarities*, 263 Astrophysical J. 54, 54 (1982).

78 Arp*, *Evidence for Discordant Redshifts*, in The Redshift Controversy 15, 37 (G. Field* et al. eds. 1973) (italics added). *See also* Arp*, Sargeant*, Willis* & Oosterbaan*, *An Eruptive BL Lacertae Object with a High Redshift*, 230 Astrophysics J. 68 (1979).

79 Arp*, *Evidence for Discordant Redshifts*, in The Redshift Controversy

15, 37-38 (G. Field* *et al.* eds. 1973) (italics added).

[80]   *Id.* at 41-42 (italics added).

[81]   *Id.* at 43 (italics added). *See also* Arp*, *Three New Cases of Galaxies with Large Discrepant Redshifts*, 239 Astrophysical J. 469 (1980).

[82]   Sulentic* & Arp*, *Evidence for Interaction in Two Discordant Redshift Pairs of Galaxies*, 297 Astrophysical J. 572, 572 (1985).

[83]   Arp* & Sulentic*, *Analysis of Groups of Galaxies with Accurate Redshifts*, 291 Astrophysical J. 572, 572 (1985).

[84]   Sulentic* & Arp*, *Evidence for Interaction in Two Discordant Redshift Pairs of Galaxies*, 297 Astrophysical J. 572, 572 (1985).

[85]   Sulentic*, *On the Density of Galaxy Quartets and the Statistical Likelihood of Discordant Redshift Groups*, 270 Astrophysical J. 417, 417 (1983).

[86]   Arp*, *Three New Cases of Galaxies with Large Discrepant Redshifts*, 239 Astrophysical J. 469, 474 (1980).

[87]   Arp*, *Further Examples of Companion Galaxies with Discordant Redshifts and Their Spectral Peculiarities*, 263 Astrophysical J. 54, 54 (1982).

[88]   Burbidge*, *Redshifts and distances*, 286 Nature 307 (1980) (italics added).

[89]   Arp*, *Evidence for Discordant Redshifts*, in The Redshift Controversy 15, 17 (G. Field* *et al.* eds. 1973) (italics added).

[90]   Amato*, *Spectral variations on a universal theme*, 130 Science News 166, 166 (1986).

[91]   *Id.* (italics added).

[92]   Wolf*, *Non-cosmological redshifts of spectral lines*, 326 Nature 363, 363 (1987) (italics added).

[93]   Wolf*, *Invariance of the Spectrum of Light on Propagation*, 56 Physical Rev. Letters 1370, 1370 (1986) ("Actually it is not difficult to conceive of sources that generate light whose spectrum is not invariant on propagation."); Wolf*, *Redshifts and Blueshifts of Spectral Lines Caused by Source Correlations*, 62 Optics Communications 12, 12 (1987) ("The spectrum of the emitted light is again found to be a line with gaussian profile, but this line may be redshifted or blueshifted relative to the spectral line of the source distribution, depending on the choice of the parameters."); Wolf*, *Redshifts and Blueshifts of Spectral Lines Emitted by Two Correlated Sources*, 58 Physical Rev. Letters 2646, 2648 (1987) ("The preceding considerations show clearly the possibility of generating, by means of correlations between source fluctuations, either redshifts or blueshifts of lines in the spectrum of radiation emitted by sources that are stationary with respect to an observer.").

[94]   Bocko*, Douglass* & Knox*, *Observation of Frequency Shifts of Spectral Lines Due to Source Correlations*, 58 Physical Rev. Letters 2649, 2651 (1987).

[95]   Morris* & Faklis*, *Effects of Source Correlation on the Spectrum of Light*, 62 Optics Communications 5, 5 (1987).

[96]   Ellis*, *Alternatives to the Big Bang*, 22 Ann. Rev. Astronomy & Astrophysics 157, 164 (1984) (second italics added).

[97] P. Marmet*, *A New Non-Doppler Redshift* 12 (1981).

[98] I. Segal*, *Mathematical Cosmology and Extragalactic Astronomy* (1976).

[99] Pecker*, Roberts* & Vigier*, *Non-Velocity Redshifts and Photon-Photon Interactions*, 237 Nature 227, 227 (1972).

[100] J. North*, *The Measure of the Universe: A History of Modern Cosmology* 229, 230-31 (1965).

[101] Crawford*, *Photon decay in curved space-time*, 277 Nature 633, 633 (1979) (italics added).

[102] Ellis*, Maartens* & Nel*, *Expansion of the Universe*, 184 Royal Astronomical Soc. Monthly Notices 439 (1978).

[103] Ellis*, *Alternatives to the Big Bang*, 22 Ann. Rev. Astronomy & Astrophysics 157, 176-77 (1984) (italics added, footnotes omitted).

[104] Collins*, *Comments on the static spherically symmetric cosmologies of Ellis, Maartens and Nel*, 24 J. Math. Phys. 215 (1983).

[105] Hanes*, *Is the Universe expanding?*, 289 Nature 745, 745-46 (1981).

[106] I. Segal*, *Mathematical Cosmology and Extragalactic Astronomy* (1976).

[107] Nicoll*, Johnson*, Segal* & Segal*, *Statistical invalidation of the Hubble Law*, 77 Proc. National Acad. of Sciences 6275 (1980) ("the Hubble law lacks an objective statistical foundation"); Nicoll* & Segal*, *Nonparametric Elimination of the Observational Magnitude Cutoff Bias*, 82 Astronomy & Astrophysics L3 (1980) (quadratic relation between redshift and distance).

[108] Hawkins*, *Letter*, 194 Nature 563 (1962).

[109] H. Alfvén*, *Cosmic Plasma* 129, 131 (1981).

[110] Pecker*, Roberts* & Vigier*, *Non-velocity redshifts and photon-photon interactions*, 237 Nature 227, 228 (1972).

[111] Hoyle* & Narlikar*, *On the nature of mass*, 233 Nature 41, 41 (1971) (italics added).

[112] Allen*, *The Big Bang Is Not Needed*, 6 Foundations of Physics 59, 59 (1976) (italics deleted).

[113] *Id.* at 60 (italics added, some italics deleted).

[114] *Glossary of Terms Used in Cosmology** 4-5 (P. Schewe* ed. 1982).

[115] Alfvén* & Mendis*, *Interpretation of observed cosmic microwave background radiation*, 266 Nature 698, 698 (1977).

[116] Alfvén*, *Cosmology: Myth or Science?*, 5 J. Astrophysics & Astronomy 79, 91 (1984).

[117] Alfvén & Mendis*, *Interpretation of observed cosmic microwave background radiation*, 266 Nature 698, 699 (1977) (italics added).

[118] Oldershaw*, *The Continuing Case for a Hierarchical Cosmology*, 92 Astrophysics & Space Science 347, 356 (1983).

[119] Wright*, *Thermalization of Starlight by Elongated Grains: Could the Microwave Background Have Been Produced by Stars?*, 255 Astrophysical J. 401, 401 (1982).

[120] Schoonover*, *Big Bang Theory Fizzles*, Fusion, March-April 1979, at

66, 66.

[121]   F. Hoyle, *The Intelligent Universe* 181 (1983) (italics added).

[122]   Hoyle, *The Big Bang in Astronomy*, 92 New Scientist 521, 522-23 (1981) (italics added).

[123]   Narlikar*, *Was there a big bang?*, New Scientist, July 2, 1981, at 19, 20-21 (italics added).

[124]   Oldershaw*, *The Continuing Case for a Hierarchical Cosmology*, 92 Astrophysics & Space Science 347, 352 (1983).

[125]   Rees*, *Origin of pregalactic microwave background*, 275 Nature 35 (1978).

[126]   Grøn*, *Repulsive gravitation and inflationary universe models*, 54 Am. J. Physics 46, 48 (1986) (italics added).

[127]   J. Trefil*, *The Moment of Creation: Big Bang Physics* 48 (1983).

[128]   Tipler*, *How to Construct a Falsifiable Theory in Which the Universe Came Into Being Several Thousand Years Ago*, 2 Philosophy of Science Association 873, 880 (1984).

[129]   Schwarzschild*, *Deep redshift survey of galaxies suggests million-Mpc³ void*, Physics Today, Jan. 1982, at 17, 19.

[130]   Grøn*, *Repulsive gravitation and inflationary universe models*, 54 Am. J. Physics 46, 48 (1986) (italics added).

[131]   Rees*, *Origin of pregalactic microwave background*, 275 Nature 35 (1978).

[132]   Allen*, *The Big Bang Is Not Needed*, 6 Foundations of Physics 59 (1976).

[133]   P. Marmet*, *A New Non-Doppler Redshift* (1981).

[134]   Margon*, *The Origin of the Cosmic X-Ray Background*, 248 Scientific Am. 104, 104, 108-09 (1983) (italics added).

[135]   Clube*, *The Material Vacuum*, 193 Royal Astronomical Soc. Monthly Notices 385 (1980).

[135A]   Carr*, *Pregalactic Stars and the Origin of the Microwave Background*, 195 Royal Astronomical Soc. Monthly Notices 669 (1981).

[135B]   Peterson* et al., *Spectrum of the Cosmic Background Radiation at Millimeter Wavelengths*, 55 Physical Rev. Letters 332 (1985); Smoot* et al., *Low-Frequency Measurements of the Cosmic Background Radiation Spectrum*, 291 Astrophysical J. L 23 (1985); Witersky* et al., *New Measurements of the Cosmic Background Radiation at 3.3 Millimeter Wavelength*, 310 Astrophysical J. 145 (1986).

[136]   Rees*, *Origin of pregalactic microwave background*, 275 Nature 35 (1978).

[137]   Note 36.

[138]   Note 52.

[139]   Note 61.

[140]   Note 62.

[141]   Note 58.

[142]   Note 71.

[143]   Note 73.

[144] Notes 77-81.

[145] Note 82.

[146] Note 83.

[147] Note 86.

[148] Note 88.

[149] Note 92.

[150] Note 94.

[151] Note 101.

[152] Note 97.

[153] Note 98.

[154] Note 103.

[155] Note 111.

[156] Note 112.

[157] Note 58.

[158] Note 117.

[159] Note 121.

[160] Note 123.

[161] Note 126.

[162] J. Trefil*, *The Moment of Creation: Big Bang Physics* 48 (1983) (italics added).

[163] Grøn*, *Repulsive gravitation and inflationary universe models*, 54 Am. J. Physics 46, 48 (1986) ("the flatness problem may also be stated as follows. Since the actual density departs more and more from the critical density as time goes on, according to the Friedman models, the present flatness is very mysterious.") (italics added).

[164] Silk* mentions problems (a), (b)-(c), and (d): "The Big Bang theory has not yet resolved three fundamental issues—what happened prior to the initial instant, the nature of the singularity itself, and the origin of the galaxies." J. Silk*, *The Big Bang* 315 (1979).

[165] R. Jastrow*, *God and the Astronomers* 109 (1978).

[166] P. Davies*, *The Runaway Universe* 27 (1980); F. Hoyle*, *The Nature of the Universe* 125 (1950).

[167] Narlikar* & Padmanabhan*, *Creation-field cosmology: A possible solution to singularity, horizon, and flatness problems*, 32 Physical Rev. D 1928, 1928 (1985) (italics added).

[168] P. Davies*, *Superforce: The Search for a Grand Unified Theory of Nature* 198 (1984) (italics added).

[169] A. Krauskopf* & A. Beiser*, *The Physical Universe* 645 (3d ed. 1973).

[170] Shapley*, *On the Evolution of Atoms, Stars and Galaxies*, in Adventures in Earth History 77, 79 (P. Cloud* ed. 1970) (italics added).

[171] J. North*, *The Measure of the Universe* 401 (1965).

[172] C. Sagan*, *Cosmos* 246 (1980).

[173] R. Jastrow*, *God and the Astronomers* 125 (1978) (italics added).

[174] H. Alfvén*, *Worlds-Antiworlds* 17 (1966). *See also* G. Abell*, *Exploration of the Universe* 648 (4th ed. 1982).

[175] A. Krauskopf* & A. Beiser*, *The Physical Universe* 645 (3d ed. 1973) ("A

number of scientists are unhappy with the big bang theory. . . . For one thing, it leaves unanswered the questions that always arise when a precise date is given for the creation of the universe: Why was all matter concentrated in one tiny region? What was the universe like before the explosion started?").

[176] Tipler*, *How to Construct a Falsifiable Theory in Which the Universe Came Into Being Several Thousand Years Ago*, 2 Philosophy of Science Association 873, 879 (1984).

[177] Narlikar*, *Was there a big bang?*, New Scientist, July 2, 1981, at 19, 19.

[178] P. Davies*, *Superforce: The Search for a Grand Unified Theory of Nature* 185 (1984).

[179] Lake*, *Windows on a New Cosmology*, 224 Science 675, 678 (1984) (italics added).

[180] Leslie*, *Cosmology, Probability, and the Need to Explain Life*, in Scientific Explanation and Understanding 53, 54 (N. Rescher* ed. 1983) (italics added).

[181] *Id.*

[182] Burbidge*, *Was there really a Big Bang?*, 233 Nature 36, 40 (1971) (italics added).

[183] Gott*, *Recent Theories of Galaxy Formation*, 15 Ann. Rev. Astronomy & Astrophysics 235, 263 (1977).

[184] F. Hoyle, *The Intelligent Universe* 184-85 (1983) (italics added).

[184A] Finkbeiner*, *Isotropy or Anisotropy*, 16 Mosaic 42 (1985).

[184B] Corliss*, *Stars, Galaxies, Cosmos* 184 (1987) ("it is rather embarrassing that no one has explained their origins. . .. Most astronomers and cosmologists freely admit that no satisfactory theory of galaxy formation has been formulated. In other words, a major feature of the universe is without explanation.").

[185] Hoyle, *The Big Bang in Astronomy*, 92 New Scientist 521, 523 (1981) (italics added).

[186] Section 6.1.

[187] Note 162.

[188] Note 165.

[189] Note 167.

[190] Note 168.

[191] Note 176.

[192] Note 173.

[193] Note 174.

[194] Note 177.

[195] Note 178.

[196] Note 179.

[197] Note 182.

[198] Note 180.

[199] Note 185.

[200] F. Hoyle, *The Intelligent Universe: A New View of Creation and Evolution* 179, 186 (1983).

[201] Narlikar*, *Was there a big bang?*, New Scientist, July 2, 1981, at 19, 21 (italics added).

[202] Allen*, *The Big Bang Is Not Needed*, 6 Foundations of Physics 59 (1976).

[203] Bondi*, *Letter*, 87 New Scientist 611 (1980).

[204] Narlikar*, *Was there a big bang?*, New Scientist, July 2, 1981, at 19.

[205] H. Alfvén*, *Cosmic Plasma* 123 (1981).

CHAPTER 8

Summary of the Scientific Issues: The Theory of Abrupt Appearance and the Theory of Evolution

> *If there is a lesson for us in examining the history of discovery, it is the increase of our knowledge and the increasing reverence for science may lead us to underestimate the amount of our ignorance.*
>
> *History reminds us that every supposedly complete discovery has been incomplete. . . .*
>
> *Professions are organized for the maintenance of the traditional approaches to knowledge, and every profession tends to be concerned with . . . classic controversies—topics that it is proper to argue about.*
>
> —University of Chicago historian of science (now Librarian of Congress) Daniel J. Boorstin*[1]

*Scientists cited in this chapter, unless otherwise indicated, are not proponents of, and their quoted statements are not intended as endorsements of, either the theory of abrupt appearance or the theory of creation. However, their quoted statements are acknowledging data that involve weaknesses of the theory of evolution.

Volume I began with Darwin's* empirical caution "that scarcely a single point is discussed in this volume on which facts cannot be adduced, often apparently leading to conclusions directly opposite to those at which I have arrived," so that a "fair result can be obtained only by fully stating and balancing the facts and arguments on both sides of each question . . .."[2] This volume properly ends with Boorstin's* historical caution that apparently complete scientific explanations seldom are, and scientism may lead to over-confidence in such theories.

That possibility of incompleteness of and overconfidence in the theory of evolution, and the danger of dogmatic refusal to consider the theory of abrupt appearance, can be seen in the following quotations from evolutionist authorities. *Each quotation should be read in its full context that has been given earlier in this volume and in light of the hundreds of other citations in each chapter.*

Figure 8.1
Darwin* in the year before his death

8.1 Definitions of the Theories of Evolution and Abrupt Appearance

a. The Scientific Meanings of Evolution and Abrupt Appearance

As defined in one of the "[t]wo textbooks of evolution [that] now dominate the field" (Gould[*3]), "the concept of evolution has been applied not only to the living world" (biological evolution), but to "the origin of life . . . as the outcome of precellular chemical evolution" and to "the evolution of the entire universe, the solar system and the physical earth" ("cosmic evolution") (Dobzhansky*, Ayala*, Stebbins*, and Valentine[*4]). Thus, a proper definition "distinguishes between evolution and mere change," and recognizes that "[t]ransformation is a better concept than 'change' " (*id.*[5]).

The theory of abrupt appearance involves the same aspects: the discontinuous abrupt appearance in complex form of the universe (cosmic abrupt appearance), of the first life (biochemical abrupt appearance), and of plants and animals (biological abrupt appearance). That theory builds on the empirical evidence of abrupt appearance that many evolutionists recognize, but adds discontinuity rather than continuity as the more logical scientific interpretation of that evidence (so that its advocates are here called discontinuitists). The theory of abrupt appearance differs from the historical theory of creation, particularly in the totally nonreligious and empirical basis of the theory of abrupt appearance and its categorization into affirmative lines of scientific evidence. However, they share some historical roots in the great scientists such as Agassiz of Harvard, who held to a scientific theory of creation that found data that organisms appear "endowed from the beginning of their existence with all their characteristics" (Agassiz[6]). Darwin* himself referred to the "theory of creation" and to the "term of creation, by which I really meant 'appeared' by some wholly unknown process" (Darwin[*7]), and the next generation understood too that "[c]reation implies an abrupt appearance" (Draper[*8]). In its context at the time of Darwin*, the "word 'creation' in English scientific writings of the mid-nineteenth century . . . does not imply God" (Cannon[*9]). This book is about the theory of abrupt appearance, as contrasted with the theory of creation.

b. The Religious Meanings of Evolution and Creation

There are no religious bodies that hold to a belief in the theory of abrupt appearance, but there are many religious groups that have a doctrinal belief in evolution, such as Theological Liberalism, Neo-

Orthodoxy, Religious Humanism, Neo-Modernist Catholicism, Reform Judaism, and Buddhism. The religious denominations that have theological beliefs in creation are equally diverse, and hold a view very different in content from the theory of abrupt appearance, in that the former but not the latter includes God, days of creation, created kinds, Adam and Eve, a fall into sin, Noah's flood, and other biblical concepts. This is fully discussed in Chapter 14.

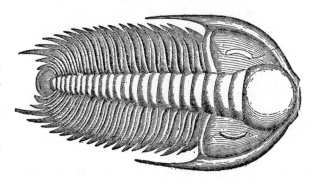

Figure 8.2
The abrupt ap-
pearance of most
lower and higher
categories in
discontinuous
complex form
(picture of the
trilobite)

8.2 The Theory of Biological Abrupt Appearance of Living Organisms

The theory of biological abrupt appearance consists of at least seven lines of affirmative scientific evidence for discontinuous abrupt appearance of plants and animals in complex form. Those lines of evidence are based on the empirical data of systematic abrupt appearances, systematic gaps, systematic similarity, and stasis, extensive anomalies in classification, comparative anatomy, and comparative biochemistry, as well as the natural laws of information science, statistics, and genetics. That basis establishes the scientific nature of biological abrupt appearance.

a. The Paleontology Argument of Systematic Abrupt Appearances

Many evolutionists acknowledge that "[n]ew species almost always appeared suddenly in the fossil record with no intermediate links to ancestors in older rocks of the same period" (Gould*[10]), and that "[u]nfortunately, the origins of most higher categories are shrouded in mystery; commonly new higher categories appear abruptly in the fossil record without evidence of transitional ancestral forms" (Raup* and Stanley*[11]). Those and other evolutionist spokesmen do not mean to endorse the theory of abrupt appearance and particularly its element of discontinuity; they instead embrace the theory of macroevolution with continuity from single-celled life to fish, to amphibians, to reptiles, to mammals. However, the scientific evidence that they observe is more logically explained by the theory of abrupt appearance, according to its advocates. The problem is not "that the fossil record is woefully incomplete," because "the record is of sufficiently high quality to allow us to undertake certain kinds of analysis" (Stanley*[12]). The abrupt appearances are not just the exceptional cases: of the "25 major living subdivisions (phyla) of the animal kingdom alone," "[m]ost taxa at these high levels appear abruptly in the fossil record" (Ayala* and Valentine*[13]), and "whether at the level of orders or species, we find—over and over again—not gradual evolution, but the sudden explosion of one group at the expense of another" (Ager*[14]). Darwin* conceded that "The Sudden Appearance of Whole Groups of Allied Species" posed a serious difficulty for his theory (Darwin*[15]), while Thompson* admits that, "[r]ather than supporting evolution, the breaks in the known fossil record support the creation of major groups with the possibility of some limited variation within each group" (Thompson*[16]).

b. The Paleontology Argument of Systematic Gaps

"The extreme rarity of transitional forms in the fossil record persists as the trade secret of paleontology" (Gould*[17]). In fact, "the record fails to contain a single example of a significant transition" (Woodruff*[18]). Those gaps are systematic: "The regular absence of transitional forms is an almost universal phenomenon," "is true of almost all orders of all classes of animals, both vertebrate and invertebrate," "is true also of the classes ... and of the major animal phyla, and . . . is apparently also true of analogous categories of plants" (Simpson*[19]). Such "discontinuities are almost always and systematically present at the origin of really high categories" (Kitts*[20]). Huxley* had conceded that, "if it could be shown that this fact [gaps between widely distinct groups] had always existed, the fact would be fatal to the doctrine of evolution" (Huxley*[21]), and Good* admits that the "gaps in many places" leave open the "distasteful" possibility of "some other explanation" such as "de novo" appearance (Good*[22]). Such "morphological breaks in the stratigraphic record" are affirmative data, just as "stasis is data" (Gould* and Eldredge*[23]).

The evolutionary tree begins with "the gap between Protista and the animal kingdom, . . . Metazoa, [which] is so great that the origin of Metazoa is still obscure" (Dobzhansky*, Ayala*, Stebbins*, and Valentine*[24]). The next branch in the tree is "fishes that . . . have their origins firmly based in nothing" (White*[25]), and then between fish and amphibians is a "broad evolutionary gap not bridged by fossil materials" (Romer*[26]). For the next branch "there is no fossil evidence of the stages through which the remarkable change from reptile to bird was achieved" (Swinton*[27]); *Archeopteryx* fossils "do not count" (Gould* and Eldredge*[28]). In the limb to mammals, " [m]issing links' have for the most part remained missing" (Russell*[29]), and for all thirty-two mammal orders "[i]n most cases the break is so sharp and the gap so large that the origin of the order is speculative and much disputed" (Simpson*[30]). Moving to the top of the tree, "[i]n spite of recent findings, the time and place of origin of order Primates remains shrouded in mystery" (Simons*[31]), and "man . . . evolved from some ape-like creature . . . without leaving any fossil traces of the steps of the transition" (Zuckerman*[32]). Thus, "we cannot totally ignore the possibility that occasionally . . . there may have been an event of a different kind" involving "de novo" appearance (Good*[33]).

c. The Comparative Morphology Argument of Systematic Similarity and Stasis

Grassé* notes that, "in their basic structure, present living beings differ [hardly] at all from those of the past" (Grassé*[34]), and in all features, many organisms of all higher categories are so nearly identical to their oldest traces that they are called "living fossils" (Eldredge* and Stanley*[35]). Yet "the most obvious single fact about biological evolution—nonchange—has seldom, if ever, been incorporated into anyone's scientific notions of how life actually evolves" (Eldredge* and Tattersall*[36]). That stasis is not just the exception, but the rule: "Most species exhibit no directional change during their tenure on earth. They appear in the fossil record looking much the same as when they disappear" (Gould*[37]). Darwin* lamented that "[a]ll these men [Cuvier, Owen, Agassiz, Barrande, Falconer, Forbes, Lyell, Murchison, and Sedgwick] were paleontologists or geologists, and special creation . . . was commonly recognized by them to have strong empirical evidence in the fossil series which seemed to support the idea that species appeared full-blown suddenly, endured unchanged, and became extinct" (Gillespie*[38])—affirmative evidence that also supports the theory of abrupt appearance.

d. The Information Content Argument of Vast Complexity

The "genetic programmes of higher organisms [consist] of something close to a thousand million bits of information, equivalent to the sequence of letters in a small library of one thousand volumes, ... specifying and ordering the growth and development of billions and billions of cells" (Denton*[39]). Similarly, the "information content of the human brain expressed in bits is ... 10^{14} bits," which "would fill some twenty million volumes" (Sagan*[40]). And for human enzymes "the information content ... is represented by the number $10^{40,000}$," so that the "chance that higher life forms might have emerged in this way is comparable with the chance that 'a tornado sweeping through a junk-yard might assemble a Boeing 747 from the materials therein" (Hoyle and Wickramasinghe[41]).

Darwin* conceded that, "[i]f it could be demonstrated that any complex organ existed, which could not possibly have been formed by numerous, successive, slight modifications, my theory would absolutely break down," although he assumed that none would be found (Darwin*[42]). Goldschmidt* listed seventeen of the almost innumerable complex features with vast information content: "hair in mammals; feathers in birds; segmentation of arthropods and vertebrates; the transformation of the gill arches in phylogeny; teeth; shells of mollusks; ectoskeletons; compound eyes; blood circulation; alternation of generations; statocysts; ambulacral system of echinoderms; pedicellaria of the same; cnidocysts; poison apparatus of snakes; whalebone; and primary chemical differences like hemoglobin versus hemocyanin" (Goldschmidt*[43]). Those examples are probably only a small part "of further as yet undreamt of depths of ingenuity and complexity" (Denton*[44]). Proponents of the theory of abrupt appearance suggest that "the enormous information content of even the simplest living system ... cannot in our view be generated by what are often called 'natural' processes" (Hoyle and Wickramasinghe*[45]).

e. The Probability Argument of Greater Statistical Plausibility

At an international conference on "mathematical challenges to the neo-Darwinian interpretation of evolution," one participant (who reflects a widespread view in Europe) said, "to conclude, . . . there is a considerable gap in the neo-Darwinian theory of evolution, . . . of such a nature that it cannot be bridged within the current conception of biology" (Schutzenberger*[46]). Another participant determined, "from a probabilistic point of view, the randomness postulate is highly implausible and . . . an adequate scientific theory of evolution must await the discovery and elucidation of new natural laws" (Eden*[47]). Other scientists have calculated that for the emergence of new species "the probability is so small in terms of the known age of the universe that it is effectively zero" (Ambrose*[48]). These improbabilities are multiplied in the numerous cases of symbiosis, such as between the yucca plant and yucca moth and the "innumerable structures which permit insects and other metazoans to house the bacteria, yeasts or other micro-organisms, which supply enzymes for the better utilization of the food of the host," by "sometimes almost incredible adaptations" (Mayr*[49]). Even non-discontinuitists such as John Stuart Mill* have found that "the adaptations in Nature afford a large balance of probability in favour of creation by intelligence" (Mill*[50]), while discontinuitists suggest that "[a]ny theory with a probability of being correct that is larger that one part in $10^{40,000}$ must be judged superior to evolution," so that the "theory that life was assembled by an intelligence . . . has a probability vastly higher" (Hoyle and Wickramasinghe[51]). While it is true that the force of this probability argument is greatest if the theories of abrupt appearance and evolution are the only alternatives, some persuasive force remains otherwise in the estimation of discontinuitists.

f. The Genetics Argument of Limited Change

Although no one questions whether genes sometimes change by mutation, there is much dispute whether the scope and frequency of those changes can produce macroevolution rather than just microevolution. In connection with the scope of mutations, "genes are limited in their capacity for viable change" at the level of the "major types" (Boyden*[52]), and "mutations do not produce any kind of evolution" at the species level either because of genetic limits (Grassé*[53]). "Viable mutations are of the same order as the trivial differences between intra-speci[es]... and as such seem quite incapable of giving rise to the major divergences of structuro-functional organisation," contrary to "the faith which the Neo-Darwinians place" in mutation and natural selection (Russell*[54]). Most significant traits are governed by more than one gene, and the "improbability increases at an enormous rate as the number of genes increases" (Ambrose*[55]). In connection with the frequency of mutations, it "is most unlikely that fewer than five genes could ever be involved in the formation of even the simplest new structure," and the "probability now becomes one in one thousand million million," because the probability of each favorable gene mutation is at best one in a thousand (Ambrose*[56]). Then "to establish one such change as a regular characteristic in a species seems to take something of the order of 10 million years" (Wald*[57]). Thus, Alfred Russel Wallace*, the cotheorist with Darwin* of the evolutionary mechanism of natural selection, noted the antagonism of Mendel's genetic laws as limits: "But on the general relation of Mendelism to Evolution I have come to a very definite conclusion. This is, that it has no relation whatever to the evolution of species or higher groups, but is really antagonistic to such evolution!" (Wallace*[58]). Instead, discontinuitists such as Blyth note that natural selection fulfills a "conservative function" (Blyth[59]), explaining the stasis within and the gaps between natural groups, by the mechanism that is now known to be the genetic laws.

g. *The Comparative Discontinuity Argument of Extensive Anomalies*

There are serious anomalies in the comparative fields of classification, comparative anatomy, and comparative biochemistry that puzzle many evolutionists. In classification, "cladistics is theoretically neutral so far as evolution is concerned" and "has nothing to say about evolution" (Patterson*[60]), but instead " 'Transformed Cladistics' is—'natural order systematics' " (Charig*[61]). In a second of the three schools of classification, "some more radical numerical taxonomists have abandoned the goal of building a taxonomy that reflects evolutionary descent" (Luria*, Gould*, and Singer*[62]). Some evolutionists concede that the existence of natural groups, which transformed cladists and radical numerical taxonomists use, "has always been massive empirical evidence for the typological model of nature" (Denton*[63]), which is the discontinuous view of the theory of abrupt appearance.

In comparative anatomy, anomalies are called convergences or parallelisms, and "convergence is everywhere" (Patterson*[64]), while "parallelisms occur plentifully in whatever direction we look" (Gates*[65]). "[T]here are few kinds of characters which are not convergent in some groups (Boyden*[66]), and there are "repeated similarities between groups considered to be far apart by paleontologists" that are categorized as "parallelisms, convergences, and so on" (Forey*[67]). At the same time, the "attempt to find homologous genes has been given up as hopeless," and it "is useless to speculate on any explanation in the absence of facts" (de Beer*[68]); instead, "apparently homologous structures are specified by quite different genes in different species" (Denton*[69]). Thus, "the facts of comparative anatomy provide no evidence for evolution in the way conceived by Darwin," and are instead "counter-evidence against the whole notion of transmutation" (Denton*[70]).

In comparative biochemistry, serious anomalies exist with almost every area of study, such as cytochrome c, hemoglobin and myoglobin, hormones, and hereditary material. It "seems disconcerting that many exceptions exist to the orderly progression of species as determined by molecular homologies; so many in fact that I think the exceptions, the quirks, may carry the more important message," which "the neo-darwinian hypothesis is insufficient to explain" in some cases (Schwabe*[71]). For example, one study of hormones indicates that amphibians are closer to mammals than reptiles or birds are to mammals, and that reptiles are nearer to fish than amphibians are to fish (King* and Millar*[72]). "Each class at a molecular level is unique, isolated and unlinked by intermediates," conforming to a "non-evolutionary and intensely circumferential pattern that was long ago perceived by the great comparative anatomists of the nineteenth century" (Denton*[73])—mostly discontinuitists (Section 15.2).

Those anomalies are serious: some nondiscontinuitists see classification as more consistent with natural groups than evolutionary assumptions, find comparative anatomy with convergences and parallisms "everywhere" but homologous genes nowhere, and wonder at comparative biochemistry that regularly finds evolutionary cousins more similar than evolutionary sisters and that sounds like a broken molecular clock of perverse chimes. Those anomalies are so regular that they go beyond weakening the theory of macroevolution, and support the theory of abrupt appearance in the view of its advocates, which is very similar to how the leading systematists and anatomists at the time of Darwin* interpreted them (Stansfield*[74]).

Figure 8.3
The "horse ser-
ies" or phylog-
eny (from the
text used by
Scopes): "a very*
deceptive picture"
that "is so per-
suasive that most
readers will be
shocked to learn
that it is an illu-
sion" (Saiff and*
Macbeth)*

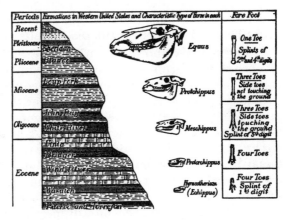

8.3 The Theory of Biological Evolution of Living Organisms

The theory of biological evolution can be assessed in terms of definitions, approaches, mechanisms, evidence, and stages. Various evolutionists find the theory noncompelling at each point.

a. The Definition of Biological Macroevolution

Biological evolution includes both microevolution, which discontinuitists accept, and macroevolution, which is the more controversial postulate that all plants and animals "have arisen by descent from a common ancestor" (Gould*[75]), so that macroevolution proceeded "from primordial life, through unicellular and multicellular organisms, invertebrate and vertebrate animals, to man" (Dobzhansky*[76]). Biological evolution also includes Darwinism, which is the "hypothesis" that "[m]icroevolution is sufficient to account for macroevolution" (Riddiford* and Penny*[77]); "evolution and Darwinism are not synonymous" (Good*[78]). While microevolution is an undisputed fact, macroevolution or " '[t]ransspecific evolution' is generally recognized as a reality, but its explanation on the basis of recognized processes is still in the stage of partly demonstrated theory" in the form of Darwinism (Dobzhansky*, Ayala*, Stebbins*, and Valentine*[79]). Macroevolution itself "must always remain an assumption" that cannot be proved (Boyden*[80]), and is properly called "a theory" (Eldredge*[81]).

b. The Darwinian, Anti-Darwinian, and Anti-Evolutionist Approaches to Macroevolution

Of six scientific approaches to macroevolution besides the theory of abrupt appearance, classical Darwinism is "wrong" on key issues, neo-Darwinism and punctuated equilibria cancel each other by denying the sufficiency of the other's mechanism, and three approaches are anti-Darwinian with one opposing and a second being agnostic toward macroevolution. Classical Darwinism "was wrong" that fossils "would fill in these gaps" (Eldredge* and Tattersall*[82]), that gradualism could explain the "extreme rarity of transitional forms" (Gould*[83]), and that acquired traits could be inherited by a "pangenesis theory" (Rosen*[84]). Neo-Darwinism is also "effectively dead, despite its persistence as textbook orthodoxy" (Gould*[85]), has had its "obituary" written (Platnick*[86]), is "very flimsy" in its "explanation of macroevolution" (Saunders*[87]), and is "incoherent" (Cracraft*[88]), according to punctuated equilibria proponents and others. Punctuated equilibria in turn is not "an important explanation for the evolution of complex adaptations" or macroevolution (Dawkins*[89]), neo-Darwinians reply.

Anti-Darwinians consist of "a significant minority of first-rate biologists who have never been able to bring themselves to accept the validity of Darwinian claims" (Denton*[90]), such as evolutionary saltationists, neutral selectionists, structuralists, nonequilibrium thermodynamics advocates, and others. Examples are Løvtrup's recent *Darwinism: The Refutation of a Myth* (1987), Ho's* and Saunder's* *Beyond Neo-Darwinism* (1984), Ambrose's* *The Nature and Origin of the Biological World* (1982), and Grassé's* *The Evolution of Living Organisms* (trans. 1977). Transformed cladists operate "in a non-evolutionary domain" and are "neutral or opposed to evolutionary theorizing" (Ball*[91]), such as Patterson* who has "been kicking around non-evolutionary or even anti-evolutionary ideas" while concluding that macroevolution "seems somehow to convey antiknowledge" (Patterson*[92]).

Anti-evolutionists include Denton's* *Evolution: A Theory in Crisis* (1985) with its "anti-evolutionary thesis" (Denton*[93]), Sermonti's* and Fondi's* *Dopo Darwin: Critica all' Evoluzionismo* (1980), and others who find that "the evidence is still lacking" for most macroevolutionary postulates (Kerkut*[94]). In such a climate of scientific dispute, it is clear to all but the blinded zealots that Darwinism and macroevolution are not compellingly established or immune to criticism.

c. The Postulated Mechanisms of Macroevolution

*Macro*evolution at present lacks any persuasive Darwinian mechanism (although there is no question that *micro*evolution has occurred and is occurring). In fact, each major school of evolutionists denies the sufficiency of the mechanism for macroevolution proposed by the other school,[95] and then confronts additional problems as well.[96] Natural selection, the "fundamental process directing evolutionary change" according to the neo-Darwinian synthesis (Dobzhansky*, Ayala*, Stebbins*, and Valentine*[97]), is tautologous or nonexplanatory (Section 10.2), or nontestable or unfalsifiable (Sections 10.3-10.4), according to scores of biologists and philosophers of science; "is based on not one sure datum (Grassé*[98]); and "inevitably results in accepting virtually any data as being 'consistent' with the theory," and thus "has failed as a rigorous theory" (Cracraft*[99]). Species selection, which "must largely determine the overall course of evolution" under the punctuated equilibria model (Stanley*[100]), "doesn't seem to do anything much" toward macroevolutionary change (Schopf*[101]), does not explain what traits are species-level traits rather than individual traits on which selection can act (Maynard Smith*,[102] Dawkins*,[103] Grene*,[104] Hoffman*[105]), has the problem that "the evidence is still lacking for species selection" (Hoffman* and Hecht* [106]), and is "not causal" but merely a "description" (*id.*[107]). Without a credible mechanism, macroevolution is not compellingly established, particularly in view of the noncompelling evidence that macroevolution has occurred at all.

d. The Postulated Evidence for Macroevolution

Each of the various alleged evidences for macroevolution and Darwinism is noncompelling, in the view of many evolutionist scientists. Of the scores of sources, the following are typical.

(1) The paleontology argument "contributed . . . nothing to evolutionary biology" (Hoffman*[108]), and in fact the "extreme rarity of transitional forms in the fossil record persists as the trade secret of paleontology" (Gould*[109])

(2) The phylogeny argument has a "chief question with respect to

phylogenetic reconstruction" of "its feasibility" (Hull*[110]), has produced only "meaningless waffle" (Charig*[111]), has an "Achilles' heel" of "circularity in the [evolutionary] approach" (Thomson*[112]), and has been "another miserable failure" (Saiff*[113]).

(3) The classification argument "has nothing to say about evolution" according to the transformed cladist school of classification (Patterson*[114]), while part of the phenetics school has "abandoned the goal of building a taxonomy that reflects evolutionary descent" (Luria* and Gould*[115]). The classification system devised by pre-Darwinian creationists "has undergone surprisingly little change" (Mayr*[116]), and modern classification has not cured the "ignorance concerning these relationships [that] is still great" (Mayr*[117]).

(4) The "facts of comparative anatomy provide no evidence for evolution" (Denton*[118]). "[T]here exists no a priori relation between the appearance of two structures and their relatedness" (Schwabe* and Warr*[119]), and the greatest proofs are that "[n]ature abounds in examples of convergence" and parallelism that involve similar structures in unrelated organisms (Denton*[120]), and that the "attempt to find 'homologous' genes . . . has been given up as hopeless" (de Beer*[121]).

(5) The embryological argument only offers a biogenetic law that has "been demonstrated to be wrong by numerous subsequent scholars" (Bock*[122]), a conundrum that "[a]natomically homologous parts in different related organisms appear to have quite different origins" (Oldroyd*[123]), and a vestigial organ argument that "provide[s] no evidence for evolutionary theory" (Scadding*[124]).

(6) The comparative biochemistry argument offers a "serious . . . challenge to the whole evolutionary framework" rather than support (Denton*[125]), by widespread anomalies that require "a robust rejection of a generalized molecular clock hypothesis of DNA evolution" (Vawter* and Brown*[126]), and by "nothing about present techniques for analysing molecular distance data [being] satisfactory" (Farris*[127]).

(7) The population genetics argument has made "no direct contribution to what Darwin obviously saw as the fundamental problem: the origin of species" (Lewontin*[128]), simply "is not, however, a theory of evolution" (Saunders* and Ho*[129]), has come "perilously close" to "explain[ing] nothing" (Lewontin*[130]), and is so circular that is "is merely 'the blind leading the blind' " (Forey*[131]).

(8) Finally, the artificial selection argument "furnished no evidence of the correctness of Natural Selection" (Macbeth*[132]), and

"selective breeding is not analogous to the action of 'natural selection' " (Russell*[133]).

Moreover, several of these arguments may well better support the theory of abrupt appearance than the theory of macroevolution, such as the paleontology argument (Sections 2.1-2.2), the population genetics argument (Section 2.6), the classification argument (Section 2.7(a)), and the comparative biochemistry argument (Section 2.7(c)), discontinuitist scientists point out.

e. The Postulated Stages of Macroevolution

The ten alleged stages of macroevolution are supported by much ardent belief but little persuasive evidence, as many scientists have concluded who are not advocates of either abrupt appearance or creation.[134] One example is Kerkut*:

> There is a theory which states that many living animals can be observed over the course of time to undergo *changes* so that *new species are formed*. This can be called [*microevolution* or] the "Special Theory of Evolution" and can be demonstrated in certain cases by experiments. On the other hand there is the theory that *all the living forms in the world have arisen from a single source* which itself came from an inorganic form. This theory can be called [macro*evolution* or] the "General Theory of Evolution" and the evidence that supports it is *not sufficiently strong* to allow us to consider it as anything more than a working hypothesis. It is *not clear whether the changes that bring about speciation are of the same nature as those that brought about the development of new phyla*. The answer will be found by future experimental work and not by dogmatic assertions that the General Theory of Evolution must be correct because there is nothing else that will satisfactorily take its place.[135]

The stages of biological macroevolution simply do not have a compelling status, and reasonable difference of opinion is possible, in the view of many scientists[136] along with Kerkut* (but not necessarily in the view of the following scientists).

(1) Macroevolution from prokaryotes to eukaryotes is an "area of speculation" (Whitfield*[137]) with many "microbial Just So Stories" (Levin* and Lenski*[138]). "It is not known just what were the ancestors of Protozoa" (Hickman*[139]), and there is "as yet no definite evidence about the way in which the Viruses, Bacteria or Protozoa are interrelated" (Kerkut*[140]).

(2) Macroevolution from early eukaryotes to invertebrate animals (early Metazoa) "cannot be documented from fossil evidence," so that "the origin of Metazoa is still obscure" (Dobzhansky*, Ayala*, Stebbins*, and Valentine*[114]). The "first and most important steps

of animal evolution remain even more obscure than those of plant evolution" (Weiss*[142]), although nine phyla appeared so that the "seas were swarming with highly differentiated aquatic plants and animals" (Barghoorn*[143]) and so that such invertebrates are "largely immune to the 'poor fossil record' argument" (Stanley*[144]).

(3) Macroevolution from invertebrate to chordate and vertebrate fish is assumed, although "[h]ow this earliest chordate stock evolved, what stages of development it went through to eventually give rise to truly fish-like creatures, we do not know" (Ommanney*[145]), and although the "geological record has so far provided no evidence as to the origin of fishes" (Norman*[146]). There are fossils of "numerous fishlike vertebrates" (Romer*[147]), but "every other major group of fishes" have "their origins firmly based in nothing" (White*[148]).

(4) Macroevolution from fish to amphibians is such that "the gap remains unbridged and the best place to start the evolution of the vertebrates is in the imagination" (Smith*[149]). The "origin of the vertebrates [is] an unsolved problem" (Stahl*[150]), and the replacement for plausible evidence is "phantoms" and "will-o'-the-wisps" (Patterson*[151]). Macroevolution from earlier amphibians to " 'modernized' forms is almost completely a blank" too (Romer*[152]), and "speculations about the evolution of the group" are what remain (Stahl*[153]).

(5) Macroevolution from amphibians to reptiles has "no direct proof from the fossil record" (Stirton*[154]), and "the major distinguishing adaptation of the reptiles, the amniotic egg," is unexplained and "baffling" (Denton*[155]).

(6) Macroevolution from reptiles to birds also offers "no fossil evidence of the stages through which the remarkable change . . . was achieved" (Swinton*[156]), and for imagining such complex changes "the difficulties become overwhelming" (Macbeth*[157]). Although *Archaeopteryx* is often proposed as a transitional form, its fossils "do not count" (Gould* and Eldredge*[158]), "stand[] in splendid isolation" (Romer*[159]), "do not provide a sufficient basis" for the transition (Denton*[160]), and in fact are "already birds" (Russell*[161]), are " 'all bird' " (Huxley*[162]), are younger than a fairly modern bird (Marx*[163]), and are "highly improbable" to be "on the main line" to modern birds (Ostrom*[164]).

(7) Macroevolution from reptiles to mammals confronts the difficulty that "[e]ach species of mammal-like reptile that has been found appears suddenly in the fossil record and is not preceded by

the species that is directly ancestral to it" (Kemp*[165]). Such "mammal-like reptiles" (on the basis of skeletons) may be "in fact in terms of their overall biology only distantly related" (Denton*[166]), possibly "were completely reptilian" (Jerison*[167]), and are described as "mammal-like reptiles" primarily on the "inadequate" basis of their jaw structure (Gow*[168]) and middle ear structure (Lombard*[169]). Macroevolution from lower mammals to higher mammals faces an absence of transitional forms that "is true of all the thirty-two orders of mammals" (Simpson*[170]), and " 'missing links' [that] have for the most part remained missing" (Russell*[171]). The horse series that has been made famous by textbook and museum "iconography" (Gould*[172]) has "had to be discarded or modified" (Raup*[173]), is "very deceptive" (Saiff* and Macbeth*[174]) and "unfortunate" (Hardin*[175]), is "largely apocryphal" (Denton*[176]) and "wrong" (Gould*[177]), and for the important changes in side toes and size is "flatly fictitious" (Simpson*[178]) and "relatively trivial" (Denton*[179]).

(8) Macroevolution from other mammals to primates is "not documented by fossils" (Kelso*[180]), and "we know very little" about the evolutionary details of the New World monkeys and the "record simply does not exist" for the Old World monkeys (*id.*[181]). "When and where the first Primates made their appearance is also conjectural" (Hill*[182]).

(9) Macroevolution from primates to man is not supported by "any fossil traces" (Zuckerman*[183]), so that some biologists acknowledge "the frailty of the conventional history" (Gribben* and Cherfas*[184]), others conclude that human fossil study "reveals more about how humans view themselves than it does about how humans came about"—which "is heresy" (Pilbeam*[185]), and some biologists concede that "the mythic element is greatest" in human evolutionary "stories" that "frequently arise unprompted by data" (Hill*[186]). "Many interpretations are possible," Hill*, a Harvard anthropologist, notes (*id.*[187]). The illustrations "suggest far more knowledge of human evolution than we actually possess" such as skeletal details without complete skeletons and hair without direct evidence (Campbell*[188]), and that yields "the completely different portraits that have been drawn for the facial features of a creature such as *Zinjanthropus*" (Oxnard*[189]), and also enables artists to have "been rehabilitating *Homo erectus*" (Rensberger*[190]). As a leading researcher cautions,

> But we have merely to remember cases like Piltdown Man, which turned out to be a fraudulent composite of a genuine fossil skull cap, and a

modern ape jaw, or Hesperopithecus, the ape of the West, which eventually was discovered to be a peccary [pig], or even of the completely different portraits that have been drawn for the facial features of a creature such as Zinjanthropus (Campbell 1964), to realize that this method also has many inherent difficulties. [Oxnard*[191]]

Each stage of human evolution has similar difficulties, in the assessment of many researchers.

(10) Finally, macroevolution from early life to plants confronts, "to the unprejudiced, the fossil record . . . in favour of special creation" and evolutionary proposals that mostly "would break down before an inquisition" (Corner*[192]). For early land plants, "our phyletic charts need extensive revision" (Axelrod*[193]), and for flowering plants, "no forms have been found in pre-Cretaceous rocks linking the angiosperms with any other group of plants" (Denton*[194]).

Macroevolution and Darwinism, in light of this extensive authority and weak evidence, are simply noncompellingly established. Thus, alternative scientific views are possible.

Figure 8.4
Louis Pasteur, the famous microbiologist, whose discoveries are the basis of the biogenesis argument and the isomers argument

8.4 The Theory of Biochemical Abrupt Appearance of the First Life

The theory of biochemical abrupt appearance comprises five or more affirmative scientific arguments for discontinuous abrupt appearance of the first life in complex form. Those arguments are grounded in the natural laws of information science, statistics, biogenesis, and thermodynamics, as well as in the empirical evidence of isomer preferences. From those grounds, it is clear that biochemical abrupt appearance is scientific, whether or not it is correct.

a. The Information Content Argument of Incredible Complexity

Every "simple cell" has "information content . . . comparable to about a hundred million pages of the *Encyclopaedia Britannica*," Sagan* estimates, because it is "a marvel of detailed and complex architecture" (Sagan*[195]). The "progression from [molecules] to that of the amoeba is at least as great as from amoeba to man" (Simpson*[196]). So vast is the information content of the least complex life that only a short nonliving protein could have evolved in a billion years (Yockey*[197]). The genetic coding system in each cell adds a "baffling circle," because "the machinery by which the cell . . . translates the code 'consists of at least fifty macromolecular components which are themselves coded in DNA' " (Popper*[198]). Even an evolutionist, Haskins*, reluctantly acknowledges that to "a pre-Darwinian (or a skeptic of evolution after Darwin) this puzzle surely would have been interpreted as the most powerful sort of evidence for special creation" (Haskins*[199]).

b. The Probability Argument of Statistical Plausibility

The probability of biochemical evolution of a single-celled organism has been calculated variously as 1 chance in $10^{2,000,000}$ (Ambrose*[200]), 1 in 10^{450} (Golay*[201]), "not a believable possibility" (Keosian*[202]), and "virtually zero" (Monod*[203]). Similar calculations have been made for the biochemical evolution of proteins and DNA. Even when the calculations are modified for introns and exons, multiple pathways and structures, and unrealistic assumptions, "the probability for a de novo or independent emergence of a protein is practically non-existent" (Erbrich*[204]). Thus, as unparalleled a logician as John Stuart Mill* found "a large balance of probability in favour of creation," recognizing this as affirmative and persuasive evidence (Mill*[205]). Similar reasoning yields a large balance of probability in favor of abrupt appearance.

The probability of biochemical abrupt appearance is very high if it is the only alternative explanation, and is higher than the exceedingly small probability of evolution even if there are other alternatives, in the assessment of many discontinuitist scientists. Those probability considerations are based on the mathematical laws of statistics that reflect biochemical laws, in the sense that such statistical frequencies measure the operation of natural laws of biochemistry, just as statistical frequencies of particular traits reflect the operation of natural laws of genetics.

c. The Isomers Argument of Left-Handed Amino Acids and Right-Handed Sugars

"The amino acids found in proteins of living organisms are all levorotatory or L-amino acids, and the sugars are dextrorotatory or D-sugars," yet "[o]utside the living world, everything is racemic, which means that it consists of equal amounts of right-handed [D] and left-handed [L] molecules" (Ponnamperuma*[206]). Those isomers in living organisms appear to be essential: "life cannot and never could exist without molecular dissymmetry" (Terentév* [207]). "How and why the complete separation of stereoisomers in living tissue was started remains an enigma" (Bresler*[208]). That "enigma" is better explained by the theory of biochemical abrupt appearance, its proponents suggest, than by the theory of biochemical evolution.

d. The Biogenesis Argument of Life from Life

The law of biogenesis is the "principle that a living organism can arise only from another living organism, a principle contrasting with concepts such as that of the spontaneous generation of living from non-living matter" or abiogenesis (Oxford Dictionary [208A]), that life biochemically evolved from nonlife. Related biochemical considerations are that "spontaneous dissolution is much more probable, and hence proceeds much more rapidly, than spontaneous synthesis" (Wald*[209]). That is evident in the origin of life experiments, where "the reactions that are invoked to synthesize such compounds are seen to be much more effective in decomposing them" (Hull* and Bernal*[210]). The law of biogenesis and the biochemical tendency away from life require abrupt appearance of the first life, and conflict with its evolution.

e. The Thermodynamics Argument of Increasing Disorder

Many researchers state that among thermodynamic laws "the second law applies equally well to open systems," and that the concept is in "error" that "the second law of thermodynamics fails for [nonequilibrium or open] systems" (Ross*[211]). Prigogine* applies classical thermodynamics to the origin of life and concludes that "spontaneous genesis of life in its present form is therefore highly improbable even on the scale of the billions of years during which prebiotic evolution occurred" (Prigogine* *et al.*[212]). Although he suggests that nonequilibrium thermodynamics solves the problem, it still must make water run uphill, steep and high. Even under nonequilibrium theory, "the spontaneous generation of life is highly improbable" (Yockey*[212A]). Biochemical abrupt appearance is as consistent as biochemical evolution is inconsistent with the downward process toward disorder of nonequilibrium thermodynamics, discontinuitist scientists point out.

Figure 8.5

The "information encoded in a single human chromosome is equivalent to several thousand volumes of small print" (Leslie)*

8.5 The Theory of Biochemical Evolution of the First Life

The theory of biochemical evolution requires a special early atmosphere, a special primordial soup, pond, or other matrix, and particular stages, all of which have been called "myths" by some evolutionist researchers. The laboratory experiments are also sometimes mythologically extrapolated.

a. The Postulated Early Atmosphere of Biochemical Evolution

The oxygen-free early atmosphere that is necessary to biochemical evolution is more a matter of wishful thinking than of scientific fact, and strong scientific evidence directly contradicts the possibility of such an atmosphere, according to a number of evolutionist scientists. There is "no evidence for . . . but much against" a primitive oxygen-free and methane-ammonia-rich atmosphere (Abelson*[213]), and "the concept of early oxidizing atmospheres . . . is becoming the new orthodoxy" (Henderson-Sellers*[214]) with much evidence for an early oxygen-rich atmosphere. Yet "the synthesis of compounds of biological interest takes place only under reducing [no free oxygen] conditions," according to Miller* and Orgel*.[215]

(1) The absence of red beds in some older strata is "contentious and ambiguous" evidence on the question of an oxygen-free early atmosphere (Clemmey* and Badham*[216]), and the presence of banded iron formations is inconclusive. In fact, the geologic evidence does not exist that would be produced by an oxygen-free atmosphere, while the atmospheric evidence "contraindicate[s]" such an atmosphere (Abelson*[217]). Some red beds exist in older strata (Clemmey* and Badham*[218]), while missing red beds are better explained by diagenesis and other factors (id.; Pettijohn*[219]).

(2) Several considerations rule out an early oxygen-free atmosphere. First, geological factors "indicate the existence of a Precambrian atmosphere containing much oxygen" (Dimroth* and Kimberley*[220]). Second, ultraviolet light would have split water vapor into oxygen and hydrogen in quantities greater than surface minerals could absorb (Carver*[221]). Third, ultraviolet light also would have caused methane and ammonia to be "rapidly destroyed by atmospheric photochemical reactions . . . and destroyed by chemical reaction with the hydroxyl radical (OH) formed by the photolysis of atmospheric [water] vapor . . . ," so that "the lifetimes of methane and ammonia in the early atmosphere must have been very short—hundreds of years . . ." (Levine*[222]).

b. The Postulated Primordial Soup of Biochemical Evolution

Shapiro* and Sillen* refer to "the myth of the prebiotic soup"[223] as a place for formation, concentration, and combination of organic molecules (Shapiro*[224]), and Hull* says that the "physical chemist

... cannot offer any encouragement to the biochemist, who needs an ocean full of organic compounds to form even lifeless coacervates" (Hull*[225]). The problems with a primordial soup are rife, and most of those problems are shared by the evaporating pool and mineral adsorption alternatives.

(1) A geologic problem is that a primordial soup would leave distinctive geological remains, but "no such materials have been found" (Brooks* and Shaw*[226]). No geological evidence exists for evaporating pools either (Dose*[227]).

(2) A cross-reaction problem includes the "reactions between abiotically formed amino acids and sugars, and more generally between aldehydes and amines," which would have brought the "rapid formation of this insoluble polymeric material ... and would thus have prevented the formation of an 'organic soup' " (Nissenbaum*, Kenyon* and Oro*[228]). Similarly, "DNA is unstable in aqueous solution" and "tends to hydrolyze" (breaking apart) (Shapiro*[229]), proteins would have formed cross-linkages by reacting with formaldehyde (Walker*[230]), and "[f]atty acids form insoluble salts with magnesium and calcium, and hence would be removed from the soup" (Abelson*[231]).

(3) A decomposition problem involves "chemical and physical processes, such as adsorption on sinking materials, polymerization and aggregation to humic type polymers or ... to particulate matter," such that organic molecules could not accumulate in the ocean (Nissenbaum*[232]). Other aspects are hydrolysis of "all the major biopolymers" (Cairns-Smith*[233]), whether in a primordial ocean or evaporating pools, and racemization of L-amino acids and D-sugars into biologically unusable mixtures of D and L forms (Dillon*[234]).

(4) A radiation problem from ultraviolet light would make amino acids "formed in such an atmosphere ... immediately vulnerable" and would cause "97 per cent" to be "decomposed before it could reach the surface," whereas amino acids formed in or reaching the ocean still would face "decomposition by ultra-violet radiation" that would "clearly preclude the possibility of accumulating useful concentrations of organic compounds over eons of time" (Hull*[235]). The "circulation of the ocean" would have "exposed the amino acids from greater depths to ultraviolet light also" (Dose*[236]). Thus, "the concentration of amino acids in the 'soup' would have been about the same as their concentrations in the oceans now" (Dose*[237]).

(5) The final difficulty, a dilution problem, throws question on whether "the 'primordial soup' could have existed at all," and leaves

it "generally accepted that the concentration of the 'soup' was probably too small for efficient synthesis, particularly of biopolymers" (Nissenbaum*, Kenyon*, and Oro*[238]). A number of researchers acknowledge "the problem of the concentrations of the monomers in primordial waters" (Cairns-Smith*[239]), and that the "dilution factor . . . imposes especially great difficulties upon the origins of the biological materials" (Dillon*[240]). The primordial soup would leave amino acids "hopelessly low as starting material for the spontaneous generation of life" (Hull*[241]), and "by far too low for direct formation of polymers and more complicated structures" (Dose*[242]).

(6) Evaporating pools might solve the dilution problem, but would magnify the radiation problem (Cairns-Smith*[243]), and would still encounter the geological problem (Dose*[244]), the cross-reaction problem, and the decomposition problem, while adding a new problem of evaporation of such essential compounds as aldehydes and hydrogen cyanide (Horowitz* and Hubbard*[245]). Bernal's adsorption on clays would not solve the dilution problem, because "[a]dditional factors would still be needed to concentrate the molecules sufficiently," and would add a new binding problem, that "[n]one of these types of molecule binds very strongly to ordinary clays" (Cairns-Smith*[246]). The geologic, cross-reaction, and decomposition problems would remain.

That "myth of the prebiotic soup," combined with the "myth" of an oxygen-free early atmosphere,[247] invites cynicism about how much other mythology is included in biochemical evolution.

c. The Postulated Stages of Biochemical Evolution

Each stage of biochemical evolution, even in the eyes of many advocates, is "the subject of either controversy or complete bewilderment" (Scott*[248]), necessitates that "[s]peculation is bound to be rife" with many proposals sharing "much with imaginative literature and little with theoretical inference,"[249] and "adds another dimension of unreality to an unreal line of thought" (Cairns-Smith*[250]).

(1) Evolution of amino acids confronts the ultraviolet radiation, cross-reaction, decomposition, and dilution problems that were discussed above.

(2) Evolution of proteins encounters difficulties of cross-reactions that make the starting materials impure (Nissenbaum*[251]); dilution such that "the concentration of the 'soup' was probably too small for efficient synthesis, particularly of biopolymers" (Nissenbaum*,

Kenyon*, and Oro*[252]); destruction of proteins by the very temperatures necessary to form them, which "pyrolize amino acids, depolymerize polypeptides, and degrade microspheres" (Sagan*[253]), as
well as by hydrolysis (Dose*[254]); formation of biologically useless
polymers with "a substantial portion of peptide bonds . . . not of the
α-peptide type" (Temussi* *et al.*[255]); and formation of biologically
useless proteins not made of "exclusively the L-enantiomers of the
amino acids" (Williams*[256]).

(3) Evolution of sugars is generally believed to have begun
through the formose reaction, but no less an authority than Orgel*
does "not believe that the formose reaction . . . is a plausible model
for the prebiotic accumulation of sugars" (Reid* and Orgel*[257]).
Difficulties include destruction of much of the formaldehyde in the
ancient atmosphere or ocean (Abelson*[258]); destruction of simple
sugars by cross-reactions with amino acids or by decomposition
from their instability (Cairns-Smith*[259]); a concentration of sugars
far too low, and a prevalence of "caramel"-like useless polymers
(Cairns-Smith*[260]); and biologically useless molecules from the
equal presence of L-sugars along with D-sugars (Williams*[261]).

(4) Evolution of enzymes must have overcome the problems of
necessary "specificity of catalysts" (Cairns-Smith*[262]), and necessary multiple evolutions of each enzyme (Dillon*[263]).

(5) Evolution of lipids involves such a complex chain of biochemical reactions that "[n]o satisfactory synthesis of fatty acids is presently available" (Miller* and Orgel*[264]); such "problems of discrimination," as using the *cis* configuration exclusively over the more
probable *trans* configuration, that are "so difficult that there almost
seems to be a conspiracy not to discuss them" (Cairns-Smith*[265]);
and further difficulties of cross-reactions to form "insoluble salts
with magnesium and calcium" (Abelson*[266]).

(6) Evolution of the genetic coding system requires developments
so complex that researchers "speculate endlessly, unfettered by
inconvenient facts" (Dickerson*[267]); involves "the major problem in
understanding the origin of life [of] trying to guess what the simpler
system might have been" (Crick*[268]); includes a "gigantic implausibility" of evolution of nucleic acids for nineteen listed reasons
(Cairns-Smith*[269]); requires evolution of the gene-protein link that is
"shrouded in almost complete mystery" (Scott*[270]); and necessitates
an evolution of the translating machinery that is "difficult to
imagine" because that "translating machinery consists of at least
fifty macromolecular components which are themselves coded in

DNA" (Monod*[271]), as well as the emergence of the enzyme editing process that is "a major unsolved problem" (Lambert*[272]).

(7) Evolution of life itself "is a jump of fantastic dimensions," and yet "available facts do not provide a basis for postulating that cells arose on this planet" (Green* and Goldberger*[273]), but instead "a very large gap separates the most complex model systems from the simplest contemporary living cells" (Kenyon* and Nissenbaum*[274]). One requirement for life is self-replication, and yet its origin is a "defect of evolutionary theory" because there are "almost no ideas" (Kempthorne*[275]), and its origin poses the "seemingly self-contradictory condition . . . that, while genetic mechanisms can exist only within living things, the organisms themselves could not have come into being without such a device" (Dillon*[276]). Another requirement for life is protein synthesis, and that involves "great difficulties even if heterotrophs had an adequate supply of organic molecules to consume, such as the need "to recognise molecules, or at the very least to distinguish between classes of them," and "some kind of structure [that] would seem to be needed that could form specific sockets" that are "much more difficult to engineer than the [recognized] molecule itself" (Cairns-Smith*[277]).

Biochemical evolution could not be effectuated by natural selection, because, "to have natural selection, you have to have self-reproduction," so that "[p]rebiological natural selection is a contradiction in terms" (Dobzhansky*[278]). A "preliminary kind of semi-Darwinian evolution, where microsystems are not able to reproduce but they are already subject to selection," is not possible (Cairns-Smith*[279]).

d. The Laboratory Experiments
for Biochemical Evolution

Although "so powerful has been the effect of Miller's* experiment on the scientific imagination that to read some of the literature on the origin of life (including many elementary texts) you might think that it had been well demonstrated . . .," actually "these experiments allow us to see . . . just why prevital nucleic acids are highly implausible" (Cairns-Smith*[280]), and indeed that biochemical evolution is highly implausible. Their significance is vastly reduced because they "use pure starting materials, afford poor yields, . . . are run under conditions which are not compatible with one another," ignore that nucleic acid components "would tend to hydrolyze," and "would be inhibited by . . . related substances which would react preferentially with them" (Shapiro*[281]).

(1) The experiments synthesizing amino acids "may have little relevance concerning the origin of life on Earth" (Clemmey* and Badham*[282]), and reflect the principle that "an experiment designed to produce nucleic acids produces little else" (Keosian*[283]). The experiments depend on a trap that "we have to imagine" in a primordial soup, because "the course of reaction may be different if the products are not preferentially removed" (Sagan*[284]); and also depend on other "crippling provisos" that "are mainly a catalogue of difficulties that have been getting worse" (Cairns-Smith*[285]). Even then, the Miller* experiment forms "[o]nly two of these fifty" building blocks of necessary molecules (Shapiro*[286]).

(2) The experiments synthesizing proteins have only "scarce relevance to the prebiotic synthesis of natural amino acids" (Temussi* et al.[287]). The experiments actually only synthesize proteinoids that "have scarce resemblance to natural peptidic material" because of nonbiological peptide bonds (Temussi* et al.[288]), and that have such randomness of composition that "[i]t is deceptive . . . to suggest that thermal polypeptides are similar to proteins" (Miller* and Orgel*[289]). The experimental products also have "a mixture of D and L forms" of amino acids, although purity of the L form is essential to life (Stansfield*[300]).

(3) Experiments involving the genetic coding system do not resolve the massive difficulties of evolving bases and sugars, nucleosides, nucleotides, nucleotide chains, gene-protein linkage, translation machinery, and a replication system, as discussed above.

(4) Experiments proposing protocell models still leave "a very large gap" from life (Kenyon* and Nissenbaum*[301]), and "are specious in that they bear apparent behavioral similarities to living things but lack the real requisites of even the simplest protobionts" (Dillon*[302]). The "protocells" are about as lifelike as "soap bubbles" and are "notoriously unstable" (Day*[303]), and they invoke such "unnatural conditions and often complex organic substances required for their formation" that "doubts inexorably arise concerning the suitability of these colloids for a role as protobiont ancestors" (Dillon*[304]). The coacervate and proteinoid microsphere models "no longer can be considered meaningful in the context of the origins of life on earth," and "[n]either they nor any other artificial systems are adequate to provide concrete evidence to show clearly how life and the requisite genetic apparatus actually did arise" (Dillon*[305]).

(5) The vast improbability of biochemical evolution has been cal-

culated by many researchers, at levels such as 1 chance in $10^{2,000,000}$ (Ambrose*[306]), and 1 chance in 10^{94} (Yockey*[307]). Thus, some conclude "that belief in currently accepted scenarios of spontaneous biogenesis is based on faith" (Yockey*[308]).

Figure 8.6
The "laws of
thermodynamics
...indicated that
the Universe had
a beginning"
(Jastrow)*

8.6 The Theory of Cosmic Abrupt Appearance of the Universe

The theory of cosmic abrupt appearance consists of six or more affirmative lines of scientific evidence for discontinuous abrupt appearance of the universe, galaxies, stars, and earth. Those arguments are based on the natural laws of thermodynamics and information science, in addition to the empirical evidence of the anthropic principle, heterogeneity of matter, special conditions for galaxy formation, and polonium halos in the earth's crust.

a. The Thermodynamics Argument

The thermodynamics laws "argue strongly for a created universe" (Stansfield*[309]), and "indicated that the Universe had a beginning" (Jastrow*[310]), many evolutionists concede. Many big bang advocates agree that the "Universe cannot have existed forever—there must have been a creation" (Davies*[311]), while their opponents concur that "[t]o avoid the issue of creation it would be necessary for all the material of the Universe to be infinitely old, and this it cannot be" because "there could be no hydrogen left in the Universe" (Hoyle*[312]). The counterargument of an eternally oscillating universe also fails because its mass "is some twenty times less than the mass density required for a closed universe" (Wald*[313]), or at least "ten times too small" (Jastrow*[314]), notwithstanding black holes and speculations about the "missing mass." The counterargument that matter and antimatter exist in equal quantities conflicts with "the prevailing opinion among astronomers and astrophysicists . . . that matter dominates over antimatter" (Wilczek*[315]), and that there is "very little if any antimatter" (Weisskopf*[316]), and has serious problems of its own (Silk*[317]). The matter and energy of the universe appeared abruptly and discontinuously as required by the thermodynamic laws, many scientists conclude.

b. The Information Content Argument

"Everywhere we look in the Universe . . . we encounter order. . . . [W]here did all the information that makes the world such a special place come from originally?" (Davies*[318]). The universe contains "a high degree of order," yet "*a priori* one should expect that the world would be rendered lawful only to the extent that we intervene with our ordering intelligence" (Einstein*[319]). The complexity is so great that the improbability of its emergence from a big bang singularity is 1 chance in 1,000,000,000,000,000 (Raymo*[320]). As Newton recognized three centuries ago, "it is not to be conceived that mere mechanical causes could give birth to so many regular motions," but the better interpretation is instead an abrupt appearance of a complex universe (Newton[321]).

c. The Anthropic Principle Argument

Under the strong anthropic principle, the "Universe must have those properties which allow life to develop within it at some stage" (Barrow* and Tipler*[322]). Those properties are not the most likely and expected ones, but are extremely improbable ones, so that "there is a grand design in the Universe that favours the development of intelligent life" (Press*[323]). Instead, those highly improbable properties are better explained by an abruptly appearing universe in initial complex form according to some nonevolutionist scientists. First, the universe's "rate of expansion [must be] very close to a critical value," and in fact must be "fine-tuned" to one part in a billion billion (Davies*[324]), if not one part in 10^{50} (Lake*[325]).

Also, the inhomogeneity level of the early universe, in order to make cosmic evolution anything but impossible, had to have "highly specific initial conditions" such that "the recessional velocity" was "equal to the escape velocity" (Gale*[326]). Second, the four forces had to be at critical levels. If the strong nuclear force changed, it would prevent "hydrogen compounds or long-lived stable stars" in one direction and would prevent "[e]lements heaver than hydrogen" in the other direction (Barrow* and Tipler*[327]). If the weak force changed, it would leave no hydrogen in one direction and all hydrogen in the other, rather than the essential mix of light and heavy elements (Leslie*[328]). Third, physical features of the universe must also be at critical levels to permit any imaginable form of life, such as planets, suns, etc. (Barrow* and Tipler*[329]). Whether or not cosmic evolution can produce a complex universe once so many special initial conditions are present, it can neither produce nor explain so many improbable special conditions, and their abrupt appearance seems much more likely to many scientists.

d. The Heterogeneity Argument

The heterogeneity of the universe involves a "inhomogeneity right up to the largest observable scales," with the discovery of "ever-larger inhomogeneities in the distribution of matter: stars, stellar clusters, galaxies, groups of galaxies, clusters of groups, and clusters of clusters" (Oldershaw*[330]). That heterogeneity could result only from abrupt appearance in that complex form or from an explosion with the exceedingly improbable special condition that "the recessional velocity is exactly equal to the escape velocity" (Gale*[331]). That clustering involves a "distribution of galaxies [that] is highly inhomogeneous" probably for the "entire universe" (Gregory* and Thompson*[332]), and between the galaxies vast and uneven voids (Waldrop*[333]). By contrast, "[t]he standard Big Bang model does not give rise to lumpiness" but to "a universe that is uniform, ... with no organization of any kind" (Patrusky*[334]), except by adding the "assumption" with "no explanation" of a big bang starting "in a peculiar state of extraordinary but not quite perfect uniformity"—the "smoothness problem" (Guth* and Steinhardt*[335]). The more natural interpretation of heterogeneity is abrupt appearance of the universe in that form, many nonevolutionist scientists suggest.

e. The Galaxy and Star Formation Argument

The formation of galaxies, galactic clusters, stars, and solar systems simply does not result from an explosion such as the big bang, nonevolutionist scientists such as Hoyle suggest.[336] Even if the expanding debris from an explosion were not inert, "there is no reasonable astronomical scenario in which mineral grains can condense."[337]

Formation of galaxies required not just incredibly accurate critical levels of expansion rate and smoothness, but a process whereby "galaxies could have formed in a universe which is flying apart so fast" (Leslie*[338]) despite that, "[a]fter the decoupling of radiation and matter, it was not possible for the very small irregularities then present in the distribution of the gas to increase quickly enough to form entire galaxies" (Breuer*[339]). Formation of stars confronts similar obstacles, because for gas clouds "ordinarily the internal pressure is much stronger than the gravitation" (Cameron*[340]). Thus, "[o]ne of the chief problems in cosmology is to explain why in an expanding universe matter becomes aggregated into galaxies" (Harrison*[341]), and "[t]he conclusion in the present state of the subject would be that the [solar] system cannot exist" (Jeffreys*[342]).

f. The Radiohalos Argument

The polonium halo argument has been described by an evolutionist as follows:

> The polonium halos, especially those produced by ^{218}Po, are the center of a mystery. The half life of the isotope is only 3 minutes. Yet the halos have been found in granitic rocks . . . in all parts of the world, including Scandinavia, India, Canada, and the United States. The difficulty arises from the observation that there is no identifiable precursor to the polonium: *it appears to be primordial polonium.* If so, how did the surrounding rocks crystallize rapidly enough so that there were crystals available ready to be imprinted with radiohalos by α particles from ^{218}Po? This would *imply almost instantaneous cooling and crystallization* of these granitic minerals, and we know of no mechanism that will remove heat so rapidly: the rocks are supposed to have cooled over millennia, if not tens of millennia (Kazmann*[343]).

The original experimentation on the subject has been performed by a creationist physicist working with many evolutionist colleagues, and has been reported in more than a dozen scholarly articles sometimes jointly written with evolutionist coauthors (Gentry[344]). A method of falsification has been offered (Gentry[345]). The objection that the polonium was a decay product of uranium, rather than an original element in the rocks containing the halos, has been countered by numerous experiments using sophisticated techniques such as fission track and neutron flux methods, electron microscope x-ray fluorescence, fossil alpha recoil analysis, and iron microprobe mass spectrometry, which showed that the polonium did not migrate into and the uranium (or thorium) did not migrate out of the rocks (Gentry[346]), and that the lead isotopes present resulted from polonium rather than uranium decay (Gentry[347]). Although the theory of abrupt appearance is not dependent on this particular affirmative evidence, it is strongly supported by the apparent solidity of the experimental results.

Figure 8.7
The "evidence in favour of a big bang cosmology is much less definite than is widely realized"; "there is still no really conclusive evidence in favour of such a universe" (Burbidge*)

8.7 The Theory of Cosmic Evolution of the Universe

The big bang theory and inflationary universe theory can be examined in terms of evidence and stages. Neither is compellingly established, in the view of a large number of physicists and astronomers.

a. The Primary Evidence for Cosmic Evolution

"[S]ome cosmologists, albeit a minority, do sometimes wonder whether the confidence so often claimed in the big bang picture is justified by our observational knowledge of the Universe" (Narlikar*[348]), and to future cosmologists, it is "probable that our present cosmological ideas on the structure and evolution of the universe. . . will appear hopelessly premature and primitive" (Vaucouleurs*[349]). In fact, the "evidence in favour of a big bang cosmology is much less definite than is widely realized," and "there is still no really conclusive evidence in favour of such a universe" (Burbidge*[350]). Instead, "[t]here are then a variety of possibilities available," and the big bang theory "is one of this family but is by no means the only conceivable member; further possibilities are not completely excluded experimentally or theoretically" (Ellis*[351]).

(1) The "red shift, observed in the spectral lines of distant galaxies and interpreted as a Doppler effect, is the key to cosmology" and the primary evidence for the big bang theory (Sagan*[352]). However, "high-redshift objects [quasars] were associated with nearby low-redshift objects" (Arp*[353]), and in studies of 260 galaxies, "companion galaxies in these groups have significantly higher redshifts," meaning that "these companions contain a component of nonvelocity redshift" to explain the different red shifts of companions (Arp* and Sulentic*[354]). Discordant red shifts of associated galaxies include numerous examples with interacting double galaxies in the neighborhood of spiral galaxies, multiple interacting companions, chains of galaxies, and galaxies connected by luminous filaments (Arp*[355]). Consequently, "redshifts cannot be universally applied as distance indicators" (Sulentic* and Arp*[356]). Although the objection has been raised that these objects are accidentally aligned but non-associated, "more quasar-galaxy . . . and galaxy-galaxy . . . discordant redshift associations exist than are expected by chance" (Arp* and Sulentic*[357]), and " 'near misses' which should be found much more frequently are not, in fact, found" (Arp*[358]). Burbidge* laments that this "strong evidence that not all red shifts are of cosmological origin" "is largely ignored," and suggests that the reason might be that "astronomers knowing that their subject in this area already rests on rather shaky foundations . . . cannot face up to the opening of Pandora's box" (Burbidge*[359]).

Many alternative explanations of red shifts have been offered. Wolf* calculates that "the normalized spectrum of light will, in general, change on propagation in free space," and "can produce red-shifts" that are noncosmological (Wolf*[360]); and that theoretical conclusion has been experimentally verified (Bocko* et al.[362]). Crawford* gives the alternative explanation for much red shift of "a gradual energy loss of photons due to their interaction with curved space-time" (Crawford*[362]), which others join in (Marmet*,[363]

Segal*[364]). Ellis* suggests a "static two-centered universe . . . where the redshifts observed for distant galaxies are purely cosmological gravitational redshifts" (Ellis*[365]). Thus, "it will clearly become necessary to arrive at a theory of discrepant redshifts," and it is unlikely that "discrepant redshifts will be explained adequately . . . as simple Doppler peculiar motions" (recession) (Hoyle and Narlikar*[366]).

In any event, the universe's "expansion implies little regarding an initial cosmic state," and "[e]specially . . . does not imply the big bang model" (Allen*[367]).

(2) The other "persuasive evidence" for the big bang theory is the "blackbody background radiation" (Sagan*[368]). However, the "claim that it is strong evidence in support of hot big bang cosmology . . . is completely unjustified" (Alfvén*[369]). In fact, the strength of the microwave background should be "between ten and a thousand times more powerful" if it resulted from a big bang event (Hoyle[370]), and its spectrum shows "deviations from the Planckian spectrum that are considered statistically significant" (Narlikar*[371]). Moreover, the "horizon problem" is that "one should not expect that different regions of the universe had the same temperature," and "the observed isotropy of the cosmic background radiation has no natural explanation" under the big bang theory (Grøn*[372]). Instead, various explanations other than a big bang have been offered for the microwave background.

b. The Stages of Cosmic Evolution

The stages of cosmic evolution embody serious difficulties. There are the "four fundamental problems" of "why there is so little antimatter," "how the galaxies could have formed in the time alloted," the horizon problem of large scale isotropy, and the flatness problem of a critical mass level (Trefil*[373]).

(1) In addition, the problem of the origin of matter and energy involves the dilemma on the one side of the "disturbing fact" that "hydrogen is used up in stars" so that unburned hydrogen precludes an eternally oscillating universe (Jastrow*[374]), and on the other side of the thermodynamic law of "conservation of energy" that "is violated in the big-bang model" or inflationary model that requires energy and "matter to come into existence" (Narlikar* and Padmanabhan*[375]). The inflationary universe model does not solve the "mystery" of "how space (strictly spacetime) came to exist" and "[h]ow did the universe arrive in the false vacuum state in the first

place?" (Davies*[376]). The "outstanding theoretical problem" (Tipler*[377]) with the next stage, the compression of the universe, is that it requires "assuming . . . some unknown force" (Jastrow*[378]), about which "[p]roponents of the theory turn extremely vague" (Alfvén*[379]).

(2) The problems with the explosion and expansion stages are "how did this explosion occur" (Narlikar*[380]) and how to escape the "extreme improbability that such a coherent, synchronized eruption would occur spontaneously" (Davies*[381]), and then how the expansion was "tuned to an accuracy of one part in 10^{50}" (Lake*[382]). The "vexed question of the origin of galaxies" is such that the big bang offers "no physical understanding of the situation" but only an assumption of incredibly precise inhomogeneities (Burbidge*[383]); "it is hard to see how galaxies could have formed in a universe which is flying apart so fast" from an explosion (Leslie*[384]). The origin of complex information similarly conflicts with an explosion whose "[i]nternal motions die away adiabatically" and "lead to a universe that is dead . . . almost from its beginning" (Hoyle[385]).

* * *

Kerkut* suggests to a student, who is uncritically espousing evolutionary arguments, "that he might have looked at the book by Radl, *The History of Biological Theories.*"[386] Just as virtually every biological theory in history has been abandoned, Darwinism may someday be viewed as an erroneous guess. Cairns-Smith* draws the analogy between Darwinian evolution and phlogiston theories, which have been long discarded:

One of the troubles with starting well is that you may lock onto a point of view and then stay with it long after it has failed to maintain its initial promise. There are many examples from the history of science. The phlogiston theory was one. This was the idea that an inflammable material contained a 'principle of fire'—phlogiston—which was given off when the material was burnt. This explains the obvious facts of combustion so well that it was quite natural to accept it and then interpret new data in terms of it. Suppose that as a respectable eighteenth century phlogistonist, you had been asked to explain why a candle goes out when a jar is put over it. Would you have taken this as a puzzle or an anomaly? Neither, you would have taken it as a confirmation of the phlogiston idea because it is so easily explained: the air in the jar has become saturated with phlogiston and cannot take up any more. What about the gain in weight when a metal is converted to a calx (i.e. oxide)? Here you would have put on a more patient expression. This is not so much a puzzle, you would explain, as a misunderstanding: phlogiston is the principle of fire, you see, not an isolable substance: metals all contain this principle (which is why incidentally they have so many properties in common). When the corpuscles of metals are imbued with phlogiston the effect of gravity is lessened... *You would, I daresay, have been able to ward off all comers with such explanations.* Nothing would force you to change sides. (Nothing ever forced Priestly).[387]

Richard Dawkins* of Oxford, who is no friend to either the theory of abrupt appearance or the theory of creation, acknowledges that "[t]he obvious way to decide between rival theories is to examine the evidence"—and the rival theories to which he refers are Darwinian evolution, Lamarckism, " 'neutralism', 'mutationism' and creationism."[388] That is what Volume I has attempted, and what it is hoped that other studies of origins will do. Refusal to admit that any rival theories exist is a pretense that assures victory in one's own mind but that denies a fair contest, as Huston Smith* of Syracuse University and formerly of Massachusetts Institute of Technology points out:

This reduction of the field of evidence in which it [Darwinism] stands already exaggerates its stature. . . . To gain acceptance in science a working hypothesis does not need to show much in the way of proof; all it need do is stay ahead of its competitors. If its competitors are weak, the lead hypothesis can look strong without actually being so. And if it has no competitors? . . .[389]

Charles Darwin* himself recognized the pervasive impact of bias on the subject of origins, and his words are a fitting close to this volume:

Although I am fully convinced of the truth of the views given in this volume under the form of an abstract, I by no means expect to convince experienced naturalists whose minds are stocked with a multitude of facets all viewed, during a long course of years, from a point of view directly opposite to mine. . . .[390]

Notes

[1] *Interview with Daniel J. Boorstin*, U.S. News & World Report, April 1984, at 73.

[2] C. Darwin*, *The Origin of Species* 2 (1st ed. 1859, repr. 1964).

[3] Gould*, *Darwinism Defined: The Difference between Fact and Theory*, Discover, Jan. 1987, at 64, 65.

[4] T. Dobzhansky*, F. Ayala*, G. Stebbins* & J. Valentine*, *Evolution* 9 (1977).

5 *Id* at 8. *See also* Gruner*, *On Evolution and Its Relation to Natural Selection*, 16 Dialogue 708, 709 (1977).

6 Agassiz, *Prof. Agassiz on the Origin of Species*, 30 Am. J. Science 142, 149 (1860), excerpted from 3 L. Agassiz, *Contribution to the Natural History of the United States* (1860).

7 2 *The Life and Letters of Charles Darwin* 202-03 (F. Darwin* ed. 1903).

8 J. Draper*, *History of the Conflict Between Religion and Science* 246-47 (1896).

9 Cannon*, *The Bases of Darwin's Achievement: A Revaluation*, 5 Victorian Studies 109, 131 (1961).

10 Gould*, *Evolution's Erratic Pace*, Natural History, May 1977, at 12, 12.

11 D. Raup* & S. Stanley*, *Principles of Paleontology* 382 (2d ed. 1978).

12 S. Stanley*, *Macroevolution* 1 (1979).

13 F. Ayala* & J. Valentine*, *Evolving: The Theory and Processes of Organic Evolution* 258 (1979).

14 Ager*, *The Nature of the Fossil Record*, 87 Proc. Geological Association 131, 133 (1976).

15 C. Darwin*, *The Origin of Species* 302 (1st ed. 1859, repr. 1964).

16 A. Thompson*, *Biology, Zoology, and Genetics: Evolution Model vs. Creation Model* 2, 76 (1983).

17 Gould*, *Evolution's Erratic Pace*, Natural History, May 1977, at 12, 14.

18 Woodruff*, *Evolution: The Paleobiological View*, 208 Science 716, 716 (1980).

19 G. Simpson*, *Tempo and Mode in Evolution* 107 (1944); G. Simpson*, *The Major Features of Evolution* 360-61 (1953).

20 Kitts*, *Paleontology and Evolutionary Theory*, 28 Evolution 458, 467 (1974).

21 T. Huxley*, *Three Lectures on Evolution* 619 (1882).

22 R. Good*, *Features of Evolution in the Flowering Plants* 383 (1974).

23 *Id.* at 116.

24 T. Dobzhansky*, F. Ayala*, G. Stebbins* & J. Valentine*, *Evolution* 373, 397 (1977).

25 White*, *Presidential Address*, 177 Proc. Linnean Society 1, 8 (1966).

26 A. Romer*, *Vertebrate Paleontology* 36 (3d ed. 1966).

27 Swinton*, *The Origin of Birds*, in 1 Biology and Comparative Physiology of Birds 1 (A. Marshall* ed. 1960).

28 Gould* & Eldredge*, *Punctuated equilibria: The tempo and mode of evolution reconsidered*, 3 Paleobiology 115, 147 (1977).

29 E. Russell*, *The Diversity of Animals* 130 (1962).

30 G. Simpson*, *Tempo and Mode in Evolution* 105-06 (1944).

31 Simons*, *The Origin and Radiation of the Primates*, 167 Annals of N.Y. Acad. Sciences 318 (1969).

32 S. Zuckerman*, *Beyond the Ivory Tower* 64 (1970).

33 R. Good*, *Features of Evolution in the Flowering Plants* 384 (1974).

34 P. Grassé*, *Evolution of Living Organisms* 84 (trans. 1977).

[35] *Living Fossils* (N. Eldredge* & S. Stanley* eds. 1984).

[36] N. Eldredge* & I. Tattersall*, *The Myths of Human Evolution* 8 (1982).

[37] Gould*, *Evolution's Erratic Pace*, Natural History, May 1977, at 13, 14.

[38] N. Gillespie*, *Charles Darwin and the Problem of Creation* 26 (1979)(U. of Chicago Press).

[39] M. Denton*, *Evolution: A Theory in Crisis* 351 (1985).

[40] C. Sagan*, *Cosmos* 278 (1980). *See* ch. 4 n. 7.

[41] *Hoyle on evolution*, Nature, Nov. 12, 1981, at 105, 105.

[42] C. Darwin*, *The Origin of Species* 189 (1st ed. 1859, repr. 1964).

[43] R. Goldschmidt*, *The Material Basis of Evolution* 6-7 (1940).

[44] M. Denton*, *Evolution: A Theory in Crisis* 342 (1985).

[45] F. Hoyle & N. Wickramasinghe, *Evolution from Space* 150 (1981).

[46] Schutzenberger*, *Algorithms and the Neo-Darwinian Theory of Evolution*, in Mathematical Challenges to the Neo-Darwinian Interpretation of Evolution 73, 74-75 (P. Moorhead* & M. Kaplan* eds. 1967).

[47] Eden*, *Inadequacies of Neo-Darwinian Evolution as a Scientific Theory*, in Mathematical Challenges to the Neo-Darwinian Interpretation of Evolution 109, 109 (P. Moorhead* & M. Kaplan* eds. 1967).

[48] E. Ambrose*, *The Nature and Origin of the Biological World* 142 (1982).

[49] Mayr*, *Accident or Design, The Paradox of Evolution*, in The Evolution of Living Organisms 1, 2-3 (G. Leeper* ed. 1962).

[50] J. Mill*, *Three Essays on Religion* 174 (2d ed. 1874).

[51] F. Hoyle & N. Wickramasinghe, *Evolution from Space* 130 (1981).

[52] A. Boyden*, *Perspectives in Zoology* 27, 35 (1973).

[53] P. Grassé*, *The Evolution of Living Organisms* 87, 88 (trans. 1977).

[54] E. Russell*, *The Diversity of Animals* 123 (1962). *See also* McDonald*, *The Molecular Basis of Adaptation: A Critical Review of Relevant Ideas and Observations*, 14 Annual Rev. Ecology & Systematics 77, 97 (1983).

[55] E. Ambrose*, *The Nature and Origin of the Biological World* 123-24 (1982).

[56] *Id.* at 120-21 (1982).

[57] Wald*, *Discussion*, in Mathematical Challenges to the Neo-Darwinian Interpretation of Evolution 12, 19 (P. Moorhead* & M. Kaplan* eds. 1967).

[58] Letter from A. Wallace* to A. Reid* (Dec. 28, 1909), in *Alfred Russel Wallace Letters and Reminiscences* 340 (J. Marchant* ed. 1916).

[59] M. Pitman, *Adam and Evolution* 75-76 (1984) (creationist author).

[60] C. Patterson*, *The Goals, Uses, and Assumptions of Cladistic Analysis* (1981), quoted in Beatty*, *Classes and Clades*, 31 Systematic Zoology 25, 31 (1982).

[61] Patterson*, *Cladistics*, 27 Biologist 234 (1980).

[62] S. Luria*, S. Gould* & S. Singer*, *A View of Life* 676 (1981).

[63] M. Denton*, *Evolution: A Theory in Crisis* 105 (1985).

[64] Address of Dr. Colin Patterson* at American Museum of Natural History, tr. at 9 (Nov. 5, 1981).

[65] R. Gates*, *Human Ancestry from a Genetical Point of View* 3 (1948) (Harvard U. Press).

[66]   A. Boyden*, *Perspectives in Zoology* 27 (1973).

[67]   Forey*, *Neontological Analysis Versus Palaeontological Stories*, in Problems of Phylogenetic Reconstruction 119, 149 (K. Joysey* & A. Friday* eds. 1982).

[68]   *See* G. de Beer*, *Homology: An Unsolved Problem* 15 (1971).

[69]   M. Denton*, *Evolution: A Theory in Crisis* 149 (1985).

[70]   *Id.* at 155.

[71]   Schwabe*, *On the validity of molecular evolution*, 11 Trends in Biochemical Sciences 280, 280 (1986).

[72]   King* & Millar*, *Heterogeneity of Vertebrate Lutenizing Hormone-Releasing Hormone*, 206 Science 65, 67 (1979).

[73]   M. Denton*, *Evolution: A Theory in Crisis* 290 (1985).

[74]   W. Stansfield*, *The Science of Evolution* 99 (1977). Of course, comparative biochemistry did not then exist.

[75]   S. Luria*, S. Gould* & S. Singer*, *A View of Life* 767 (1981).

[76]   Dobzhansky*, *Evolution*, in 10 Encyclopedia Americana 734, 748 (1982).

[77]   Riddiford* & Penny*, *The scientific status of modern evolutionary theory*, in Evolutionary Theory: Paths into the Future 1, 4-5 (J. Pollard* ed. 1984).

[78]   R. Good*, *Features of Evolution in the Flowering Plants* 5 (1974).

[79]   T. Dobzhansky*, F. Ayala*, G. Stebbins* & J. Valentine*, *Evolution* 5 (1977).

[80]   Boyden*, *Systematic Zoology: A Critical Appraisal, Pt. I*, 15 Physiological Zoology 109, 117 (1982).

[81]   N. Eldredge*, *The Monkey Business: A Scientist Looks at Creationism* 28-29 (1982).

[82]   N. Eldredge* & I. Tattersall*, *The Myths of Human Evolution* 45-46 (1982).

[83]   Gould*, *Evolution's Erratic Pace*, Natural History, May 1977, at 13, 14.

[84]   Rosen*, *Book Review*, 27 Systematic Zoology 370, 370 (1978).

[85]   Gould*, *Is a new and general theory of evolution emerging?*, 6 Paleobiology 120-21 (1980).

[86]   Macbeth*, *How To Defuse a Feud*, Kronos, Summer 1982, at 1, 3-4.

[87]   Saunders*, *Book Review*, New Scientist, Feb. 21, 1985, at 44, 44.

[88]   Cracraft*, *Book Review of Beyond Neo-Darwinism*, 1 Cladistics 300, 303 (1985).

[89]   R. Dawkins*, *The Blind Watchmaker* 266 (1986).

[90]   M. Denton*, *Evolution: A Theory in Crisis* 327 (1985).

[91]   Ball*, *On Groups, Existence and the Ordering of Nature*, 32 Systematic Zoology 446, 446 (1983).

[92]   Address of Dr. Colin Patterson* at American Museum of Natural History, tr. at 1, 4 (Nov. 5, 1981).

[93]   M. Denton*, *Evolution: A Theory in Crisis* 16, 353 (1985).

[94]   G. Kerkut*, *Implications of Evolution* 150 (1960).

[95]   Section 3.2(b)-(c).

[96]   Section 3.3 (a) & (f).

[97]   T. Dobzhansky*, F. Ayala*, G. Stebbins* & J. Valentine*, *Evolution* 32, 504 (1977).

[98]   P. Grassé*, *The Evolution of Living Organisms* 170 (trans. 1977).

[99]   Cracraft*, *Book Review of Beyond Neo-Darwinism*, 1 Cladistics 300, 301 (1985).

[100]   Stanley*, *A Theory of Evolution Above the Species Level*, 72 Proc. National Acad. Sciences 646, 648 (1975). *See also* Stanley*, *Macroevolution and the Fossil Record*, 36 Evolution 460, 471 (1982).

[101]   Schopf*, *A Critical Assessment of Punctuated Equilibria*, 36 Evolution 1144, 1156 (1982).

[102]   Maynard Smith*, *Current controversies in evolutionary biology*, in Dimensions of Darwinism 273, 279 (M. Grene* ed. 1983).

[103]   R. Dawkins*, *The Blind Watchmaker* 266 (1986).

[104]   Grene*, *Introduction*, to Dimensions of Darwinism 1, 10 (M. Grene* ed. 1983).

[105]   Hoffman*, *Paleobiology at the crossroads: a critique of some modern paleobiological research programs*, in Dimensions of Darwinism 241, 249 (M. Grene* ed. 1983).

[106]   Hoffman* & Hecht*, *Species selection as a causal process: A reply*, 19 Evolutionary Biology 275, 280 (1985).

[107]   *Id.* at 275, 276.

[108]   Hoffman*, *Paleobiology at the crossroads: a critique of some modern paleobiological research programs*, in Dimensions of Darwinism 241 (M. Grene* ed. 1983).

[109]   Gould*, *Evolution's Erratic Pace*, Natural History, May 1977, at 14.

[110]   Hull*, *Thirty-One Years of Systematic Zoology*, 32 Systematic Zoology 315, 333-35 (1983).

[111]   Charig*, *Systematics in Biology: A Fundamental Comparison of Some Major Schools of Thought*, in Problems of Phylogenetic Reconstruction 411-12 (K. Joysey* & A. Friday* eds. 1982).

[112]   Thomson*, *Marginalia: The Meanings of Evolution*, 70 Am. Scientist 529, 529-30 (1982).

[113]   E. Saiff* & N. Macbeth*, Evolution (unpublished ms. 1982).

[114]   C. Patterson*, *The Goals, Uses, and Assumptions of Cladistic Analysis* (1981), quoted in Beatty*, *Classes and Clades*, 31 Systematic Zoology 25, 31 (1982).

[115]   S. Luria*, S. Gould* & S. Singer*, *A View of Life* 676 (1981).

[116]   E. Mayr*, *Systematics and the Origin of Species* 276 (1942).

[117]   E. Mayr*, *The Growth of Biological Thought* 217-18 (1982).

[118]   M. Denton*, *Evolution: A Theory in Crisis* 155 (1985).

[119]   Schwabe* & Warr*, *A Polyphyletic View of Evolution: The Genetic Potential Hypothesis*, 27 Perspectives in Biology & Medicine 465, 468 (1984).

[120]   M. Denton*, *Evolution: A Theory in Crisis* 178 (1985).

[121]   G. de Beer*, *Homology: An Unsolved Problem* 15 (1971).

[122]   Bock*, *Book Review*, 164 Science 684, 684 (1969).

[123] Oldroyd*, *Charles Darwin's Theory of Evolution: A Review of Our Present Understanding*, 1 Biology & Philosophy 133, 154 (1986).

[124] Scadding*, *Do "Vestigial Organs" Provide Evidence for Evolution?*, 5 Evolutionary Theory 173, 173 (1981).

[125] M. Denton*, *Evolution: A Theory in Crisis* 291 (1985).

[126] Vawter* & Brown*, *Nuclear and Mitochondrial DNA Comparisons Reveal Extreme Rate Variation in the Molecular Clock*, 234 Science 194, 194 (1986).

[127] Farris*, *Distance Data in Phylogenetic Analysis*, in Advances in Cladistics 3, 22 (V. Funk* & D. Brooks* eds. 1981).

[128] R. Lewontin*, *The Genetic Basis of Evolutionary Change* 159 (1974) (Columbia U. Press).

[129] Saunders* & Ho*, *Is Neo-Darwinism Falsifiable?—And Does It Matter?*, 4 Nature & System 179, 185 (1982).

[130] R. Lewontin*, *The Genetic Basis of Evolutionary Change* 11-12, 189 (1974).

[131] Forey*, *Neontological Analysis Versus Palaeontological Stories*, in Problems in Phylogenetic Reconstruction 119, 124 (K. Joysey* & A. Friday* eds. 1982).

[132] Macbeth*, *Danger: analogies ahead*, 79 Rivista di Biologia (Biology Forum) 191, 194 (1986).

[133] E. Russell*, *The Diversity of Animals* 134 (1962).

[134] Section 3.2 (d)-(f).

[135] G. Kerkut*, *Implications of Evolution* 157 (1960) (italics added).

[136] Section 3.5.

[137] Whitfield*, *Book Review of Symbiosis in Cell Evolution*, 18 Biological J. Linnean Soc. 77, 78-79 (1982).

[138] Levin* & Lenski*, *Coevolution in bacteria and their viruses and plasmids*, in Coevolution 99, 126-27 (D. Futuyma* & M. Slatkin* eds. 1983).

[139] C. Hickman*, *Integrated Principles of Zoology* 111 (3d ed. 1966).

[140] G. Kerkut*, *Implications of Evolution* 151 (1960).

[141] T. Dobzhansky*, F. Ayala*, G. Stebbins* & J. Valentine*, *Evolution* 373, 397 (1977).

[142] P. Weiss*, *The Science of Biology* 732 (1963).

[143] Barghoorn*, *The Oldest Fossils*, Scientific Am., May 1971, at 30, 41.

[144] S. Stanley*, *Macroevolution* 88 (1979).

[145] F. Ommanney*, *The Fishes* 60 (1964).

[146] J. Norman*, *A History of Fishes* 296 (rev. ed. 1963).

[147] A. Romer*, *Vertebrate Paleontology* 15 (3d ed. 1966).

[148] White*, *Presidential Address: A little on Lung-fishes*, 177 Proc. British Linnean Society 1, 8 (1966).

[149] H. Smith*, *From Fish to Philosopher* 26 (1953).

[150] B. Stahl*, *Vertebrate History: Problems in Evolution* 34 (1973).

[151] Patterson*, *Phylogenies and Fossils*, 29 Systematic Zoology 216, 217 (1980).

[152] Romer*, *Book Review*, 162 Science 250, 250 (1968).

[153] B. Stahl*, *Vertebrate History: Problems in Evolution* 240-41 (1973).

[154] R. Stirton*, *Time, Life and Man* 416 (1957).

[155] M. Denton*, *Evolution: A Theory in Crisis* 218 (1985).

[156] Swinton*, *Biology and Comparative Physiology of Birds* 1 (A. Marshall* ed. 1960).

[157] Macbeth*, *The Hypothesis of Divergent Ancestry*, 5 Historia Natural 321, 326 (1985).

[158] Gould* & Eldredge*, *Punctuated equilibria: The tempo and mode of evolution reconsidered*, 3 Paleobiology 115, 147 (1977).

[159] A. Romer*, *Notes and Comments on Vertebrate Paleontology* 144-45 (1968).

[160] M. Denton*, *Evolution: A Theory in Crisis* 176 (1985).

[161] E. Russell*, *The Diversity of Animals* 118 (1962).

[162] Gould*, *The Archaeopteryx Flap*, Natural History, Sept. 1986, at 16, 18.

[163] Marx*, *The Oldest Fossil Bird: A Rival for Archaeopteryx?*, 199 Science 284, 284 (1978).

[164] Lecture by John Ostrom* at Iona College (Nov. 5, 1983).

[165] T. Kemp*, *Darwin Up To Date* 33 (1982).

[166] M. Denton*, *Evolution: A Theory in Crisis* 181-82 (1985).

[167] *Id.* at 180-81, quoting J. Jerison*, *Evolution of the Brain and Intelligence* 153-55, 213 (1973).

[168] Gow*, *An Ictidosaur Fossil from North America*, (Feb. 1983).

[169] R. Lombard*, *Evolution* 1230 (1979).

[170] G. Simpson*, *Tempo and Mode in Evolution* 105 (1944).

[171] E. Russell*, *The Diversity of Animals* 130 (1962).

[172] Gould*, *Life's Little Joke*, Natural History, Apr. 1987, at 16, 18, 24-25.

[173] Raup*, *Conflicts between Darwin and Paleontology*, Field Museum of Natural History Bull., Jan. 1979, at 22, 25

[174] E. Saiff* & N. Macbeth*, Evolution (unpublished ms. 1982).

[175] G. Hardin*, *Nature and Man's Fate* 225-26 (1961).

[176] M. Denton*, *Evolution: A Theory in Crisis* 182 (1985).

[177] Gould*, *Life's Little Joke*, Natural History, Apr. 1987, at 16, 18, 24-25.

[178] G. Simpson*, *The Major Features of Evolution* 263 (1953).

[179] M. Denton*, *Evolution: A Theory in Crisis* 85-86 (1985).

[180] A. Kelso*, *Physical Anthropology: An Introduction* 142 (2d ed. 1974).

[181] *Id.* at 150-51.

[182] 1W. Hill*, *Primates* 25-26 (1953).

[183] S. Zuckerman*, *Beyond the Ivory Tower* 64 (1970).

[184] Gribben* & Cherfas*, *Descent of Man—Or Ascent of Apes?*, 91 New Scientist 592, 594 (1981).

[185] Pilbeam*, *Book Review of Leakey's Origins*, 66 Am. Scientist 378, 379 (1978).

[186] Hill*, *Book Review*, 72 Am. Scientist 188, 189 (1984).

[187] *Id.*

[188] B. Campbell*, *Humankind Emerging* 34 (3d ed. 1982) (although believ-

ing that the drawings give a correct sequence and some idea of ancestors' nature).

[189]   Oxnard*, *Human Fossils: New Views of Old Bones*, 41 Am. Biology Teacher 264, 264 (1979).

[190]   Rensberger*, *Facing the Past*, Science 81, Oct. 1981, at 41, 49.

[191]   Oxnard*, *Human Fossils: New Views of Old Bones*, 41 Am. Biology Teacher 264, 264 (1979).

[192]   Corner*, *Evolution*, in Contemporary Botanical Thought at 95, 97 (A. MacLeod* & L. Cobley* eds. 1961).

[193]   Axelrod*, *Evolution of the Psilophyte Paleoflora*, 13 Evolution 264, 274 (1959).

[194]   M. Denton*, *Evolution: A Theory in Crisis* 163 (1985), quoting Axelrod*, *The Evolution of Flowering Plants*, in The Evolution of Life 227, 230 (S. Tax* & C. Callendar* eds. 1960).

[195]   Sagan*, *Life*, 10 Encyclopaedia Britannica: Macropaedia 893, 894 (15th ed. 1974).

[196]   G. Simpson*, *The Meaning of Evolution* 15-16 (1949).

[197]   Yockey*, *A Calculation of the Probability of Spontaneous Biogenesis by Information Theory*, 67 J. Theoretical Biology 377, 377 (1977). *Cf.* Section 4.2 (probability argument).

[198]   Popper*, *Scientific Reduction and the Essential Incompleteness of All Science*, in Studies in the Philosophy of Biology 259, 270 (1974), quoting J. Monod*, *Chance and Necessity* 143 (1971).

[199]   Haskins*, *Advances and Challenges in Science in 1970*, 59 Am. Scientist 298, 305 (1971).

[200]   E. Ambrose*, *The Nature and Origin of the Biological World* 135 (1982).

[201]   Golay*, *Reflections of a Communications Engineer*, 33 Analytical Chemistry 23 (June 1961).

[202]   Keosian*, *Life's Beginnings—Origin or Evolution?*, in Cosmochemical Evolution and the Origins of Life 291 (J. Oro* *et al.* eds. 1974).

[203]   J. Monod*, *Chance and Necessity* 136 (1972).

[204]   Erbrich*, *On the Probability of the Emergence of a Protein with a Particular Function*, 34 Acta Biotheoretica 53, 77-78 (1985).

[205]   J. Mill*, *Three Essays on Religion* 174 (2d ed. 1874, repr. 1969).

[206]   C. Ponnamperuma*, *The Origins of Life* 105 (1972).

[207]   Williams* & Smith*, *A Critical Evaluation of the Application of Amino Acid Racemization to Geochronology and Geothermometry*, 8 Origins of Life 91, 91 (1977).

[208]   S. Bresler*, *Introduction to Molecular Biology* 6 (1971).

[208A]   *Oxford Dictionary of Natural History* 77 (M. Allaby* ed. 1985).

[209]   Wald*, *The Origin of Life*, Scientific Am., Aug. 1954, at 44, 49-50.

[210]   Hull* & Bernal*, *Thermodynamics and Kinetics of Spontaneous Generation*, 186 Nature 693, 694 (1960).

[211]   Ross*, *Letter*, Chemical & Engineering News, July 7, 1980, at 4.

[212]   Prigogine*, Nicolis* & Babloyantz*, *Thermodynamics of Evolution*,

Physics Today, Nov 1972 at 23 23.

212A Yockey*, *A Calculation of the Probability of Spontaneous Biogenesis by Information Theory*, 67 J. Theoretical Biology 377, 380 (1977).

213 Abelson*, *Chemical Events on the Primitive Earth*, 55 Proc. National Acad. Sciences 1365, 1365 (1966).

214 Henderson-Sellers*, Benlow* & Meadows*, *The Early Atmospheres of the Terrestrial Planets*, 21 Quarterly J. Royal Astronomical Soc. 74, 81 (1980).

215 S. Miller* & L. Orgel*, *The Origins of Life on ι.,e Earth* 33 (1974).

216 Clemmey* & Badham*, *Oxygen in the Precambrian Atmosphere: An Evaluation of the Geological Evidence*, 10 Geology 141, 141-42 (1982).

217 Abelson*, *Chemical Events on the Primitive Earth*, 55 Proc. National Acad. Sciences 1365, 1365 (1966). *See also* Dimroth* & Kimberley*, *Precambrian Atmospheric Oxygen: Evidence in the Sedimentary Distributions of Carbon, Sulfur, Uranium, and Iron*, 13 Canadian J. Earth Sciences 1161 (1976).

218 Clemmey* & Badham*, *Oxygen in the Precambrian Atmosphere: An Evaluation of the Geological Evidence*, 10 Geology 141, 141 (1982).

219 F. Pettijohn*, *Sedimentary Rocks* 596 (3d ed. 1976).

220 Dimroth* & Kimberley*, *Precambrian Atmospheric Oxygen: Evidence in the Sedimentary Distributions of Carbon, Sulfur, Uranium, and Iron*, 13 Canadian J. Earth Sciences 1161, 1161 (1976).

221 Carver*, *Prebiotic atmospheric oxygen levels*, 292 Nature 136 (1981).

222 Levine*, *The Early Atmosphere: A New Picture*, Science Activities, Feb.-Mar. 1986, at 7, 10, 11.

223 *E.g.*, T. Dobzhansky*, F. Ayala*, G. Stebbins* & J. Valentine*, *Evolution* 349-64 (1977); S. Luria*, S. Gould* & S. Singer*, *A View of Life* 686-90 (1981); G. Stebbins*, *Darwin to DNA, Molecules to Humanity* 174-84 (1982).

224 R. Shapiro*, *Origins: A Skeptic's Guide to the Creation of Life on Earth*, 112-13 (1986).

225 Hull*, *Thermodynamics and kinetics of spontaneous generation*, 186 Nature 693, 694 (1960).

226 J. Brooks* & G. Shaw*, *Origins and Development of Living Systems* 360 (1973).

227 Dose*, *Peptides and Amino Acids in the Primordial Hydrosphere*, in The Origin of Life and Evolutionary Biochemistry 69, 75 (K. Dose* *et al.* eds. 1974).

228 Nissenbaum*, Kenyon* & Oro*, *On the Possible Role of Organic Melanoidin Polymers as Matrices for Prebiotic Activity*, 6 J. Molecular Evolution 253, 253 (1975).

229 Shapiro*, *Damage to DNA Caused by Hydrolysis*, in Chromosome Damage and Repair 3 (E. Seeberg* & K. Kleppe* eds. 1981).

230 J. Walker*, *Formaldehyde* 399 *passim* (3d ed. 1964).

231 Abelson*, *Chemical Events on the Primitive Earth*, 55 Proc. National Acad. Sciences 1365, 1369 (1966). *See also* Wrighton*, *Photochemistry,*

Chemical & Engineering News, Sept. 3, 1979, at 29.

[232] Nissenbaum*, *Scavenging of Soluble Organic Matter from the Prebiotic Oceans*, 7 Origins of Life 413, 413, 415 (1976).

[233] A. Cairns-Smith*, *Genetic Takeover and the Mineral Origins of Life* 48 (1986).

[234] L. Dillon*, *The Genetic Mechanism and the Origins of Life* 62 (1978).

[235] Hull*, *Thermodynamics and kinetics of spontaneous generation*, 186 Nature 693, 693 (1960).

[236] Dose*, *Peptides and Amino Acids in the Primordial Hydrosphere*, in The Origin of Life and Evolutionary Biochemistry 69, 75 (K. Dose* et al. eds. 1979).

[237] Quoted in A. Cairns-Smith*, *Genetic Takeover and the Mineral Origins of Life* 46-47 (1986).

[238] Nissenbaum*, Kenyon* & Oro*, *On the Possible Role of Organic Melanoidin Polymers as Matrices for Prebiotic Activity*, 6 J. Molecular Evolution 253, 253, 259 (1975).

[239] A. Cairns-Smith*, *Genetic Takeover and the Mineral Origins of Life* 46-47 (1986).

[240] L. Dillon*, *The Genetic Mechanism and the Origins of Life* 61-62 (1978).

[241] Hull*, *Thermodynamics and kinetics of spontaneous generation*, 186 Nature 693, 693 (1960).

[242] Dose*, *Peptides and Amino Acids in the Primordial Hydrosphere*, in The Origin of Life and Evolutionary Biochemistry 69, 73 (K. Dose* et al. eds. 1979).

[243] A. Cairns-Smith*, *Genetic Takeover and Mineral Origins of Life* 47 (1986).

[244] Dose*, *Peptides and Amino Acids in the Primordial Hydrosphere*, in The Origin of Life and Evolutionary Biochemistry 69, 75 (K. Dose* et al. eds. 1979).

[245] Horowitz* & Hubbard*, *The Origin of Life*, 8 Ann. Rev. Genetics 393 (1974).

[246] A. Cairns-Smith*, *Genetic Takeover and the Mineral Origins of Life* 47-48 (1986).

[247] R. Shapiro*, *Origins: A Skeptic's Guide* 112 (1986).

[248] Scott*, *Update on Genesis*, New Scientist, May 2, 1985, at 30, 30.

[249] Anon.*, *What Future for biogenesis?*, 216 Nature 635, 635 (1967).

[250] A. Cairns-Smith*, *Genetic Takeover and the Mineral Origins of Life* 51-52 (1986).

[251] Nissenbaum*, *Scavenging of Soluble Organic Matter from the Prebiotic Oceans*, 7 Origins of Life 413 (1976).

[252] Nissenbaum*, Kenyon* & Oro*, *On the Possible Role of Organic Melanoidin Polymers as Matrices for Prebiotic Activity*, 6 J. Molecular Evolution 253, 259 (1975).

[253] Sagan*, *Simulated Natural Experiments*, in The Origins of Prebiological Systems and of Their Molecular Matrices 374-75 (S. Fox* ed. 1965).

[254]   Dose*, *Peptides and Amino Acids in the Primordial Hydrosphere*, in The Origin of Life and Evolutionary Biochemistry 69, 73-74 (K. Dose* *et al.* eds. 1979).

[255]   Temussi*, Paolillo*, Ferrara*, Benedetti* & Andini*, *Structural Characterization of Thermal Prebiotic Polypeptides*, 7 J. Molecular Evolution 105, 105, 109 (1976).

[256]   Williams* & Smith*, *A Critical Evaluation of the Application of Amino Acid Racemization to Geochronology and Geothermometry*, 8 Origins of Life 91, 91 (1977).

[257]   Reid* & Orgel*, *Synthesis of sugars in potentially prebiotic conditions*, 216 Nature 455, 455 (1967).

[258]   Abelson*, *Chemical Events on the Primitive Earth*, 55 Proc. National Acad. Sciences 1365 (1966).

[259]   A. Cairns-Smith*, *Genetic Takeover and the Mineral Origins of Life* 66 (1986).

[260]   *Id.* at 55.

[261]   Williams* & Smith*, *A Critical Evaluation of the Application of Amino Acid Racemization to Geochronology and Geothermometry*, 8 Origins of Life 91, 91 (1977); C. Patterson*, *Evolution* 157 (1978).

[262]   A. Cairns-Smith*, *Genetic Takeover and the Mineral Origins of Life* 73 (1986).

[263]   L. Dillon*, *The Genetic Mechanism and the Origins of Life* 63 (1978).

[264]   S. Miller* & L. Orgel*, *The Origins of Life on the Earth* 98 (1974).

[265]   A. Cairns-Smith*, *Genetic Takeover and the Mineral Origins of Life* 63 (1986).

[266]   Abelson*, *Chemical Events on the Primitive Earth*, 55 Proc. National Acad. Sciences 1365 (1966).

[267]   Dickerson*, *Chemical Evolution and the Origin of Life*, Scientific Am., Sept. 1978, at 70, 85.

[268]   F. Crick*, *Life Itself* 71 (1981).

[269]   A. Cairns-Smith*, *Genetic Takeover and the Mineral Origins of Life* 62 (1986).

[270]   Scott*, *Update on Genesis*, New Scientist, May 2, 1985, at 30, 32.

[271]   J. Monod*, *Chance and Necessity* 143 (A. Wainhouse* trans. 1971).

[272]   Lambert*, *Enzymic Editing Mechanisms and the Origin of Biological Information Transfer*, 107 J. Theoretical Biology 387, 400-01 (1984).

[273]   D. Green* & R. Goldberger*, *Molecular Insights into the Living Process* 407 (1967).

[274]   Kenyon* & Nissenbaum*, *Melanoidin and Aldocyanin Microspheres: Implications for Chemical Evolution and Early Precambrian Micropaleontology*, 7 J. Molecular Evolution 245, 246 (1976).

[275]   Kempthorne*, *Evaluation of Current Population Genetics Theory*, 23 Am. Zoologist 111, 111 (1983).

[276]   L. Dillon*, *The Genetic Mechanism and the Origins of Life* 65 (1978).

[277]   A. Cairns-Smith*, *Genetic Takeover and the Mineral Origins of Life* 59-60 (1986).

278 Dobzhansky*, *Synthesis of Nucleosides and Polynucleotides with Metaphosphate Esters*, in The Origins of Prebiological Systems 299, 310 (S. Fox* ed. 1965).

279 A. Cairns-Smith*, *Genetic Takeover and the Mineral Origins of Life* 60 (1986).

280 A. Cairns-Smith*, *Genetic Takeover and the Mineral Origins of Life* 56 (1986).

281 Shapiro*, *The Improbability of Prebiotic Nucleic Acid Synthesis*, 14 Origin of Life 565, 565 (1984).

282 Clemmey* & Badham*, *Oxygen in the Precambrian Atmosphere: An Evaluation of the Geological Evidence*, 10 Geology 141, 141 (1982).

283 Keosian*, *Life's Beginnings—Origin or Evolution?*, in The Origin of Life and Evolutionary Biochemistry 221 (K.Dose* et al. eds. 1974).

284 Sagan*, *Discussion of K. Harada and S. Fox: The Thermal Synthesis of Amino Acids from a Hypothetically Primitive Terrestrial Atmosphere*, in The Origins of Prebiological Systems and of Their Molecular Matrices 195-96 (S. Fox* ed. 1965).

285 A. Cairns-Smith*, *Genetic Takeover and the Mineral Origins of Life* 64 (1986).

286 R. Shapiro*, *Origins: A Skeptic's Guide to the Creation of Life on Earth* 105 (1986).

287 Temussi*, Paolillo*, Ferrara*, Benedetti* & Andini*, *Structural Characterization of Thermal Prebiotic Polypeptides*, 7 J. Molecular Evolution 105.

288 *Id.* at 105, 108-09.

289 S. Miller* & L. Orgel*, *The Origins of Life on Earth* 144 (1974).

300 W. Stansfield*, *The Science of Evolution* 57 (1977).

301 Kenyon* & Nissenbaum*, *Melanoidin and Aldocyanin Microspheres: Implications for Chemical Evolution and Early Precambrian Micropaleontology*, 7 J. Molecular Evolution 245, 246 (1976).

302 L. Dillon*, *The Genetic Mechanism and the Origins of Life* 63-64 (1978).

303 W. Day*, *Genesis of the Planet Earth* 320 (1979).

304 L. Dillon*, *The Genetic Mechanism and the Origins of Life* 60 (1978).

305 *Id.* at 64.

306 E. Ambrose*, *The Nature and Origin of the Biological World* 135 (1982).

307 Yockey*, *A Calculation of the Probability of Spontaneous Biogenesis by Information Theory*, 67 J. Theoretical Biology 377, 387 (1977).

308 *Id.* at 377.

309 W. Stansfield*, *The Science of Evolution* 57 (1977).

310 R. Jastrow*, *God and the Astronomers* 109, 111 (1978).

311 P. Davies*, *The Runaway Universe* 27 (1980).

312 F. Hoyle*, *The Nature of the Universe* 125 (1950) (emphasis added).

313 R. Wald*, *Space, Time, and Gravity: The Theory of the Big Bang* 61 (1971).

314 R. Jastrow*, *God and the Astronomers* 121-22 (1978).

315 Wilczek*, *The Cosmic Asymmetry between Matter and Antimatter,*

Scientific Am., Dec. 1980, at 82, 83.

[316] Weisskopf*, *The Origin of the Universe*, 71 Am. Scientist 473, 479 (1983).

[317] J. Silk*, *The Big Bang* 319-21 (1979).

[318] Davies*, *Chance or choice: is the Universe an accident?*, 80 New Scientist 506, 506 (1978).

[319] A. Einstein*, *Lettres à Maurice Solovine* 114-15 (1956).

[320] C. Raymo*, *The Soul of the Night* 93 (1985).

[321] I. Newton, *Mathematical Principles* 543-44 (2d ed. 1686, A. Motte* trans., F. Cajori* ed. 1946).

[322] J. Barrow* & F. Tipler*, *The Anthropic Cosmological Principle* 21, 16 (1986) (original in italics).

[323] Press*, *A place for teleology?*, 320 Nature 315, 315 (1986) (not stating his own view but summarizing Barrow* and Tipler*).

[324] P. Davies*, *Superforce: The Search for a Grand Unified Theory of Nature* 184 (1984).

[325] Lake*, *Windows on a New Cosmology*, 224 Science 675, 678 (1984).

[326] Gale*, *The Anthropic Principle*, Scientific Am., Dec. 1981, at 154, 164.

[327] J. Barrow* & F. Tipler*, *The Anthropic Cosmological Principle* 322, 327 (1986).

[328] Leslie*, *Cosmology, Probability, and the Need To Explain Life*, in Scientific Explanation and Understanding 53, 54 (N. Rescher* ed. 1983).

[329] J. Barrow* & F. Tipler*, *The Anthropic Cosmological Principle* 309, 307, 524, 541, 545, 548 (1986); Gale*, *The Anthropic Principle*, Scientific Am., Dec. 1981, at 154, 168.

[330] Oldershaw*, *The Continuing Case for a Hierarchical Cosmology*, 92 Astrophysics & Space Science 347, 349 (1983).

[331] Gale*, *The Anthropic Principle*, Scientific Am., Dec. 1981, at 154, 168.

[332] Gregory* & Thompson*, *Superclusters and Voids in the Distribution of Galaxies*, Scientific Am., Mar. 1982, at 106, 113.

[333] Waldrop*, *Delving the Hole in Space*, 214 Science 1016, 1016 (1981).

[334] B. Patrusky*, *Why Is the Cosmos Lumpy?*, Science 81, June 1981, at 96, 96.

[335] Guth* & Steinhardt*, *The Inflationary Universe*, Scientific Am., May 1984, at 116, 119.

[336] F. Hoyle, *The Intelligent Universe* 183-85 (1983); Hoyle, *The Big Bang in Astronomy*, 92 New Scientist 521, 523 (1981).

[337] Hoyle & Wickramasinghe, *Where Microbes Boldly Went*, New Scientist 413 (1981).

[338] Leslie*, *Cosmology, Probability, and the Need To Explain Life*, in Scientific Explanation and Understanding 53, 54 (N. Rescher* ed. 1983).

[339] R. Breuer*, *Contact with the Stars* 8 (1982).

[340] Cameron*, *The Origin and Evolution of the Solar System*, 233 Scientific Am. 35 (1975).

[341] Harrison*, *Universe, Origin, and Evolution of*, in 18 Encyclopaedia

Britannica 1007, 1008 (14th ed. 1974).

[342] H. Jeffreys*, *The Earth: Its Origin, History and Physical Constitution* 359 (5th ed. 1970).

[343] Kazmann*, *It's About Time: 4.5 Billion Years*, Geotimes, Sept. 1978, at 18, 19.

[344] Gentry, *Abnormally Long Alpha-Particle Tracks in Biotite (Mica)*, 8 Applied Physics Letters 65 (1966); Gentry, *Anti-matter content of the Tunguska meteor*, 211 Nature 1071 (1966); Gentry, *Alpha Radioactivity of Unknown Origin and the Discovery of a New Pleochroic Halo*, 1 Earth & Planetary Science Letters 453 (1966); Gentry, *Extinct radioactivity and the discovery of a new pleochroic halo*, 213 Nature 487 (1967); Gentry, *Fossil Alpha-Recoil Analysis of Certain Variant Radioactive Halos*, 160 Science 1228 (1968); Gentry, *Giant Radioactive Halos: Indicators of Unknown Alpha Radioactivity?*, 169 Science 670 (1970); Gentry, *Radioactive Halos in the Lunar Environment*, 1 Proc. Second Lunar Science Conf. 167 (1971); Gentry, *Radiohalos: Some Unique Pb Isotope Ratios and Unknown Alpha Radioactivity*, 173 Science 727 (1971); Gentry, *Ion microprobe confirmation of Pb isotope ratios and search for isomer precursors in Polonium radiohaloes*, 244 Nature 282 (1973); Gentry, *Radioactive Halos*, 23 Annual Rev. Nuclear Science 347 (1973); Gentry, *Radiohalos in a Radiochronological and Cosmological Perspective*, 184 Science 62 (1974); Gentry, *"Spectacle" array of 210 Pb halo radiocentres in biotite*, 252 Nature 564 (1974); Gentry, *Spectacle haloes: Reply*, 258 Nature 269 (1975); Gentry et al.*, *Radiohalos in Coalified Wood: New Evidence Relating to Time of Uranium Introduction and Coalification*, 194 Science 315 (1976); Gentry et al.*, *Evidence for Primordial Superheavy Elements*, 37 Physical Rev. Letters 11 (1976); Gentry et al.*, *Search with Synchrotron Radiation for Superheavy Elements in Giant-Halo Inclusions*, 38 Physical Rev. Letters 205 (1977); Gentry et al.*, *Evidence Against Super-Heavy Elements in Giant-Halo Inclusions Reexamined with Synchrotron Radiation*, 40 Physical Rev. Letters 507 (1978); Gentry, *Are Any Unusual Radio Halos Evidence for SHE?*, Proc. International Symposium on Superheavy Elements (Lubbock, Texas, Mar. 9-11, 1978); Gentry et al.*, *Reinvestigation of the α-activity of Conway granite*, 273 Nature 217 (1978); Gentry et al.*, *Implications of unknown radioactivity of giant and dwarf halos in Scandinavian rocks*, 274 Nature 457 (1978); Gentry, *Time: Measured Responses*, 60 E.O.S. 474 (1979); Gentry, *Polonium Halos*, 61 E.O.S. 514 (1980).

[345] Gentry, *Letter*, Physics Today, Apr. 1983, at 13, 13; Gentry, *Time: Measured Responses*, 60 E.O.S. [Trans. Am. Geophysical U.] 474, 475 (1979); Gentry, *Polonium Halos*, 61 E.O.S. 514 (1980).

[346] Gentry, *Radioactive Halos*, 23 Annual Rev. of Nuclear Science 347, 356 (1973); Gentry, *Fossil Alpha-Recoil Analysis of Certain Variant Radioactive Halos*, 160 Science 1228 (1968); Gentry, *Radiohalos in a Radiochronological and Cosmological Perspective*, 184 Science 62 (1974); Gentry, *Radioactive Halos*, 23 Annual Rev. Nuclear Science 347, 355 (1973).

[347] Gentry, *Radioactive Halos*, 23 Annual Rev. Nuclear Science 347, 360-61 (1973); Gentry, *Radiohalos: Some Unique Pb Isotope Ratios and Unknown Alpha Radioactivity*, 173 Science 727, 727 (1971); Gentry et al.*, *Ion microprobe confirmation of Pb isotope ratios and search for isomer precursors in Polonium radiohaloes*, 244 Nature 282 (1973).

[348] Narlikar*, *Was there a big bang?*, New Scientist, July 2, 1981, at 19, 19.

[349] Vaucouleurs*, *The Case for a Hierarchical Cosmology*, 167 Science 1203, 1203 (1970).

[350] Burbidge*, *Was there really a Big Bang?*, 233 Nature 36, 36, 39 (1971).

[351] Ellis*, *Alternatives to the Big Bang*, 22 Ann. Rev. Astronomy & Astrophysics 157, 181 (1984).

[352] C. Sagan*, *Cosmos* 252-53, 256 (1980).

[353] Arp*, *Evidence for Discordant Redshifts*, in The Redshift Controversy 15, 26-27, 31 (G. Field* ed. 1973).

[354] Arp* & Sulentic*, *Analysis of Groups of Galaxies with Accurate Redshifts*, 291 Astrophysical J. 88, 88 (1985).

[355] Arp*, *Evidence for Discordant Redshifts*, in The Redshift Controversy 15, 35-36 (G. Field* ed. 1973); Sulentic* & Arp*, *Evidence for Interaction in Two Discordant Redshift Pairs of Galaxies*, 297 Astrophysical J. 572, 572 (1985) (discordant interacting pairs of galaxies); Arp*, *Further Examples of Comparison Galaxies with Discordant Redshifts and Their Spectral Peculiarities*, 263 Astrophysical J. 54, 54 (1982); see also Arp*, Sargeant*, Willis* & Oosterbaan*, *An Eruptive BL Lacertae Object with a High Redshift*, 230 Astrophysics J. 68 (1979); Arp*, *Evidence for Discordant Redshifts*, in The Redshift Controversy 15, 37-38, 41-42 (G. Field* ed. 1973); Arp*, *Three New Cases of Galaxies with Large Discrepant Redshifts*, 239 Astrophysical J. 469 (1980).

[356] Sulentic* & Arp*, *Evidence for Interaction in Two Discordant Redshift Pairs of Galaxies*, 297 Astrophysical J. 572, 572 (1985).

[357] Arp* & Sulentic*, *Analysis of Groups of Galaxies with Accurate Redshifts*, 291 Astrophysical J. 88, 88 (1985).

[358] Arp*, *Three New Cases of Galaxies with Large Discrepant Redshifts*, 239 Astrophysical J. 469, 474 (1980).

[359] Burbidge*, *Redshift and distances*, 286 Nature 307 (1980).

[360] Wolf*, *Non-cosmological redshifts of spectral lines*, 326 Nature 363, 363 (1987).

[361] Bocko*, Douglass* & Knox*, *Observation of Frequency Shifts of Spectral Lines Due to Source Correlations*, ... Physical Rev. Letters ...., (1987).

[362] Crawford*, *Photon decay in curved space-time*, 277 Nature 633, 633 (1979).

[363] P. Marmet*, *A New Non-Doppler Redshift* (1981).

[364] I. Segal*, *Mathematical Cosmology and Extragalactic Astronomy* (1976).

[365] Ellis*, *Alternatives to the Big Bang*, 22 Ann. Rev. Astronomy & Astro-

physics 157, 176-77 (1984).

366 Hoyle* & Narlikar*, *On the nature of mass*, 233 Nature 41, 41 (1971).

367 Allen*, *The Big Bang Is Not Needed*, 6 Foundations of Physics 59, 59 (1976).

368 C. Sagan*, *Cosmos* 252-53, 256 (1980).

369 Alfvén* & Mendis*, *Interpretation of Observed Cosmic Microwave Background Radiation*, 266 Nature 699 (1977).

370 F. Hoyle, *The Intelligent Universe* 181 (1983).

371 Narlikar*, *Was there a big bang?*, New Scientist, July 2, 1981, at 19, 20.

372 Grøn*, *Repulsive gravitation and inflationary universe models*, 54 Am. J. Physics 46, 48 (1986).

373 J. Trefil*, *The Moment of Creation: Big Bang Physics* 48 (1983).

374 R. Jastrow*, *God and the Astronomers* 109 (1978).

375 Narlikar* & Padmanabhan*, *Creation-field cosmology: A possible solution to singularity, horizon, and flatness problems*, 32 Physical Rev. D 1928, 1928 (1985).

376 P. Davies*, *Superforce: The Search for a Grand Unified Theory of Nature* 198 (1984).

377 Tipler*, *How To Construct a Falsifiable Theory in Which the Universe Came Into Being Several Thousand Years Ago*, 2 Philosophy of Science Association 873, 879 (1984).

378 R. Jastrow*, *God and the Astronomers* 125 (1978).

379 H. Alfvén*, *Worlds-Antiworlds* 17 (1966).

380 Narlikar*, *Was there a big bang?*, New Scientist, July 2, 1981, at 19, 19.

381 P. Davies*, *Superforce: The Search for a Grand Unified Theory of Nature* 185 (1984).

382 Lake*, *Windows on a New Cosmology*, 224 Science 675, 678 (1984).

383 Burbidge*, *Was there really a Big Bang?*, 233 Nature 36, 40 (1971).

384 Leslie*, *Cosmology, Probability, and the Need To Explain Life*, in Scientific Explanation and Understanding 53, 54 (N. Rescher* ed. 1983).

385 Hoyle, *The Big Bang in Astronomy*, 91 New Scientist 521, 523 (1981).

386 G. Kerkut*, *Implications of Evolution* 5 (1960).

387 A. Cairns-Smith*, *Genetic Takeover and the Mineral Origins of Life* 63 (1986) (italics added).

388 R. Dawkins*, *The Blind Watchmaker* 287 (1986).

389 Smith*, *Two Evolutions*, in On Nature 42, 45 (L. Rouner* ed. 1984).

390 C. Darwin*, *The Origin of Species* 481 (1st ed. 1859, repr. 1964).

Author Index to Volume I

Subject Index to Volume I

abrupt appearance *and* Biochemical evolution
Lingula, 66
Lipids, problems with evolution of, 350-1
"Living fossils," as evidence for abrupt appearance theory, 66-8
"Lucy" *see Australopithecus afarensis*
Lungfishes
  as living fossils, 67
  as possible intermediates, 183
  problem of origins of, 61-2, 214

Macroevolution
  as criticized by noncreationist scientists, 136
  as "working hypothesis", 142-3
  defined as common ancestry ("molecules to man"), 139
  postulated stages of, 208-38
Mammal-like reptiles
  problems with jaws of, 221
  reptilian brains of, 220-1
Mammals
  abrupt appearance in fossil record, 55, 219
  gaps between orders of, 63, 222
  as living fossils, 68
Man *see Homo sapiens*
Mechanisms of macroevolution
  as not compelling established, 155
  confusion over, 156
  various theories of, 155-78
  (*see also* Genetic recombination, Mutation, Natural selection, Species selection)
Mesohippus, 224
Mesozoic Era, 186
Metazoa
  gap between Protista and, 61
  discontinuity in origin of, 212
Microevolution
  as change within local populations, 139
  not disputed by discontinuitist scientists, 139
Microfossils, ambiguous nature of, 53
Microsphere model, 371
Migration, as an evolutionary mechanism, 167
Miller-Urey experiment

in biochemical evolution, 364
  significant problems with, 365-6
Miohippus, 224
Missing links *see* Fossil gaps
Mitochondria, postulated origins of, 211-2
Moeritherium, 222
Molecular clock
  conceptual flaws in, 200-2
  data which contradict, 200
Monotremes, as possible intermediates, 183
Morganucodon, 221
Mutation (as an evolutionary mechanism)
  inadequacy of scope of, 165-6
  inadequacy of frequency of, 166-7
  major variation not observed, 167
Mutations
  limited scope of viable, 85-7
  low frequency of viable, 87-8
  no real evolutionary effect of, 86
  problems of coordinating, 86-8
  systemic, 176-7
  x-ray induced, 95
Myoglobin, 99

Natural groups
  as units of classification, 41
  as evidence for theory of abrupt appearance, 41-2, 92-3
  independent of evolutionary theory, 92
Natural selection
  and extinction, 164
  as mechanism of macroevolution, 158-65
  as tautologous, 159
  cannot explain macroevolution, 158-60
  inadequacy of empirical examples, 160-4
  incompatibility with fossil record, 59
  not applicable to biochemical evolution, 359-60
  not modeled by artificial selection, 206-7
Nautilus, 66
Neanderthal Man, 227, 231-2
Nebraska Man, 227-8
Nellia tenella, 66
Neo-Darwinism
  as allowing any possible observation, 174-5
  as speculative hypothesis, 142